# Highways

## Volume 2
## Highway Engineering

## Third edition

## C A O'Flaherty

BE (NUI), MS, PhD (Iowa State), C Eng, FICE, FCIT, FIE(Aust),
FIHT, MIEI
Director and Principal, Tasmanian State Institute of Technology
Formerly Professor of Transport Engineering and Director of the
Institute for Transport Studies, University of Leeds

# Edward Arnold

© 1988 C A O'Flaherty

First published in Great Britain 1967

Second edition 1974
Third edition 1988

*British Library Cataloguing in Publication Data*

O'Flaherty, C. A. (Coleman Anthony), *1933–*
    Highways.——3rd ed.
  Vol. 2: Highway engineering
  1. Roads. Engineering aspects
  I. Title
  625.7

  ISBN 0–7131–3596–4

Typeset in 10/11pt Times by Mathematical Composition Setters Ltd, Salisbury
Printed and bound in Great Britain for Edward Arnold, the educational,
academic and medical publishing division of Hodder and Stoughton Limited,
41 Bedford Square, London WC1B 3DQ, by Richard Clay, Suffolk

# Preface

The decision taken during the preparation of the second edition of *Highways*, to divide the book into two volumes, appears to have been well accepted and this has been carried forward into the third edition. Thus Volume 2: *Highway Engineering*, covers the 'hard' side of highways, i.e. their physical location, structural design, construction and maintenance, as well as the materials used in their construction. Volume 1, now entitled *Traffic Planning and Engineering*, covers the historical and administrative aspects of highways together with those other matters which are of particular interest to traffic planners and engineers.

The intention underlying the preparation of this third edition has not changed from that described in the previous editions—to provide a basic textbook for the young engineer about to centre his or her career on highways, whether it be in their planning, design, construction, maintenance, or operation.

There are a number of significant changes in this third edition of Volume 2.

Firstly and most importantly, the text has been completely revised and updated, and every chapter has been extensively modified. The published information and research on this very dynamic area of study has expanded tremendously over the past decade, and hence Volume 2 has been lengthened in order to cope with the various technical topics in a reasonable way.

Particular attention has been paid to the chapters dealing with the design of flexible pavements, bituminous surfacings and concrete pavements, so as to include the major outcomes of the test road research work carried out by the Transport and Road Research Laboratory over the past thirty years. The recently published pavement design procedures, which supersede the Road Note 29 design methods, are described in these chapters.

An additional new chapter has been provided on pavement maintenance and strengthening. As the major road building programme in Britain slows down, this area of highway engineering can be expected to become much more important.

Particular attention has also been paid in this third edition to the referencing system. As in the two previous editions, authoritative references have been quoted where it has been appropriate to authenticate certain statements and to provide the source of facts, tables and figures. In this edition, however, an attempt has been made to point the reader towards significant references as an aid to further study; on the whole, these references are fairly recent, although 'classics' are quoted in many instances. It is important for the young engineer to appreciate that a tremendous amount of research is currently being carried out in highway engineering with the result that many previously held tenets are now being questioned and discarded; even at the undergraduate level, it is necessary for the student to read the professional journals and governmental publications in order to keep abreast of these changes and to find out 'the reason why'.

Whilst this book is primarily aimed at students in Britain, the writer is conscious that this edition is being written from afar. Every attempt has been made to minimize the likelihood of error, but mistakes may inadvertently have crept in, and so the writer will welcome any advice on these. Meanwhile the reader is reminded that the factual material in the text is primarily given for demonstration purposes, and is urged to seek out the original material and to consult the most up-to-date 'official' versions of recommended practices, standards, etc., when engaged in actual planning, design and fieldwork.

Coleman A O'Flaherty

# Acknowledgements

I am indebted to the many organizations and journals which allowed me to reproduce diagrams and tables from their publications. The number in the title of each table and figure indicates the reference at the end of each chapter where the source is to be found. It should be noted that material quoted from British government publications is Crown copyright and reproduced by permission of the Controller of Her Majesty's Stationery Office.

I should also like to thank again my former colleagues at the University of Leeds, most particularly G Leake and J Cabrerra, for their encouragement during the preparation of the first and second editions, when the tone for this third edition was set.

Not only I but the publishers are grateful to Mrs G McCulloch for her excellent typing and interpretation of the handwritten word. This text has been written from afar, and this would not have been possible without the help of the many library staff at my Institute who sought and obtained numerous references on my behalf. Above all, however, I am indebted to Miss J Jensen, Librarian-in-charge, at the State Offices Library, Hobart, for her very considerable, unassuming, professional help in obtaining the reference material on which this third edition is mainly based.

Last, but far from being least, I thank my wife, Nuala, who has helped me immeasurably in this work. Not only has she participated actively in the preparation of this text, but her patience and forebearance have made it possible.

Coleman A O'Flaherty

# Contents

# 1
# Highway location, plans and specifications

The location of a major highway route requires consideration of very many complex and interrelated factors (see Table 1.1) using, as appropriate, the combined skills of the engineer, planner, economist, surveyor and geologist. In general, the aim of the alignment selection process is to find a location for the new road that will result in the lowest total construction, land, traffic and environmental costs.

Before an attempt can be made at selecting a physical location for a highway improvement, data must be available regarding traffic desires and

**Table 1.1** Compendium of factors considered in highway route location (based on reference 1)

| Subject area | Features | Factors |
|---|---|---|
| Engineering and economics | Construction costs | Topography, geology, geomorphology, soils, materials, vegetation, drainage, design criteria, safety |
| | Maintenance costs | Climate, traffic, soils, materials, topography, drainage, geomorphology |
| | User costs | Traffic, topography, travel time, safety |
| | Right-of-way costs* | Land values, land use, replacement costs, traffic, design criteria, utilities, tax base |
| | Development potential* | Agriculture, forestry, mineral extraction, trade and industry, tourism, personal mobility, political strategy |
| Social aspects | Neighbourhood locale | Population, culture, land use, tax rate, land value, institutions, transportation, historical sites, utilities and services, community boundaries, traffic, employment, dynamic change, tax base |
| Social/ecology | Recreation and conservation | Land use, vegetation, fish life, scenic areas, wildlife, drainage, topography, erodibility, sedimentation, landmarks |
| Ecology | Pollution† | Noise, air, water, spillage, thermal, chemical, waste |
| Aesthetics | Scenic value | Scenic areas, view from road, view of road, 'eye-sores', topography, vegetation, drainage |

*Right-of-way costs and the development potential of an area also affect the social aspects of that area
†Pollution also affects the aesthetic value of an area

needs, the planning intentions within the area to be traversed, and estimates of the future physical characteristics of the highway itself. Location surveys involving geologic and photogrammetric skills provide the basic information for structural design, as well as the economic analyses which have a considerable influence on the final location of the highway. The coupling of advanced computing techniques with improved methods of obtaining data ensure that, when the final costings are done and the specifications written, the highway location selected will yield the highest social return on the transport investment, and reconcile as effectively as possible the conflicting interests of the various individuals and groups affected by the facility.

In essence, both Volumes 1 and 2 of *Highways* are concerned with as many of these considerations as is deemed practical. In this chapter, however, are emphasized the methods of determining the *physical* characteristics which influence location and design. Integrated with these surveys are the plans and specifications resulting from them, so these are also described here.

## Some dos and don'ts of highway location

Before discussing the means by which the engineering data are obtained, it is worthwhile considering some detailed guiding principles which should be kept in mind when selecting the location for a highway. The following outline is not in any particular order, nor indeed is it, or can it be, complete. In addition, some of the elements tend to contradict one another; in practice, the location is selected which represents the best compromise solution.

(1)   For the highway to serve its function of allowing convenient, continuous, free-flowing traffic operation, it should be located where it can best meet the major traffic desire lines and be as direct as possible.

(2)   Keep grades and curvature to the minimum necessary to satisfy the service requirements of the highway.

(3)   Avoid sudden changes in sight distance, especially near junctions

(4)   Avoid having the beginning or end of a sharp horizontal curve on or adjacent to a pronounced vertical curve as drivers may not perceive the change before they reach it.

(5)   In urban areas site the highway through undeveloped or blighted areas, along the edges of large parklands and, in general, away from highly-developed, expensive land areas. Seek locations which result in the least amount of environmental blight (visual and audio) to affected householders.

(6)   In urban areas locate the highway as close as possible to the principal parking terminals.

(7)   In rural areas locate as much as possible of the new highway on existing ones, so as to minimize the loss of farmland and to reduce the total initial and maintenance costs.

(8)   Locate the highway along the edges of properties rather than through

the middle, so as to cause the minimum interference to cultivation and to avoid the need for subway construction.

(9)   Avoid the destruction or removal of man-made culture.

(10)   Keep the highway away from cemeteries, places of worship, hospitals, schools and playgrounds.

(11)   Consider the effect of the proposed highway on existing or future utilities above, on or under the ground. It may be such as to warrant changes in order to avoid expensive relocation of these utilities.

(12)   Never have two roads intersecting near a bend or at the top or bottom of a hill.

(13)   In the case of a motorway, the need for an interchange with another road may dictate an alignment that will intersect the other highway at a place, at an angle and in terrain that will permit the interchange to be constructed most economically.

(14)   Avoid intersections at-grade with railway lines. If possible, have the highway pass over the railway at a point where the railway goes into a cutting.

(15)   Seek favourable sites for river crossings. Preferably these should be at right-angles to the stream centreline.

(16)   Do not have a bridge or tunnel located on or adjacent to a highway curve.

(17)   Avoid the need for deep cuttings and expensive tunnel construction.

(18)   Avoid locations where rock is close to the surface as this will usually require at least some expensive excavation.

(19)   In hilly terrain reduce the maximum gradient to the lowest value possible.

(20)   To minimize drainage problems, select a location on high ground in preference to one in a valley. If a particular location is likely to be subject to frequent and expensive maintenance due to drainage, an alternative location should be sought unless the potential maintenance costs can be economically reduced by special design.

(21)   Avoid bogs, marshes and other low-lying lands subject to flooding.

(22)   Locate the highway on soil which will require the least pavement thickness above it.

(23)   Locate the highway adjacent to sources of construction materials.

(24)   When the needs of all other factors have been satisfied, the best location is the one which results in the minimum total cost of earthworks. This means that the minimum quantities of excavation should be so balanced with the quantities of embankment as to require a minimum of haulage with little need for overhaul.

(25)   In hilly terrain the highway should cross ridges at their lowest points. (This usually results in cheaper construction as well as more economical vehicle operating costs.) Avoid creating severe breaks in the natural skyline.

(26)   In hilly country also, select a location subject to sunlight, and avoid areas where the highway is shielded from the sun so that moisture on the carriageway cannot evaporate or snow and ice have difficulty in melting and dissipating[2].

(27)   Avoid the unnecessary and expensive destruction of wooded areas. If

intrusion is unavoidable, the road should be on a curve, where possible, so as to preserve an unbroken background.

(28) Avoid ground subject to subsidence or landslip.

(29) Avoid placing the highway at right-angles to a series of natural drainage channels.

(30) To relieve the monotony of driving on a long, straight road, it is an advantage to site the road so as to give a view of some prominent feature ahead.

## Location surveys in rural areas

### Structure of the location process

In general, the approach to selecting the route for a long highway can be described[3] as a 'hierarchically structured decision process'. This very logical approach is most easily considered by referring to Fig. 1.1.

The first step in the process requires fixing the end termini, and then defining a *region*, A, which will include all conceivably feasible routes between them; typically, this region will be about one-third as wide as it is long. This region is then searched and a number of broad *bands*, B and C, are selected within which it is decided to concentrate further searches and selections. For a major rural road scheme, e.g. a rural motorway, a band could be as much as 8–16 km wide. Within these bands, further searching may result in the selection of corridors D, E and F, each perhaps 3–8 km wide. A comparison of these corridors suggests that E, say, is the best and so *route* G is generated within it; typically, this route could be from 1.0–1.5 km wide. The next step is to search this area and locate within it (not shown in the figure) one or more different *alignments*, each perhaps 30 m wide and containing minor geometric differences. These alignments are compared, a final selection is made, and this is used for *design* purposes.

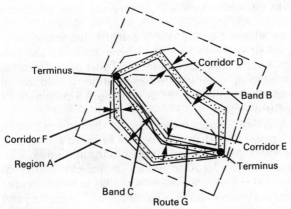

**Fig. 1.1** A hypothetical route location problem showing the spatial relationships of various actions generated and evaluated[3]

Note that the process involves continuous searching and selecting, using increasingly more detailed knowledge at each decision-making stage. Factors influencing the selection process at any instance include not only such 'tangibles' as topography, soil and geological details, land use, population distribution, travel demand, user costs, structure and maintenance costs, and safety but also 'intangible' considerations of a political, social and environmental nature which require intensive public consultations (see Volume 1, Chapters 1 and 3) before final decisions can be made.

## Location surveys

To aid in the decision-making process, a classical conceptual approach has tended to be developed with regard to gathering topographical and geotechnical information about the areas being evaluated. Generally, these can be divided into reconnaissance, preliminary location, and final location/design surveys.

### Reconnaissance survey

The purpose of a reconnaissance survey is to evaluate the feasibility of one or more corridor routes for a highway between specific points which may be many kilometres apart.

Mostly a desk study, good reconnaissance can be the greatest single money-saving phase in the construction of a new road. Hence the engineer should make ample provision in both time and finance for this stage of the highway location study. There follows a useful check-list[4] of the general information required in the first phase of the reconnaissance study for a major highway in Britain, irrespective of whether it is in a rural or an urban area.

(1) *General land survey*: (a) location of site on published maps and charts, (b) air survey, where appropriate, (c) site boundaries, outlines of structures, and building lines, (d) ground contours and natural drainage features, (e) above-ground obstructions to view and flying, e.g. transmission lines, (f) indications of obstructions below ground, (g) records of differences and omissions in relation to published maps, (h) position of survey stations and benchmarks (the latter with reduced levels), and (i) meteorological information.

(2) *Permitted use and restrictions*: (a) planning and statutory restrictions applying to the particular areas under the Town and Country Planning Acts administered by the appropriate local authorities, (b) local authority regulations on planning restrictions, listed buildings and building byelaws, (c) Department of Trade and Industry regulations governing issue of industrial development certificates, (d) rights of light, support and way including any easements, (e) tunnels, mine workings (abandoned, active and proposed), mineral rights, and (f) ancient monuments, burial grounds, etc.

(3) *Approaches and access* (*including temporary access for construction purposes*): (a) road (check ownership), (b) railway (check for closures), (c) by water, and (d) by air.

(4)    *Ground conditions*: (a) geological maps, (b) geological memoirs, (c) flooding, erosion, landslide and subsidence history, (d) data held by central and local authorities, (e) construction and investigation records of adjacent sites, and (f) seismicity.

(5)    *Sources of material for construction*: (a) natural materials, (b) tips and waste materials, and (c) imported materials.

(6)    *Drainage and sewerage*: (a) names of the sewerage, land drainage and other authorities concerned and byelaws, (b) location and levels of existing systems (including fields, drains and ditches), showing sizes of pipes, and whether foul, stormwater or combined, (c) existing flow quantities and capacity for additional flow, (d) liability to surcharging, (e) charges for drainage facilities, (f) neighbouring streams capable of taking sewage or trade effluents provided that they are purified to the required standard, (g) disposal of solid waste, and (h) flood risk to the proposed works, and/or caused by the proposed works.

(7)    *Water supply*: (a) names of the authorities concerned and byelaws; (b) location, sizes and depths of mains, (c) pressure characteristics of mains, (d) water analysis, (e) availability of water for additional requirements, (f) storage requirements, (g) water sources for fire fighting, (h) charges for connections and water, (i) possible additional sources of water, and (j) water rights and responsibilities under the Water Resources Act of 1963, which controls permissions to take water from any source.

(8)    *Electricity supply*: (a) names of the supply authorities concerned and regulations, (b) location, capacity and depths of mains, (c) the voltage, phases and frequency, (d) capacity to supply additional requirements, (e) transformer requirements, and (f) charges for installation and current.

(9)    *Gas supply*: (a) names of the supply authorities concerned and regulations, (b) location, sizes and depths of mains, (c) type of gas, thermal quality and pressure, (d) capacity to supply additional requirements, and (e) charges for installation and gas.

(10)    *Telephone*: (a) address of the local office, (b) location of existing lines, (c) requirements, and (d) charges for installation.

(11)    *Heating*: (a) availability of fuel supplies, (b) planning restrictions (smokeless zone: Clean Air Act of 1956 administered by the local authority), and (c) district heating.

Since 1805 the *Ordnance Survey* has been engaged in developing very detailed topographical information for Britain, and its maps are continually being brought up to date and extended. These maps, which are very useful in defining site conditions and in interpreting special maps such as those of geology or land use, are available in two main groups: these are the *large-scale maps* (with scales ranging from 1:1250 to 1:10 560 and *small-scale maps* (ranging from 1:25 000 to 1:625 000).

The 1:25 000 scale map (about 2.5 in/mile), which is the largest Ordnance Survey map printed in colour, is on National Grid lines and covers an area of 10 km square. This map is very useful for a first appraisal of the site, e.g. the colour blue is used to mark watercourses, areas of water, springs, marshes and their associated names; if a regular pattern of straight, artificial drainage channels is shown, this can be taken as a good indication of a high water-table. Field boundaries are shown on the 1:25 000 map, and there is a good indication of the type of vegetation in woodlands and uncultivated ground. The contour interval is 25 ft, which can help in picking out steep ground that is liable to instability. Public footpaths, bridle paths, and other rights-of-way, which are useful in getting access to a site, are clearly marked on the more recent revisions of this map.

The 1:10 560 scale maps (6 in/mile) cover the whole of Britain. As part of the metrication programme, these maps are being replaced by 1:10 000 maps with a contour interval of 5 m (10 m in the more mountainous areas).

Maps at a scale of 1:1250 (about 50.5 in/mile) cover most towns and urban areas with a population of about 20 000 or over; each such map represents an area equivalent to 500 m square. Maps at a scale of 1:2500 (about 25 in/mile) cover the whole of Britain, apart from areas of mountain and moorland.

The familiar small-scale *One-inch Map* (1:63 360)—which is currently being replaced by the 1:50 000 series—is useful for general planning and location purposes. The *Route Planning Map* (1:625 000 or about 10 miles/in) shows motorways, primary routes, and many other roads; it also identifies which highways have dual carriageways.

The decision as to which map to use at any particular stage of the reconnaissance survey depends upon the detail of the information required.

It may be noted that the sites of many ancient monuments, generally protected by Acts of Parliament, are also marked on these survey sheets, and the most up-to-date records of these should be obtained. In contrast, old Ordnance Survey maps can be very usefully perused in order to obtain information about the locations of concealed mineshafts, adits and wells; the sites of demolished buildings with possible concealed foundations and cellars; abandoned sewage farms; filled ponds, clay pits, quarries and sand and gravel pits; changes in landslip areas etc.

The British Geological Survey (BGS) is the principal source of geological data; information is readily available in the form of maps, geological handbooks, memoirs and papers. Very often also, the BGS will be able to provide information regarding the groundwater conditions in a given area, as well as details regarding boreholes at particular points, i.e. it has records on file of about a quarter of a million wells, shafts and boreholes.

The 1:63 360 BGS map series, with memoirs—which is currently being replaced by 1:50 000 scale sheets—is that which is used most often to gain an appreciation of the types of material and the geological structures occurring in a given locality; both the solid maps (which show the underlying main strata) and the drift maps (which show the superficial deposits) are normally consulted for the particular area being considered. For more detailed geological information, the 1:10 560 maps—now being replaced by 1:10 000 sheets—may be examined, e.g. the positions of many boreholes are marked on these, with brief borehole data.

The BGS has also published several maps relating to new towns and classic geological areas at a scale of 1:25 000, whilst groundwater conditions are shown on hydrogeological maps, e.g. of North and East

Lincolnshire at 1:126 720 and of the Dartford area at 1:63 360. The production of engineering geological maps of selected areas is currently being undertaken by the BGS.

A most useful source of detailed information regarding the soil conditions pertaining at a given site are the memoirs and accompanying soil maps of the *Soil Survey of Great Britain* (see also Chapter 4). The Soil Survey is seeking to prepare maps at the 1:63 360 scale for the country as a whole, but unfortunately only a small proportion has been covered to date. Some county and regional maps have been published at smaller scales. Whatever has been published, the Soil Survey has records or copies of all known, reliable pedological soil surveys, and copies of its own 1:10 560 and 1:25 000 field sheets; copies of manuscript maps may be made available to genuine enquirers before their publication.

For best engineering use, Soil Survey maps should be compared with the appropriate geological maps, e.g. it may be found that soil maps give a better picture of the drift materials, especially if the geological mapping is old. Soil maps may also give a better indication of lithological type and its variations, and poor drainage and peaty areas are readily distinguished.

An indication of the value of the Soil Survey maps can be gained from a consideration of the keys to such maps. These keys are quite full, and give both the nature of the parent material from which the soil profile has been formed and the drainage conditions of the soil (see, for example, Table 1.2). 'Excessively drained soils' are usually very coarsely textured, sandy or gravelly, whilst (at the other extreme) 'very poorly drained soils' are saturated within the upper 0.3 m for at least half the year, and are permanently saturated between 0.3 and 0.6 m. 'Gley soils'—which are soils with poor drainage—are of two kinds: in groundwater gleys the water-logged conditions extend to bedrock, whilst in the case of surface-water gleys the parent material is usually clay textured and, being impermeable to downward movement of water, has resulted in waterlogging in the upper 0.6 m of the soil profile.

It might be noted that in the USA the use of soil survey data has progressed to the stage where a correlation has been developed between the soil series shown on the maps and the Californian Bearing Ratio (*CBR*) values of the B-horizons for these soils[5].

Land use, land classification, and soil survey data are also readily available from appropriate organizations which can provide a tremendous wealth of information of use to the highway engineer. British Coal should be consulted if it is anticipated that the highway will penetrate areas where coal or oil-shale mining is/has been carried out.

The above are just a few of the sources of detailed information already available for the engineer to use in a reconnaissance survey. Details of these and other rich sources of information are readily available in an excellent publication in the literature[6].

As will be gathered from the above, the first step in the reconnaissance survey is the location and acquisition of all maps and memoirs relating to the area, as well as the most suitable air photographs. These are then thoroughly studied; a visit to the area may also be considered desirable at

**Table 1.2** Soil Survey of England and Wales—part of the key to sheet 125, Derby (1 : 63 360): explanation of mapping units (soil series)

| Geographic region | Parent material or substratum | Surface texture | Subsoil characteristics | Drainage classes, major soil groups, and soil series | | |
|---|---|---|---|---|---|---|
| | | | | Freely drained, brown earth | Imperfectly drained, brown earth with gleying | Poorly–very poorly drained, surface-water gley soil |
| Limestone uplands | Silty drift over carboniferous limestone | Silt loam | Brown or yellowish-brown clay loam | Nordrach | – | – |
| | Carboniferous limestone | Silt loam | Brown silt 1 m with shattered limestone 380 mm or less | Lulsgate | – | – |
| | Boulder clay and head from carboniferous and triassic rocks | Silt loam | Yellowish-brown clay loam | – | Ivet | – |
| Coalfield (lowlands) | Sandstone (coal measures) | Loam or silt loam | Brown silt loam over micaceous sandstone | Seacroft | – | – |
| | | Clay loam | Prominently mottled clay | – | – | Dale |
| | Shale (coal measures) | Loam | Prominently mottled clay loam or silty clay loam | – | Stanley | – |

this stage. Where appropriate, additional relevant information may be obtained from the BGS, other official bodies (e.g. local authorities), and university geology departments, and from the engineers of existing civil engineering projects in the area (e.g. site reports on roads, building foundations and pipelines). Typically, particular attention is paid to hills, waterways and land uses, e.g. low points or passes in the hills are potential fixed points in the location, as are river-crossing sites that afford suitable topography for approaches to bridges. Peat bogs and other marshy areas which may have to be avoided can also be detected at this stage. Sites for necessary flyover structures can be identified along intersecting roads and railway lines, and utility relocation problems may be anticipated.

Discovery of the above controlling factors, together with the rapid appraisal of intervening grades and horizontal alignments, is possible with the modern topographic map. In Britain, existing small-scale aerial photographs[7] can be very usefully employed to supplement the available topographical and geological maps, e.g. by helping to identify man-made features such as new roads, buildings (constructed or demolished), extensions to quarries and gravel pits, variations in field boundaries, pipelines and movement of mining spoil tips. In addition, many poor drainage and marshy areas, unstable ground, mining subsidence, abandoned streams, swallow holes and rock outcrops which are not on the maps can also be identified with the aid of these photographs.

The Air Photograph Units of the Department of the Environment, the Scottish Development Department, and the Welsh Office have comprehensive series of air photographs in their collections, including RAF and Ordnance Survey photographs. They also maintain central registers of air photography for England, Scotland and Wales for much photography held by and obtainable from commercial air photography companies. Furthermore, the Units have commissioned air photograph cover, e.g. for the whole of England and Wales in 1969 at a scale of 1:60 000, and for industrial South Wales in 1978–79 at a scale of 1:25 000. (Details of many sources of air photographs in Britain and overseas are readily available in the technical literature[8].)

Stereoscopic techniques can afford quantitative data and, when applied by a skilled photo-interpreter, they can also yield significant soil and subsurface information.

Next, armed with questions generated by the desk study, the reconnaissance engineer takes to the field and obtains an evaluation of the effect of unusual topographic features, hydrology, the nature of certain man-made works, and subsurface conditions. Table 1.3 summarizes some of the geological features that should be considered during the walk-over reconnaissance. Much preliminary information regarding alternative routes can be obtained from visual inspections of geological exposures, and by noting the state of stability of the local materials in old highway and railway cuttings. The overall objective of this phase of the study is to delimit terrain areas that are obviously unsuitable for highway construction, *without causing local disquiet and annoyance*, i.e. local people are often quick to

**Table 1.3** Engineering geology data noted in the 'walk-over' of a site[9]

| Engineering geology feature seen from the walk-over | Typical locations | Design and construction of significance to project | Additional techniques to aid identification in the reconnaissance phase | Additional techniques to evaluate in the full site investigation phase |
|---|---|---|---|---|
| River alluvium deposits | Adjacent and beneath modern rivers; Adjacent and beneath modern lakes; old infilled lake flats | Settlement, Borrow, Drainage, Variability | Local case histories, Photogeology, Simple engineering geophysics, Backhoe pits, Hand and posthole (mechanical) augers, Field engineering geological mapping, Simple index tests | Borings, Engineering geophysics, Trenches, Load tests, Trial embankments, Shafts |
| Glacial or till deposits | North of line Bristol to London. Valleys and plains | As above, plus stability | As above, especially photogeology, mapping and pits | As above, plus observational method and especially trenches |
| Fluvioglacial deposits | As above | As above | As above, especially photogeology, mapping, pits and augers | As above |
| Periglacial deposits and permafrost features | All Britain, but especially south of Wales to Bristol | As above, plus slope stability | As above, especially photogeology, mapping and pits | As above, especially pits and shafts |
| High groundwater and poor drainage | Lowlands, fens, highland bogs and moors | Settlement, Stability | As above, especially special photogeological techniques, mapping and observation holes | As above, plus observation holes |
| Rock structure/discontinuities | Everywhere on nearly all 'solid' deposits | Excavation, Borrow, Slope stability | As above, especially mapping and simple index tests | Mapping, drilling, and in situ tests and observations |
| Rock weathering | Everywhere, especially mechanical weathering in glaciated areas and chemical weathering in unglaciated areas | As above, plus settlement | As above | As above |

draw inferences—some of which may not be correct—from the presence of a highway engineering team in the area.

Also listed in Table 1.3 are additional investigatory techniques that may be used to gather supplementary information. In practice, it may be more appropriate to carry these out at a later stage in the investigation process.

Upon completion of the low-key reconnaissance survey, the engineer should be at least in a position to design the more detailed geotechnical investigations which are likely to follow, and should also have sufficient information available which, when taken in combination with the social, environmental, traffic, economic and political inputs, will enable the selection of one or more apparently feasible corridor routes. If the reconnaissance survey has been very thorough, and the necessary data are readily available, it may be possible immediately to carry out the necessary economic and environmental comparisons to aid in the determination of the best route (see Volume 1, Chapter 5, for further information on these evaluations).

The results of these studies are presented in a *reconnaissance report*[10]. In its barest essentials, this report should state the service and geometric criteria to be satisfied by the project, describe the preferred route(s), and present tentative estimates of cost. Also included should be provisional geotechnical maps for the locations under consideration, provisional longitudinal geological sections, and block diagrams showing the characteristics of the more important engineering features. Special situations which might lead to design or construction problems, or which might require special attention in a later detailed site investigation, should also be pointed out.

Major highway projects such as motorways and trunk roads deserve a comprehensive report, particularly since public hearings probably will be required. In such cases the reconnaissance report may also be designed as a public-relations device which will inform interested persons about the advantages (and disadvantages) of particular routes. It should cover matters such as the exhaustive nature of the study, concern for landowner's interests, highway safety, environmental considerations and the expected benefits from the highway to both the road user and the communities served.

**Preliminary location survey**
The preliminary survey is a large-scale study of one or more feasible corridor routes, each typically 40–240 m wide. It results in a paper location and alignment that defines the line for the subsequent, final, location survey. This paper location and alignment should show enough ties to the existing topography to permit a location party to peg the centreline. This much is a minimum; in many cases field detail for final design may also be obtained economically during the preliminary survey phase.

The preliminary survey is made for the purpose of collecting additional physical information which may affect the location of the highway within a given corridor. Thus, within each established corridor area, the shape of the ground, any potential ground subsidence problems[11,12], the limits of the catchment areas, the positions and invert levels of streams and ditches, and the positions of trees, banks and hedges, bridges, culverts, existing roads, power lines and pipelines, houses and monuments are determined and noted. These are then translated into maps, profiles and (frequently) cross-sections which can assist the engineer in the determination of preliminary grades and alignments and the preparation of cost estimates for alternative centrelines.

Two approaches are available for preliminary survey mapping: aerial surveys and ground surveys, either separately or in various combinations.

The ground method is best used in the situation where the corridor is closely defined, narrow rights-of-way are contemplated, and the problems of man-made culture are clear. Ground surveys, beginning with a traverse baseline, will probably furnish necessary data quite economically. Additional operations which can be quite easily included are the profile levels and cross-sections, and the ties to land lines and cultural objects.

The cost of a mainly desk-based aerial survey does not increase in direct relationship to the area photographed, and so this type of survey is likely to be more suitable and economical than a ground survey in the following instances:

(1)   where the reconnaissance was unable to approximate closely the final alignment—illustrations of this are entirely new locations in rugged terrain or where land uses and values vary widely,

(2)   where a wide right-of-way, such as that for a motorway, is necessitated,

(3)   where it is desired to prevent the premature or erroneous disclosure of the details of probable location—the ground-control work required for aerial surveys reveals little of the highway engineer's intentions, thereby preventing any land speculation or the premature awakening of local public concerns.

The choice of method should be an educated one, based on an advance cost analysis that takes into account the overall project schedule and the time and need requirements of the various techniques. The following discussion is concerned primarily with the carrying out of the traditional type of *ground survey*. The use of the airphoto technique is described separately in the discussion on photogrammetry and airphoto interpretation.

The first step is the carrying out of a baseline traverse. This traverse may be simply a series of connecting straight lines if the curvature necessary to connect the tangents is such that the highway curves will not deviate greatly from the tangents. Where sweeping curves with large external distances are required, they may have to be included as part of the original baseline so as to avoid unnecessary ground coverage. The baseline traverse should be stationed continuously from the beginning to the end of the survey, and the survey carried out to a degree of accuracy commensurate with the importance of the project and the nature of the topography being traversed. Angles between connecting lines should be measured in accordance with accepted highway surveying procedures and every angle point should be carefully referenced to at least two points established well outside the area that might be occupied by the highway construction.

To furnish data for a profile of the baseline, levels should be taken at all marked stations, as well as at all important breaks in the ground. Elevations should also be noted at all cross-roads, streams and other critical points on the line. Levels should always be referred to the standard datum plane of the country in which the works are being carried out. In Britain, the *Ordnance Datum* is used. This was originally referred to an approximate mean sea level at Liverpool, but was changed over forty years ago to that of the mean sea level at Newlyn in Cornwall, where it was fixed on the basis of hourly observations made over a six-year period from 1 May 1915. Thus old Ordnance Survey maps refer to the Liverpool Datum, while the current maps refer to the Newlyn Datum. The difference between the two sets of levels varies over the country from zero to about 600 mm as a result of corrections to the original survey. When old maps are being used, care should therefore be taken to determine on which datum they are based.

After the baseline has been pegged and levels run over it, the topography elevations may be taken by one of several methods. The simplest method is by cross-sections, and on fairly flat topography these are sometimes taken by the level party at the same time as the profile levels. Observations are made at right-angles from each station for as far as is considered necessary to cover the expected construction area for a given centreline. Where wider deviations of the location from the baseline are expected, the topography may be more rapidly taken by tacheometry, or (less commonly) by plane table, or by a combination of the two.

At the same time the locations of all trees, fences, buildings, etc., are noted so that they can be shown on the preliminary map.

The preliminary map prepared from the data collected by the classical ground-survey method is termed a *strip* map because it is plotted on a continuous roll of detail paper. The minimum information shown on the map is the plot of the baseline and all planimetric detail; it may or may not include the plotting of contours, depending upon the complexity of the project. In addition, it may be desirable to have it supplemented with detailed maps showing contours of those areas where complex structures or intersections are to be located.

The planimetric strip map should also show surface and subsurface information that might affect the location. For example, items that should be noted include steps in the ground in mining areas, i.e. these are most probably the result of mining subsidence; other such subsidence evidence includes compression and tensile damage in brickwork, buildings and roads, structures out of plumb, and interference with drainage patterns. Mounds and hummocks in otherwise flat country may indicate glacial till and gravel. Broken and terraced ground on hill slopes may be due to landslips; small steps and inclined tree trunks can be evidence of creep. Crater-like holes in chalk or limestone country usually suggest swallow holes filled with soft material. Low-lying flat areas in hilly country may indicate the presence of soft silty soils and peat. Unusual green patches, reeds, rushes, willow trees and poplars usually reflect wet ground conditions.

*Paper location*   The selection of a horizontal alignment, and the extent to which it may be selected to fit the ground economically, depends primarily upon the geometric design standards adopted for the highway. These, in turn, may range from the relatively low criteria for widths, curvature, grades and sight distances sufficient to accommodate sparse rural traffic at moderate speeds, to those criteria necessary for large volumes of heavy traffic travelling at high speeds. With the service classification established by the traffic requirements, and the appropriate standards of alignment thereby fixed, the combination of tangents and horizontal curvature is then sought that will best fit the topography while remaining within the limits of these criteria.

At the same time consideration will have to be given to factors other than the ground fit. These have already been listed in the 'dos and don'ts' of location (pp. 2–4).

Factors affecting the choice of a horizontal alignment will also affect the vertical alignment. One which deserves some further mention, however, is that of the earthworks required, as this is perhaps one of the most important factors to be considered with reference to construction. When the needs of all the other more important factors have been satisfied, then the best line is the one that gives the minimum total cost for earthworks. The ideal situation leads to the minimum quantities of excavation so balanced in sections with the quantities of embankment as to require a minimum of haulage without overhaul. This is usually an extremely difficult and rare condition to achieve and compromises are frequently necessary. Many factors affect earthworks decisions. For instance, the unit cost of excavation may be cheaper in one classification of material as against another, or the length of haul and the amount of required overhaul may make wastage and borrow desirable as an economical alternative. The solutions of these problems lie in economic analyses of the road user benefits and costs of the alternatives.

**Final location survey**
This survey, much of which is very often carried out as part of the preliminary survey, serves the dual purpose of fixing the centreline of the road, while at the same time collecting physical data which are necessary for the preparation of plans for construction purposes. If the previous surveys have been properly carried out, it will be found that much of the final location survey can be reduced essentially to identifying and referencing the centreline by coordinates, and obtaining critical elevations not already available.

As with the reconnaissance and preliminary surveys, the trend in carrying out the final location survey is to make as much use as possible of aerial photography and photogrammetric maps in order to reduce tedious field study. Large-scale maps procured in this way for the preliminary survey will usually provide much, if not all, of the information needed for the final location, the preparation of construction drawings, and the other operations necessary to advance the project to the construction stage.

Electronic computers are further aids to efficiency at this stage of a highway project. Now every survey party chief is normally equipped with small battery-powered electronic computers which shorten the time required for, as well as reducing the possibility of errors in, field computations; they also eliminate the need for the engineer to carry trigonometrical and other mathematical tables into the field.

Very significant savings in both office time and labour can be effected by feeding the survey data into larger electronic computers that are capable of comparing alternative centreline routes. For example, in Britain a computer program called *BRUTUS* (*B*roadband *R*o*UT*e *S*election) has been used successfully[13] to help the designer of a 30 km stretch of motorway to search for promising alternative routes within a broad band of interest. Another program called *NOAH* (*N*arrowband *O*ptimization of the *A*lignment of *H*ighways) has been used[14] to locate and design a road through exceptionally mountainous terrain in the Middle East, whilst satisfying exacting design standards; this task had proved impossible using normal manual methods. Both of these computer programs form part of the *HOPS* (*H*ighway *O*ptimization *P*rogram *S*ystem) suite[15,16] available through the Department of Transport.

The following are the general features of the final location survey. However, it should be emphasized that part of the requirements specified here will already have been satisfied in the earlier ground surveys.

*Pegging the centreline*   The centreline established at this stage should follow closely the paper location on the preliminary-survey map, conforming as much as possible to the major and minor control points and the alignments prescribed. In practice, however, this is not always possible, and local deviations may be necessary to make the best fit of the line to the topography and to allow for incomplete or inaccurate preliminary-survey information. For high-quality roads, additional detailed information may need to be gathered regarding fill sections, profiles, cross-sections, and topography; during the topography phase, particular attention will need to be directed towards recording all invert elevations, existing drainages, sanitary sewers, structures, and public utility information.

*Centreline levelling*   Profile levels are taken along the centreline at each station and at all intermediate points where there is any significant change in the slope of the ground, so that a truly representative profile is obtained. This profile should normally extend for at least 150 m beyond the beginning and end points of the scheme so as to allow for transitions to existing or new facilities. Where temporary benchmarks are found within the limits of the construction width, new permanent ones will need to be located outside the final construction area so that the points can be preserved throughout the period of the highway contract. In many instances it will be possible to locate one of these about every kilometre along the centreline and, in addition, there should be at least one such benchmark within about 60 m of each highway structure.

*Cross-sections*   Cross-sections should be taken at each station, points of significant change in ground slope, and for a reasonable distance beyond the beginning and end points of the project. (Where large-scale aerial photographs are available, this detail work can be considerably curtailed, since both profile and cross-section data can be developed in the stereo-plotter to an accuracy comparable with that obtained by the ground-survey procedure.)

*Property lines* The positions of all property corners, lines, fences, buildings and other man-made improvements are accurately determined and noted during the final location survey. The exact extent to which all property owners are directly affected by the new location should also be determined.

*Intersecting roads* The directions with respect to the pegged centreline of all intersecting roads should be measured. Profiles and cross-sections of the intersecting roads should be taken for some distance on both sides of the new centreline. It should be remembered that it is always easier to design a new junction, and 'tie-ins' between existing and proposed construction, when there are too many cross-sections rather than too few.

*Ditches and streams* All ditches and streams within the area of construction should be carefully located with respect to the pegged centreline. In addition, stream-bed profiles should be taken for some distance upstream and downstream; usually about 60 m will be adequate for all but the largest streams. Greater profile lengths and cross-sections may also have to be taken of larger streams to provide information required for the hydraulic design. Detailed information should be obtained on all existing culverts or bridges, including the type, size, number of openings or spans, elevation of culvert flow lines and stream-beds under bridges and, where available, high water elevations.

*Special site surveys* In order to obtain the detailed information needed for the design of large culverts, bridges, roundabouts, interchanges and other complex intersections or structures, special site surveys will have to be made. Information obtained should include such items as alignments of streams and intersecting roads, topography, profiles, cross-sections, elevations of grade-controlling points, foundation conditions and, for bridges and large culverts, data on adjacent structures upstream and downstream.

Site surveys for borrow pits and quarries should provide information on the quality and quantity of subbase, roadbase and surfacing materials, concrete aggregates, the availability and accessibility of fill for earthworks and reclamation, water for compaction and topsoil for final sodding purposes. If particular borrow pits or quarries are specified, elevations along lines perpendicular to one or more arbitrary baselines may be taken in each case for use in later computations of the quantities of materials removed.

## 'Real world' situation: a comment

The above has attempted to present what might be termed an idealistic approach to the surveys carried out prior to the establishment of the final

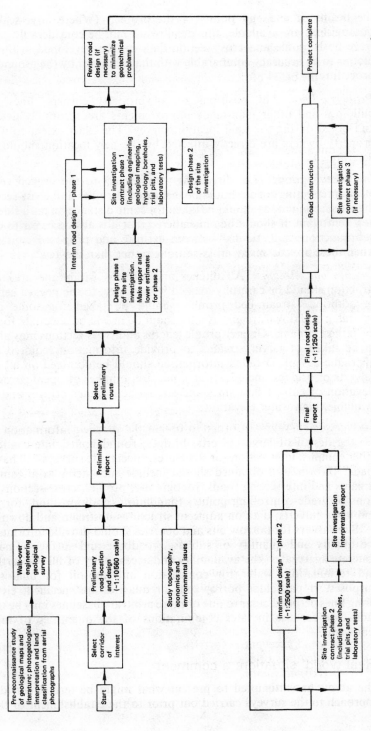

**Fig. 1.2** Flow diagram showing the major site investigation activities set in their relative position to the main highway design activities[9]

centreline of a highway in a non-controversial rural environment. In practice, of course, the situation can be very different, with the surface and subsurface geotechnical investigations prior to the final route selection stage of the project development varying from non-existent to fairly comprehensive. It is the belief of many engineers that the final route selection is mostly predicted on considerations other than geotechnical, e.g. economics, traffic patterns, environmental and social issues, politics and local concerns (see Table 1.1); as a result, it is probably true to say that there is a tendency, at the pre-design stage, for some engineers to seek to perform only the minimum geotechnical investigations required for the adequate evaluation of potential problem areas.

What is probably a fairly realistic approach to the carrying out of the appropriate surveys in Britain is summarized in Fig. 1.2. Note that this figure shows that the main surface and subsurface investigations are carried out during an integrated final location and highway design phase. In other words, the tempo and depth of detailed site investigation increases as the road location and design become more settled. In this way, the amount of wasted pre-design investigative work is minimized.

# River crossings

## Bridge surveys

In the not too distant past, it was common practice, when a new highway had to cross a river or estuary, to determine first where the most favourable bridge site was located and then to 'bend' the highway so that the crossing could be made at this point. The term 'favourable' as used in this context usually meant the cheapest right-angle crossing. Today, however, the bridge location is determined upon a more desirable basis, it being realized that the crossing having the least initial cost is not necessarily the most economical one. It is accepted that the bridge is an integral and important part of the highway, but not—unless the river is extremely wide—the controlling one. Thus the approach now taken is first to secure the most favourable location and alignment for the highway, and then to require the bridge engineer to furnish the necessary bridge to fit this scheme. This, of course, usually results in more expensive structures, since skew bridges are more costly than right-angled ones and, all other things being equal, longer bridges are more expensive than shorter ones. In the long run, however, a better and more economical highway is obtained.

Surveys for significant bridges, as with other transportation projects, can be carried out in three classical phases, i.e. reconnaissance survey, preliminary location survey, and the final location survey. The following is but a brief description of what these entail; for further details the reader is referred to an excellent report which is readily available in the literature, and on which this brief discussion is based[10].

The *reconnaissance survey* for a major water-crossing structure is carried out to obtain information regarding the location of all possible sites, their comparison with respect to feasibility, and the preparation of preliminary estimates of the cost of construction. Data gathered for the desk-based component of this study may include[4], as appropriate:

(1)   requirements of statutory bodies controlling waterways, e.g. port authorities, water authorities, planning authorities, and fisheries,

(2)   topographical and marine survey data to supplement, where appropriate, Ordnance Survey maps and Admiralty charts and publications,

(3)   available detailed information about rivers, the size and nature of catchment areas, tidal limits, flood levels, and their relationships to Ordnance Datum,

(4)   observations on tidal levels and fluctuations, velocity and directions of currents, variations in depth, and wave data,

(5)   information on scour and siltation, and the movement of foreshore material by drift,

(6)   location and effects of existing river or marine structures, wrecks, and other obstructions above and below the waterline,

(7)   observations on the conditions of existing structures, e.g. attack by marine growth and borers, corrosion of metal work, disintegration of concrete, and attrition by floating debris or bed movements.

In-depth field surveys are rarely required at this stage of the investigation, most of the required information being already available from existing records, maps, and aerial photographs. However, in certain instances it may be desirable to inspect the sites and make precursory subsurface explorations.

The reconnaissance survey having established the need for a water crossing within a limited zone, the *preliminary location survey* is carried out to define its exact alignment, and to obtain the physical data needed for the design of the project and for the acquisition of the necessary land. The operations usually include a preliminary triangulation to establish the starting coordinates for traverses at the bridge-heads and along the approaches, topographic surveys along these traverses, and the design of a more elaborate triangulation system that can be used later during the construction phase of the project.

In addition to these surface operations, the preliminary survey will normally include a hydrographic survey of the project site. This is carried out to determine the hydraulic or flow characteristics of the water at the proposed crossing, as well as the nature of the channel or estuary bottom containing the water. Also included are engineering and geological surveys of the subsurface foundation conditions. The nature of the hydrographic data required will, of course, vary with the type of crossing and the location and exposure of the structures. In general, however, it will be necessary to obtain detailed location information on such items as the water datum, tide or river flood stages, tidal and river or other currents, and water and—in cold climates—ice erosion characteristics, together with a complete estuary or river-bottom profile with cross-sections. Where embankments or causeways are being constructed using hydraulic fill procedures, some underwater studies for material borrow areas will be required.

The *final location survey* can be considered as two stages, the preconstruction survey and the construction survey. The preconstruction survey operations are performed in advance of the actual construction but are directly related to it. Examples are the establishment of the horizontal control stations and benchmarks that will constitute the fundamental framework defining lines and grades. Much of this work can be accomplished during the preliminary survey but generally some later refinement and strengthening is necessary to improve its accuracy. The construction survey operations provide the intermediate and final positioning, both horizontally and vertically, of the various components of the bridge structure. This is a most important stage since, for instance, the exact location and span distance between two main piers of a cantilever bridge are considerably more critical than the general positioning of these two piers and the remainder of the bridge within a given area. Also, these operations must be closely coordinated with the construction schedule to avoid any unnecessary and costly delays to the contractor.

The importance of attaining high accuracy in this survey cannot be overemphasized; it must be attained if wasteful delays and needless expenditure of money are to be avoided. For instance, for bridges of one-thousand metres or more in length to be properly located, surveys having an accuracy of 1 part in 100 000 may be required. This level of accuracy can usually only be attained by the use of special geodetic equipment.

## Low water crossings

It is appropriate to introduce here the concept of using low-cost water crossings in some rural areas. Whilst such crossings should never be considered for use on high-quality main highways, their usage on access roads of low priority may well be considered at the survey stage.

Low water crossings are the road—stream crossings on low-volume roads that are located and deliberately designed to be covered with flood waters approximately once per year[17], usually following the maximum annual storm. In contrast, conventional high-level bridge crossings are designed to cater for at least 25—50-year floods.

Whilst difficult at first for highway designers to accept, such crossings can be very effectively and economically utilized in certain rural areas. For example, single-use access roads (such as roads for logging operations or recreation) rarely require 100 per cent continuous access, whilst scattered farm residences usually can operate adequately with occasional road closures. Furthermore, it is quite reasonable to drive even a modern car through 10—15 cm of water. Often also, there may be alternative, but longer, access routes available when high water temporarily closes one crossing.

Another reason for giving consideration to low-level crossings is that highway embankments and constricted drainage waterways can cause flooding in broad, flat stream valleys. The construction of a low water crossing often permits the continuation of a large, natural waterway, thereby minimizing the flooding of adjacent lands, crops and homes. The alternative of high-level approach roads and a large bridge structure may not be economically feasible or environmentally desirable.

In mountainous terrain, streams on alluvial fans have widely varying, rapidly changing flows, and unstable channels. Low water crossings at such locations offer a low investment in a high-risk situation, and minimize the chance of causing a channel change.

In arid or semi-arid regions, drainage-ways carry little or no water, except during sudden, severe storms; the bridges and high-level approach roads required to cater for these infrequent floods may be prohibitively expensive. In northern climates, floods are often associated with spring runoffs, whilst flow may be low and steady during the remainder of the year, and easily provided for by low-level crossings.

Low water crossings include fords, vented fords, and low-level bridges.

*Fords* (*or dips*) are formed by lowering the road surface grade to the stream-bed level from bank to bank. They may be most appropriately used across dry drainages or where the day-to-day stream flow is low.

In its simplest form, ford location means finding access points to/from a firm, unsurfaced level crossing on the natural bed of the stream or drainage path. Further levelling of the stream-bed may be accomplished by placing a row of boulders along the downstream crossing edge and filling gravel behind the boulders; a more reliable design may utilize meshed gabions along the downstream edge. Adequate embedment of the boulders and gabions, and additional downstream boulders for stream energy dissipation, are essential to avoid the development of a downstream plunge pool and consequent undermining of the roadway crossing support. Fords may also be surfaced with concrete, bitumen or gabions to protect the crossing from erosion, and provide the crossing vehicle with a more stable, tractive surface.

*Vented fords* (*or dips with culverts*) are formed by allowing the partial lowering of the grade of the road surface so that it can be covered by water during floods, whilst culverts beneath the crossing surface handle the day-to-day water flow. This type of ford is most appropriately used at locations where the day-to-day water flow exceeds a fordable depth by vehicles.

Problems can occur with this type of ford unless it is properly located, and the sloped culvert entrances are properly formed, so as to be self-cleansing. A splash apron or cutoff wall will need to be located on the downstream side of the ford, to prevent undermining of the culverts and the roadway on top.

*Low-level bridges*, usually of concrete, up to about 45 m in length and with spans of 5–10 m, may be constructed at locations where culverts cannot handle the day-to-day water flow. However, the bridge is designed so that its surface is covered by water during the design flood.

## Highway location in urban areas

The determination of a suitable location for a major highway in an urban area can be one of the most complex problems imaginable. In theory, the traditional sequence of reconnaissance, preliminary and final location surveys is carried out; in practice, however, there are usually only two phases, these being a combination reconnaissance–preliminary survey and the final location survey.

The final location survey is similar to that described for a highway location survey in a rural area, except that it is usually much more difficult to carry out. For example, very rarely in an urban area can a continuous centreline be pegged directly. So many obstructions are met with that, until the ground is cleared for the roadworks to begin, it is always necessary to set out the centreline by means of complicated off-setting and referencing. The taking of profile and cross-section levels is always a complicated and sometimes delicate task, during which the operators not only are faced with considerable sighting problems but may also be subjected to the concerns of property owners who are not terribly enthusiastic about granting permission for survey teams to enter private property.

Notwithstanding the difficulties associated with the final location survey, it is in the earlier reconnaissance–preliminary survey that the main problems arise. This is normally a desk-based study since, in an urban area, there is usually ample information available from previous geotechnical surveys, street improvements, property locations, and utility installations to render superfluous any but the most essential field investigations. It should be pointed out that in this instance aerial surveying procedures can be invaluable in indicating features which may be invisible to the completely ground-based investigator.

The early studies leading to the location and preliminary design of a major highway in an urban area can be divided into the following six interrelated steps.

(1)  Determine the approximate traffic load along a general route suggested by traffic desire lines.
(2)  Select the type of highway, the number of lanes needed to accommodate the approximate traffic load, and the type of service to be provided.
(3)  Make plane and field sketches to establish one or more preliminary lines that approximate the desire-line location, and make sketch preliminary designs including interchange locations.
(4)  Assign traffic to one or more of the selected locations to determine design traffic volumes.
(5)  Adjust line and complete sketch preliminary plans for major alternative locations.
(6)  Analyse and compare alternative locations for selection of the preferred one by making cost estimates, analysing road user benefits and considering other controls and factors.

Most of these factors have already been discussed elsewhere (see Volume 1, Chapter 3), so the following discussion is confined to the *controls* in step (6) which may need to be taken into account.

## Urban location controls

There are very limited possibilities for locating new major highways, or improving existing streets to carry out the same functions, in an urban area. The town is an established entity and it is usually only on the very outskirts that undeveloped land can be obtained. The streets necessary for the free flow of traffic are fixed in location and size by the natural topography and by the buildings which they service. Thus the location of a new highway or the substantial improvement of an old one must inevitably result in the elimination of, or changes in, portions of the established city culture and this, just as inevitably, complicates the task of finding a suitable location.

While the anticipated traffic is a major factor controlling the location of a highway, it must always be qualified by an evaluation of its effect upon, and relationship with, land use and other similar town planning considerations. Town planning is concerned with the present and future needs of the business, industrial, residential and recreational elements of a town so that a pleasant and functional whole is assured now and in the future. Thus the highway engineer is actively participating in town planning when locating (and designing) a new highway and must be prepared to bow to policy and social needs where necessary and appropriate.

The parking problem is acute in most cities, as is the traffic congestion in the streets, and these can be alleviated or accentuated by the location of a new major route. Thus it is generally desirable to locate the new highway as close as possible to existing or potential parking areas. This is particularly important in or near central areas where, of necessity, vehicle travel and consequent traffic congestion has to be minimized. If the most suitable route location does not meet this criterion, then congestion can often be reduced by the judicious location of the on- and off-ramps which connect the major highway to appropriate town streets.

The existing transport systems are most important controls affecting the location and type of urban arterial highways. Pedestrians, cars, lorries, buses and trams use the streets and, obviously, any new facility must be integrated with the existing road system if optimum usage is to be obtained. Equally important, however, are the other transport media, e.g. railways and their terminal stations, waterways and docks, and airports; all of these facilities need servicing by major roadways if they are to fulfil their functions. With the present tendency towards cutting railway services, it may be that a railway line may offer a location possibility of value for highway purposes. Usually, the area along a railway is either rundown or sparsely developed so that it can be obtained at prices well below those of alternative locations.

As in rural areas, the topography and physical features of a town can be major controls influencing the location of a highway. Geotechnical and groundwater conditions may also affect location. For instance, subsurface conditions, such as a high water-table or rock close to the surface, will normally preclude a depressed highway, even though it may be desirable from other points of view. Poor subsoil conditions may also preclude the construction of elevated highways, or render more difficult and expensive the building of an at-grade roadway.

In an urban area, existing public utilities, such as storm-water and sewer pipes, and water, gas and electric lines and their appurtenances, can present such severe difficulties that they will affect the location of a major highway. Whether they be for at-grade or depressed highways, some adjustments in utilities are always necessary; in the case of a depressed highway the utility relocation costs may be so great as to make another site more attractive.

## Remote sensing techniques

Historically, highway engineers have had to use their ingenuity to maximize the use of scarce financial resources when carrying out surveys preparatory to the location and construction of major highways. For example, in well-populated, highly developed countries, the amount of physical investigation carried out in the field often can be minimized by making good use of the wealth of information already available from various historical sources. In the newly developing countries, and also in many of the larger highly developed ones, e.g. Canada and the USA, such historical data are often not available, with the result that very large costs have to be incurred both at the planning stage and, unfortunately, at the maintenance stage to correct errors that should have been picked up at the survey stage. For example, it is reported [18] that well over US$100m is spent annually in the USA to correct highway landslides, most of which could have been avoided by more thorough surveys before selection of the final road routes.

To meet this need for improved survey practice at relatively low cost, particularly in locations where there is a significant absence of relevant topographic and subsurface data, a family of investigative systems known as *remote sensing techniques*, capable of providing a wide range of different forms of imagery (in addition to conventional air photography), has started to become available to the highway engineer in recent years.

In this context, remote sensing is defined as the means by which information can be gathered about an object, such as the surface of the earth, without being in physical contact with it. Such information may be gathered from ground measurements, aircraft or satellites, using a range of equipment from the simple camera to the most sophisticated multispectral scanners.

Numerous papers have been written in recent years regarding the potential of remote sensing in highway location and geotechnical surveying. The following brief discussion is based mainly on some of the more useful recent publications in this field of study [1,18-22].

### Electromagnetic spectrum

All bodies in the universe emit electromagnetic radiation which travels through space as a wave, and remote sensing techniques are concerned with the detection and recording of radiant energy within the electromagnetic

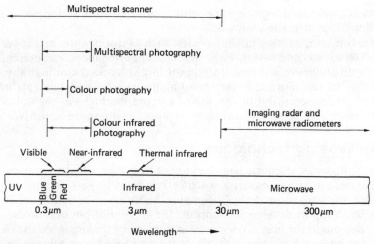

**Fig. 1.3** Spectral sensitivity ranges of imaging sensors[1]

spectrum. In general, a brightness value recorded on a photograph or scanner image represents the total intensity of electromagnetic radiation—including that received from the target or ground surface—entering a receiver at a particular point. Until the 1970s, black-and-white photography was the only form of remotely sensed data generally available to the highway engineer. Now black-and-white, infrared, false-colour infrared and colour photography, multispectral photography, multispectral scanner imagery from the Landsat satellites, and special airborne radar and scanner systems have started to become more readily available. This imagery has the potential to provide considerable additional information to the highway engineer, provided that appropriate and selective interpretative techniques are employed. In many instances, these interpretative techniques are only now being developed.

**Table 1.4** Multispectral tonal signatures for typical highway surfaces (reported in reference 19)

| Highway surface | Tonal signatures | | | |
| | Panchromatic black-and-white (0.4–0.7 $\mu$m) (No. 12 filter) | Black-and-white infrared (0.7–0.9 $\mu$m) (No. 12 filter) | Thermal infrared imagery (8–14 $\mu$m) | |
| | | | Daytime | Night-time |
|---|---|---|---|---|
| Concrete | Light | Medium | Medium light | Light |
| Asphalt | | | | |
|   fresh | Dark | Dark | Light | Light |
|   weathered | Medium light | Medium | Medium | Light |
| Gravel | Light | Light | Medium | Medium light |
| Cinders | Dark | Dark | Light | Medium light |

Figure 1.3 summarizes the spectral ranges of common imaging sensors and illustrates some of the basic distinctions.

It should be noted that the spectral characteristics of any object on the earth's surface largely depend upon its atomic and molecular structure, and are selective with regard to wavelength. As a result, remote sensing devices discriminate between different surface features on the basis of distinctive 'signatures' in respect of their reaction to electromagnetic energy. For example, Table 1.4 shows how—on the basis of an analysis of different photographic and imagery data collected over a 13-month period—different tonal signatures were identified in different spectral regions for various road surfaces occurring within a given test site. In relation to this table, it should be noted that at least three spectral regions had to be sampled in order to differentiate between and identify all of the different types of highway surface.

## Conventional aerial photography

The *human eye* is a most efficient remote sensor within the wavelength band 0.3–0.7 $\mu$m. This information can be supplemented by the use of *black-and-white* and *colour aerial photography*, usually with the aid of a suitable filter combination which enhances certain surface features. For example, the green and red wavelength bands (0.5–0.7 $\mu$m) are best suited for land use classification or vegetation black-and-white mapping, whilst the infrared (0.7–0.9 $\mu$m) band will clearly distinguish healthy from unhealthy vegetation. Since water totally absorbs infrared radiation, this type of photography can be particularly useful in delineating land–water boundaries, rivers, drainage areas, and areas with underground water supplies.

The use of aerial photographs in highway location and geotechnical surveying is a well-accepted highway engineering practice, and hence is discussed separately in this chapter. However, it is appropriate to note here that historically airphoto interpretation has been mainly based on photography taken for photogrammetric purposes, the great majority of which is typically on 9-inch panchromatic monochrome film in large cameras at a scale of between 1 : 20 000 and 1 : 50 000. Recent trends have been towards the use of specially commissioned different colour film emulsions for interpretative purposes, i.e. the additional information extracted from colour photographs can be most significant since colour photography contains hue and chroma data as well as tonal and textural information, and the human eye is capable of separating at least 100 times more colour combinations than grey scale ones. Thus, whilst the use of colour films may be more costly, the added expense may be more than offset by the additional information interpreted more quickly for material surveys and the discrimination of soils, geology and other ground features. This is why in many terrain investigations the standard techniques of airphoto interpretation are now being most effectively complemented by the use of colour and false-colour infrared films in multispectral photography for detailed investigations.

## Scanning systems

*Thermal scanners*, which sample the thermal infrared part of the spectrum, can operate during both the day and the night. In fact, night-time operation is to be preferred, as there are then no solar effects and only the thermal radiation emitted from the ground surface is recorded. After processing, a form of 'thermal map' is obtained which may be black-and-white or colour coded. Hidden subsurface conditions and geological features that influence highway location and design can then be detected by what is in effect a sensing of subtle surface temperature differences, e.g. the location of water-saturated slopes, soft organic soils, underground cavities and subsurface voids, volcanic and hydrothermal activity, buried utilities and conduits, and subsurface drainage systems [19]. Local differences in the proximity of the water-table to the ground surface—a factor which has a considerable effect upon the stability of a highway pavement—also have been detected using this technique.

Whilst multispectral thermal imagery could well have a tremendous potential for the future, it is at this time a relatively expensive process. In practice, therefore, its usage is probably most justified when a highway alignment has already been found in a poorly-explored area, but a more-finely-detailed geotechnical analysis is required. A much more exciting possibility in terms of practical usage by the highway engineer is the *visual multispectral scanner* (*MSS*) imagery currently available from the orbiting Landsat satellites.

A multispectral scanner which moves over the surface of the earth is able to receive incoming radiant energy which is split into its various spectral components, and then converted into electrical signals by means of photoelectric detectors. These signals are normally recorded on magnetic tape or they can be displayed immediately on a cathode ray oscilloscope screen. Whilst scanner imagery is very much like multispectral photography in that it can record radiation in the visible and photographic infrared range, and in spectral bands extending through the ultraviolet and thermal infrared, it has the additional advantage that spectral bands outside the photographic range can be included (see Fig. 1.3). Furthermore, the movement of successive scan lines is proportional to the forward motion of the carrying vehicle, i.e. an aircraft or satellite, so that these scanners can provide a continuous image of the earth's surface.

At the present time there are at least 4000 satellites circling the earth; as is well recognized, they are used for many and varied purposes. Since the launching of the first Earth Resource Technology Satellite (ERTS-1, later renamed the Landsat satellite) on 23 July 1972, however, these satellites have been used to provide many hundreds of thousands of images of the earth's surface to a central receiving station in Sioux Falls, South Dakota, USA; in addition, receiving stations are now operating in Argentina, Australia, Brazil, Canada, India, Italy, Japan, South Africa, and Sweden [20]. The orbits of the Landsat 5 satellite—this, the last of the series, was launched on 18 May 1984—are so arranged for the satellite to pass at a height of 705 km in a north–south direction over the same piece of earth every 16 days, and on command the satellite will transmit a synoptic image of any area 185 km² to these receiving stations.

The most important feature of the Landsat satellites is their multispectral scanners which permit simultaneous data collection over four wavebands in the visible and near-infrared (0.4–1.1 μm) spectral range. Whilst most of the data collected so far are issued to customers either as a computer-compatible tape (CCT) or as photographs at a scale of 1 : 10⁶, Landsat data are also available in photographic form at a scale of 1 : 250 000; CCTs are also now being produced. Each photograph is composed of a combination of picture elements (pixels), each with a theoretical ground resolution of 79 m × 59 m. Various rectification programs are available which, when suitable ground-control points can be established, will geometrically rectify a 185 km² scene to within 50–100 m absolute positional accuracy.

To date, the level of detail available from Landsat imagery has not been sufficient to meet the needs of highway location in well-developed countries such as Britain. Its potential for use in less-developed countries is considerable, however, e.g. the paucity of background information available on landforms, geology, soils, hydrology, and other features of these countries can be largely offset if the interpretation and analysis of Landsat data is combined with established land classification and field survey procedures. The following illustrate some uses to which Landsat data have been put (see also Table 1.5).

### Examples
Ethiopia has not been well mapped or surveyed. As a consequence, Landsat imagery at a scale of 1 : 2 × 10⁶ was judged in 1977 to be the most appropriate way to compile a land region mosaic of the whole of the country in a relatively short time. Amongst the objectives of this project was the compilation of a nationwide inventory of naturally occurring road construction materials. The mapping of Ethiopia has been extended into northern Kenya, to assist in a reconnaissance survey for land use potential and regional development. The area involved in this extension study was 240 000 km², and six months was allowed from inception of the work to the delivery of the draft report.

Individual Landsat scenes at scales of between 1 : 500 000 and 1 : 10⁶ have been used in a study of the terrain of the Wad Medani-Kosti area of the Sudan, to locate gravel materials for road construction for two major projects in the area. In this case the interpretation of the satellite images was assisted by the use of colour composites as well as black-and-white pictures, and by a density slicing technique which was used to enhance the appearance of the red quartzitic gravels being sought and make them stand out more clearly.

The Transport and Road Research Laboratory has also used Landsat data to assess the reserves of calcrete available for road construction within a corridor 400 km long by 40 km wide in central Botswana. Calcrete is a calcareous natural gravel that forms within the Kalahari sands, most abundantly in large bare depressions (pans), but also in smaller quantities beneath the sand itself away from pans. The purpose of the study was to

**Table 1.5** Summary of road alignment survey activities that are typically augmented by the use of widely available remote sensing techniques[20]

| Project stage | Aim | Activity | Remote sensing techniques | | Specialized remote sensing techniques |
| --- | --- | --- | --- | --- | --- |
| | | | Landsat MSS and RBV* | Existing black-and-white air photography | |
| Pre-project phase | To identify main sources of information and to put project into context with respect to the terrain | Collect together all relevant published material relating to the project to assess requirements for mapping and interpretation during survey stages | Purchase Landsat MSS imagery in a form suitable for the requirements of the project. Select images from several dates or seasons, if necessary. Make false-colour composite images at 1:250 000–1:500 000. Purchase Landsat RBV imagery, if available, at 1:100 000–1:250 000 | Make enquiries in Europe or of host government to purchase air photography and airphoto mosaics | Find out if specialized air photography or other form of remote sensing coverage has been made for some previous project in the area |
| Reconnaissance | To identify possible alternative routes and to define strategy for construction programme | Define project in terms of size, political and physical constraints, and geotechnical complexity. Examine possible routes on maps and satellite images and airphoto mosaics, if available. Undertake broad terrain classification for collation of regional information. Visit site to check interpretations; report on findings and plan next stage | Examine MSS photo products in conjunction with maps (scale as above). Interpret influence of major terrain features on road alignment, e.g. changing course of major rivers; catchment area of major river systems; extent of flooding of low-lying areas; possible sources of water for construction; possible sources of construction materials (e.g. alluvial terraces and fans); pattern of regional instability; extent of erosion; spread of deforestation; assessment of land acquisition/site clearance problems | Airphoto mosaics at approximately 1:100 000 used in conjunction with Landsat material | |

| Project stage | Aim | Activity | Remote sensing techniques | | |
|---|---|---|---|---|---|
| | | | Landsat MSS and RBV[*] | Existing black-and-white air photography | Specialized remote sensing techniques |
| Feasibility | To appraise route corridors and select best route | Make detailed interpretation of conditions on all routes; if necessary, make a more detailed terrain classification of the area. Interpret foundation conditions, earthworks (borrow and spoil areas), drainage, materials sources (gravels), major bridge sites, and hazard zones. Carry out site investigation of alternative routes, noting key physical and geotechnical features. Make cost comparisons. Carry out selected laboratory and field testing. Recommend best route and prepare report | Use MSS and RBV as base map if no more detailed mapping is available. Supplement airphoto interpretation with colour information from MSS | Use airphotos for all detailed classification study (scale 1 : 20 000–1 : 60 000, as available). (1) Carry out foundation conditions survey. (2) Calculate catchment areas and locations of culverts. (3) Identify spoil areas, also possible borrow areas. Minimize erosion risk. (4) Identify possible sources of construction material. (5) Locate all possible bridge sites. (6) Identify major hazard areas (poorly-drained soils, spring lines, unstable areas, erosion in river courses). | Commission specialized air photography (possibly small format) at a scale appropriate to size of task and degree of ground complexity (approximately 1 : 10 000–1 : 30 000). Examine Landsat computer-compatible tapes in interactive processor (scales 1 : 20 000–1 : 100 000) |
| Design | To make a detailed study of selected route to engineering design standards | Make a comprehensive site investigation of selected route, with full sampling and testing programme. Prepare final design documents | — | Use air photography to support all field survey activities | — |
| Construction, and post-construction maintenance | To build road and to carry out repairs prior to handing-over | Carry out road construction activities | — | Use air photography to locate access roads for construction traffic, in difficult terrain | Large-scale air photography may be used to monitor changes taking place at important sites as construction proceeds. It may also be used to record damage caused by landsliding, for design of rehabilitation measures |

[*] RBV = return beam vidicon

determine whether the relocation of the existing sand track through areas containing more calcrete would be justified.

## Radar imagery

Imaging radar and microwave radiometers produce images much like a scanner image but in spectral bands well beyond the thermal range (see Fig. 1.3). Thus *side-looking airborne radar*[23] (*SLAR*) is a self-illuminating imaging sensor capable of operating within a wide range of frequencies. Unlike the techniques previously discussed, however, these longer wavelength sensors employ antennae on planes as receivers rather than optical detectors.

The side-scan geometry of SLAR produces a small-scale image that is similar in appearance to a shaded relief presentation of the terrain. The contrasts in radar return (reflectivity) values are electronically processed to produce grey tones on film that can be related to a number of land surface conditions.

Radar imagery would appear to have a considerable potential with respect to providing the highway engineer working in remote and poorly-mapped areas with a display of very useful terrain data. It is reported[19] to have been successfully used for the preliminary selection of highway routes, the location of construction material sources, the detection of subsurface voids, the estimation of the bearing strength of cohesive soils from determinations of moisture content, differentiation of surface roughness and areas of abnormal soil moisture, and for specific hydrological, agricultural, vegetation and land use studies.

Particular advantages of SLAR are as follows.

(1)  Its all-weather, day and night, operational capability makes it an excellent survey tool for tropical areas that are perennially cloud covered.
(2)  It is generally produced at a relatively small scale, e.g. typical scales range from 1 : 100 000 to 1 : 400 000 and afford a synoptic display of terrain data.
(3)  The image geometry produces a display that is similar in appearance and usage to a shaded relief topographic map.
(4)  Objects or clusters of objects (including most cultural features) that are good reflectors of electromagnetic energy, and which might normally be lost on conventional small-scale mosaics of aerial photography, appear as high return or bright spots on SLAR imagery.
(5)  In comparison with photographic mosaics at the same scale, radar imagery strips present a relatively unconfused display of regional terrain patterns and landforms.
(6)  In forested areas the radar beam will partially penetrate the tree cover and reveal topographic details beneath.

## The future

The above has attempted to provide a very brief overview of the different types of remotely sensed data and interpretation techniques that have fairly recently become available to highway engineers. With the exception of conventional aerial photography, these earth surveillance methods are still in the developmental stage. However, refinements in sensing systems and improvements in data handling will ensure not only that future raw imaged data will be more sensitive to terrain conditions, but also that methods of analysing these data will improve.

What is inevitable is that remote sensing is a method of analysis that has a significant future, particularly in respect of strengthening location and geotechnical appraisals for highway projects in poorly-mapped, poorly-surveyed terrain.

Data of both a regional and a detailed nature are required for both route location and materials' surveys at different stages of major highway projects. Where large regional areas have to be surveyed, the multispectral scanner and SLAR imagery techniques are able to provide the broad type of coverage that is appropriate to this scale of examination, whereas conventional aerial photography is more suitable for use in studies of a more detailed nature. In other words, no single technique is applicable to all the various investigatory stages of such projects. As is suggested in Table 1.5, what is required is the use of the appropriate sensing technique at the proper stage in the overall project.

## Basic photogrammetry and airphoto interpretation

Aerial photography, which is part of the remote sensing family of investigative techniques, provides an effective means by which a comprehensive and economic survey of the ground surface can be carried out. The first really successful airphoto—a view of Boston, USA—was taken from a tethered balloon in 1890[22], whilst the first taken from an aeroplane was in 1909. Following the development of airphoto techniques in World War I, the first British air photography company was founded in 1919, and since then the use of the technique has continued to grow. For example, the Ordnance Survey has for many years made extensive use[24] of air survey in its mapping programmes, e.g. for those at scales of 1 : 1250, 1 : 2500 and 1 : 10 000. Highway engineers continually make use of airphotos to plan routes, to update their survey maps and plans and, to a lesser extent, for geotechnical interpretative purposes. More recently, the application of aerial photography to agricultural and land use development planning has also become commonplace.

### Photogrammetry

Photogrammetry has been simply defined[25] as the technique of obtaining reliable measurements by means of photography. It is usually divided into categories according to the type of photographs used or the manner of their use.

*Ground* or *terrestrial photogrammetry* is the term used when the photographs are taken from points on the ground surface. It might be noted here that, in recent years, increasing attention has been focused on the use of terrestrial photogrammetry for ground surveys, particularly in under-developed regions where basic ground information may be lacking, in steep broken ground where accessibility is difficult (e.g. steep valleys or gorges), and in circumstances where the constraints of time or limited availability of suitably skilled staff make it appropriate. Photo-theodolite stereo-pair ground photographs can be used to prepare accurately-contoured maps and plans, e.g. they have been used to make detailed plans of landslides in the mountainous areas of Columbia and Nepal[26] at scales between 1 : 200 and 1 : 10 000 with contour intervals between 0.5 and 5 m. The technique has also been used to measure rock slopes, and in surveys of highway cuttings and alignments.

*Aerial photogrammetry* is the term used to describe the use of photographs which have been taken from airborne vehicles: these can be either vertical or oblique photographs.

High oblique photographs are aerial photographs taken with the axis of the camera up to about 20 degrees from the horizontal, so that the horizon is included. In appearance these resemble a ground photograph taken from a commanding height; they provide true perspective views of the land surface and as such they may be analysed in terms of the laws of perspective. In practice, high oblique photographs are used primarily for pictorial and illustrative purposes because of the facility with which they can provide a panoramic view in familiar perspective.

Low oblique aerial photographs are taken with the camera axis inclined at such an angle as not to show the horizon. If the angle as measured from the vertical axis is large, a perspective view is obtained similar to that which is obtained with a high oblique photograph. If the angle is small, the result obtained very closely resembles a vertical photograph.

As is implied by the name, a vertical photograph is one taken with the optical axis of the camera coinciding with the direction of gravity. In fact, however, true vertical photographs are rarely obtained. The major factor which invariably causes non-verticality is the inability of the pilot to keep the plane exactly level, with the result that the camera axis deviates from the vertical. Nevertheless, 'vertical' aerial photographs are the best known and most used in aerial surveying for highway purposes, and so the following discussion is concerned with them and the manner in which they are used in practice.

## Vertical aerial photography

Aerial photography can be defined as the science of taking a photograph from a point in the air for the purpose of making some type of study of the surface of the earth. One useful way of obtaining an understanding of the basic features of vertical aerial photography is to consider part of the terminology which is commonly used.

### Photographic scale

A most important characteristic of a photograph is its scale. Unlike a map drawing, on which any measured distance bears a *fixed* and uniform relationship with the corresponding distance on the ground, the scale on a vertical air photograph will rarely remain constant but will vary from photograph to photograph and from point to point on a photograph. A photograph is actually a perspective projection, not an orthographic one, and thus areas on the ground lying closer to the centre of the photograph will appear larger than corresponding areas lying further away from the camera. In addition, the scale of a vertical air photograph will vary from location to location, depending upon the elevations of the ground area. This is illustrated in Fig. 1.4, which represents relationships established when a photograph is taken at a fixed height, $H$, above some datum plane, say sea level. The focal length of the camera is $f$ and the principal or nadir point of the photograph is at o. The elevation of the ground point A is $H_A$ and it appears as an image on the photograph at a; point B has an elevation of $H_B$ and appears on the photograph at b. By similar triangles the scales at a and b can be determined thus

$$\frac{d_{ao}}{d_{AO_A}} = \frac{f}{H - H_A} \quad \text{and} \quad \frac{d_{ob}}{d_{O_B}B} = \frac{f}{H - H_B}$$

respectively, where $d$ signifies the distance between the points as subscripts. Therefore

$$S_h = \frac{f}{H - h}$$

where $S_h$ is the scale at any elevation $h$, $f$ is the focal length of the camera, and $H$ is the flying height above the datum plane.

When planning photographic studies an average scale is used for rough calculation purposes. This average scale, $S_{ave}$, is given by the equation

$$S_{ave} = \frac{f}{H - h_{ave}}$$

where $h_{ave}$ is the average elevation of the terrain being photographed.

It is appropriate to note here that the accuracy of photogrammetric height measurement is about 1/500th part of the flying height[27]. Such accuracy is ensured when the ground vegetation is sufficiently low and

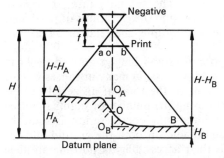

**Fig. 1.4**   Determining the scale of an air photograph

herbaceous, or of a shrubby, discontinuous character, so that the ground surface is faithfully imaged on the photograph.

Scales of 1:10 000 and 1:20 000 are widely used in Britain for general purpose air photography. However, it should be appreciated that no single photographic scale will satisfy all of the requirements for the variety of engineering studies performed. For example, it is quite common for medium- and larger-scale aerial photography to be stereoscopically examined in association with specially constructed controlled or uncontrolled photo-mosaics at scales of 1:80 000 to 1:150 000. Scales of 1:2400 to 1:6000 have been used for pavement-condition surveys, scales of 1:8000 to 1:12 000 for detailed soils mapping, scales of 1:15 000 to 1:50 000 for terrain analyses, and scales of 1:60 000 to 1:1 000 000 obtained from high altitude aircraft photography have been used for route selection and regional planning studies[1].

**Ground control**
Control surveys are an essential part of any mapping carried out by photogrammetric methods, i.e. if horizontal and vertical measurements are desired from the air photographs it is necessary to establish the positions and heights of a number of air-visible ground-control points. The horizontal control points are used to determine the scale and true orientation of each photograph, to provide a basis for correcting cumulative errors which arise when strips of photographs are assembled, and to link the photographs to the standard geographic (National Grid) coordinates. The vertical control points are needed before contour lines or point-elevations can be obtained from the photographs.

The accuracy with which the photo-control surveying is carried out should be commensurate with the map scale, desired map accuracy, and the required contour interval. Thus, for example, less accurate surveying is acceptable in isolated areas where the topography is rugged and land values are low; conversely, more accurate maps and surveys are required in areas where the topography is less uneven, land use is intense, and land values are high.

Ground-control establishment is divided into two parts. The first part, called the *basic control*, establishes a basic reference network of pillars and beacons, which includes triangulation and traverse stations and benchmarks, over the survey area as a whole. The second phase, the *photo control*, establishes the horizontal locations and the elevations of particular points which can be identified on the photographs and related to the basic control points.

The geodetic survey for the purpose of establishing ground control can be a most expensive and time-consuming process; in many instances its cost may account for as much as 50 per cent of the total of an aerial survey. Hence great care must be taken in choosing the number of points required and their exact location. The most important consideration is that the points must be easily and clearly identifiable on both the ground and the photograph. Another main factor is their accessibility. Choosing an ideal point on a photograph is of little value if it cannot be reached and referenced in the field. A vertical photo-control point should always be selected so that it is part of an area of no elevation change. Typical suitable points are the intersection of two existing road centrelines, or the base of a telephone pole in a flat field.

The number of photo-control points which have to be established depends entirely upon the purpose for which the aerial survey is being carried out. For instance, if a controlled mosaic of an area is to be constructed, no vertical control points are required, while only a limited number of horizontal photo-control points may be necessary. Whereas, if a topographic map is to be constructed from the air photographs, four vertical and two horizontal control points may be required on each overlap area of the initial and final pairs of overlapping photographs. In these cases the vertical control points are placed at the corners of the overlap in order to establish the datum above which the elevation can be measured. The two horizontal control points are located towards the centre of overlap so as to fix the scale of the map. In between, ground control should be maintained at the rate of one horizontal point near the centre of every fifth photograph and two vertical points, one near each edge of every third or fourth photograph. Additional control points may then be 'bridged-in' to intervening pictures with a first-order stereoplotting machine. If no vertical bridging is done, then two points will be needed for each photograph.

**Mosaic**

A mosaic is an assembly of individual aerial photographs fitted together systematically so that they provide a composite view of the entire area covered by the photographs. Thus the mosaic gives the appearance of a single photograph of the earth's surface that is both comprehensive and complete, and which can generally be used and appreciated without the need for special photogrammetric training. It is particularly valuable both for obtaining a complete picture of the terrain and as a public relations instrument to explain highway schemes to the interested public.

In order to provide distinction between the many ways of compiling mosaics, they are generally classified as being either controlled or uncontrolled. An *uncontrolled mosaic* is a compilation of photographs so oriented as to match as closely as possible corresponding images on adjacent photographs, but with no attempt being made to tie-in particular horizontal control points. They are useful when a rapid composite picture of an area is required, and where relative rather than absolute positions of terrain features are required. A *controlled mosaic* is composed of an assembled group of photographs, each of which has been corrected for major tilt distortions beforehand so that ground-control points are more accurately positioned.

A mosaic that is of particular interest to the highway engineer is the *strip mosaic*. This is prepared from a single strip of photographs taken along a single course or flight strip. It can be either controlled or uncontrolled, although for technical work the controlled strip mosaic is obviously of greater value.

**Planimetric and topographic maps**

A planimetric map, irrespective of whether it is derived from aerial photographs or from a ground survey, is one which illustrates the horizontal locations of particular features, whereas a topographic map also shows the relief of the mapped area, very often in the form of contour lines. A contour is defined as a line of equal elevation on the terrain. The chief characteristics of contours are as follows.

(1)   All points on any one contour have the same elevation.
(2)   Every contour closes on itself, either within or beyond the limits of the map. If a contour does not close within the limits of the map, it will run to the edge of the map.
(3)   A contour that closes within the limits of the map indicates either a summit or a depression. In depressions there will usually be found a pond or a lake. Where there is no water the contours are usually marked in some special way to indicate a depression.
(4)   Contours cannot cross each other, except where there is an overhanging cliff, and here there must be two intersections, i.e. where the lower ground contour line enters and emerges from below the overhanging cliff-line.
(5)   On a uniform slope, contours are equally spaced. The steeper the slope, the smaller is the spacing; the flatter the slope, the larger is the spacing.
(6)   On a plane surface, contours are straight and parallel to each other.
(7)   In crossing a valley, the contours run up the valley on one side and, turning at the stream, run back on the other side. Since the contours are always at right-angles to the lines of steepest slope, they are always at right-angles to the thread of the stream at the point of crossing.
(8)   Contours also cross ridge lines (watersheds) at right-angles.
(9)   In general, the curve of the contour in a valley is convex towards the stream.
(10)   All contour lines are noted as multiples of their intervals.

**Digital ground models**

It should be pointed out that, as a result of the very significant developments which have taken place in electronic computing over the past two decades, there has been an ever-increasing requirement for survey data describing the shape and disposition of the ground surface to be held in computer databanks, for subsequent interrogation and analysis by purpose-written programs. Now, instead of producing drawn topographic maps—which are essentially three-dimensional models of the ground surface shown in two-dimensional graphic form—for later use, it is accepted that the survey data may be of considerably greater value to the potential technical user if presented to the computer in the form of horizontal and vertical coordinates $(x, y, z)$ which represent the shape of the ground. A mathematical model of the ground surface derived from such data is known synonymously as a *digital ground model* (*DGM*) or a *digital terrain model* (*DTM*). Data acquisition for digital ground models can be via ground survey[28] or aerial survey[27] methods.

The last decade in particular has seen very significant advances in the development of modern surveying instruments which have increased both the speed of data acquisition and the accuracy of the data obtained by ground survey methods. Nonetheless it is now held by many that aerial survey methods for DGM data collection are generally more effective than ground methods, e.g. accessibility problems do not exist so that all points required to define the surface model can be measured directly, subject to their being clear of ground cover. A German project[29] to check a photogrammetrically-determined DGM showed that much better control was provided by photogrammetry (using large-scale photography) than by the ground survey.

As will be gathered from the above, DGMs are comprised of a pattern of data points of known horizontal coordinates and heights which represent the shape of the ground; the models also include interpolation procedures which enable the heights of any intermediate points of known horizontal coordinates to be determined. Several models are available with different patterns of data points and associated interpolation procedures[30]: these are known as ordered, semi-ordered, and random DGMs.

*Ordered* models have the survey points located in a square grid pattern, e.g. at the intersections of 10 m by 10 m multiples of the National Grid, which occur arbitrarily with respect to ground features. With this type of model, the photogrammetric process by which the perspective views of adjacent overlapping photographs are converted into orthographic projection involves an operator guiding a 'floating mark' to each succeeding ordered intersection position using a stylus moving over a control sheet that is gridded in the terrestrial system and properly oriented on the instrument's drawing table. When the planimetric location of a given point has been established, the photogrammetrist sets the reference mark onto the surface of the model and then, by pressing a button, is able to record the $(x, y, z)$ coordinates before moving to the next grid intersection.

*Semi-ordered* digital ground models result from the $(x, y, z)$ coordinates being determined for discrete points in strings along contour lines, on straight sections, or along characteristic terrain lines at significant breaks of slope (e.g. at the toe of an embankment). Modern photogrammetric instruments are able to output such $(x, y, z)$ coordinates at preset intervals of distance or time; thus, for example, whilst the operator is following a contour on the three-dimensional model, the digital ground model can be recorded automatically.

*Random*-type digital ground models are comprised of the coordinates of points selected in a random manner.

Digital ground models have been used extensively to describe the shape of the ground, in the design of new roads and road junctions. They are an integral part of several suites of highway design computer programs, e.g. the Department of Transport's *British Integrated Program System for Highway Design* (*BIPS*). They are used in the design of earthworks, drainage and structures and in the calculation of landtake for highways. Optimization programs which require DGMs as data input have been developed to derive the cross-sections, profiles, and cut and fill quantities required to minimize earthworks. Perspective drawings produced by computer programs have been used to show the shape of the ground in conjunction with motorist visibility distances along highways and aesthetic features of the design (including the appearance of bridges). Recordings of subsurface data have been included in digital ground models for road design. Subsurface modelling has also been used to define the distribution of soils in the ground, and to highlight zones of difficult soils where more detailed survey is required.

Digital ground models can be used very powerfully at all stages in the location of a highway. At the reconnaissance stage, it is obviously desirable to study the widest range of possible route alternatives; this can be done most effectively by developing a DGM for the area under consideration, and then automatically determining the corresponding ground profile for each alternative horizontal alignment considered. As the location of the alignment progresses, the bands of interest (i.e. strips of ground) through which the highway may possibly pass become more defined; if data regarding terminal points, curves and straights for any given alignment are fed into the computer, the detailed effects of these locational changes on, for example, cut and fill volumes can be determined without any costly re-surveying.

**Flight line, flight height and overlap**
A flight line is the path followed by a plane as photographs are being taken. Along this flight line, photographs are taken at continuous intervals, so that successive ones overlap each other by about 60 per cent and thus alternate photographs will overlap each other by about 20 per cent. This forward overlap of consecutive photographs is necessary for stereoscopic examination purposes; the overlap between successive alternate photographs is required because of the need to have an area common to two consecutive photographs in order to extend horizontal and vertical control by photogrammetric means.

For mapping purposes, flight lines are generally parallel to each other, and adjacent flight strips normally overlap each other by about 25 per cent. This ensures complete coverage of the ground, and ties-in adjacent strips.

The flying height for survey photography is dependent upon the following factors:

(1)   desired scale of mapping or profiling for which photography will be used,
(2)   vertical interval of contouring or height accuracy required,
(3)   intended interpretation usage, e.g. geology, vegetation, traffic, soils, or land use,
(4)   operational ceiling of aircraft above ground level (this may be governed by prevailing air traffic regulations in the area),
(5)   type of photogrammetric plotting equipment available, and techniques for mapping,

(6) desired film material, i.e. colour, infrared (or false) colour, or panchromatic,
(7) cost.

A most useful draft specification for vertical air photography is available in the technical literature[31]. The emphasis in this specification is on defining acceptable standards which can be achieved in practice rather than ideal standards which can only be achieved in exceptional weather conditions or by adopting special procedures which would unnecessarily increase the cost of photography for general use. The specification can also be modified or extended to meet particular requirements.

**Stereoscopic vision**
Stereoscopic perception is the facility which makes it possible for a person to see the image of a scene in three dimensions. Normally two-eyed vision is needed to realize and measure the depth dimension. An understanding of how this occurs can be gained by considering Fig. 1.5. Cover up the two black dots b and b' in Fig. 1.5(a) and look hard at the dots a and a', i.e. focus the eyes as if beyond the page. It will be found that four images will initially be seen but that the two middle ones can be made to superimpose to form another image in between the two real dots a and a'. A little practice is required before the fusion is clear; holding a postcard between them and at

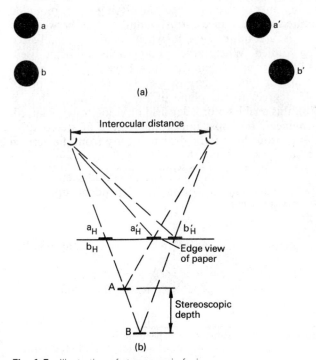

**Fig. 1.5** Illustration of stereoscopic fusion

right-angles to the page may help. Next uncover b and b' and look at all four dots in the same way. It will be found that the additional four 'middle' dots which appear can be made to fuse into two. To be sure that all four dots are represented in the superimposed image, check that the letters a and a' are adjacent to the upper dot while b and b' should be beside the lower one. When the fusions have taken place, it will be seen quite dramatically that the upper dot seems to be floating in space relative to the lower one. Figure 1.5(b) illustrates why this is so. Here $a_H$ and $a_H'$ represent the upper pair and $b_H$ and $b_H'$ the lower pair of dots as seen when viewing the plane of the paper as an edge. The rays from the eyes to a and a' intersect at A and those to b and b' intersect at B. These intersections, A and B, are the positions in space at which the stereoscopic images appear to be, with the B intersection located behind A.

If two air photographs are taken of the same land area, but from two different exposure stations, they can be oriented and viewed simultaneously so that, as illustrated in Fig. 1.5, the observer has the impression of viewing a three-dimensional model of the topography. In other words, the two positions of the camera, perhaps a kilometre apart, substitute for the observer's eyes.

In order to facilitate three-dimensional examination of pairs of photographs, a viewing instrument known as the *stereoscope* is used. There are two main types of stereoscope: the direct lens or refraction type, and the reflection mirror type. The direct type (see Fig. 1.6(a)) is the simpler and more compact, consisting only of two matched magnifying lenses mounted on supports and separated by a distance corresponding to that between the eyes. These stereoscopes are quite suitable when relatively small-sized photographs are being studied. When larger photographs are being used, they have to be spread further apart than the normal eye distance and this necessitates using the mirror type of stereoscope. This consists simply of four mirrors set at 45 degrees to the plane of the photographs and, as illustrated in Fig. 1.6(b), this enables a broader field of vision to be obtained.

To the highway engineer, the most important feature of stereoscopic vision is that it enables contour lines to be drawn directly from the vertical air photographs. A crude way of doing this is to sketch the contour lines under the stereoscope with the aid of numerous known spot elevations on

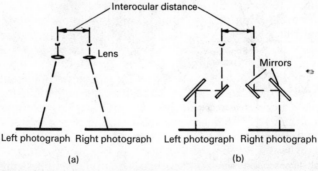

**Fig. 1.6**   Basic types of stereoscope: (a) direct type and (b) mirror type

each photograph. Much better results are obtained with the aid of mechanical or optical contouring devices, known as *stereoscopic plotting machines* or *stereoplotters*, which produce three-dimensional models of the ground surface without calculations or the determination of coordinates of points in the model. Without attempting to go into detailed discussions of the functioning of these machines, which can be either manually operated or automated, it is possible to describe briefly a basic manner in which the contours may be drawn.

A pair of consecutive or parallel air photographs is viewed in a binocular system, with each photograph being held in a mechanical reconstruction of the original air camera system. When the two 'cameras' are correctly oriented, the observer is provided with a three-dimensional view of the terrain in which the depth dimension appears exaggerated. The reconstruction of the ray paths from objects on the ground through the air camera lens is simulated in the plotting instrument by mechanical rods or light rays, each of which pivots about a point corresponding to the perspective centre of the original taking camera. The monocular system for each eye contains a reference dot which is engraved in the optical train. Viewed stereo-scopically, the two dots fuse together to provide a floating reference mark which can be moved horizontally or vertically. This is, of course, only a subjective impression since, in fact, the marks remain stationary and it is the upper ends of the space rods which move. Thus, when the space rods intersect at a corresponding image point in the model, the fused dot appears to the observer to be in contact with the ground at this point. By this means it is possible to trace a contour line, or any other such topographical detail, by keeping the reference dot always in contact with the ground surface as it appears in the model. The contour trace can then be passed to another instrument in which the contour lines are 'traced' by a reference marker and the $(x, y, z)$ coordinates of these lines are automatically recorded for entry into a computer (see also the discussion on digital ground models, pp. 38–40).

## Airphoto interpretation

Aerial photographs contain a complete record of the observable land surface and can be interpreted to predict subsurface conditions and provide information on many features important to engineering design. Whilst interpretation is often based on photography taken for photogrammetric purposes[20], typically at a scale between 1:20 000 and 1:50 000, it should be appreciated that, as discussed previously, no single scale of imagery will satisfy all the requirements of a variety of engineering studies.

Interpretation from aerial photographs differs from direct observation in scope, perspective and time relations. The large area imaged permits the stereoscopic observer to perceive and make deductions regarding relations between objects and their surroundings which to a ground observer might not be evident. The stereoscopic effect permits the interpreter to perceive the shape of objects; in this respect the exaggeration of vertical distance, which is present in stereoscopic pairs, is particularly helpful in emphasizing small but important differences in elevation and separating objects from their background. The permanence and fidelity of the photographic image permit the interpreter to conduct a close and careful study of an area under more favourable conditions than could be obtained by direct observation; in addition, the photographs lend themselves well to comparative and before-and-after studies.

However, airphoto interpretation resembles direct observation in one most important respect. The amount and reliability of the information obtained depends entirely upon the training and aptitude of the observer and upon the nature of the scene observed. For example, the soils interpreter must be able to recognize basic landforms and geomorphological processes—see references 21, 32, 33 and 34 for excellent discussions on these topics—as indicated by the following pattern elements on the photographs[20]: (a) image tone, e.g. colour or shade of grey, texture, uniformity, and sharpness of boundary, (b) topography, e.g. size, shape, and elevation, (c) drainage, e.g. form, type, and texture, (d) erosion, e.g. form and type, (e) vegetation, e.g. type, associations, and indicator communities, and (f) culture, e.g. man's influence on the landscape and adjustment to variations in landforms and environment. Whilst basic descriptions and examples of these pattern elements are well documented in the literature[35], it is really only through practice in interpretation that an observer having a solid base of technical knowledge can develop a proper understanding of the meanings of the characteristics and patterns of photographic images.

**Examples**
Without attempting to go into any detail regarding airphoto interpretation, it is useful to comment briefly on some of the more obvious features which aid in the interpretative process. For example, the size of an object is one of the most useful clues to its identity. Simply by measuring an unknown object on an aerial photograph, an interpreter can eliminate from consideration whole groups of possible identifications. Shadows are particularly helpful in the identification of man-made features, e.g. tall, slender objects, such as church spires, water towers, tanks and smoke-stacks, would frequently be almost indistinguishable but for their shadows. Shadows allow mounds to be distinguished from depressions, tips from pits, embankments from cuttings, and rectangular or cylindrical structures or tanks from lined pits of the same form. Shape is also a key to interpretation. Typically, geometric shapes tend to be man-made, e.g. linear roads and ditches, rectangular buildings, and circular tanks and stock ponds, whilst a break in slope is very often associated with a change in ground materials.

Joints, faults, shear zones and brecciated zones all have features which readily reveal their presence to the skilled photogeologist. Thus, for instance, very recent faults can generally be recognized where graded surfaces, such as alluvial fans or pediments, have been displaced; rocks on both sides of a fault will fail to match in type or attitude, or both.

Old landslides and areas susceptible to landslides are readily detected from aerial photographs by characteristic steep scarps, hummocky surfaces, ponded depressions, and disturbed drainage conditions. Recent land movements appear sharply delineated against the contiguous contact area, and the character of the vegetation on the moved slope will generally differ from that on the undisturbed adjacent slope. If older aerial photographs are available, a comparison of these with the newer ones will indicate the progress of the moving slope. (An excellent treatise[36] on the theoretical and practical aspects of land movements and the methods available for their investigation, prevention and control is readily available in the technical literature.)

Patterns, i.e. arrangements of (usually) similar features in relation to each other, are also important in the interpretative process. Obvious examples of well-defined patterns are trees regularly arranged in orchards or irregularly in woodland, ploughed fields, crops in fields, geological out-crops, land drains, allotments, spoils in open cast mining, and lineations such as soil or crop marks left by buried pipelines.

Soils can be interpreted in aerial photographs by studying the patterns created by the nature of the parent rock, the mode of deposition, and the climatic, biotic and physiographic environment. Drainage patterns, such as those indicated in Fig. 1.7, suggest the origin and composition of the underlying geological formation. A dendritic drainage pattern is commonly found in glacial topography. Trellis drainage is to be found in areas of folded sedimentary rocks; the characteristic pattern is due to the ridges being cut by stream gaps. The radial pattern can reflect water draining into an enclosed basin but, more often, it indicates a high dome or hill, or a volcanic cone. A parallel drainage pattern usually indicates a regional sloping terrain condition or a system of faults or rock joints. The classical annular drainage system is usually indicative of tilted sedimentary rock about an igneous intrusion. Whenever a drainage pattern appears rectan-gular, it is nearly certain that rock is at or close to the ground surface, and that the drainage is controlled by rock joints, fissures or faults. (Reference 37 provides a fundamental overview of the use of drainage patterns in the identification of soils and bedrocks from airphotos.)

Colour perception can also be most important in airphoto interpre-tation. In black-and-white photography, distinctions between hues are lost and objects are observed in tones of grey; to the skilled soil engineer interpreter, these are still major clues which enable soils to be classified or particular geological features to be identified. For example, water generally

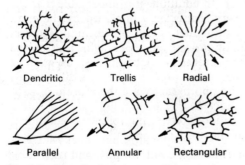

Dendritic     Trellis     Radial

Parallel     Annular     Rectangular

**Fig. 1.7** Some basic drainage patterns

appears dark unless turbid, whilst exposed wet soils are normally darker than similar dry soils. Clayey soils are usually dark-toned, whilst shallow calcareous areas where limestone or chalk is brought to the surface by ploughing are usually light-toned. On the positive (reverse) image of infrared colour, water shows up as a strong cyan blue which, against a magenta background of living vegetation, will indicate pools of stagnant water or sections of a river visible between a forest canopy. Colour photography taken when the sun is at its maximum is very successful in minimizing the vegetation shadows in wooded areas, thus permitting the optimum viewing of the ground beneath; image resolution in shadow areas is also better using colour emulsions as compared with panchromatic ones. Furthermore, colour can be used to identify particular types of tree-form, which in turn act as indicators of swamp areas, narrow watercourses, etc.

Erosional features, particularly the shapes of gullies, provide clues to soil texture and structure, profile development, and other conditions. For instance, U-shaped gullies are found in wind-deposited loess soils or similar, but stratified, sandy or silty soils; the characteristic and near-vertical sides of the gullies reflect the fact that there is relatively little clay present and that these soils crumble fairly easily. A broad saucer-shaped gully is indicative of a cohesive clay or silty clay soil, while V-shaped gullies are found in semi-granular soils with some cohesiveness.

Vegetation can also be an important indicator of soil conditions, with areas having the same natural plant cover tending to contain the same soils. Similarly, land use is often directly related to soil type, profile development, porosity and other conditions of interest to the highway engineer.

## Uses of aerial surveys

Aerial photographs have become most valuable tools in the hands of the highway engineer. As a means by which an instantaneous record of ground information at a point in time can be viewed at will, they are particularly useful as visual aids in technical conferences and at public hearings, as well as being obviously helpful in determining the most suitable topographic location for a highway.

Usage of colour emulsions for the above purposes is continually increasing. There are various reasons for this, not least of which is the enhanced technical appeal of colour. In addition, it is undeniable that the information content provided is very significantly increased by the extra dimension of colour. Another reason is that colour processing is increasingly being carried out by automatic processing devices which lessen the need for skilled personnel in the processing laboratories; as well as improving the quality of the photographic product, the cost differentials between colour and black-and-white photography are therefore diminishing, although they still remain significant[38].

In the hands of skilled airphoto interpreters, the following additional information can be provided to the highway engineer[10]:

(1)   the location of sand and gravel deposits, borrow pits, and rock areas suitable for quarrying,

(2)   the rating of soil-bearing capacities as good, fair or poor,
(3)   the outlining of soils as to their texture, and the estimation of the depths of organic deposits,
(4)   the classification of bedrocks as to physical types and their relative depths below the surface,
(5)   the estimation of the depths of glacial drift and wind-blown materials,
(6)   the estimation of hydrological factors,
(7)   the delineation of active and potential areas involving problems such as sink holes, landslides, rock falls and frost heave,
(8)   the location of underground utilities placed by cut-and-cover methods.

New aerial photographs provide the most up-to-date information regarding current land use, and this is of particular importance at the reconnaissance phase of a highway location study, particularly if it is being carried out in an urban area. Similarly, these photographs can be easily used to locate important intermediate control points, so that possible band routes can be selected. At this stage of the reconnaissance a small-scale mosaic will provide sufficient detail to enable elimination of all but a couple of possible bands.

To enable the choice to be narrowed, an enlarged mosaic can be viewed in conjunction with a topographic map. A simple technique is to assemble one or more mosaic bands and to overlay them with topographic maps that are enlarged to the same scale and drawn on transparent material. Trial lines for each route can then be sketched on the mosaics and profiles plotted directly from the contours of the overlay. When route profiles are found which indicate alignments that might satisfy the highway's design standards, they can be compared on a cost–benefit basis to aid in the final selection.

Large-scale photography is necessary at both the *preliminary* and *final location* phases of a location survey. The manner in which the data can be automatically processed has already been described, and so will not be further discussed here.

Airphoto interpretative methods can be used to cut down the amount of soil survey field work which is normally carried out during the final location survey. As part of the routine field studies, it is customary to carry out auger investigations at fixed intervals along the location line, and then to carry out other detailed studies as indicated by the results obtained. Much of this routine augering and subsequent laboratory analysis may be eliminated if the airphotos are used to delineate ground areas with similar physical characteristics. Then it is only necessary to go to the field and test a limited number of points within each delineated area. Similarly, considerable areas of ground can be explored in a short period of time when searching for sources of suitable highway materials. With the aid of aerial photography, the materials engineer can select the most promising sites for further detailed study, thereby minimizing the amount of random field investigation and subsequent laboratory testing.

Air photography can also be used successfully to locate ground instability that should be avoided when building a highway. Examples range from the direct identification of the sites of solifluction slides and mud flows, to predictions regarding water conditions and deductions regarding the nature and sequence of unstable materials in depth below proposed highway centrelines. In this latter respect, for example, infrared photography has been used successfully[39] to detect hidden subsurface conditions and geological features such as muck pockets, underground cavities, volcanic and hydrothermal activity, and subsurface drainage systems. In addition, many indirect phenomena affecting highway pavement and structure foundation designs can be recognized on air photographs, e.g. spring line and seepage areas, gulley developments, eroding and accreting sections of streams, constancy of river channels, and probable flood levels. Whilst some of these may require checking in the field, good interpretative data will result in many dangerous sites being avoided, and the necessary foundation investigations being concentrated on a limited number of likely sites.

When large-scale aerial photography is used to prepare the necessary maps, it may be possible to complete the plans and specifications for a highway and to let the construction contract without actually placing a centreline peg in the ground. When this occurs, the final location line need not be pegged until the contractor is about to begin construction, in which case the final location survey becomes a combined location and construction survey.

The most important *advantages* of aerial photogrammetric procedures in highway engineering can be summarized as follows.

(1)   On a large highway scheme the time required to locate the facility and prepare plans for contract is considerably reduced.
(2)   Cost savings of a significant nature can be made by comparison with conventional ground survey methods. The less well mapped the terrain in which the highway is being located, the greater are the savings.
(3)   Skilled technical personnel are released from dull routine work and can be used more profitably on more demanding problems.
(4)   Topographic maps prepared from air photographs can be more reliable than those produced from ground surveys.
(5)   The ability to survey large areas of land ensures that the most suitable location is not accidentally overlooked.
(6)   Highway profiles and cross-sections can be measured without physically encroaching on private lands. Thus there is the minimum of obstructive field work, landowners are not upset, and land values are not affected.
(7)   A most complete inventory of all surface features is obtained. This is always available for use and may be referred to at any time. Futhermore, it can be analysed at any time, and this is not affected by poor weather or lighting conditions.
(8)   Public relations are considerably facilitated and enquiries aided by the use of aerial photographs intelligible to the general public.

In general, it can be said that the use of aerial photographs greatly facilitates the location and design of highways. Nevertheless, there are certain *disadvantages* associated with their use.

(1) First and most important, the taking of air photographs cannot be guaranteed at any particular time. Good photography requires clear atmospheric conditions and photographs taken on wet or misty days, or in haze or smoky conditions, may be of limited value.

(2) A topographic map cannot be accurately obtained if the ground is covered by snow or obscured by the leaves of trees. In the latter case, air photographs of, for instance, heavily-wooded tropical areas can be of considerably less value than might normally be expected. In temperate areas, where the ground has a deciduous cover, the taking of aerial photographs must await the time of leaf-fall.

(3) If the area to be studied is relatively small and well mapped, it will usually be more economical to use ground survey methods rather than aerial procedures.

## Subsurface explorations

Subsurface explorations are made for the purpose of obtaining information regarding the types, location and extent in plan and profile of soil and rock which will be encountered in connection with the proposed highway location. Whilst they are an important part of all engineering surveys for location purposes, they are essential at the final location and design phase(s) because they provide pertinent information on the following subjects[40]:

(1)  the location of the road, both vertically and horizontally,
(2)  the location and selection of borrow materials for fills and subgrade treatment,
(3)  the design and location of ditches, culverts and drains,
(4)  the need for subgrade treatment and the type of treatment required,
(5)  the design of the roadway cross-section,
(6)  the location of local sources of construction materials for the pavement,
(7)  the selection of the type of surface and its design.

Such investigations ensure[4]: (a) the overall suitability of the highway site and its environs for the proposed works, (b) that an adequate and economic design can be prepared for both temporary and permanent works, and (c) the planning of the best method of construction.

As has been indicated in previous discussions (see, for example, Fig. 1.2), a subsurface exploration cannot and must not be considered as a separate, detached function in the location and design of a highway, but rather as an integral part of the development of the scheme. Thus, from the moment that consideration is given to the approximate location of the proposed new highway until the highway is actually constructed, information is continually required regarding subsurface conditions so that the proper analyses and decisions can be made.

Although subsurface investigations are, naturally enough, concerned primarily with soils and soil conditions, they should not be considered as soil surveys only. A comprehensive subsurface investigation for highway purposes may well consist of a study of not only the critical soil layers and the extent of adverse ground conditions, such as swamps or peat bogs, but also the depths to bedrock and the water-table. In areas of foundations for major structures or proposed deep rock cuts, geological cross-sections may also be required. If the proposed new highway passes through an area that has been used for another purpose in the past, the in situ ground materials obviously can have a significant effect on an otherwise very suitable location; examples of such problems are available in the literature[4]. Where an old roadway is already in existence on or adjacent to the site, data may also be obtained which will relate the existing pavement condition to the characteristics of the underlying materials, provide possible reasons for failure, and suggest corrective measures for the project under examination.

Before discussing the carrying out of these subsurface surveys, it is useful to note that, following an extensive analysis of 99 major road projects in Scotland over the period 1969–74, it was determined[41] that the proportion of the total cost of these projects spent on formal site investigation to assess ground conditions (including basic soil testing) varied from zero to 5.66 per cent. Whilst there appeared to be no correlation between site investigation expenditure and the size, project complexity, or ground conditions, a correlation was determined between low expenditure on site investigation and high inaccuracy of estimation of project time (scheduling) and cost (budgeting). Furthermore, there was a wide variation in the accuracy of estimation of earthworks' quantities on these projects; most usually there was a substantial underestimate of the quantities or costs involved.

The most striking conclusion from this study was that the majority of failings on these projects came not from inadequacies with regard to the state of the art of site investigation, but rather from inadequacies in respect of the state of application of the art. For example, in the site investigations that were carried out, very little regard was paid to a planned approach, e.g. one investigation of a 'main' type was generally expected to suffice, whereas a 'preliminary' investigation—which could have derived valuable information from available data—was often not used, and few or no records were kept of the results.

## Sequence of operations

The classical sequence of operations used in a subsurface exploration is[42]:

(1)  preliminary work,
(2)  site examination,
(3)  determination of the soil profile and collection of samples,
(4)  location of the water-table.

In practice, of course, the last three stages may be taken out of sequence or may overlap.

### Preliminary work
Whilst the extent of any subsurface exploration is obviously determined by the character and variability of the ground and groundwater, it is still true

to say that its cost is generally low in comparison with the overall cost of the project. Furthermore, the cost of such explorations may be very considerably reduced by making the maximum use of existing available knowledge to provide information on ground conditions, and to aid in the forward planning of the investigation. At all times, however, it should be remembered that the major factors controlling the scope and method of exploration are the technical requirements of the project, not its cost.

The preliminary work is essentially a desk-based study which searches out and gathers together all possible technical information regarding the conditions likely to be met. The sources of such information are readily available in the literature[6] and some of these have already been discussed in this text and will not be repeated here. However, it is appropriate to mention again that Britain is superbly endowed with 1:10 560 coverage of geological maps, which have been the continuing work of the (now) British Geological Survey (BGS) since the 1830s. These maps, and the appropriate *memoirs*, are usually published in two editions, *Drift* and *Solid*; the former shows the superficial deposits of glacial origin and the solid rocks exposed at the surface, while the latter shows the solid rocks as they would appear if the cover of superficial deposits were removed. It is also desirable to consult the authorities at the BGS and the Geological Museum, as they have much useful unpublished information. For instance, the Mining Industry Act of 1926 imposed a statutory obligation that the BGS be notified of all sinkings and borings to a depth of more than 30.5 m for minerals and the Water Acts of 1945 and 1946 required the same, to more than 15.25 m for water; thus a very large amount of unpublished but valuable underground information is collected and available for preliminary study.

In countries where such geological maps and memoirs are not normally available, regional photogeological maps and regional zonation maps have been very successfully developed over the past forty years; many of these have stemmed from original engineering photogeological work or from specially commissioned ground surveys.

In all countries the pedological maps prepared as part of soil survey programmes are invaluable when carrying out exploration in non-urban areas. These maps, which are prepared primarily for agricultural purposes, provide most useful information regarding soil conditions to a depth of about 1.25 m below ground level.

Subsurface explorations previously carried out for other engineering projects in the vicinity usually provide very valuable information. Local experience gained in the execution of road, railway or building works in the area should be tapped, as should the tremendous amounts of data already available in local authority offices, e.g. from sewer studies, and in service undertakings, e.g. gas, electricity and water. Geotechnical information typically available from such sources includes soil gradation and plasticity data, soil moisture contents and depths to the water-table, soil strength and its consolidation characteristics, and the suitability of the underlying material for use in embankments.

A unique arrangement has existed in Britain since 1967, whereby copies of all site investigation reports prepared in relation to new motorways and trunk roads are deposited with the Transport and Road Research Laboratory. In the case of other existing roadways, highway maintenance records should be scanned for information concerning areas which have given trouble because of frost heave, seepage water, pumping of pavement joints, excessive or uneven settlement of the roadbed, landslides, or any other difficulties associated with subsurface behaviour. Knowing the positions of such areas in advance will enable the highway engineer to make better decisions affecting both the location of the centreline and the design of the highway alignment.

Upon completion of the desk-based study, it should be possible to prepare provisional geotechnical maps (perhaps using the geological maps as a base) and sections summarizing the information obtained. Special care should be taken at this stage to show such unfavourable ground conditions as: (a) unstable slopes, (b) materials which require extra flat slopes in cuttings, (c) unrippable rock above formation level, (d) soft material requiring excavation below highway formation level, (e) areas with material above formation that is unsuitable as fill, (f) areas liable to flooding, springs, and areas requiring special drainage measures, (g) locations liable to snow-drifting, fog, icing, or excessive winds, (h) mineworkings and shafts, swallow holes, cavernous ground, and areas liable to subsidence, and (i) mineral deposits[6].

**Site examination**
In areas where preliminary information is limited, further essential terrain information can be obtained by on-site examination. For example, soils observed along roads in the vicinity of the proposed highway line should be studied and changes in the soil (or rock) profile noted as they occur in highway cuts. These notes should include a complete description of the soil (or rock) profile for each type observed.

A careful visual inspection of the site and the vegetation it sustains may reveal clues suggesting man-made interferences with the natural subsoil conditions at some time in the past.

Some indications of the depth of the water-table below the surface can often be obtained from an inspection of streams or ponds. Lush growths of vegetation, such as rushes, cotton-grass or willows, indicate that the water-table is near the surface for at least part of the year; whereas bracken and gorse growths indicate that the soil is well drained.

Geological faults may be indicated by such topographical features as a step in the line of an escarpment or a depression where the shattered rock has been more rapidly eroded than the surrounding rock. These places should receive detailed inspection, as igneous intrusions may involve excavation, while, in certain circumstances, a fault may also give rise to constructional difficulties. Potential rock-fall and soil-fall slides can often be foreseen simply by recognizing geological conditions that are likely to produce overhanging or oversteep cliffs. Some of the geological settings that fall into this category are illustrated in reference 36. Careful note should also be made, especially on sloping clay formations, of any irregularities in the ground that may be due to landslides or a lack of stability.

At this stage it may be desirable to prepare a corrected strip map covering the most likely centreline(s). In complex terrain, especially if adverse ground conditions exist, this map will be vital in establishing the final location line, as well as identifying points for further detailed exploration.

**Determination of soil profile**
The field work for this phase of the investigation consists of making examinations of the subsurface by means of auger borings, test pits, road cuttings or, if necessary, by geophysical surveying methods. There is no hard and fast rule to follow as to where these tests should take place, except that the profile should be examined at close enough intervals to determine the boundaries of each significant soil type occurring on the scheme. This interval, which is normally uniform, may be varied as follows.

(1)   If the soil profile is uniform, the interval may be increased.
(2)   When the character of the soil profile changes, intermediate borings should be made until it is clear that all variations have been mapped.
(3)   Where the topography is rolling, and the grade changes rapidly from cut to fill, detailed data may be necessary only in cuts.
(4)   Where the original ground line or old highway grade is to be covered with fill material, no examination is normally necessary, unless the character of the support is unknown.

One practical recommendation is that tests for motorways should be carried out at every 300 m in uniform soils, and every 16 m for quickly changing ground such as glacial deposits. A closer spacing between points of exploration, e.g. 10 m, will often be appropriate for structures; such exploration should be made at a minimum of three points and to a depth below each footing of at least 1.5 times the width of the loaded area.

All subsurface explorations should normally be carried out to a depth of 2–3 m below the existing ground level when little cut or fill is required. For cuttings, they should be carried out to the same depth below the formation level. The investigation depths may vary, however, according to the following stipulations.

(1)   When the highway lies within uniform layers of the soil profile, the study should be extended down to the first layer below the ditch-line which would stop percolation, or through the previous layer which would carry water.
(2)   When embankment material is to be borrowed from ditches or pits alongside the road, the investigations should be extended to the estimated depth of borrow.
(3)   If frost action is a problem, studies should extend to at least the mean depth of frost in those materials showing a high affinity for frost accumulation.
(4)   Where high embankments (7.5–9.0 m) are concerned, they will produce appreciable bearing pressures and so soil borings should be extended to a depth of at least 2.5 times the height of the embankment.

(5)  With low embankments (<3 m), the ground pressures are not very great and exploration to a depth of 3.0–4.5 m will usually be sufficient.
(6)  When the new location line follows an already existing road, the subsurface may be adequately mapped by examining exposed cuts, but supplementary investigations should be carried out if areas show adverse pavement performance.

If the proposed centreline crosses a peat bog, soundings should normally be taken at about 15 m intervals along the centreline and 7.5 m to the right and left for a distance of 30 m. If there is an appreciable difference in the depth of swamp material between 15 m intervals, the boundaries of change should be established by additional soundings.

In the case of bedrock, sufficient data are required to obtain an accurate outline of the bedrock contact occurring in all road cuts. Where necessary, samples of the bedrock should be examined to determine the uniformity and nature of the underlying rock.

*Sampling*   At least one sample should be taken from each stratum found at each test location and sent to the laboratory for further investigation. The soil tests usually carried out are those required for identification and classification purposes, i.e. mechanical analysis, liquid limit, plastic limit, compaction and, where necessary, strength tests. Table 1.6 gives some guidance as to the amount of soil required for each series of tests. (The identification and classification tests are described in Chapter 4.)

**Table 1.6**   Mass of soil sample required for various laboratory tests[4]

| Purpose of sample | Soil type | Mass required (kg) |
|---|---|---|
| 1  Soil classification, including Atterberg limits, sieve analysis, moisture content, and sulphate content tests | Clay, silt, sand | 1 |
| | Fine and medium gravel | 5 |
| | Coarse gravel | 30 |
| 2  Compaction tests | All | 25–60 |
| 3  Comprehensive study of construction materials, including soil stabilization | Clay, silt, sand | 100 |
| | Fine and medium gravel | 130 |
| | Coarse gravel | 160 |

*Reporting*   Generally, the subsurface exploration report will contain six types of information[43]:

(1)  graphical representation of test locations and soil profiles,
(2)  a written report for special use of materials or potential problem areas,
(3)  photographs which show the landforms,
(4)  profiles of surface and subsurface materials,
(5)  properties, strength and grading,
(6)  usual problems and recommended solutions.

The graphical representation of tests is based on the data obtained from the test log, which is a summary of the information obtained at each test location. Typical information recorded in this log includes: (a) test number,

(b) test location, (c) date of test, (d) names of field personnel, (e) compaction of existing ground to determine swell or shrinkage factors, (f) blows per unit depth to advance casings, sampling spoon, probes, etc., plus mass of hammer, (g) reason for termination of test, (h) location of sample and type of sample obtained, (i) soil strata locations with description, identification and classification of material, (j) the percentage recovery in bedrock, (k) ground elevation, (l) footing or grade elevation, when possible, and (m) groundwater elevation.

In relation to (i) above, the agricultural soil name of the profile should also be given (wherever feasible) for possible future correlation purposes. The number, sequence and thickness of each soil layer should be noted. Each layer should be described according to texture, structure, organic content, relative moisture content, and degree of cementation.

*Mapping the profile*   The data obtained from the subsurface investigation should be plotted on a profile sheet to assist in the making of location and design recommendations. One excellent method of so doing—this is indicated in Fig. 1.8—is to establish the range of subsurface profile characteristics for each type (map unit) identified during the survey, and then to indicate the boundaries of the different types on a plan or strip map of the proposed highway location. The location of borings, points where samples were taken, and supplementary notes on drainage, landform, and soil or rock types are usually included. Normally a profile sketch is provided in addition to the plan view to show the subsurface conditions that are likely to influence the position of the grade line.

### Location of water-table

If no trace of soil moisture is found in a test hole at its full depth, it can be assumed that the water-table is below this depth, and the investigation continued elsewhere. If, however, water is indicated, the hole should be left for 12 to 24 hours to allow the water to rise to its final level. The most convenient way of then measuring the depth of the water level is to lower a measure until its lower end just touches the water surface.

It occasionally happens that a boring will pierce a layer of impervious clay which is covering a permeable layer in which the water is under considerable pressure. This artesian condition is indicated by water rising *above* the level at which it was first found seeping into the hole. It very often requires special drainage facilities, and thus additional borings should be made nearby to check the magnitude and extent of the water condition. These checks should be carried out in all instances where free water is encountered.

The colour of the subsoil will often indicate whether the water-table is fluctuating. While it is desirable to make the water-table determination in winter time when the water level can be expected to be at its highest, obviously this is not always possible and a mottled subsoil will assist in the identification of a location with a fluctuating water-table. In clay soils this mottling is very noticeable as grey and blue colorations interspersed with brown, yellow or rust colorations.

## Exploration methods

Many methods have been devised for securing information regarding the subsurface, and each one of them has particular advantages. Thus it is not necessary to recommend one method as against another, but rather to state that the method, tools and equipment used in any given case will vary with the location and topographical features encountered. In fact, in many instances it will be found desirable to use more than one method on a given scheme.

Before discussing the various methods, one further point should be emphasized in relation to obtaining and analysing subsurface data. Subsurface exploration has always been a highly specialized art in which there is little room for the unsupervised or inexperienced. Although this type of

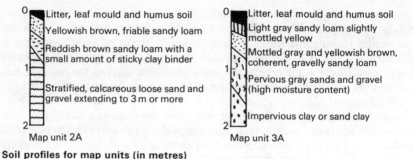

**Soil profiles for map units (in metres)**

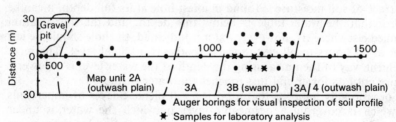

**Plan for highway right of way**

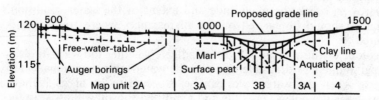

**Soil profile on centreline**

**Fig. 1.8**  Example of subsurface profile mapping, illustrating the determination of the limits of soils identified by soil profiles (after reference 40)

exploration is based on sound engineering principles, it is still heavily dependent upon considerable experience if valuable results are to be obtained. This experience and ability cannot just come from a book, which—however erudite—can only provide a very general background to a vast field of study.

## Test pits

If it is possible to say that one method of obtaining data is 'better' than others, then certainly it is that of digging test pits and examining the profile in situ. Test pits, dug by hand or machines, are open excavations large enough to permit an investigator to enter and examine formations in their natural condition. Although this method makes it possible to obtain samples in either a disturbed or an undisturbed condition, it can be a relatively expensive procedure, which may make it impractical on many sites.

Test pits are unquestionably the best way of examining and sampling non-cohesive soils containing boulders, cobbles or gravel. However, safety requirements may well necessitate the use of shoring for excavations in excess of about 1.5 m. They can be excavated very rapidly with the aid of a backhoe, in non-flowing soils, to depths of up to about 5 m, while bulldozers can dig pits or trenches to depths of over 3 m. It is usually very expensive to excavate pits by hand-labour, but this may be necessary in particular instances, e.g. when examining the profile of an existing roadway.

## Soil auger borings

Two basic types of hand-operated tools are used for auger borings. One of these is the common farm posthole auger, which consists of a spiral-shaped bucket, about 100 mm in diameter by 150 mm long, fastened to a shaft of narrow piping with a T-handle at the top for rotating the auger. The second type consists of a helical-shaped bit of about 25.0–37.5 mm in diameter fastened to a length of piping with a T-handle at the top. In either case, the tool is rotated into the ground until the bit has penetrated a distance equal to its length, after which it is withdrawn directly and the retained soil examined and sampled as necessary. The process is then repeated until the required depth is obtained. If the hole caves in, it may be necessary to use a section, or sections, of pipe of slightly larger diameter than the auger to form a casing to protect the walls.

On large projects it may be economically feasible to use augers operated by motor power. Particularly suitable for sampling cohesive soils, these vehicle-mounted augers normally use a continuous-flight borer with a hollow stem of, typically, 75–125 mm internal diameter (which can also drill holes at an angle). By continuous-flight is meant that the auger can be lengthened by extension pieces, and need not be withdrawn when drilling. When augering, the hollow stem is closed at its bottom end with a plug; when a soil sample is required, the plug is removed and a sampler lowered down through the stem and driven into the soil below the auger bit. Unlike hand augers whose operation in suitable ground conditions is confined to depths of about 5 m, these mechanical augers can obtain samples from as deep as 30–50 m.

Subsurface exploration by means of hand-operated auger borings has many disadvantages. The principal one is that, in stony or granular soils, or at sites with a high water-table, the soil wall usually flows into the hole and the excavated material falls from the auger as it is being withdrawn. Furthermore, not only is the sample obtained in a very disturbed condition, but it is also often contaminated with scrapings from different strata from the side of the hole.

Nevertheless, hand- or mechanically-operated auger boring represents what is probably the most effective 'value-for-money' method of obtaining subsurface information. It is quick, i.e. a large number of holes can be bored in a day, which makes it very useful for highway location and design purposes. In many ways, auger boring is the ideal investigative tool for borrow pit surveys and location of materials when a random sampling method is employed. In addition, hand-operated auger boring is a particularly useful way of determining the depth to a relatively shallow (< 3 m) water-table.

**Boring rigs**
Boring rigs are employed to sample deeper boreholes such as might be required in deep cuttings or in the foundation investigation for a major structure.

*Shell-and-auger* boring is one of the cheapest, simplest and most often used ways of investigating soil and weak weathered rock. Boring is by means of a percussive rig equipped with a friction winch to raise and drop a wire rope carrying the drill tools. A casing may be used to keep the hole open. A maximum borehole depth of about 60 m in suitable strata is achievable with this type of rig.

In the case of sands and gravels, a shell or 'baler', consisting of an open-ended 150–300 mm diameter cylinder with a cutting-edge and flap-valve, is used to break up and recover the soil or rock. The lower part of the shell must be covered with water, however, in order for the boring to be carried out effectively in cohesionless materials, and this results in the sample recovered being in a very disturbed state.

In cohesive soils, a 'clay cutter' is used instead of the shell in a dry borehole. This cutter is similar to the shell but does not have the flap-valve. A chisel is substituted to break up rock, boulders or other hard materials.

A method rarely used in Britain, but widely used overseas to investigate sands, silts and clays, is known as *wash boring*. With this method of drilling, a casing is driven into the soil, one length at a time, by a drop-hammer action similar to that used in pile driving. After each length of casing has been driven, the contained soil is cleaned out by forcing water under pressure through hollow rods or a narrow pipe inside the casing. A chisel-shaped chopping bit is attached to the end of these thin pipes and the whole unit is then alternatively raised and dropped and turned so that the resulting churning-cum-jetting action loosens the soil within the casing and it is washed to the surface.

An experienced operator handling the wash pipes is able to 'feel' a significant change in material and, when this occurs, the churning is stopped and the casing washed clean of all loosened soil. After the wash rods or pipes are raised from the hole, a sampling tool is substituted for the churning bit and driven to obtain a sample. On removal of the sample for further examination, the sample tool is replaced by the chopping bit and the drilling continued until another material change is noticed.

**Rock drilling**
When rock is met within a cut section, its nature and condition must be established in sufficient detail for a reasonable estimate of the cost of excavation to be made. A rotary drilling process, either the *rotary open hole* method or the *rotary core* method, is usually employed to obtain these specimens. In either case, the drill bit is rotated at high speed at the bottom of the borehole and a drilling fluid—most usually water—is forced into the hole through hollow drill rods; this water serves a dual purpose, that of cooling the bit and bringing the pulverized rock debris to the surface of the borehole.

By far the more commonly used method is the rotary core one. With this process, an annular-shaped bit studded with industrial diamonds—or, in the case of soft rocks, tungsten carbide inserts—is screwed onto the bottom of a cylindrical core barrel, which in turn is fastened to extension rod sections of hollow steel tubing. As the bit cuts into the rock, the isolated core feeds into the barrel, and this is raised at regular intervals to the surface for extraction.

With the rotary open hole method, which is also known as *shot drilling*, a plain bit is used and chilled steel shot is fed down through the hollow rods, with the lubricating medium, to act as the cutting agent. If this process is used with small-diameter boreholes, all of the rock material within the annulus may be removed; for this reason, shot drilling tends to be used to obtain samples from large-diameter (>150 mm) boreholes, when it is generally more economical to use steel shot rather than industrial diamonds as the cutting agent.

Most boreholes cut into rock tend to be vertical. However, when previous study suggests that near-vertical bedding planes, joint systems or faults exist, inclined holes must be cut if a complete picture of the geological pattern is to be obtained.

**Soundings**
Also known as probings, these consist of simply pushing or driving sections of steel rod down through the soil as far as they can be made to penetrate. The oldest, simplest type of sounding equipment consists of a 25 mm diameter pointed steel rod which is driven into the ground by an operator wielding a sledge hammer; mechanically-operated hammers may also be used for this purpose. More elaborate sounding equipment is available which provides a pipe surrounding the rod to eliminate side friction, and measures the resistance to penetration of the rod by recording the number of blows or force of a jack required to advance it a given distance. The

penetration resistance readings obtained with these penetrometers are then compared with the results obtained in known profiles for interpretation purposes.

The results which can be interpreted from soundings are limited especially with regard to subsurface boundaries. The method is most appropriately used where other means of site investigation have disclosed relatively thin layers of soft soils overlying harder ones, and it is desired to check the thickness of the soft stratum over a wide area very quickly and very economically. However, it must always be remembered that, when used in other uncalibrated situations, and the penetrometer is driven to refusal, the only real information obtained is that bedrock does not exist above the depth to refusal—what is not known is whether the refusal is due to bedrock or a boulder or perhaps a bed of gravel.

**Geophysical methods**
Geophysical exploration is a form of field investigation utilizing a blend of physics and geology, in that physical measurements made at the surface by specially developed instruments are interpreted in terms of the subsurface geological conditions. Two methods of geophysical exploration, the electrical resistivity and seismic refraction methods, have found most application to the shallow depths met with in highway work.

The great advantage of these methods lies in the speed with which certain subsurface explorations, e.g. depth to bedrock, can be carried out over a large site, whilst check test pits, boreholes, etc., can be restricted to areas where anomalous readings are obtained. They can also be employed to determine the amount of rock to be removed from road cuts, resolve doubts as to whether subsurface obstructions are bedrock or boulders, and worked or unworked coal seams[44], facilitate deductions of subsurface irregularities which often are missed by borings, locate buried sources of roadfill material, i.e. buried sand pits, gravel pits, etc., and aid in determining the extent of known sources of road materials.

Geophysical survey methods offer a means of quick and relatively inexpensive subsurface exploration, and as such they are very attractive to the engineer faced with a comprehensive investigation programme for a large highway scheme. However, the inexperienced engineer should consider carefully before attempting to apply these procedures, even though a skilled instrumentalist be at hand. Although the tests may be carried out flawlessly, they are of little value unless the results are interpreted correctly, and correct interpretation can only be expected from experienced persons with a basic understanding of geophysical theories and procedures, and of the branches of engineering dealing with soils and geology.

*Electrical resistivity method*  The resistivity of a substance is defined as the electrical resistance offered by a unit cube of the substance to the flow of an electric current perpendicular to one of its faces. It is usually denoted by the symbol $\rho$ and expressed in units of ohm-centimetres.

With the exception of certain metallic minerals which are very good conductors, the constituent minerals of the earth are more or less insulators,

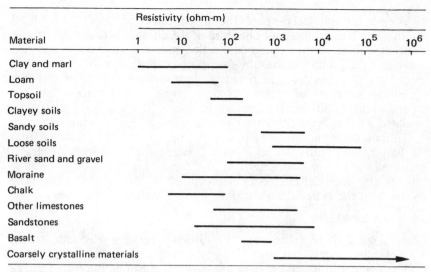

**Fig. 1.9** Resistivity values for natural materials (reported in reference 45)

and the resistivities of the various subsurface formations are almost entirely dependent upon the salinity of the moisture contained in them. Thus, as is suggested in Fig. 1.9, it is by noting the differences in the resistivities of different materials at a site and comparing these with results obtained for known conditions that predictions can be made regarding the subsurface materials.

To carry out an electrical resistivity test, an electric current is applied to the ground through two metal rods called current electrodes; these are connected by insulated wires through a milliammeter to a battery or generator. As is illustrated in Fig. 1.10(a), the current flows through the ground so that the lines of flow make a pattern similar to the lines of magnetic force about a bar magnet. In theory, the lines of current flow extend to an infinite depth, but, since the intensity diminishes quite rapidly

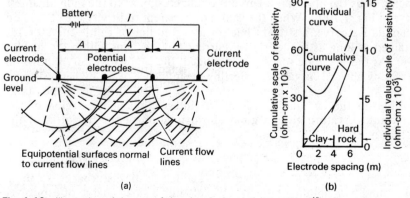

(a)                                                    (b)

**Fig. 1.10** Illustration of the use of the electrical resistivity method [46]

with depth, for practical purposes the current can be considered as confined within a depth equal to about one-third of the distance between the current electrodes. Two further electrodes, called potential electrodes, are next inserted in the ground so that the four electrodes are in a straight line and spaced at equal intervals. The potential electrodes are actually porous pots containing solutions of copper sulphate, some of which seeps into the ground so that good electrical contacts are made. The pots are connected by insulated wires to a potentiometer so that voltages can be measured.

To determine the resistivity of the ground, the current $I$ flowing from the battery and through the ground between the current electrodes is measured on the milliammeter. At the same time the voltage drop $V$ between the potential electrodes is measured on the potentiometer. The resistivity of the material is then given by an equation of the form:

$$\rho = 2\pi A V/I$$

where $\rho$ = resistivity (ohm-cm), $A$ = distance between electrodes (cm), $V$ = potential drop (volts), and $I$ = current (amperes).

The manner in which the data are interpreted can be illustrated by the following simple example. A soil of relatively low resistivity is overlying a rock with high resistivity. When the electrode spacing is very small compared with the thickness of the upper layer, practically all the current will flow through the uppermost depth and the resistivity measured will approximate closely the actual resistivity of that layer. If the electrode spacing is increased, the depth of current penetration increases and the resistivity measured represents an average for all material existing within the depth $A$ below the surface. As the electrode spacings are progressively expanded, the current flow lines eventually encounter the underlying rock formation. This material, which has an appreciably higher resistivity than the overlying soil, then begins to affect the average resistivity values; as the spacings are further increased, the effect of the lower bed increases proportionally until, eventually, the resistivity measured approaches closely the resistivity of the rock.

When the resistivity $\rho$ is plotted as an ordinate against the electrode spacing $A$ as the abscissa, a curve is obtained similar to the individual test curve in Fig. 1.10(b). When the values of apparent resistivity are plotted on a cumulative curve, a straight line (or a curved line of gentle curvature) is obtained as long as the 'effective' current flow remains within the surface layer. As the electrode spacing is expanded, the cumulative curve shows an increasing upward curvature, reflecting the influence of the higher resistivity of the rock. If straight lines are then drawn through as many points as possible on the cumulative curve, the intersection in the region of the increasing curvature gives a good approximation of the thickness of the surface material.

*Seismic refraction method*   The seismic method is based primarily on the measurement of the time required for a sudden elastic disturbance, set up in the ground by a hammer blow or by exploding a small charge of explosive, to be picked up by a number of vibration detectors or seismometers located on the ground surface at known distances from the shot point. The seismometers transform the ground vibrations into electrical impulses which are transmitted to a recording apparatus . The instant of explosion and time markings are also recorded and the interval of time between the instant of explosion and the arrival of the first vibration impulse at each seismometer can then be determined. Knowing these data, the velocity at which the seismic waves are moving through the various underlying strata can be graphically calculated, after which the thickness of the various layers can be determined from a simple mathematical relationship.

The basis of the method is most easily understood by considering an example[47]. Figure 1.11(a) represents the advance of a wavefront in a two-layer structure consisting of about 24.5 m of gravel on top of bedrock. The wave travels at about 1525 m/s in the gravel, and at about 6100 m/s in the bedrock. In such a condition the wavefront has approximately the shape of a sphere of 15.25 m radius 0.010 s after it leaves the shot point. About 0.016 s after the shot, it reaches the rock surface at point A. From this point of contact a wavelet starts into the rock with a velocity of 6100 m/s, so that 0.020 s after the shot the wavelet has reached the distance noted by that circle in the diagram, not only vertically below A, but also radiating in all directions within the rock; thus the 0.020 s wavefront reaches the point B along the gravel–rock interface. Along the interface, however, the wave in the rock starts a new series of wavelets into the gravel, directed towards the gravel surface. The ones at B and C are but two of many such wavelets, and their envelope is the new refracted wave DE as shown 0.025 s after the shot.

Figure 1.11(b) shows the continued advance of the wavefront through the gravel until more than 0.040 s after the explosion. It is clear that the wavefront travels to the nearer seismometers at a speed of 1525 m/s. Equally obvious is the fact that, at some distance along the line of seismometers, a refracted wave will travel the shorter distance to the surface and be picked up before the original wavefront reaches the same point through the gravel. Beyond this 'critical distance' the refracted wave is always picked up first by the seismometers.

A plot of the arrival times at the seismometers versus distance from the shot point is also shown in Fig. 1.11(b). The earlier seismometers record the velocity of the gravel; note that the plotted points fall along a straight line, the slope of which is 1525 m/s. The further seismometers record values which plot along a line whose slope equals 6100 m/s; this is the velocity of the bedrock. The distance from the shot point to the point of intersection of these two lines is controlled by the thickness of the gravel, and the greater this is the greater will be the distance of the intersection from the shot point.

In seismic tests the velocity of the transmitted sound waves generally increases with an increase in the density of the transmitting medium (see Fig. 1.12). However, predicting the material from its velocity requires considerable skill and judgement, and so calibration tests over known subsurface formations are essential for a successful interpretation of the data obtained.

In the interpretation of seismic data it is convenient to represent the propagation of the seismic waves by means of wave rays. By definition, a

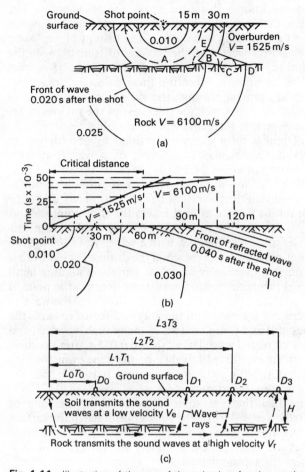

**Fig. 1.11**  Illustration of the use of the seismic refraction method

wave ray is a wave path which is normal to the progressing wavefront at every instant and is, therefore, a path of minimum time. Figure 1.11(c) shows the path of the wave rays between the shot point and four seismometers spaced along the ground for the simple level two-layer structure already discussed. The equation for the determination of the depth to solid rock may be developed as follows:

$$V_e = L_0/T_0$$

$$T_3 = H/V_e + L_3/V_r + H/V_e = 2H/V_e + L_3/V_r$$

and    $$T_2 = H/V_e + L_2/V_r + H/V_e = 2H/V_e + L_2/V_r$$

Therefore

$$V_r = \frac{L_3 - L_2}{T_3 - T_2}$$

and $\quad H = \dfrac{V_e T_3}{2} - \dfrac{V_e L_3}{2 V_r}$

where $H$ = depth to solid rock (m), $V_e$ = velocity of the sound wave in the soil (m/s), $V_r$ = velocity of the sound wave in the rock (m/s), $T_0$, $T_1$, $T_2$, $T_3$ = time for sound wave to reach seismometers $D_0$, $D_1$, $D_2$, $D_3$ (s), respectively, and $L_0$, $L_1$, $L_2$, $L_3$ = distance to seismometers $D_0$, $D_1$, $D_2$, $D_3$ (m), respectively.

In this equation $V_e$ is calculated from the results obtained from the seismometers located within the critical distance. The velocity $V_r$ is determined from results obtained at seismometers beyond the critical distance.

Excellent descriptions of how to carry out and interpret seismic refraction surveys are available in the technical literature[48,49].

*Comparison of the geophysical methods*   The seismic test is particularly useful for determining the presence or absence of dense, solid rock since the high velocities associated with such formations make the determination quite dependable (to within 10 per cent of the depth). Although the resistivity method will, in most instances, indicate the depth of overburden to a high-resistivity formation such as rock, it cannot always, in the absence of confirming geological data, furnish completely dependable evidence for predicting the presence of rock. Sand and gravel can show surface anomalies similar to those shown by solid rock. In areas where solid rock layers are interbedded with less dense materials such as shales, the resistivity test is the better tool, since it can detect the change from the hard rock to the softer and less resistant shales. The seismic test under such conditions is limited to an indication of the depth of overburden above the high-velocity sandstone or limestone, and the lower-velocity shales cannot be located.

| Material | Seismic wave velocity (km/s) | | | | | | | |
|---|---|---|---|---|---|---|---|---|
| | 0 | 1 | 2 | 3 | 4 | 5 | 6 | 7 |
| **Soils:** | | | | | | | | |
| *Above water-table* | | | | | | | | |
| Sediments | | — | | | | | | |
| Moraine | | — | | | | | | |
| *Below water-table* | | | | | | | | |
| Coarse sand | | | — | | | | | |
| Clay | | | = | | | | | |
| Gravel | | | — | | | | | |
| Moraine | | | — | | | | | |
| **Rocks:** | | | | | | | | |
| Shale and clay shale | | — | | | | | | |
| Chalk | | — | | | | | | |
| Limestones and sandstones | | – – – – – –——————— | | | | | | |
| Quartzite | | | | | | — | | |
| Gneiss | | | | – – – –————————— | | | | |
| Igneous rocks | | | | – – – –————————— | | | | |

**Fig. 1.12**   Seismic values for natural materials (reported in reference 45)

Provided that saturated soils do not exist above the water-table, the depth to the water-table in soil can be determined using either the seismic or the resistivity method. Generally, however, only the resistivity method can be used to locate the water-table in bedrock.

The resistivity test offers a practical means for the rapid investigation of larger areas in search of localized deposits of gravel, sand or other granular materials useful in highway construction. The seismic method is not so well adapted to an area survey, but is best applied to the determination of conditions at a single designated spot or limited area. Even in the limited areas, if differential weathering has resulted in pinnacles and deep valleys in the subsurface rock—a condition sometimes encountered in limestone formations—the resistivity test may prove the more valuable method.

An important advantage of the seismic method is that the seismic compression velocity of a rock or soil has been broadly correlated with its rippability with a certain size of tractor. However, the use of explosives may be prohibited in built-up areas and this may place a handicap on the use of the seismic method in certain instances. The electrical resistivity method is more difficult to apply in saline groundwater conditions, or where there are buried metals, e.g. water or gas pipes. The development of reliable and relatively cheap electronics means that it is now much easier to carry out a seismic refraction survey than previously.

## Preparation of plans

The drawings for a highway scheme are, in effect, the graphical instructions as to how the roadway is to be constructed. As such they are an integral part of the contract drawn up between the highway authority and the contractor. Hence great care must be taken in their preparation so that the contractor knows exactly what has to be done and costly variations are not necessary after the contract is awarded.

### Component parts

A basic set of plans for a highway improvement may contain the following.

(1)   A location map of the proposed improvement—this shows the location of the proposed line, major topographical features, possible detour routes, and other general features of introductory interest.

(2)   A detailed plan of the proposed highway—this should show the chainages and exact locations of all pegs; bearings of tangent lines, radii and other geometrical data affecting the layout of all horizontal curves, boundaries of the right-of-way, and streams, railways, buildings, fences, public utility lines, and other structures contained within it; existing and proposed drainage structures; locations of benchmarks; any other details to be considered in the course of construction. Contours showing the topographical nature of the terrain may also be included.

(3)   A profile section of the longitudinal line of the road—this should show the required surface or formation line of the highway and the natural ground or existing road line; all necessary existing and required elevations at marked pegs; all required vertical curve data; percentages of grade for each continuous grade; elevations of floors of culverts and bridges, and the beds of streams; any other information necessary for the vertical design of the highway.

(4)   Earthworks cross-sections at all necessary locations—each cross-section should be clearly located and indicate the elevations and line of the existing ground and the proposed roadway formation, and the areas of cut and fill for each section.

(5)   Typical roadway cross-sections at selected locations—these should provide all information required to construct the pavement, shoulders, footways, side slopes, drainage ditches, and other such structural items.

(6)   A mass-haul diagram—this indicates the amount of cut or fill to particular locations along the line of the roadway, and shows where excavated material may be economically moved to create embankments.

(7)   Construction details of such items as culverts and bridges—these are very often separate contracts—guard rails and fences, traffic islands, kerbs, gutters and drainage inlets, pavement joints, superelevation, and other such items should be shown.

(8)   Special requirements of the scheme should be shown.

## Steps in preparation

A basic approach to the preparation of highway plans is as follows.

(1)   Prepare the location map.
(2)   Draw the highway plan.
(3)   Plot the profile section and establish the vertical alignment of the road.
(4)   Develop preliminary concepts relative to cross-sections, drainage requirements, and minor structures.
(5)   Visit field and test the feasibility of concepts.
(6)   Prepare cross-section details.
(7)   Estimate earthworks quantities.
(8)   Prepare construction details of all structural items.
(9)   Complete and check plans.
(10)  Visit field and verify that the plans are operational.

The first four stages involve what might be termed the preparation of the preliminary plans. After they have been prepared, it is good practice to visit the field and, by inspection, check the extent to which such features as proposed drainage structures are feasible, and how they and other such features affect, and are affected by, field conditions. At this stage also, any further data required to complete the plans are obtained.

The remaining stages involve the preparation of the final plans. When they are considered complete, the designer again traverses the entire length of the scheme, and verifies that each item is as desired.

**Establishing the vertical alignment**

The first step in the establishment of the vertical alignment is the determination of the ruling grade for each section of the highway. As discussed in Volume 1, Chapter 6, there are maximum ruling grades for highways: these depend upon the type and location of the roadway. Below these maximum values, however, a number of other conditions influence the choice of grade at particular locations.

In many cases the grade chosen for a particular section will be controlled by adjacent topographical features or man-made culture. For instance, when the terrain is low lying and swampy it is necessary to establish a line well above the existing ground level. Bridges, intersections with other roadways, etc., are fixtures which require that the highway be graded to meet them. In urban areas the grade is controlled by the requirements of street intersections and footpaths, drainage needs, and the value of adjacent property.

Where the existing ground grades are within the maximum permitted for the highway, the establishment of the grade lines is primarily a matter of fitting the new grades to the existing ones so that a comfortable riding surface is obtained which produces a pleasing appearance with the minimum of earthworks. Good drainage is also obtained in this way. In rolling topography, particularly in rural areas, the selection of grades will be strongly influenced by the amount of earth-moving that has to be carried out, i.e. in most instances the natural ground level will not be the same as that required for the highway and considerable earth-moving operations may be required to construct the subgrade to the desired grades. If the grades are properly selected, and the horizontal alignment is well chosen, then the material cut from the high areas should ideally balance the amount of earthworks required to make up the low areas; a most economical earthworks construction is then said to prevail. If, however, earthworks material has to be wasted and/or expensive fill has to be imported at the subgrade construction stage, then consideration may have to be given to changing the vertical alignment (or perhaps the horizontal one) to ensure a more economical highway construction.

A measure of the importance of earthworks in highway construction in Britain can be gathered from the data in Table 1.7, which illustrates the huge amounts of earthworks that had to be shifted for major road construction only, in one year. Currently, much consideration is being given to using 'waste' materials in highway embankments where the use of

**Table 1.7**   Earthworks operations for major roads in Britain in 1969[50]

| Operation | Volume ($10^6$ m$^3$) | Estimated mass ($10^6$ t) |
|---|---|---|
| Cut to fill | 27 | 54 |
| Rock excavation | 5 | 10 |
| Cut to waste | 3 | 6 |
| Imported fill | 13 | 26 |

imported fill is essential, i.e. materials such as colliery shale, spent oil shale, wastes from coal-fired power stations, quarry wastes, chalk and incinerator wastes (see also Chapter 3). Where such usage is practically and economically feasible, it can have the additional advantages of conserving scarce natural raw materials, e.g. gravel and sand, improving the environment by removing unsightly and often-damaging waste materials from spoil tips, and releasing valuable derelict land for other uses.

In modern-day design offices, the vertical alignment is now normally established following computer analysis. Nonetheless, the process involved is simply illustrated by the following non-computerized, but well-proven method.

First, a trial grade line is established by visually attempting to balance the cut and fill volumes. This can be done by stretching fine thread over the profile and holding it in place with pins located at intersection points, the use of pins permitting easy changes to study the effects of different grades without the need for tediously erasing pencil lines. In choosing suitable grades, the cross-section data should be frequently inspected since the centreline elevation is very often different from the side elevations. When the grades have been decided upon, vertical curves are calculated, located on the profile drawing, and then checked to ensure that the sight distances are adequate; often the vertical curves have to be flattened in order to lengthen the available sight distance.

**Estimating earthworks quantities**
The determination of earthworks quantities is usually based on cross-section data gathered in the field or interpolated from digital ground models. These cross-section data show the extent of the excavation (cut) in cuttings and the filling (fill) for embankments at regular intervals—usually about every 15–30 m—and where major surface irregularities occur along the centreline of the proposed highway.

Current practice, of course, is to make the maximum use of the computer in the determination of earthworks quantities for optimum highway location and design purposes. Thus what used to be very tedious and repetitive calculations, often made the responsibility of the most junior engineers in the design office, are now handled much more speedily and effectively with the aid of modern-day office equipment.

Notwithstanding the above, the following discussion assumes that earthworks quantities are still determined 'manually', as it is on the basis of fundamentals such as these that the computer programs are developed.

*Determining cross-sectional areas*   When the ground surface is level or regular, the area of a cross-section is most easily determined by dividing the enclosed space into triangles and trapesiums and using standard formulae in the calculations. If the ground surface is irregular, the area of a cross-section can be obtained using the coordinate method. By geometry, it can be shown that the enclosed area, $A$, in Fig. 1.13 is given by

$$A = \tfrac{1}{2}[y_1(x_4 - x_2) + y_2(x_1 - x_3) + y_3(x_2 - x_4) + y_4(x_3 - x_1)]$$

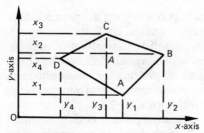

**Fig. 1.13**   Determining area by the coordinate method

From this the following simple rule can be postulated.

> Moving about the closed figure in an anticlockwise direction, multiply each ordinate ($y$-value) by the algebraic difference between the prior and following abscissas ($x$-values), find the algebraic sum of the products and divide the result by 2. If the enclosed figure is to the left of the $y$-axis, movement should take place in a clockwise direction.

The use of the above relationship in calculating a cross-sectional area is illustrated by the following example.

Let it be assumed that the cross-sectional area of the embankment shown in Fig. 1.14, which is to be constructed across sloping ground, is required. The width of the embankment is to be 10 m.

For convenience in calculation the embankment will be divided into two parts, $A_1$ and $A_2$. The coordinates of each corner are written in fractional form and are referenced with respect to the centreline and the top of the embankment. Thus the 'fraction' $\frac{7}{11}$ means that the point referenced is 7 m below the top of the embankment and 11 m from the centreline.

Considering area $A_1$, begin at any corner and proceed anticlockwise about the enclosed area so as to obtain

$$A_1 = \tfrac{1}{2}[4(0 - 5) + 0(11 - 0) + 0(5 - 0) + 6(0 - 11)] = -43 \text{ m}^2$$

Considering area $A_2$, begin at any corner and proceed clockwise about the enclosed area so as to obtain

$$A_2 = \tfrac{1}{2}[7(0 - 19) + 7(11 - 5) + 0(19 - 0) + 0(5 - 0) + 6(0 - 11)]$$

$$= -157 \text{ m}^2$$

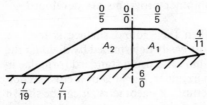

**Fig. 1.14**   Determining the cross-sectional area of an embankment by the coordinate method

Therefore

$$A_1 + A_2 = -200 \text{ m}^2$$

The minus sign has no significance other than it indicates that an embankment is being considered. If the calculations are carried out for a cutting, i.e. with the centreline and the bottom of the embankment as the reference lines, then a positive answer will be obtained. In the case of a side-hill section involving both cut and fill, the vertical reference axis should be taken through the point of intersection of the formation or carriageway and the natural ground level so that the areas in cut and fill can be determined separately.

*Determining earthworks volumes*  When the cross-sectional areas of excavation and embankment are known, the volumes can be calculated. The simplest and most common procedure for measuring volume is by means of the *trapezoidal* or *average-end-area method*. This merely involves the estimation of each of the end cross-sectional areas of a length of roadway, the calculation of their mean, and the multiplication of the mean area by the distance between the ends. Thus, in Fig. 1.15, if the area delineated by points A, B, C and D is denoted by $A_1$ and that delineated by points I, J, K and L is denoted by $A_2$, then

$$V = \tfrac{1}{2}D(A_1 + A_2)$$

where $V$ = volume (m³), $D$ = distance between the end areas (m), and $A_1$, $A_2$ = end areas (m²).

For a series of successive cross-sections spaced at uniform distances $D$ apart, with areas $A_1$, $A_2$, $A_3$,..., $A_n$, the volume enclosed between the first and last sections is given by the expression

$$V = \tfrac{1}{2}D(A_1 + A_2) + \tfrac{1}{2}D(A_2 + A_3) + \tfrac{1}{2}D(A_3 + A_4)$$
$$+ \ldots + \tfrac{1}{2}D(A_{n-1} + A_n)$$
$$= D[\tfrac{1}{2}(A_1 + A_n) + A_2 + A_3 + A_4 + \ldots + A_{n-1}]$$

The above formula is exact only when the end areas are equal. When they are not, as is usually so, the results given by the equation are larger than the true values. In practice, however, it is found that the total error on

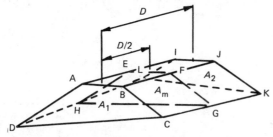

**Fig. 1.15**  Determining volumes by the average-end-area and prismoidal formulae

a long line is rarely more than a few per cent; hence this very simple method is very often used to calculate earthworks quantities.

When more precise results are required, and when the field data are sufficiently exact to warrant them, volumes may be determined by means of the *prismoidal formula*. Referring again to Fig. 1.15, if $A_1$ and $A_2$ are as indicated before and the mid-section area delineated by points E, F, G and H is denoted by $A_m$, then

$$V = \tfrac{1}{6} D(A_1 + 4A_m + A_2)$$

Note that $A_m$ is not the average of the end areas: it is the area of the cross-section at the point midway between the end areas. For a series of successive and equally spaced cross-sections with areas $A_1$, $A_2$, $A_3$,...,$A_n$, and when $n$ is an *odd* number, the volume enclosed between the first and last sections is given by

$$V = \tfrac{1}{6} D(A_1 + 4A_2 + 2A_3 + 4A_4 + 2A_5$$
$$+ ... + 2A_{n-2} + 4A_{n-1} + A_n)$$

Where such precise results are required as to justify the use of the prismoidal formula, they will also warrant correcting the volumes on curves for errors involved in assuming the centreline to be straight. On curves, the cross-sections are taken as near radially as possible, so that the volume being estimated is a curved solid between two non-parallel plane ends; this is shown in Fig. 1.16. This volume can be closely determined by means of Pappus' second theorem, as follows.

If a plane area rotates about an axis in its own plane which does not divide it into two parts, the volume of the solid thereby formed is equal to the area multiplied by the length of the path of the centre of mass of the area.

In Fig. 1.16, let $A_1$ and $A_2$ be two adjacent end areas that are at a distance $D$ from each other. Let the centroids of $A_1$ and $A_2$ be distances of $e_1$ and $e_2$, respectively, from the centreline, which has a radius of curvature $R$. If the average area is $\tfrac{1}{2}(A_1 + A_2)$, then by Pappus

$$V = \tfrac{1}{2}(A_1 + A_2) \times (\text{arc distance between the centroids})$$

However,

$$D = R\theta$$

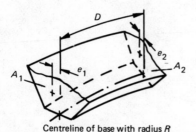

Centreline of base with radius $R$

**Fig. 1.16**   Determining volumes on a curved centreline

where $D$ = length of curve, $R$ = radius of curve, and $\theta$ = angle subtended at the centre of the curve. Therefore

$\theta = D/R$ radians

The average eccentricity is $\frac{1}{2}(e_1 + e_2)$; hence the arc distance between the centroids is given by

centroid arc distance $= \theta[R + \frac{1}{2}(e_1 + e_2)] = D[1 + (e_1 + e_2)/2R]$

Thus the volume is given approximately by

$V = \frac{1}{2}D(A_1 + A_2)[1 + (e_1 + e_2)/2R]$

In the above equation the correction factor is actually $D(e_1 + e_2)/4R$. Thus it can be seen that if $D$ is quite small and $R$ is large, the correction can be relatively unimportant. If the eccentricity of the centroid of the average section is within the inside of the curve, the correction factor is subtracted from, instead of being added to, the volume as determined by ignoring the curve.

**Distributing earthworks quantities**
As discussed earlier, the location of a highway and the selection of its vertical alignment should ideally be such that the volume of material excavated within the limits of the scheme is equal to that required in embankment. If all the excavated material can be hauled from the cuttings to the embankments, then wastage and the need to borrow materials are eliminated and a most economical design is obtained. In order to cost the scheme, i.e. the prices in the bill of quantities are normally based on the unit volume of soil before excavation or the unit volume after compaction, it is necessary therefore to analyse the relationships between cut and fill materials along the proposed line of the road.

*Shrinkage* When calculating earthworks quantities, an allowance has to be made for the excess of excavation required to form a given embankment volume. The term shrinkage is almost universally used to explain the condition whereby a unit volume of excavation soil will occupy less space when placed in a compacted embankment. The *shrinkage factor* is the term used to describe the relationship between the two volumes. This can, however, be a very confusing term as its value depends upon how it is determined. If the shrinkage factor is defined as the ratio of a volume of embankment to a fixed *volume of excavation* containing the same mass of dry material, then

$SF = V_f/V_e$

where $SF$ = shrinkage factor, $V_f$ = volume of embankment, and $V_e$ = volume of excavation. However,

$M = D_f V_f = D_e V_e$

where $M$ = mass of dry material to fill a given volume of either excavation or embankment, $D_f$ = dry density of embankment material and $D_e$ = dry density of excavation material. Therefore

$$SF = \frac{M/D_f}{M/D_e} = \frac{D_e}{D_f}$$

This means that if the density of the undisturbed excavation material is $1520 \text{ kg/m}^3$, and the density of the embankment is expected to be $1680 \text{ kg/m}^3$, then $1 \text{ m}^3$ of excavated material will theoretically occupy $0.905 \text{ m}^3$ in the embankment; in other words, $SF = 0.905$. The percentage shrinkage, expressed on the basis of a unit excavation volume, is given by

% shrinkage $= (1.000 - SF)100 = (1.000 - 0.905)100 = 9.5$

Payment for earthworks is usually based on excavation quantities; hence, for design purposes, the earthworks calculations are often determined on the basis of the volume of excavated material required to occupy a *given volume of embankment* containing the same mass of material. Using the same method of analysis as before, it can be shown that on this basis

$$SF = D_f/D_e$$

Thus, using the same example as above,

$$SF = 1680/1520 = 1.111$$

In other words, $1.111 \text{ m}^3$ of excavation is needed to obtain $1 \text{ m}^3$ of embankment. The percentage shrinkage expressed on this basis is

% shrinkage $= (SF - 1.000)100 = 11.1$

Whatever the basis of comparison, shrinkage is generally small; indeed in some instances there may be a negative shrinkage, i.e. a net bulk-up. However, materials such as chalk and sand generally show shrinkages when in embankment of 0–15 per cent and 0–10 per cent, respectively[51].

One final point that should be made here is that shrinkage should not be confused with wastage. *Wastage* of good material may occur, for example, as a result of constructing haul roads, or over-filling embankments, or removing soil from the site because it is contaminated by rain. On a typical highway project in Britain, such wastage generally amounts to about 5 per cent.

*Swell*  When a given volume of soil or rock is excavated, it will swell up (bulk up) so that $1 \text{ m}^3$ of material before excavation becomes more than $1 \text{ m}^3$ in the transporting vehicle. This must be taken into account when assessing the amount of transport required for costing and constructing purposes. The ratio of the bulk volume to the 'natural' or unexcavated volume is known as the *swelling factor* or *bulking factor*. Typical swelling factors for various types of material in Britain are given in Table 1.8[51].

When transported material is laid in the embankment and made more dense by compaction, the net result may be (as discussed previously) a net shrinkage. In the case of rocks, however, this will not be so. Typical net swelling factors for weak and hard rocks compacted in embankments are 1.0–1.1 and 1.05–1.20, respectively.

**Table 1.8** Typical swelling factors for various types of material in Britain

| Material | Swelling factor |
| --- | --- |
| *Soil* | |
| Sand—uniform or well graded, loose or compact | 1.10–1.15 |
| Gravel, sandy gravel | 1.10–1.15 |
| Clay—soft, firm, stiff, gravelly, organic, glacial | 1.20–1.40 |
| Loam, peat, topsoil | 1.25–1.45 |
| *Rock* | |
| Granite, basalt/dolerite, gabbro | 1.50–1.80 |
| Limestone, marble | 1.45–1.75 |
| Quartzite, sandstone, chert, flint | 1.40–1.70 |
| Coal | 1.35 |
| Gneiss, schist, slate, shale | 1.30–1.65 |
| Chalk—upper, middle, lower | 1.30–1.40 |

*Haul, free-haul and overhaul* In earthworks calculations the term haul has a dual meaning. It is used to describe the *distance* over which material is moved and, also, the *volume-distance* of material used.

In earthworks contracts the contractor can be paid a specified price for excavating, hauling and dumping material, provided that the haulage distance does not exceed a certain amount. This distance, which is called the free-haul, can be as little as 150 m on small road schemes and 350 m or more on large motorway construction schemes. Within the free-haul distance the contractor is paid a fixed amount per cubic metre of material, irrespective of the actual distance through which it is moved. When the haulage distance is greater than the free-haul, however, the contractor can be paid at a higher rate for the overhaul. The unit overhaul price is based on the cost per station-metre of moving material beyond the free-haul distance, i.e. the length measurement begins at the end of the free-haul distance.

*Economic-haul* When the haul distances are large it may be more economical to waste excavation material and borrow from a more convenient source than pay for overhauling. On any given scheme, the economic-haul distance will vary considerably, as it depends upon the availability of both suitable borrow materials and nearby sites where excavated material can be wasted.

The economic-overhaul distance can be determined by equating the cost of roadway excavation plus overhaul and tipping in embankment with the cost of borrowing pit material (which includes original cost as well as cost of excavating, hauling and tipping borrow in embankment), plus excavation, haul and wasting roadway material within the free-haul distance.

Thus, if $a$ = cost of roadway excavation per m$^3$, $b$ = cost of overhaul and tipping per m$^3$ per station, $c$ = cost of borrow material per m$^3$, and $L$ = economic-overhaul distance in stations, then

$$a + bL = c + a$$

Therefore

$$L = c/b \text{ stations}$$

If the free-haul distance is denoted by $F$ stations, then the economic-haul distance is given by

$$F + L = F + c/b \text{ stations}$$

*Mass-haul diagram* To enable the contractor to have a knowledge of the amount and extent of free-haul and overhaul on a project, so that a bid can be submitted, it is common practice to include a mass-haul diagram in the plans for the scheme. This diagram is a simple graphical representation of the amount of earthworks involved in the highway scheme, and the manner in which they may be most economically handled. It shows accumulated volume at any point along the proposed centreline and from this the economical directions of haul and the positioning of borrow pits and spoil heaps can be estimated.

An example of a mass-haul diagram is shown in Fig. 1.17. It consists of a graph showing the algebraic summation of excavation and embankment proceeding along the centreline of the roadway. The accumulated total at each station is the summation of the differences between cut and fill. Prior to summation, however, the embankment areas were adjusted so that all volumes are expressed in terms of excavated volumes.

Before discussing how it is used in practice, it is worthwhile outlining the characteristics of the diagram, as follows.

(1)  The ordinate at any station along the curve represents the earthworks accumulation to that point.
(2)  The maximum ordinate (+) indicates a change from cut to fill proceeding along the centreline from an arbitrarily assumed origin. The minimum ordinate (−) represents a change from fill to cut. These

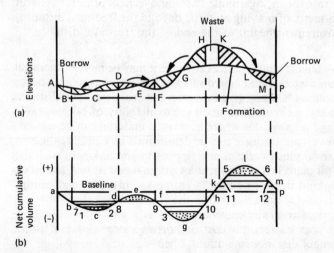

**Fig. 1.17**  Example of a mass-haul diagram: (a) longitudinal section and (b) mass diagram

maximum and minimum points may not necessarily coincide with the apparent points of transition as indicated by the profile section: this depends upon whether or not there are side-hill transitions at these points.
(3)   A rising curve at any point indicates an excess of excavation over embankment material at this point. A falling curve indicates the reverse.
(4)   A steeply rising or falling curve indicates heavy cuts or fills. Flat curves show that the earthworks quantities are small.
(5)   The shapes of the loops indicate the direction of haul. A convex loop shows that the haul from cut to fill is from left to right, while a concave loop indicates that the haul is from right to left.
(6)   Since the ordinates of a curve are plotted from cut volumes and adjusted fill volumes, then any line parallel to the baseline which cuts off a loop intersects the curve at two points between which the amount of cut is equal to the fill. Such a line is called a 'balancing line' and the intersection points are called 'balancing points'.
(7)   The area between a balance line and the mass-haul curve is a measure of the haul (in station-cubic-metres) between the balance points. If this area is divided by the maximum ordinate between the balance line and curve, the value obtained is the average distance that the cut material must be hauled in order to make the fill. This distance can also be estimated by drawing a horizontal line through the midpoint of this maximum ordinate until it intersects the loop at two points; the length of this line is very close to the average haul distance when the shape of the loop is 'smooth'.
(8)   Balance lines need not be continuous; the vertical break between any two balance lines merely indicates unbalanced earthworks between two adjacent points of termination of the lines. Adjacent balance lines should never overlap, as this means using the same part of the mass-haul diagram twice.

One way of using a mass-haul diagram is illustrated in Fig. 1.17. This figure has two parts, Fig. 1.17(a) being a profile section showing the ground contour and the proposed road formation, while Fig. 1.17(b) is the mass diagram illustrating the volumes of fill and excavation plotted as an additive curve beginning at a. First of all, the limits of economic-haul are noted; these are drawn as the balance lines bd, fh, and km between B and D, F and H, and K and M, respectively. Therefore the earthworks quantities are not only balanced in volume but economically so as well. The manner in which haulage should take place is indicated by the arrows; note that haulage takes place downhill to the embankments so that the empty vehicles can travel uphill to the excavation sites.
The limits of free-haul are indicated by the balance lines 12, 34, and 56. The free-haul station-meterage is indicated by the dotted areas 1c2, 3g4, and 5l6. In this case, by pure coincidence, the balance line of df is equal to the free-haul distance and, as a result, the area def is also free-haul station-meterage.
The overhaul volume for the section BCD is given by the ordinate difference between c to bd and c to 12. The average length of overhaul is estimated by drawing the balance line 78 through the median of the overhaul ordinate. Since the curve is smooth, the points 7 and 8 will lie

directly below the centres of mass of the overhaul volumes, and thus the average distance that this excavated material is moved is given by the distance 78. Since the free-haul is given by 12, the average overhaul is equal to the distance 78 less the distance 12.

It is rarely that the attempt to choose an economical grade line results in the earthworks being completely balanced from beginning to end. In Fig. 1.17 the earthworks are not balanced and so material must be borrowed in order to build embankments between A and B, and M and P. The earthworks quantities involved are given by the ordinates at b and m. Between H and K the excavated material will have to be wasted on a spoil tip since it is not an economical proposition to overhaul and use it in the preparation of the embankments.

It might be noted that the Transport and Road Research Laboratory has developed a computer program *THEUS*[52] (*TH*eoretical *E*arthwork *U*tilization *S*ystem) which allows the engineer to evaluate the most cost-effective earthworks strategies for major road construction projects. Given a vertical alignment and the position, capacity, and cost of access of spoil tips and borrow pits along the length of road to be constructed, THEUS analyses the mass-haul curve and produces details of the volumes of material to be moved over the various distances together with the required usage of the spoil heaps and borrow pits. It also takes into account variations in excavation costs along the route, the effect of haul length on haulage cost, haulage barriers, and the overall percentage of unsuitable material, as well as particular percentages for individual lengths, in order to determine the cheapest earthworks for the alignment under consideration.

## Preparation of quantities

When a road improvement has been located and designed and the final plans drawn, the next phase is the drawing-up of a bill of quantities for the scheme. A bill of quantities consists of a detailed tabulation of all items of work expected to be met with during the course of construction, the estimated quantities of each, and the unit and total cost of every item. On the basis of these quantity data, the engineer can estimate whether the cost of the scheme will be within the allowed budget.

When the work is to be advertised for tenders from interested contractors, a bill of quantities is normally included as a part of the plans for the scheme. In this, the unit prices and total costs are not, of course, included, as it is up to the contractor to make estimates of these costs for tendering purposes. When a contract has been entered into, it is the function of the *priced* bill of quantities to provide for the valuation of the works executed. (A useful procedure according to which a bill of quantities may be prepared and priced, and the quantities of work expressed and measured, is readily available in the literature[53].)

A measure of the scope of a typical bill of quantities for a major highway project may be gathered from the following, which is listed in the normal preparation sequence used in practice in Britain[54]:

(1) preliminaries,

(2) roadworks,
(3) each bridge, viaduct or other structure,
(4) service areas,
(5) maintenance compounds,
(6) accommodation works,
(7) works for statutory undertakers,
(8) testing,
(9) dayworks.

Detailed lists of items for roadworks, service areas, maintenance compounds, accommodation works, and works for statutory undertakers are usually grouped as appropriate under the following headings: site clearance, hedges, fencing, drainage and service ducts, earthworks, subbase and roadbase, flexible surfacing, concrete pavement, kerbs and footways, and traffic signs and road markings.

The lists of items in the bill for each bridge or viaduct are normally grouped under the following construction headings: special preliminaries, special foundations, substructure (subdivided into end supports and intermediate supports), superstructure, finishings, and testing. Those for other structures are normally grouped under the following headings: special preliminaries, special foundations, structure, finishings, and testing.

## Specifications

Whereas the highway plans provide the graphical information necessary for the construction of the highway, the specifications are the written instructions which set the standards to which the work must be carried out. These standards are based on the result of experience and research knowledge acquired over many years as to the quality of materials and workmanship which can be demanded, and expected, on particular types of scheme. It is most important that the specifications should describe every construction item which enters into the contract, the materials to be used and the tests they must meet, methods of construction in particular situations, the method of measurement of each item, and the basis on which payment should be calculated.

Since substantial parts of highway schemes are repetitive, most highway authorities have at their disposal standard specifications for highway construction. These specifications are usually printed in permanent book form. On any given scheme, however, it will be found that particular problems arise which necessitate deviating from the standard specifications and thus the final specifications will include supplementary provisions that cover the conditions peculiar to local needs.

In Britain, the standard specification publications are the Department of Transport's *Specification for Highway Works*[55] and its associated *Notes*[56].

Specifications can be broadly divided into two main types: performance or end-result specifications and method or 'recipe' specifications. The aim of both types is to bring certainty of cost to the project contract—in the former method by transferring away the problems of unknown quantities to the contractor, and in the latter method by designing them out. In practice, a combination of both types of specification tends to be used in Britain.

With *performance specifications* the quality of the end product is described in terms of some functional standard, and the contractor is allowed to use ingenuity and experience to win the contract by devising the most economical solution to the construction problems. For example, in the case of an earthworks contract, the end-result specification may be that acceptable soils shall be compacted to 90–95 per cent of the maximum dry density as achieved by the appropriate British Standard compaction test. This specification places on the contractor the main responsibility for selecting the soils to be used, the thickness of layer to be compacted at any given time and place, the compaction equipment to be used, and the number of plant passes to be made. It will usually require the contractor to carry out numerous field trials to determine the optimum combinations for each soil used. An on-site field laboratory will also probably need to be established to enable the degree of compliance with the compaction specification to be checked.

With *method specifications* the contractor is provided with clearly defined descriptions of how the various components of the project should be produced. In this instance, the onus of responsibility for the satisfactory completion of the work—provided that the contractor carries out the contract according to specification—rests with the supervising (design) engineer. In the case of an earthworks contract, for example, this type of specification would normally state options with regard to the type of compaction equipment to be used, the thickness of layer, and the number of passes to be carried out on each type of soil.

Specifications are integral parts of the contract documents and their preparation should not be taken lightly. The legal importance of specifications means that their preparation requires not only considerable knowledge of highway practice, but also expertise in the law of contracts, so legal opinion should always be sought before specifications are placed for contract. To enable the legal advisers to prepare documents so that later recriminations are avoided, the engineer engaged in writing a specification should know exactly what is required and what is economically attainable. Careless and loose wording can also result in the use of poor-quality materials and poor workmanship, and the specifications should be tightly written so that this can be avoided. However, the requirements specified should not be so exacting that either they are impossible to attain or the costs of so doing are not justified by the results (see reference 57 for a useful discussion on the problem of specifying unachievable accuracies for survey, setting out and construction).

## Selected bibliography

(1) Beaumont TE, *Techniques for the Interpretation of Remote Sensing Imagery for Highway Engineering Purposes*, TRRL Report LR753, Crowthorne, Berks., The Transport and Road Research Laboratory, 1977.

(2) Milloy MH, *The Influence of Topography on the Duration of Ice-forming Conditions on a Road Surface*, RRL Report LR271, Crowthorne, Berks., The

Road Research Laboratory, 1969.

(3) Turner AK, Route location and selection, in: *Proceedings of the Conference on Computer Systems in Highway Design*, held in Copenhagen, 2–9 September 1972, and organized by the Royal Technical University (Copenhagen), Planning and Transport Research and Computation (International) Company Ltd (London), and the Laboratory for Road Data Processing (Copenhagen), London, Planning and Transport Research and Computation (International) Company Ltd, 1972.

(4) BS 5930: *Site Investigations*, London, The British Standards Institution, 1981.

(5) Scherocman JA and Sinclair HR, Use of soil surveys for planning and designing low volume roads, *Transportation Research Record 702*, 1979, pp. 125–132.

(6) Dumbleton MJ and West G, *Preliminary Sources of Information for Site Investigations in Britain*, TRRL Report LR403, Crowthorne, Berks., The Transport and Road Research Laboratory, 1976 (revised edition).

(7) Anon, Aerial photography in DoE, *DoE Construction*, 1972, **4**, pp. 24–26.

(8) Dumbleton MJ, *Photographs for Investigating Natural Changes, Past Use, and Present Condition of Engineering Sites*, TRRL Report LR1085, Crowthorne, Berks., The Transport and Road Research Laboratory, 1983.

(9) Fookes PG, Site reconnaissance and the engineering geologist, in: Dumbleton MJ (Ed), *Available Information for Route Planning and Site Investigation*, TRRL Report LR591, Crowthorne, Berks., The Transport and Road Research Laboratory, 1973.

(10) Committee on Engineering Surveying, *Report on Highway and Bridge Surveys*, New York, The American Society of Civil Engineers, 1962.

(11) *Report on Ground Subsidence*, London, The Institution of Civil Engineers, 1977.

(12) Malkin AB and Wood JC, Subsidence problems in route design and construction, *Q. Jl Engng Geol.*, 1972, **5**, pp. 179–194.

(13) Stott JP, Calogero V, Hickman D and Roumeliotis P, *Broad Band Route Selection by Program BRUTUS: Test on a Section of Motorway*, TRRL Report LR985, Crowthorne, Berks., The Transport and Road Research Laboratory, 1981.

(14) Broughton J, *Design of a Feasible Highway Alignment Through Mountainous Country Using Program NOAH*, TRRL Report LR914, Crowthorne, Berks., The Transport and Road Research Laboratory, 1979.

(15) Stott JP, The optimization of road layout by computer methods, Part 2, *Proc. Inst. Civ. Engrs*, 1973, **55**, pp. 67–85.

(16) Highway Engineering Computer Branch, *Highway Optimization Program System HOPS*, HECB/R/1-5 HOPS, London, The Department of Transport, 1972 (reprinted December 1977).

(17) Coghlan G and Davis N, Low water crossings, *Transportation Research Record 702*, 1979, pp. 98–103.

(18) Beaumont TE and Charman JH, Remote sensing techniques applied to highway engineering and transportation planning in developing countries, in: *Highway Design and Maintenance in Developing Countries*, PTRC Report P177, pp. 145–153, London, Planning and Transport Research and Computation (International) Company Ltd, July 1979.

(19) Beaumont TE, Remote sensing survey techniques, *The Highway Engineer*, 1979, **26**, No. 4, pp. 2–14.

(20) Beaven PJ and Lawrence CJ, *Terrain Evaluation for Highway Planning and Design*, TRRL Report SR725, Crowthorne, Berks., The Transport and Road Research Laboratory, 1982.

(21) *Terrain Evaluation and Remote Sensing for Highway Engineering in Developing Countries*, Proceedings of a symposium held at OECD, Paris, 12–14 September 1979, TRRL Report SR690, Crowthorne, Berks., The Transport and Road Research Laboratory, 1982.

(22) Jupp DLB, Heggen SJ, Mayo KK, Kendall SW, Bolton JR and Harrison BA, *The BRIAN Handbook*, CSIRO Natural Resource Series No. 3, Canberra, ACT, The Commonwealth Scientific and Industrial Research Organization, 1985.

(23) Barr DJ and Miles RD, *Techniques for Utilizing Side-looking Airborne Radar (SLAR) Imagery in Regional Highway Planning*, Special Report 102, pp. 49–56, Washington DC, The Highway Research Board, 1969.

(24) Fagan PF, Photogrammetry in the national survey, *Photogrammetric Record*, 1972, 7, No. 40, pp. 405–423.

(25) Dumbleton MJ and West G, *Air-photograph Interpretation for Road Engineers in Britain*, RRL Report LR369, Crowthorne, Berks., The Road Research Laboratory, 1970.

(26) Heath W and Dowling JWF, *Examples of the Use of Terrestrial Photogrammetry in Highway Engineering*, TRRL Report SR602, Crowthorne, Berks., The Transport and Road Research Laboratory, 1980.

(27) Scott L, Data collection for digital ground models using aerial survey methods, in *Surface Modelling by Computer*, pp. 15–24, London, The Institution of Civil Engineers, 1977.

(28) Howes LA, Data acquisition for digital ground models by ground survey methods, in: *Surface Modelling by Computer*, pp. 9–14, London, The Institution of Civil Engineers, 1977.

(29) Tempfli K and Kure J, Large scale surveys: aerial versus ground survey methods, *ITC Journal*, 1980, 4, pp. 696–715.

(30) Stott JP, Review of surface modelling, in: *Surface Modelling by Computer*, pp. 1–8, London, The Institution of Civil Engineers, 1977.

(31) Scott L, English JS, Lewry D, Mott PG and O'Brien CIM, Specification for vertical air photography, *Photogrammetric Record*, 1979, 9, No. 54, pp. 739–756.

(32) Brunsden D, Doornkamp JC, Fookes PG, Jones DKC and Kelly JMH, Geomorphological mapping techniques in highway engineering, *The Highway Engineer*, 1975, 22, No. 12, pp. 35–41.

(33) *Terrain Evaluation for Highway Engineering and Transport Planning*, TRRL Report SR448, Crowthorne, Berks., The Transport and Road Research Laboratory, 1978.

(34) Belcher DJ, The engineering significance of soil patterns, in: *Investigation and Development of Materials Resources*, Transportation Technology Support for Developing Countries Compendium 6, Text 2, Washington DC, The Transportation Research Board, 1979.

(35) *Manual of Remote Sensing*, Falls Church, Virginia, American Society of Photogrammetry, 1975.

(36) Schuster RL and Krizek RJ, *Landslides: Analysis and Control*, Special Report 176, Washington DC, The Transportation Research Board, 1978.

(37) Parvis M, Drainage pattern significance in airphoto identification of soils and bedrocks, in: *Drainage and Geological Considerations in Highway Location*, Transportation Technology Support for Developing Countries Compendium 2, Text 12, Washington DC, The Transportation Research Board, 1978.

(38) Heath W, *Inexpensive Photography for Highway Engineering and Traffic Studies*, TRRL Report SR632, Crowthorne, Berks., The Transport and Road Research Laboratory, 1980.

(39) Matalucci RU and Abdel-Hady M, *Surface and Subsurface Exploration by Infrared Surveys*, Special Report 102, pp. 1–12, Washington DC, The Highway Research Board, 1969.

(40) AASHO, Standard methods of surveying and sampling soils for highway purposes: AASHO Designation T86-54, *Book of Standard Specifications for Highway Materials and Methods of Sampling and Testing: Part II*, Washington DC, The American Association of State Highway Officials, 1961.

(41) Matheson GD and Kerr WG, *Site Investigation in Scotland*, TRRL Report LR828, Crowthorne, Berks., The Transport and Road Research Laboratory, 1978.

(42) Road Research Laboratory, *Soil Survey Procedure*, Road Research Technical Paper No. 15, London, HMSO, 1954.

(43) Finn FN, Subsurface soils exploration, in: *Drainage and Geological Considerations in Highway Location*, Transportation Technology Support for Developing Countries Compendium 2, Text 3, Washington DC, The Transportation Research Board, 1978.

(44) Cowan DR, *Geological and Geophysical Investigations on Part of the M90 Kelty By-pass*, RRL Report LR255, Crowthorne, Berks., The Road Research Laboratory, 1969.

(45) *Manual of Applied Geology for Engineers*, London, The Institution of Civil Engineers, 1977.

(46) Moore RW, Applications of electrical resistivity measurements to subsurface investigations, *Public Roads*, 1957, **29**, No. 7, pp. 163–169.

(47) Linehan Rev. D, Seismology as a geologic technique, *Highway Research Board Bulletin*, 1948, **13**, pp. 77–85.

(48) Greenhalgh SA and Whiteley RJ, Effective application of the seismic refraction method to highway engineering projects, *Australian Road Research*, 1977, **7**, No. 1, pp. 3–20.

(49) Stewart M and Beaven PJ, *Seismic Refraction Surveys for Highway Engineering Purposes*, TRRL Report LR950, Crowthorne, Berks., The Transport and Road Research Laboratory, 1980.

(50) Sherwood PT, *The Use of Waste and Low-grade Materials in Road Construction: (1) Guide to Materials Available*, TRRL Report LR647, Crowthorne, Berks., The Transport and Road Research Laboratory, 1974.

(51) Horner PC, *Earthworks*, London, Thomas Telford, 1981.

(52) *Optimisation of Earthworks Mass Haul Strategy: Computer Program HECB/R/3 (THEUS)*, Advice Note 1/78, London, The Department of Transport, 1978.

(53) Institution of Civil Engineers, *Civil Engineering Standard Method of Measurement*, London, Thomas Telford, 1985 (2nd edition).

(54) Department of Transport, *Method of Measurement for Road and Bridge Works*, London, HMSO, 1977.

(55) Department of Transport, *Specification for Highway Works*, London, HMSO, 1986 (6th edition).

(56) Department of Transport, *Notes for Guidance on the Specification for Highway Works*, London, HMSO, 1986 (6th edition).

(57) Joint Institution of Highway Engineers and Institution of Civil Engineers Working Party, *Survey Standards, Setting Out and Earthworks Measurements*, London, The Institution of Highway Engineers, September 1982.

# 2
# Surface and subsurface moisture control

Water is the enemy of earthworks and roads. It is no exaggeration to state that the entire serviceability of a highway is greatly dependent upon the adequacy of its drainage system. Water standing on the carriageway is a danger to high-speed traffic; this danger is accentuated when freezing temperatures occur. Water seeping into the pavement and subgrade leads to the development of soft spots which result in the break-up of the surfacing and the need for expensive reconstruction.

By their nature, highways cut across natural drainage-ways, or wind along valleys adjacent to stream-beds. As a result, there are innumerable locations where highway and drainage-ways must cross, and where streams have the power to destroy a roadway by force, or to hold up traffic by flooding a carriageway.

Thus it can be said with total justification that proper drainage design is an essential and integral part of economic highway design. Indeed, when it is remembered that drainage costs can typically amount to about 20 per cent of total highway construction costs it can be understood why drainage considerations are not only a major design consideration, but also an important influence on the location of the highway itself. Thus good drainage design begins with good highway location, and locations which avoid poorly-drained areas, unstable soil, frequently flooded areas, and unnecessary stream crossings greatly reduce the drainage problem.

Road drainage considerations can conveniently be divided into those relating to the flow of surface water and those relating to the flow of subsurface water. *Subsurface moisture control* is concerned with the flow of water within soils. *Surface drainage* is concerned with the measures taken to control the movement of water over the ground on and adjacent to the highway, so that it is directed to suitable disposal points with the least detrimental effects.

## Surface drainage

There are a number of common technical situations with which the highway engineer has to cope when locating/designing a highway section [1].

### Common surface drainage problems

First, and most obvious to the motorist, there are *bridge problems*. Bridges sit astride rivers and streams which drain large areas, and the flows to be catered for can be relatively large. Bridge problems commonly require a knowledge of the peak discharge, and perhaps the hydrograph, arriving at a bridge opening. Expert advice from, and the cooperation of, the appropriate waterway authorities should be obtained when deciding on the form and scale that bridging structures should take.

*Culvert problems* differ from bridge problems in terms of scale and, of course, form. Culverts normally drain smaller streams and, as a result, gauging records are less often available. Otherwise, the hydrology needs for culverts are similar to those for bridges.

The *drainage of the carriageway* is another aspect that is closely related to storm drainage design. The engineer is concerned that precipitation falling on the road surface should be removed as quickly and efficiently as possible, so as to minimize the danger to moving vehicles. The removed rainwater must then be carried to outfall points, without unacceptably aggravating downstream conditions.

The highway engineer also has to be concerned about the need (or otherwise) for a *flood detention reservoir* to handle excess runoff. Worldwide, the development of storage facilities in, for example, parkland has become popular in urban areas in recent years. Where properly utilized, such detention storage areas can often result in considerable economies in respect of downstream drainage facilities.

In certain instances, it may be more economical and technically feasible for the highway engineer to consider *relocating channels* rather than providing expensive bridges and other drainage features to accommodate natural but fickle stream channels. In recent years, however, channel relocations have become more difficult to initiate as a result of the public's greater interest in the effects of the changes upon the natural environment.

*General river problems* also arise as a result of highway construction projects which affect the ecology, sediment transport regime, flood-control characteristics, and other river aspects.

The *urban hydrologic regime* can be significantly different from that in rural areas. Downstream flooding conditions are very often aggravated by land developments in urban areas. Most of the major roads yet to be constructed/reconstructed in Britain will be located in and about urban areas, so that the highway engineer must be particularly concerned with the peculiarities of urban hydrology.

*Water quality variations* resulting from mankind's activities, including the construction of highways, have become of greater interest to the general public over the past decade. Highways in urban areas can be particularly expected to affect the quality of runoff, both because of the composition of their pavements and (sometimes) embankments, and because of the many deposits which fall on carriageways and are then washed away during rainstorms. In rural areas, the problem is similar but generally of less concern.

In respect of the above, it is convenient to divide a surface drainage study into two parts. Firstly, there is the problem of deciding the amount of water which must be catered for, i.e. the amount of water arriving at the inlet, drainage ditch or culvert, and, secondly, there is the design of the facility needed to handle this amount of water. The first part of such an investigation is termed the hydrological study, while the second part is called the hydraulic study.

## Hydrological study

Hydrology can be described as the science which deals with the operations governing the circulation of moisture in its various forms, above, on, and beneath the earth's surface. As such it involves the study of the various phases of the hydrologic cycle, i.e. precipitation, surface runoff, infiltration, evaporation, and transpiration. The two main phases of the hydrologic cycle in which the highway engineer is most interested are precipitation and runoff.

### Precipitation

Water can be precipitated in the form of rain, hail, snow or sleet. In practice, however, the engineer is mostly concerned with the moisture which falls in the form of rain; it is only in countries which are normally very cold and subject to rapid upward changes in temperature that special consideration has to be given to the provision of extra drainage for moisture from melting-snow accumulations on the ground.

Whilst the average annual precipitation over the whole of the UK is about 1100 mm, it can vary considerably, e.g. in the mountainous regions of North West Scotland the average can be as high as 5000 mm[2]. Over the past century a daily rainfall of 160 mm or more has been measured about once every four years somewhere in Britain, most frequently in the South West and least frequently in the Midlands and the South East. The maximum daily rainfall recorded anywhere in Britain is about 280 mm.

*Rainfall intensity*  Ultimately, the highway engineer is concerned with the runoff from the catchment area being studied, and average rainfalls as described above have only a peripheral effect upon this. Of much more importance are the rainfall intensities for given periods of time at the location being evaluated. In this respect it might be noted that, regardless of topography, rainfall intensities during short ( < 1 h) storms are generally fairly similar at different locations in small countries such as Britain, e.g. the quantity of rainfall expected in 60 minutes, with a frequency of once in five years, is 18 mm ± 3 mm over 85 per cent of the country. However, the variations due to geographical location increase significantly as the storm durations and return periods are increased.

A fundamental feature of rainfalls is that the intensity of rainfall throughout a given storm is inversely proportional to the length of the storm, i.e. as the duration of a rainfall increases, its average intensity decreases (see Table 2.1). This is perhaps to be expected since the meteorological forces which cause a heavy rainfall are also continually causing it to move quickly from one area to another.

While an engineer designing a large bridge or a complete flood-control system is mainly interested in storms which cover large areas and last for

**Table 2.1** Rainfall intensities (mm/h) at Crowthorne, Berks. (National Grid Reference 4833E 1633N), as a function of duration and frequency [3]

| Duration (minutes) | Return period (years) | | | | | | |
|---|---|---|---|---|---|---|---|
| | 1 | 2 | 5 | 10 | 20 | 50 | 100 |
| 2.0 | 75.6 | 93.4 | 120.5 | 138.3 | 158 | 187 | 213 |
| 2.5 | 76.5 | 87.5 | 113.4 | 130.4 | 149 | 177 | 202 |
| 3.0 | 66.3 | 82.3 | 107.2 | 123.4 | 141 | 168 | 192 |
| 3.5 | 62.8 | 77.8 | 101.7 | 117.3 | 135 | 161 | 184 |
| 4.0 | 59.6 | 73.8 | 96.8 | 111.8 | 128 | 154 | 176 |
| 4.1 | 59.1 | 73.1 | 95.9 | 110.8 | 127 | 152 | 174 |
| 4.2 | 58.5 | 72.3 | 95.0 | 109.8 | 126 | 151 | 173 |
| 4.3 | 57.9 | 71.6 | 94.1 | 108.8 | 125 | 150 | 172 |
| 4.4 | 57.4 | 71.0 | 93.2 | 107.9 | 124 | 149 | 170 |
| 4.5 | 56.9 | 70.3 | 92.4 | 106.9 | 123 | 148 | 169 |
| 4.6 | 56.3 | 69.6 | 91.6 | 106.0 | 122 | 146 | 168 |
| 4.7 | 55.8 | 69.0 | 90.8 | 105.1 | 121 | 145 | 166 |
| 4.8 | 55.3 | 68.3 | 90.0 | 104.2 | 120 | 144 | 165 |
| 4.9 | 54.8 | 67.7 | 89.2 | 103.4 | 119 | 143 | 164 |
| 5.0 | 54.3 | 67.1 | 88.5 | 102.5 | 118 | 142 | 163 |
| 5.1 | 53.9 | 66.5 | 87.7 | 101.7 | 117 | 141 | 162 |
| 5.2 | 53.4 | 65.9 | 87.0 | 100.9 | 116 | 140 | 160 |
| 5.3 | 53.0 | 65.4 | 86.3 | 100.1 | 115 | 139 | 159 |
| 5.4 | 52.5 | 64.8 | 85.6 | 99.3 | 115 | 138 | 158 |
| 5.5 | 52.1 | 64.3 | 84.9 | 98.5 | 114 | 137 | 157 |
| 5.6 | 51.7 | 63.7 | 84.2 | 97.8 | 113 | 136 | 156 |
| 5.7 | 51.2 | 63.2 | 83.5 | 97.0 | 112 | 135 | 155 |
| 5.8 | 50.8 | 62.7 | 82.9 | 96.3 | 111 | 134 | 154 |
| 5.9 | 50.4 | 62.2 | 82.3 | 95.6 | 110 | 133 | 153 |
| 6.0 | 50.0 | 61.7 | 81.6 | 94.9 | 110 | 132 | 152 |
| 6.2 | 49.3 | 60.7 | 80.4 | 93.5 | 108 | 130 | 150 |
| 6.4 | 48.5 | 59.8 | 79.2 | 92.2 | 107 | 129 | 148 |
| 6.6 | 47.8 | 58.9 | 78.1 | 90.9 | 105 | 127 | 146 |
| 6.8 | 47.1 | 58.0 | 77.0 | 89.6 | 104 | 125 | 144 |
| 7.0 | 46.4 | 57.2 | 75.9 | 88.4 | 102 | 124 | 143 |
| 7.2 | 45.8 | 56.4 | 74.9 | 87.3 | 101 | 122 | 141 |
| 7.4 | 45.2 | 55.6 | 73.9 | 86.1 | 100 | 121 | 139 |
| 7.6 | 44.5 | 54.8 | 72.9 | 85.0 | 99 | 119 | 138 |
| 7.8 | 44.0 | 54.1 | 71.9 | 84.0 | 97 | 118 | 136 |
| 8.0 | 43.4 | 53.4 | 71.0 | 82.9 | 96 | 117 | 135 |
| 8.2 | 42.8 | 52.7 | 70.1 | 81.9 | 95 | 115 | 133 |
| 8.4 | 42.3 | 52.0 | 69.3 | 81.0 | 94 | 114 | 132 |
| 8.6 | 41.8 | 51.4 | 68.4 | 80.0 | 93 | 113 | 131 |
| 8.8 | 41.2 | 50.7 | 67.6 | 79.1 | 92 | 112 | 129 |
| 9.0 | 40.8 | 50.1 | 66.8 | 78.2 | 91 | 110 | 128 |
| 9.2 | 40.3 | 49.5 | 66.0 | 77.3 | 90 | 109 | 127 |
| 9.4 | 39.9 | 49.0 | 65.3 | 76.4 | 89 | 108 | 125 |
| 9.6 | 39.4 | 48.4 | 64.6 | 75.6 | 88 | 107 | 124 |
| 9.8 | 39.0 | 47.9 | 63.8 | 74.8 | 87 | 106 | 123 |
| 10.0 | 38.6 | 47.4 | 63.1 | 74.0 | 86 | 105 | 121 |
| 10.5 | 37.6 | 46.1 | 61.5 | 72.1 | 84 | 102 | 118 |
| 11.0 | 36.7 | 44.9 | 59.9 | 70.2 | 82 | 100 | 116 |
| 11.5 | 35.8 | 43.8 | 58.4 | 68.5 | 80 | 97 | 113 |
| 12.0 | 35.0 | 42.8 | 57.0 | 66.9 | 78 | 95 | 111 |
| 12.5 | 34.2 | 41.8 | 55.7 | 65.4 | 76 | 93 | 108 |
| 13.0 | 33.4 | 40.8 | 54.4 | 64.0 | 75 | 91 | 106 |
| 13.5 | 32.7 | 39.9 | 53.3 | 62.6 | 73 | 89 | 104 |
| 14.0 | 32.0 | 39.1 | 52.1 | 61.3 | 72 | 87 | 102 |
| 14.5 | 31.4 | 38.3 | 51.0 | 60.0 | 70 | 86 | 100 |
| 15.0 | 30.8 | 37.5 | 50.0 | 58.8 | 69 | 84 | 98 |
| 16.0 | 29.6 | 36.1 | 48.1 | 56.6 | 66 | 81 | 94 |
| 17.0 | 28.6 | 34.8 | 46.3 | 54.6 | 64 | 78 | 91 |
| 18.0 | 27.6 | 33.5 | 44.7 | 52.7 | 62 | 76 | 88 |
| 19.0 | 26.7 | 32.4 | 43.2 | 51.0 | 60 | 73 | 85 |
| 20.0 | 25.9 | 31.4 | 41.8 | 49.3 | 58 | 71 | 83 |

hours and perhaps days, the highway engineer engaged in designing for a culvert or a drainage ditch is primarily interested in the high-intensity, short-duration storms, i.e. the storms which result in the peak rate of runoff from the catchment area. Internationally, the storm duration which is most often chosen for design purposes is based on the assumption that the maximum discharge at any point in a drainage system occurs when the entire catchment area tributary to that point is contributing to the flow, and that the rainfall intensity producing this flow is the average rate of rainfall which can be expected to fall in the time required for a raindrop that falls on the most remote point of the catchment area to flow to the point under investigation.

As used above, the 'most remote point' refers to the point from which the time of flow is the greatest; this may or may not be at the greatest linear distance, depending upon the topography and other conditions. The least time taken by the raindrop to make this trip is called the *time of concentration*. This may have two components: the entry time and the time of flow. If the drainage point being considered is at the inlet to the drainage system, then the entry time is equal to the time of concentration. If, however, the design point is within the drainage system, then the time of concentration is equal to the entry time plus the time required by the raindrop to traverse the system to the point under study.

In normal urban drainage design, an *entry time* of 2 minutes is most commonly used, increasing up to 4 minutes for areas with exceptionally large paved areas with slack gradients[3]. There is little point in attempting to estimate entry times to an accuracy greater than, say, 0.5 minute, as the effect upon the design intensity is fairly insignificant (see Table 2.1) as compared with the capacity available within the practical range of pipe sizes, e.g. one increment change of pipe size from 150 to 230 mm roughly trebles the flow-carrying capacity. The *time of flow* along a pipe is calculated assuming full-bore velocities. The most satisfactory formula for the calculation of the velocity of flow for a given pipe size and gradient is the Colebrook–White formula; tables which simplify the use of this formula are readily available[4].

A British study[5] of five experimental rural catchments, with areas ranging from 2.77 to 21.30 km$^2$, differing shapes and slopes, and dissimilar average annual rainfalls, gave the following formula for the time of concentration:

$$T = 2.48(LN)^{0.39}$$

where $T$ = time of concentration when all the catchment is contributing to the flow (h), $L$ = catchment length, i.e. the plan distance from the outfall to the upstream divide, measured approximately along the centre of the catchment (km), and $N$ = dimensionless slope number = $L/Z$, in which $Z$ = rise in height from the outfall to the average height of the upstream divide (km).

A feature common to all the above catchments is that they were all relatively impermeable and contained soils based on clays or boulder clays, i.e. typical of many of those likely to be encountered in Britain. The

*L*-distance sometimes required a 'cranked' line but, in general, the location of this line was not critical.

Once the time of concentration has been determined, the next step involves determining the design intensity of rainfall for a storm length equal to the time of concentration. Ideally, the design intensity can be determined from a rainfall table (or graph) for the area under consideration. Tables similar to that shown in Table 2.1 may be obtained from the Meteorological Office provided that the appropriate National Grid Reference is quoted. Alternatively, if records are available, it may be possible for some intensity–duration–frequency relationships to be directly established.

Various countries have also developed empirical formulae to aid in the estimation of the design intensity. Typical of the early ones used in Britain are the *Ministry of Health formulae*[6]:

$$I = 762/(t + 10) \qquad \text{(for } 5 < t \leqslant 20)$$

and

$$I = 1016/(t + 20) \qquad \text{(for } 20 < t \leqslant 100)$$

where $I$ = intensity of rainfall (mm/h) and $t$ = duration of storm, or time of concentration (minutes).

It might be noted that the second of the above two formulae is also known as the *Birmingham formula*, and was originally devised by Lloyd-Davies in 1906[7].

Note also that the Ministry of Health formulae take no account of storm frequency. In fact, the results given by the equations approximate to those likely to occur once every two years for storms of short duration (up to about 0.5 h), and once a year for storms of long duration (0.5–2.0 h).

In 1935, the *Bilham formula* was published[8] which related rainfall intensity, duration and frequency, as follows:

$$n = 1.213\ 56 \times 10^5 t_r (r + 2.54)^{-3.55}$$

where $n$ = occurrence frequency for a quantity of rain, $r$, in ten years, $t_r$ = duration of rain (h), and $r$ = quantity of rainfall in time $t_r$ (mm).

Following manipulation[9], the Bilham formula has been expressed as follows:

$$I = (60/t)(Nt \times 2.0226 \times 10^2)^{1/3.55} - 2.54$$

where $I$ = intensity of rainfall (mm/h), $N$ = frequency of storm occurrence, expressed in the more usual terms of one in $N$ years, and $t$ = storm duration (minutes).

Research by the Meteorological Office has shown that the Bilham equation overestimates the probabilities of rainfalls with intensities greater than about 33 mm/h. This has given rise to the *modified Bilham formula*[10] which rearranged can be expressed as follows:

$$\ln \left( \frac{10}{[NIt \times (It + 0.1)^{-3.55}]/60} \right) = 1 - 0.8I$$

where ln signifies natural logarithms, and the other values are as defined above. An iterative procedure for solving this equation and calculating intensities greater than 33 mm/h, together with a computer program listing in the form of a Fortran function subprogram, is available in the literature[9].

*Storm frequency*   There are significant differences of opinion amongst engineers as to what storm frequency or *return period* should be used for road design purposes. As is suggested by Fig. 2.1, the annual cost of highway drainage facilities is likely to be very high if heavy floods or high return periods are used; however, only designing for small, frequent floods can be costly as damage to property, and consequent repairs, may be high. Somewhere between the two extremes, for every project, there is an economical and acceptable design which the highway engineer seeks to identify. Ideally, the engineer should select several storm frequencies and carry out hydraulic designs for each, until the optimum design is obtained. In practice, however, and notwithstanding that economic evaluation methodologies have been developed to aid in this process (see, for example, reference 11), the real relationship between rainfall frequency, flooding frequency and cost is usually unknown, so that the selection is mostly based on experience and tradition.

As a generalization, it can be said that the factors which mainly influence the selection of the return period are always local in character, and cannot be determined by any specific formula. The most influential is the general location vulnerability of the highway section under consideration, e.g. at one location a given volume of floodwater might only hinder traffic for a short time, whilst at another serious damage and possible disaster could result from the flooding of valuable or 'sensitive' properties, such as hospitals.

In Britain, recommended[3] design frequencies for piped drainage systems range from once per year for separate surface-water sewers in

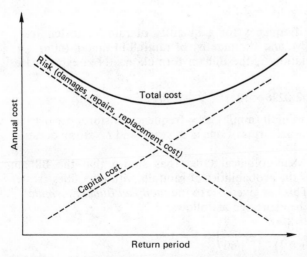

**Fig. 2.1**   Conceptual relationship between drainage costs and storm frequency

modern housing estates or roads, to once per 50–100 years for combined sewage and stormwater sewers in older urban developments with basements. In contrast, most large American cities use a 5–10-year return period for most roads, with the shorter periods being associated with urban areas of flatter terrain. Roadside and central-reserve drainage ditches flanking motorways in urban areas in American cities are normally designed to carry the runoff from a 10-year storm without the floodwaters encroaching upon the highway shoulders; at locations where there is danger of water ponding on the carriageway (e.g. in underpasses, sag vertical curves, and depressed sections), the storm frequency selected may be about five times that selected for usage at locations where water will not pond[12].

Culverts and small bridges under major roads in Britain are normally designed on the basis of a 50- or 100-year return period, whilst a 25-year return period may be utilized on less important roads.

Table 2.2 summarizes a qualitative approach recommended for selecting the design return period for major rural highways in the USA. The importance of one factor or a combination of factors in this table can be used to give the designer some guidance regarding the choice of storm frequency.

Whilst British drainage practice has been criticized as inferior to American practice, it should be remembered that the piped stormwater drains most commonly used in urban areas in Britain are almost invariably laid at least 1 m below ground level. As a result, they are usually able to accommodate a fairly large flood surcharge—possibly to the extent of increasing the design capacity of the drain by 100 per cent—before water is unable to feed into gulleys or starts coming out of manholes.

**Table 2.2** Flood frequency selection chart used in the drainage design of rural highways in the USA[13]

| Factor* | Design frequency (years) | | |
| --- | --- | --- | --- |
| | 10–25 | 25–50 | ⩾50 |
| Non-highway damage | Low | Medium | High |
| Highway damage | Low | Medium | High |
| Potential loss of life | Low | Medium | High |
| Height of fill (m) | <6.10 | 6.10–15.25 | >15.25 |
| Cost of replacement | Low | Medium | High |
| Average daily traffic flow (number of vehicles) | <100 | 100–750 | >750 |
| Detours available | Yes | Poor | No |
| Roadway overflow section | Yes | Nominal | No |
| Number of known floods > $Q_{50}$ | None | One | Several |
| National Defense Highway | No | No | Yes |
| Impact on local economy (e.g. school buses and food) | Low | Medium | High |

*Additional factors may be added

## Runoff

Ultimately, the highway engineer is concerned with the maximum rate of surface runoff from the catchment area, i.e. the difference between the amount of rainfall during the time of concentration and the losses due to infiltration, evaporation, transpiration, interception and storage. It can be a difficult value to determine for the following reasons: it is dependent upon a number of factors which are difficult to quantify, it is never constant over a given catchment area, and it can vary considerably during a single storm. Major factors governing runoff are as follows.

(1)  *Type and condition of the soil with respect to infiltration*  All the rainfall from a given storm does not reach the culvert, sewer or drainage ditch. For instance, if the soil is granular and/or very dry, little precipitation from the initial part of the storm will run off. Once the ground is saturated, however, the greater part of the precipitation will flow easily over the ground surface and the runoff may be more than twice the initial flow. Similarly, if the ground is frozen, the runoff is high.

(2)  *Kind and extent of cultivation and/or vegetation*  These obviously also affect the rate of overland flow, e.g. runoff over hard, bare ground will occur at a faster rate than over freshly-tilled soil or lush grassland. Summer vegetation, such as weeds, tree leaves, and crops, increases floodplain storage and ground infiltration. Whether a row crop, such as corn, is planted in rows normal to or parallel with the general direction of the runoff plain can, during the latter part of the growing season, make nearly 50 per cent difference in the runoff [14].

(3)  *Length and steepness of slopes*  Next to catchment area size, these are probably the most important characteristics affecting runoff. The steeper and shorter the slopes, the greater chance there is that more rainfall will contribute to the runoff.

(4)  *Number, arrangement, slope and condition of the natural and man-made drainage channels in the catchment area.*

(5)  *Irregularity of ground surface*  Depressions in the ground surface will hold back runoff water until they are filled. Karst topography and volcanic terrain produce little surface runoff. The presence of ponds, lakes or swamps in the catchment area considerably reduces the amount of runoff that might otherwise occur. (Note that in certain instances it may be desirable for the highway engineer to consider constructing retarding ponds in the catchment area, as the beneficial effect of such storage on peak runoffs can be quite large.)

(6)  *Size and shape of catchment*  Surface runoff for small streams in the same geographical area is generally proportional to the size of the catchment area. As catchment areas increase, the peak runoff becomes proportional to some power (usually in the range 0.5–0.8) of the area. Long, narrow watersheds are generally considered to give lower peaks than square-, fan- or pear-shaped catchment areas, other characteristics being equal.

(7)  *Temperature of air and water*  If the air temperature is warm, quite a significant amount of precipitated water may return to the atmosphere

before it reaches the culvert or ditch. If the temperature is relatively low, the water is more viscous and the rate of overland flow will be slowed.

(8) *Changes in land use* It must be kept in mind that changes in land use during the life of a drainage structure may increase the rate of runoff. For example, urbanization can increase the flood peaks on small streams by 1.5 to 2.0 times over predevelopment conditions.

In view of these considerations, it can be seen why there is great difficulty in arriving at any one design figure which will take all factors into proper account. The approach therefore usually taken is for the engineer to utilize a compromise factor which will adequately meet the most severe design requirements but still be within the economic scope of the scheme.

Many researchers and practitioners have concentrated on obtaining values of relative imperviousness such as the ultimate impermeability factor, i.e. the ratio of runoff to rainfall for the drainage area after a long period of rainfall, e.g. >15 minutes. In these studies, most emphasis has been placed upon runoff determinations for urban areas as compared with rural areas. An examination of the rural data leads to the values given in Table 2.3, whilst Table 2.4 is representative of those published for urban areas in Britain. Another well-known set of recommendations[15] for built-up areas assumes that all garden and unpaved land is entirely permeable, and all paved and roofed surfaces have an ultimate impermeability factor of 0.8.

Once the appropriate impermeability factor (or combination of factors) has been selected for a given type of development, it is multiplied by the intensity of rainfall in order to determine the rate of runoff for the area under examination.

Very many formulae have been developed which attempt to measure the quantity of runoff from a storm over a given drainage area (see reference 16 which reviews eighteen such methods). Two which have gained particular credibility in Britain are the Rational and the Transport and Road Research Laboratory (TRRL) methods.

**Table 2.3** Ultimate impermeability values suggested for rural areas

| Type of surface | Impermeability factor |
| --- | --- |
| Concrete or bituminous surfacings | 0.8–0.9 |
| Gravel or macadam surfacings | 0.4–0.7 |
| Bare, impervious soils* | 0.4–0.7 |
| Impervious soils, with turf* | 0.3–0.6 |
| Bare, slightly pervious soils* | 0.2–0.4 |
| Slightly pervious soils, with turf* | 0.1–0.3 |
| Pervious soils* | 0.1–0.2 |
| Wooded areas | 0.1–0.2 |

* These values are applicable to relatively level ground. When the slopes are greater than 2 per cent, the impermeability factor should be increased by 0.2 (to a maximum of 1.0) for every 2 per cent increase in slope

**Table 2.4**  Ultimate impermeability values suggested for urban areas in Britain[2]

| Type of surface | Impermeability factor |
|---|---|
| Urban areas | |
| with considerable paved areas | 1.00 |
| average | 0.50–0.70 |
| residential | 0.30–0.60 |
| industrial | 0.50–0.90 |
| playgrounds, parks, etc. | 0.10–0.35 |
| Housing development (houses/ha) | |
| 10 | 0.18–0.20 |
| 20 | 0.25–0.30 |
| 30 | 0.33–0.45 |
| 50 | 0.50–0.70 |
| General development | |
| paved areas | 1.00 |
| roofs | 0.75–0.95 |
| lawns, depending upon slope and subsoil | 0.35–0.50 |
| heavy clay soils | 0.70 |
| average soils | 0.50 |
| light sandy soils | 0.40 |
| vegetation | 0.40 |
| steep slopes | 1.00 |

*Rational method*  Also known in Britain as the *Lloyd-Davies method*, this runoff formula is variously attributed to an Irishman in 1850[17], an American in 1889[18], and a Welshman in 1906[7]. Currently used to design storm-drainage in about 90 per cent of the design offices in Britain and the USA, the Rational method relates the peak rate of runoff from a given sub-catchment (or catchment) to rainfall of given average intensity by means of the following equation:

$$Q = 0.167(60/t)Apr$$

where $Q$ = discharge (m$^3$/minute), $t$ = time of concentration (minutes), $A$ = catchment area (ha), $p$ = proportion of total rainfall running off after allowing for soakage and evaporation (a weighted average should be used if the surface of the catchment area varies), $r$ = total rainfall during time of concentration (mm), and 0.167 = runoff in m$^3$ per minute per ha for a rainfall of 1 mm per hour on a completely impervious surface.

Now if $I$ is the rainfall intensity, in mm/h, for a storm of duration $t$ minutes, then

$$r = (t/60)I$$

If this value for $r$ is inserted in the above equation, then

$$Q = 0.167AIp$$

If $Q$ is expressed in litres per second, then the equation becomes

$$Q = 2.78AIp$$

The manner in which the Rational (Lloyd-Davies) method is used to design a drainage system is as follows.

*Step 1*   Prepare a key plan of the proposed system. For example, Fig. 2.2 shows a possible urban piped system, based on a contour plan of the entire catchment area. Note that the inlet points are identified, as are the manholes and pipe lengths in between. Each pipe length is numbered, with the longest sewer upstream from the outfall identified and numbered 1, and its individual sections numbered 1.0, 1.1 ,.... The point in sewer 1 at which the first branch enters the system is next identified; the longest branch to this point is numbered 2, and individual sections are numbered 2.0, 2.1,..., and so on for branches 3–7.

*Step 2*   Set up a design table as shown in Table 2.5 and complete columns 1–4 for all sections.

*Step 3*   Determine the areas in hectares of the directly connected surfaces which contribute runoff to the pipe section being considered. Apply to each area appropriate ultimate impermeability values from Table 2.4, and convert them into 'equivalent' impermeable areas (columns 9–12).

*Step 4*   Assume a suitable pipe size for each section (column 14) and using accepted tables (see, for example, reference 19) determine the full-bore velocity (column 5) and the time of flow in each section (column 6), calculated from columns 3 and 5.

*Step 5*   Calculate the time of concentration (column 7) for flow from the most remote part of the catchment contributing to the pipe length under consideration. This is the sum of the time of entry (2 minutes in this example) plus the total time of pipe flow up to and including the section under consideration. Where two drains join, the time of concentration is assumed to be the greater time to the manhole concerned.

*Step 6*   Select a suitable storm return period, and determine from appropriate data (Table 2.1 in this example) the intensity of rainfall (column 8) for a storm equal to the time of concentration. Since the concentration time

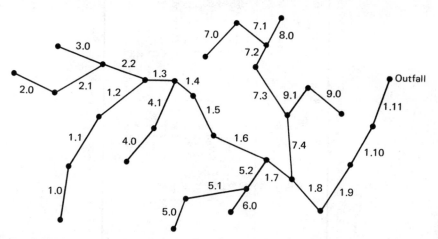

**Fig. 2.2**   Example key plan of a piped drainage system in an urban area

**Table 2.5** Example design table for Rational method calculations[3]

| 1 | 2 | 3 | 4 | 5 | 6 | 7 | 8 | 9 | 10 | 11 | 12 | 13 | 14 |
|---|---|---|---|---|---|---|---|---|---|---|---|---|---|
| Pipe length number | Difference in level (m) | Length (m) | Gradient | Velocity (m/s) | Time of flow (minutes) | Time of concentration (minutes) | Storm intensity (mm/h) | Impermeable area (ha) Roads | Buildings, yards, etc. | Total (9+10) | Cumulative | Rate of flow (l/s) | Pipe diameter (mm) |
| 1.0 | 1.10 | 63.1 | 1 in 57 | 1.33 | 0.79 | 2.79 | 67.9 | 0.089 | 0.053 | 0.142 | 0.142 | 26.8 | 150 |
| 1.1 | 1.12 | 66.1 | 1 in 59 | 1.70 | 0.65 | 3.44 | 62.5 | 0.077 | 0.109 | 0.186 | 0.328 | 56.9 | 225 |
| 1.2 | 0.73 | 84.7 | 1 in 116 | 1.46 | 0.97 | 4.41 | 57.4 | 0.081 | 0 | 0.081 | 0.409 | 65.2 | 300 |
| 2.0 | 1.40 | 44.8 | 1 in 32 | 2.32 | 0.32 | 2.32 | 72.5 | 0.113 | 0.081 | 0.194 | 0.194 | 39.1 | 225 |
| 2.1 | 0.01 | 49.1 | 1 in 80 | 1.77 | 0.46 | 2.78 | 67.9 | 0.045 | 0.105 | 0.150 | 0.344 | 64.9 | 300 |
| 3.0 | 0.98 | 48.5 | 1 in 49 | 1.43 | 0.56 | 2.56 | 70.5 | 0 | 0.129 | 0.129 | 0.129 | 25.2 | 150 |
| 2.2 | 1.65 | 54.3 | 1 in 33 | 2.74 | 0.33 | 3.11 | 65.5 | 0.101 | 0.073 | 0.174 | 0.647 | 117.7 | 300 |
| 1.3 | 1.22 | 27.7 | 1 in 23 | 3.29 | 0.14 | 4.55 | 56.9 | 0.121 | 0.235 | 0.356 | 1.412 | 223.2 | 300 |
| 4.0 | 0.88 | 54.9 | 1 in 62 | 1.66 | 0.55 | 2.55 | 70.5 | 0.093 | 0.093 | 0.186 | 0.186 | 36.4 | 225 |
| 4.1 | 0.58 | 45.7 | 1 in 79 | 1.48 | 0.52 | 3.07 | 66.3 | 0.069 | 0.040 | 0.109 | 0.295 | 54.2 | 225 |
| 1.4 | 0.52 | 22.9 | 1 in 43 | 2.77 | 0.14 | 4.69 | 55.8 | 0.069 | 0 | 0.069 | 1.776 | 275.3 | 375 |
| .... | .... | .... | .... | .... | .... | .... | .... | .... | .... | .... | .... | .... | .... |

*Notes:* Storm return period = one in one year. Roughness coefficient = 0.6 mm. Time of entry = 2 minutes.

varies from one pipe section to another, the design intensity will change accordingly.

*Step 7* Calculate the expected peak rate of flow, $Q$, in each pipe length using the Rational formula, where $I$ is obtained from column 8 and $Ap$ from column 12.

*Step 8* Compare the full-bore capacity of each pipe section with the expected peak flow in that section. If any pipe length is found inadequate, a larger pipe diameter is assumed and steps 4–8 are repeated.

It is useful at this stage to emphasize some of the assumptions underlying the use of the Rational method, so that the reader can realize why it is that in practice the calculated results are very often qualified by engineering judgement.

(1) The rainfall intensity $I$ is selected for a storm of duration equal to the time of concentration, and the entry time component of this time is usually selected by measurements based on the assumption that the raindrop moves perpendicularly to the ground contour-lines. If too low a time of concentration is chosen, this will result in the selection of too high a rainfall intensity and the overestimation of the runoff. Furthermore, the frequency of peak runoff is assumed to be equal to the frequency of the rainfall causing it.

(2) The rainfall intensity value used is assumed to be steady throughout the catchment area during the storm. If the area is very large and/or the topography is very variable, this assumption may well not be valid.

(3) The impermeability factors which are used in the calculations are assumed to be constant, and independent of rainfall intensity, duration and frequency. Furthermore, they only take into direct account the type of surface and slope, and assume that the other influencing factors are covered by these.

(4) The velocity of flow in a pipe drain is assumed to be equal to the full-bore velocity, and to remain constant throughout the time of concentration.

From these and other considerations, it can be seen that the design precision of the Rational method is somewhat limited. In general, it can tend to overestimate the maximum runoff, and the extent to which this occurs increases with the size of the catchment area. As a result, it is probable that use of the Rational method should be confined to urban areas and relatively small catchment areas in rural locations. In urban areas in Britain it is recommended[3] that its usage be confined to the design of drainage systems for housing estates or villages where the diameter of the largest pipe is unlikely to exceed 600 mm. (A computer program[20] is available for analysis purposes.) Suggested upper limits on the size of rural catchments vary from publication to publication. For example, the American Asphalt Institute states[21] that for the design of drainage structures the use of the Rational method should be restricted to drainage areas of less than 80 ha; the US Federal Highway Administration recommends that 200 ha should not be exceeded, with 80 ha being its preferred maximum.

The Transport and Road Research Laboratory has developed an empirical runoff formula which can be used in the drainage design of highways (e.g. culvert sizes) in natural rural catchments[5]. The formula used, which resembles the Rational formula, but is different from it, is as follows:

$$Q = F_A A R_B / 3.6T$$

where $Q$ = peak discharge (m$^3$/s), $F_A$ = annual rainfall factor (dimensionless) = $0.00127R_A - 0.321$, in which $R_A$ = average rainfall (mm) (valid up to 2440 mm), $A$ = catchment area (km$^2$), $R_B$ = expected total rainfall (mm) for the time of concentration (valid up to 48 h) and the selected return period calculated from the Bilham formula, and $T$ = time of concentration, obtained from the previously discussed formula $T = 2.48(LN)^{0.39}$ (see p. 88).

A table of values for the ratio $R_B/T$, for a range of return periods and durations, is readily available in the literature[5].

*TRRL hydrograph method*    The TRRL hydrograph method was first developed in the 1950s and early 1960s as a simple sewer design tool for use in large urban areas[22]. The data required for that and subsequent versions are no more than for the Rational method. However, the calculations can normally be carried out only by an electronic digital computer—it was the first significant design method developed specifically for use on the computer—and details of the processes involved are readily available in the literature[3].

The TRRL method as originally developed assumed that only sewered impermeable areas contributed significantly to the peak flow in a storm sewer. Using these areas a time–area diagram was constructed with the routing velocity in each pipe assumed to be equal to the full-bore velocity. The flow was then calculated for a given rainstorm using the time–area method, after which the hydrographs derived from the time–area calculation were re-routed through a reservoir storage equation, ostensibly to allow for storage in the pipes.

In early versions of the TRRL hydrograph method, the storage correction was applied to the system as a whole using measured outfall–flow recession curves or assuming a uniform proportional depth throughout the system. With later versions, however, the routing procedure was applied to each pipe section in turn using the uniform proportional depth assumption (currently 0.85), and this has enabled the method to be used as a design procedure. When the calculated flow is greater than that of the pipe at full capacity, the size of the pipe is increased by an appropriate increment, and the calculations repeated for that pipe length.

Since its introduction, the simplicity of use, economy and flexibility associated with the computer approach have resulted in the TRRL method coming into wide usage in Britain; it has also gained attention in the USA and Australia. It is reported[16] that a survey of over 350 British design agencies in late 1974 found that 62 per cent used this method—a high figure when it is appreciated that the continued use of the Rational method is acceptable for urban drainage systems with pipes of less than 600 mm diameter.

## Hydraulic study: basic hydraulic design

Once the peak runoff has been determined for a particular catchment, the highway engineer's next step is the hydraulic design of the drainage system to carry it. The following discussion is mainly concerned with open-channel drainage ditches and the culverts which lie within them.

On all roads also, it is useful to consider the drainage design of the carriageway surface.

### Channels

Two types of channel are of particular interest to the highway engineer. These are the longitudinal channels (or ditches) which run approximately parallel to the centreline of the highway and the open-channel natural drainage ditches that are intercepted by the roadway (and in which road culverts lie).

*Longitudinal ditches* These may be placed alongside roadways in order to intercept surface water running off the carriageway and shoulders. In hilly terrain and in cut sections, they serve to prevent water running down the back slopes and invading the roadway pavement.

Longitudinal ditches on low-cost roads are usually V-shaped because they can be very economically formed and maintained by a grader. They are, however, susceptible to erosion and are usually incompatible with roadside safety requirements.

On high-quality roads, e.g. motorways and dual carriageways, longitudinal ditches are usually designed with flattened side slopes and rounded bottoms. Whilst this shape is normally selected so as to provide a traversable section, and thus minimize the hazard to errant vehicles which leave the carriageway, it is also compatible with hydraulic efficiency.

Normally, small roadside ditches are not hydraulically designed, due to the lack of economical justification. Instead, the ditch side walls are simply cut to at least the natural angle of repose of the soil and to a depth which is usually between 0.3 and 0.6 m; in this latter respect great care should always be taken to ensure that, at the very least, the depth is such that sustained flow in the bottom of the ditch never rises above the bottom of the pavement. On roads such as motorways, however, ditches should always be checked for their hydraulic capabilities to ensure that they are able to handle the expected flows without danger either to traffic or to the road structure itself. This is especially important if the ditches carry water from adjacent back slopes as well as from the roadway. As is discussed in Volume 1, Chapter 6, vehicle safety considerations usually govern the ditch side slopes chosen on these roads, preference being given to the use of relatively flat slopes, especially on the side closest to the carriageway.

*Open-channel drainage ditches* Highway drainage channels can be classified according to their function, e.g. gutters, chutes, roadside channels, toe-of-slope channels, intercepting channels, median swales, and channel changes[23].

*Gutters* are the surface channels at the edges of the carriageway or the shoulder formed by a kerb or by a shallow depression. They are normally paved with concrete, brick, stone blocks, or some other structural material. Gutters are most commonly associated with urban road drainage, although they may also be employed in mountainous regions, areas of poor soil stability, and for particular locations such as highway interchanges and underpasses. On highways constructed on high embankments, shoulders may be designed to serve as gutters with kerbs constructed at the outer edges to confine the water; the water collected in the gutters is normally discharged down the side slopes with the aid of chutes located at suitable intervals.

*Chutes*, also called *flumes* or *spillways*, are open or closed channels used to carry water down cut or embankment slopes. Open chutes can be of metal, or paved with concrete, bituminous material, stone or sod, depending upon the volume or velocity of water to be carried. On long slopes, closed (pipe) chutes may be used to prevent the high-velocity water from jumping out of the channel, eroding the slope, and destroying the chute. Energy dissipators are normally required at the chute outlet.

*Roadside channels* are those which are provided in cut sections to remove the runoff from rain falling on the carriageway and on the cut slopes. When paved they are also sometimes called gutters. Factors governing their safety design (for traffic) are described in Volume 1, Chapter 6.

*Toe-of-slope channels* are located at or near the toe of an embankment when it is necessary to convey water collected by the roadside channel to the point of disposal. On the downhill side of a highway, this channel can often be laid on a mild slope and the lower end flared to spread the water over the hillside. Where this is likely to cause erosion or softening of the embankment, the toe-of-slope channel should convey the stormwater to a natural watercourse.

*Intercepting channels* are located on or in the natural ground near the top edge of a cut slope or along the edge of the right-of-way, to intercept the runoff from a hillside before it reaches the highway. They minimize erosion and decrease the likelihood of flooding the highway. A surface interception channel constructed by forming a dyke with borrow material is better than an excavated channel, because the latter destroys the natural ground cover and is more likely to erode.

*Median swales* are the shallow, depressed longitudinal surface drains, at or near the centre of central reservations of dual carriageways, that are used to drain the central reservation and portions of the carriageways (see also Volume 1, Chapter 6). The swale is sloped longitudinally for drainage, and at intervals the water is intercepted by inlets and discharged from the highway.

*Channel changes*, as the name implies, alter the alignment or cross-section of natural watercourses. Channel changes should only be initiated after careful consideration, e.g. replacing a long, sinuous natural channel with a shorter one can increase the water velocity sufficiently to damage the embankment near the stream or cause scour about structure footings. Motorist safety considerations do not normally enter into open-channel ditch designs which are not parallel to roadways, even though they may intersect highways at particular locations. In these latter instances the features which govern the design are primarily hydraulic ones, and the highway engineer is expected to provide protective mechanisms, e.g. guardrails, to ensure that motorists cannot err into the drainage channel.

By definition, an open channel is a conduit which is open to the atmosphere and, as a result, flow takes place not because of a pressure difference between points—as in a horizontal closed pipe—but because of a difference in elevation between two points. The basic hydraulic formula for determining the flow of water in open channels is written as follows:

$$V = C(RS)^{1/2}$$

where $V$ = average velocity of flow (m/s), $C$ = a coefficient of roughness whose value depends upon the nature of the surface over which the water is flowing, $R$ = mean hydraulic radius (m) = $A/P$, in which $A$ = cross-sectional area of flow (m$^2$) and $P$ = wetted perimeter (m), and $S$ = hydraulic gradient. Furthermore,

$$Q = AV$$

where $Q$ = discharge (m$^3$/s).

The former, known as the Chézy formula, is the basis of practically all the open-channel hydraulic formulae which are in use today. The great array and complexity of these formulae can often be very confusing to the engineer who is not a hydraulics specialist. Fortunately or unfortunately—depending upon how one looks at it—there is often relatively little agreement between the results obtained by very many of these formulae. Hence, under the many-variable conditions prevalent in the field, the engineer is wise to settle upon some basic formulae for use in routine work and to use them sufficiently often to become well acquainted with the effects of the various coefficient values used in their equations.

Perhaps the most widely investigated formula used in highway drainage design is the Manning formula[24]. This formula gives the value for $C$ in the Chézy formula as:

$$C = R^{1/6}/n$$

where $n$ = Manning's roughness coefficient.

The simplified Manning formula is

$$V = R^{2/3}S^{1/2}/n$$

Thus

$$Q = AV = AR^{2/3}S^{1/2}/n$$

Values for $n$ for various channel surfaces which were recommended by the US Corps of Engineers are given in Table 2.6. In the reference from which this table is abstracted, the bare soil values were given for soils classified by the Unified Classification System; here, for convenience, the value given for each soil is its nearest equivalent (and very similar) classification according to the British Soil Classification System (see Chapter 4). Also shown in Table 2.6 are maximum permissible velocity values for various types of ditch lining, below which significant erosion will not normally occur.

It might be noted that, as a general principle, drainage channels should make use of native natural lining materials, e.g. grass, crushed rock and earth, wherever possible. Properly employed flexible linings of this nature are less costly to construct, have self-healing qualities which reduce maintenance costs, permit infiltration and exfiltration of water, and present a more aesthetically pleasing, natural appearance. (Reference 26 provides very detailed information regarding flexible channel linings.) By contrast, the initial construction costs of rigid linings are normally higher, whilst maintenance costs may also be increased because of their vulnerability to undercutting, hydrostatic uplift and erosion along the longitudinal interface between the rigid lining and the unlined section. Smooth, rigid linings also result in higher flow velocities which cause scour at the terminus of the lined portion of the channel, unless controlled by energy dissipating devices such as riprap.

Before illustrating the manner in which the Manning formula is used in ditch design problems, there is one further item which must be discussed: *critical velocity* and its relationship to the *critical discharge* and *critical slope* of an open channel. In a uniform open channel the depth of flow at any point is dependent upon the shape of the cross-section, the roughness of the channel, the slope of the channel, and the discharge. This depth of flow, called the normal depth, is relatively great when the channel slope is gentle and the water is in tranquil or subcritical flow. If the slope is increased, a normal depth of flow—called the critical depth—will be reached; at steeper slopes the flow becomes supercritical. At this stage, for instance, a discontinuity of flow in the form of a hydraulic jump may be caused downstream which will result in the generation of intense local turbulence at and just downstream of the jump; this may be very erosive and cause severe damage to the walls and bed of the ditch. The gradient at which the change occurs is called the critical slope, the velocity at this slope is called the critical velocity, and the discharge is termed the critical discharge.

Technically, critical flow at a point in an open channel can be said to occur when the discharge is a maximum for a given energy head or, alternatively, when for a constant discharge the energy head is a minimum. The energy head at any point in the channel is the depth of water plus the velocity head, $V^2/2g$, where $V$ is the velocity of the water at that point and $g$ is the acceleration of free fall. Increasing the slope of the channel beyond the critical slope does not increase the discharge but simply makes the water flow faster at a depth less than the critical depth. In any channel in which (in theory) the water is flowing at the critical depth, the velocity head is equal to one-half of the mean depth of flow, where the mean depth is defined as the water cross-sectional area divided by the width of the free-water surface. In

**Table 2.6** Manning's '*n*' and maximum permissible velocity of flow in open channels (based on reference 25)

| Ditch lining | Manning's '*n*' | $V_{max}$ (m/s) |
|---|---|---|
| *Natural earth* | | |
| (1) Without vegetation | | |
| Rock | | |
| (a) smooth and uniform | 0.035–0.040 | 6.1 |
| (b) jagged and irregular | 0.040–0.045 | 4.5–5.5 |
| Soils | | |
| GW | 0.022–0.024 | 1.8–2.1 |
| GP | 0.023–0.026 | 2.1–2.4 |
| GC | 0.020–0.025 | 0.6–1.5 |
| GF | 0.024–0.026 | 1.5–2.1 |
| SW | 0.020–0.024 | 0.3–0.6 |
| SP | 0.022–0.024 | 0.3–0.6 |
| SC | 0.020–0.023 | 0.6–0.9 |
| SF | 0.023–0.025 | 0.9–1.2 |
| CL and CI | 0.022–0.024 | 0.6–0.9 |
| MI and ML | 0.023–0.024 | 0.9–1.2 |
| CH | 0.022–0.023 | 0.6–0.9 |
| MH | 0.023–0.024 | 0.9–1.5 |
| MO | 0.022–0.024 | 0.6–0.9 |
| Pt | 0.022–0.025 | 0.6–0.9 |
| (2) With vegetation | | |
| Average turf | | |
| (a) erosion-resistant soil | 0.050–0.070 | 1.2–1.5 |
| (b) easily eroded soil | 0.030–0.050 | 0.9–1.2 |
| Dense turf | | |
| (a) erosion-resistant soil | 0.070–0.090 | 1.8–2.4 |
| (b) easily eroded soil | 0.040–0.050 | 1.5–1.8 |
| (c) clean bottom with bushes on sides | 0.050–0.080 | 1.2–1.5 |
| (d) channel with tree stumps | | |
| (i) no sprouts | 0.040–0.050 | 1.5–2.1 |
| (ii) with sprouts | 0.060–0.080 | 1.8–2.4 |
| (e) dense weeds | 0.080–0.120 | 1.5–1.8 |
| (f) dense brush (floodplains) | 0.100–0.140 | 1.2–1.5 |
| (g) dense willows (floodplains) | 0.150–0.200 | 2.4–2.7 |
| *Paved* | | |
| Concrete with all surfaces | | |
| (a) trowel finished | 0.012–0.014 | 6.1 |
| (b) float finished | 0.013–0.015 | 6.1 |
| (c) formed, no finish | 0.014–0.016 | 6.1 |
| Concrete bottom, float finished, with sides of | | |
| (a) dressed stone in mortar | 0.015–0.017 | 5.5–6.1 |
| (b) random stone in mortar | 0.017–0.020 | 5.2–5.8 |
| (c) dressed stone or smooth concrete rubble (riprap) | 0.020–0.025 | 4.6 |
| (d) rubble or random stone (riprap) | 0.025–0.030 | 4.6 |
| Gravel bottom with sides of | | |
| (a) form | 0.017–0.020 | 3.0 |
| (b) random stone in mortar | 0.020–0.023 | 2.4–3.0 |
| (c) random stone or rubble (riprap) | 0.023–0.033 | 2.4–3.0 |
| Brick | 0.014–0.017 | 3.0 |
| Asphalt | 0.013–0.016 | 5.5–6.1 |

other words, supercritical flow does not occur when the velocity head is less than one-half of the mean depth of flow.

Once the discharge volume has been estimated by means of hydrological study, the next stage is the hydraulic design of the drainage ditch which has to carry this volume. A simple design procedure which utilizes the Manning formula may be outlined as follows.

*Step 1*   For the soil in which the drain will be running, select the maximum permissible velocity to avoid erosion, the Manning roughness coefficient *n*, and the side slopes of the channel. The first two of these values can be obtained from Table 2.6. The side slopes are normally controlled by the angle of natural repose of the soil; a commonly used value which suits most soils is a slope of 1 vertical to 2 horizontal. If a longitudinal ditch is being evaluated, flatter side slopes should be used because of traffic safety considerations.

*Step 2*   Using the Manning formula, calculate the maximum permissible hydraulic radius.

*Step 3*   Using the equation of continuity, calculate the minimum permissible cross-sectional area required by the given discharge and permissible velocity.

*Step 4*   Calculate the wetted perimeter for this area.

*Step 5*   Using the expressions obtained in steps 3 and 4, solve simultaneously for the bottom width of the ditch and the depth of flow.

*Step 6*   Check that the depth of flow is greater than the critical depth.

*Step 7(a)*   If the depth of flow is greater than the critical depth, add a suitable freeboard and modify the section for practicality. In the case of a longitudinal ditch, the freeboard should at least equal the height above the bottom of the pavement. For other channels, an arbitrary value of about 0.5 m is often chosen for ditches other than longitudinal ditches.

*Step 7(b)*   If the depth of flow is less than the critical depth, then surface discontinuities in the form of a hydraulic jump, slug or roll-wave flow, or air entrainment are likely to occur downstream, provided that the channel characteristics do not change. In such instances consideration should automatically be given either to reducing the slope of the channel or to determining how it might be protected by the installation of channel linings. Such linings vary in cost, durability, hydraulic roughness and appearance. Types most used include gabions, Portland cement concrete, bituminous asphalt, mortar rubble, sections of various types of pipe, manufactured blocks, articulated riprap, and plastic soil-cement.

If a large section of the channel is to be provided with a rigid lining it will be advisable to steepen the side slopes to angles of 60 degrees and obtain a new design on the basis of the most 'economical section', i.e. a design based on the channel cross-section which gives the greatest flow for the minimum of excavation. This design treatment can be found in detail in any good textbook on hydraulics and so is not further discussed here.

**Example 1 of channel hydraulic design**
Determine the ditch cross-section necessary to carry a design flow of 3 m³/s.

The ditch will be cut in material which is classified as a CL-soil. The natural slope of the ground is approximately 0.04 per cent. Assume a (rounded) trapezoidal channel with 2:1 side slopes.

*Solution*
For this ditch the following coefficients apply: $S = 0.04$, $V_{max} = 0.66$ m/s and $n = 0.022$. Thus substituting in

$$V = R^{2/3} S^{1/2} / n$$

gives

$$0.66 = R^{2/3} (0.0004)^{1/2} / 0.022$$

Therefore

$$R \leqslant 0.6275 \text{ m}$$

Thus

$$A \geqslant Q/V = 3/0.66 = 4.5 \text{ m}^2$$

and

$$P = A/R \geqslant 4.5/0.6275 = 7.17 \text{ m}$$

However,

$$A = h(b + 2h) = 4.5 \tag{1}$$

and

$$P = b + 2h(1 + 2^2)^{1/2} = b + 4.48h = 7.17 \text{ m} \tag{2}$$

where $h$ = depth of flow (m) and $b$ = bottom width (m). Solving equations (1) and (2) simultaneously gives $b = 3.09$ m and $h = 0.915$ m.

The critical depth $= V^2/g = (0.66)^2/9.81 = 0.045$ m. Obviously, in this case the flow is supercritical (i.e. depth $> 0.045$ m), and so no secondary design (e.g. lining of the channel) is necessary. Adding 0.5 m for freeboard, the desired depth of channel is 1.4 m.

**Example 2 of channel hydraulic design**
An existing highway in cutting in glacial till topography is to have longitudinal ditches to drain both the roadway and the back slopes. The maximum discharge in each side channel is expected to be 1 m$^3$/minute. Each ditch is to have a (rounded) trapezoidal shape, with side slopes of 3:1 and bottom width of 1 m. The bottom of the ditch will be 10 cm below the pavement and on a gradient of 4 per cent. Determine whether the side channel is capable of handling this discharge without the water eroding the sides or entering the pavement.

*Solution*
The soil is classified as GF and the ditch will be grassed after construction.

Therefore use a value of $n = 0.070$. Then

$$V = \frac{R^{2/3}S^{1/2}}{n} = \frac{1}{n}\left[\frac{(b+sh)h}{b+2h(1+s^2)^{1/2}}\right]^{2/3}S^{1/2}$$

$$= \frac{1}{0.070}\left[\frac{(1+3\times0.1)0.1}{1+2\times0.1(1+3^2)^{1/2}}\right]^{2/3}(0.04)^{1/2} = 0.529 \text{ m/s}$$

This is well below the maximum permissible velocity so erosion should not be a problem here.

$$Q = AV = (b+sh)hV = (1+3\times0.1)0.1\times0.529\times60$$

$$= 4.12 \text{ m}^3/\text{minute}$$

Therefore the ditch is well capable of discharging the design volume without water penetrating the pavement and gaining ready access to the subgrade.

## Culverts

A culvert can be defined as a conduit which conveys water through an embankment. Since a bridge performs the same function, it might be said that a culvert is also a bridge, although it is not normally considered as such. Perhaps the easiest distinction between the two is that a bridge surface forms part of the carriageway, whereas the top of a culvert is always beneath the pavement. One further difference is that culverts may very often be designed to flow full, whereas bridges are normally designed to pass floating debris and, possibly, boats.

As with road pavements, there are two types of culvert: flexible culverts and rigid culverts. Flexible culverts are either thin-walled steel pipes or galvanized, corrugated metal pipes; they rely only partly upon the strength of the pipe walls to resist the external loads, and instead they are designed to deflect under the loads. When deflection takes place, the horizontal diameter of the culvert increases and compresses the soil at the sides and in this way employs the passive resistance of the soil to help to support the applied loads. When failure of a flexible culvert does occur it is primarily because of excessive deflection. In contrast to the flexible pipes, rigid culverts are composed of reinforced concrete, cast iron or vitrified clay and their load-carrying ability is primarily a function of the stiffness of the walls of the culverts. When failure of a rigid culvert does occur it is usually due to rupture of the walls of the culvert.

Culverts are utilized in pipe, arch or box form, although pipe culverts are by far the most common. Pipe and arch culverts are formed from both rigid and flexible materials, whereas box culverts—they have rectangular cross-sections—are always made rigid. Most of the larger culverts are provided with concrete headwalls or wingwalls, regardless of the material from which the culverts themselves are made. The main function of a headwall is to aid in the smooth movement of water from the ditch to the culvert. In so doing it not only increases the design capacity of the culvert, but, by reducing the vortices caused by secondary flow at the entrance, it also protects the surrounding soil from excessive erosion. Headwalls and wingwalls also: (a) retain embankment material and reduce slope erosion, (b) provide structural stability to the culvert ends and serve as counter-weights to offset buoyant or uplift forces, and (c) inhibit piping, i.e. the removal of fill material via seepage along the outside of the culvert barrel. Endwalls and aprons are very often provided at the culvert exits so that the emerging water is prevented from scouring the ditch into which it empties.

*Location* Proper location is a prime prerequisite to the efficient and economical operation of a culvert within a drainage system. Improper location can lead to the softening and possible failure of a roadway, as well as undesirable ponding and damage to adjacent property on the upstream side of the embankment. Culvert location in both plan and elevation is particularly important in ensuring sediment-free culvert barrels.

Deposition factors to be aware of when locating culverts are as follows: (a) at moderate flow rates, the culvert cross-section is greater than the stream cross-section, so that the flow depth and sediment transport capacity are reduced, (b) abrupt changes to a flatter slope in a culvert or in the channel adjacent to a culvert will cause sediment deposition, and (c) culvert inlets placed at bends in a stream will be subjected to deposition in the same way that sand bars are formed on the inside of stream bends.

A culvert is simply an enclosed channel which serves to carry an open stream under a highway. If it is to be an efficient substitute for the open-ditch section it must be placed so that the water has both a direct entrance and a direct exit. Thus, as is illustrated in Fig. 2.3(a), the culvert is ideally placed in the natural ditch-bed so that its alignment conforms closely to that of the original situation. Often this means that the culvert must be located at a skew angle rather than at a right-angle to the centreline of the road. If the stream meanders and/or its location in the natural channel would require an inordinately long culvert, some stream modification may be in order, provided that care is taken in the design of the channel change to avoid erosion and silting problems. As is suggested by Figs 2.3(b), (c) and (d), this will usually involve cutting a new ditch into which the water can be diverted prior to the culvert. Once the water has passed through the culvert it should normally be returned to its original channel as quickly as possible. It should be noted that culvert locations normal to the centreline of a highway should not be used if they require severe or abrupt changes in channel alignment either upstream or downstream of the culvert.

The slope of a culvert should normally conform as closely as possible to the natural grade of the stream; this is usually the one which produces least silting or scouring in conjunction with an economical length of culvert. The silt-carrying capacity of a stream varies as the square of its velocity and hence considerable sedimentation can occur if the velocity of the water is reduced by changing the slope. If sedimentation is expected, as for instance when draining particular bare soil areas, it may be advisable to set the invert of the culvert several centimetres or more above the stream-bed but at the same slope, so that the carried material is prevented from being deposited *within* the conduit. Indeed, if the embankment is high and ponding of the water is allowable, the culvert can very often be placed at a level above that

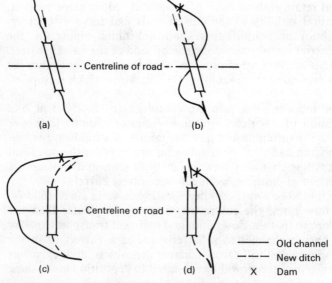

**Fig. 2.3**  Various methods of locating culverts in roadways

of the stream-bed, so that its length is reduced significantly and its replacement or relocation, should this ever become necessary, is simplified. It is generally considered that culverts should be placed at a minimum slope of about 0.5 per cent if significant sedimentation is to be avoided.

If the slope of the culvert is greater than the natural slope of the watercourse, then the increased water velocity may cause scouring of the sides and base of the ditch at the outlet to the culvert. In this latter respect special care has to be taken when an embankment is constructed on the side of a steeply sloping hill so as to ensure that erosion of the downstream side slope does not take place as water emerges from the culvert.

*Hydraulic design*  If a culvert were to be the same size and shape as the drainage ditch which it services, then its hydraulic design would be relatively easy. Unfortunately, however, this is not so and a culvert normally has the effect of a constriction to the streamflow. The efficient design of this constriction may be very difficult depending upon the governing factors. These factors and some of their effects are as follows.

(1)  *Depth of the headwater pond*  For a given design flood, the depth of the pond formed at the entrance is a function of the size and shape of the culvert. Conversely, the manner in which flow takes place in the culvert is affected by the head of water available at the inlet. Laboratory experiments indicate that the entrance to a culvert can be considered as hydraulically submerged when the depth above the invert of the inlet is greater than about 1.2 times its diameter.

(2)  *Depth of the tailwater pond*  If both the inlet and the outlet are submerged during the design flood, the culvert will usually run full,

although there are certain instances when it will not do so. If the outlet is not submerged, it is still possible for the culvert to run full if the inlet is submerged and the culvert is long.

(3) *Type of entrance* If the culvert has a poorly-designed entrance, then considerable turbulence will occur at the inlet and energy will be dissipated which would otherwise be available for moving water through the culvert. Studies have shown that culverts with flared or wing-type entrances are much more hydraulically efficient than ones with straight, square-edged headwalls or where the culverts project into the headwater pond. For instance, culverts with submerged inlets having flared entrances may flow full, whereas those with poor inlets will not. Good entrance design is a most important feature of the design of short culverts and long culverts on steep slopes, but is of less importance with long culverts on gentle slopes.

(4) *Roughness of the interior walls* Other things being equal, a rough-textured culvert which runs full will discharge less water than a smooth one also running full, since much of the energy head is used up in overcoming the resistance to flow. The longer the culvert, the more important is the roughness factor.

(5) *Length of the culvert* As discussed above, the length of the culvert dictates whether or not the type of entrance and the roughness of the interior walls are major or minor features of the hydraulic design.

(6) *Slope of the culvert* Other considerations being equal, it is the culvert slope which dictates whether or not the culvert operates as a free surface channel. If the slope is too gentle, the culvert will tend to flow full and the depth of the headwater pond will be increased.

As can be gathered from the few basic examples given above, the manner in which the hydraulic flow occurs in a culvert is dependent upon a number of interrelated factors. Some of the more important of these interrelationships are illustrated in Fig. 2.4.

Figure 2.4(a) illustrates the case, commonly experienced in flat or slightly rolling country, where both the inlet and the outlet culvert are submerged. The culvert then normally operates as a pipe. It will certainly do

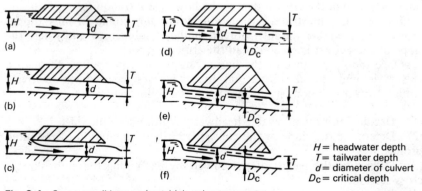

**Fig. 2.4** Some conditions under which culverts operate

so if the level of the tailwater pond plus the headloss due to friction in the culvert is greater than the elevation of the crown of the culvert at the inlet. It will not operate as a pipe if the culvert has a poorly-designed inlet and is on a steep slope. In this instance the inlet acts as a sluice and the culvert will not run full, except beyond the hydraulic jump which will form near the outlet; in time, however, the air space created between the entrance to the culvert and the jump will gradually disappear due to the air-entraining action of the hydraulic jump. If the velocity of the water is sufficiently high, the hydraulic jump may be formed outside the outlet with the result that it is not submerged.

Figures 2.4(b) and (c) illustrate the situations which are likely to occur in hilly topography where the slope of the downstream ditch is sufficiently steep to carry the water away from the outlet and prevent the formation of a tailwater pond. Normally, a culvert with a well-shaped inlet will flow full in such a location, provided that the inlet is hydraulically submerged. If, however, the culvert has a sharp-edged projecting or square-edged inlet, the flow entering the culvert may be contracted to a depth less than the height of the culvert. The culvert is said to be hydraulically 'short' if it is sufficiently steep and/or short for the water to be carried through so quickly that part-full flow will occur throughout its entire length; this is illustrated in Fig. 2.4(c). If the inlet is poorly designed but the slope of the culvert is very gentle while its length is considerable, then the velocity of the flow may be sufficiently low to allow the depth of flow to increase so that the free-water surface reaches the top of the culvert and full flow occurs; in this case the culvert is said to be a 'long' culvert.

Figures 2.4(d) and (e) illustrate conditions where both the inlet and the outlet are not hydraulically submerged. The condition shown in Fig. 2.4(d) can be found when the depth of the tailwater pond is between the critical depth and the crown of the culvert at the outlet. Since the slope is less than the critical slope and the flow is tranquil, this condition is only likely to occur at locations where the culvert empties into a deep, narrow outlet ditch on a flat slope. When the culvert discharges into a channel which has a relatively flat slope and a wide, flat floodplain, the flow condition in Fig. 2.4(e) may be experienced. Here, although the depth of the tailwater pond is less than the critical depth, the flow is still tranquil.

Figure 2.4(f) illustrates a situation, commonly found in hilly topography, where neither the inlet nor the outlet is submerged and where the slope of the culvert is greater than the critical slope.

Once the importance of the basic features influencing flow through a culvert is understood, the actual hydraulic design becomes relatively straightforward. It consists essentially of the following steps.

(1) Decide upon the allowable headwater depth above the inlet.
(2) Determine the slope of the culvert from an examination of the ditch profile.
(3) Determine the length of the culvert by examining the embankment cross-section.
(4) Determine the elevations of the inverts of the inlet and outlet of the

culvert. These can also be obtained from the embankment cross-section.
(5)  Select a size and type of culvert which it is considered will be suitable at the particular location.
(6)  Identify the hydraulic method of operation.
(7)  By means of an appropriate hydraulic equation, calculate the headwater depth for the design flood and culvert discharge.
(8)  If the calculated depth is greater or significantly lower than the allowable depth, select a new culvert and repeat the procedure.

It is not possible to describe here all the equations and nomographs which have been developed for use in step 7. For practical purposes, however, it is very often sufficient to obtain an approximate solution by using charts such as those shown in Fig. 2.5, which are readily available in

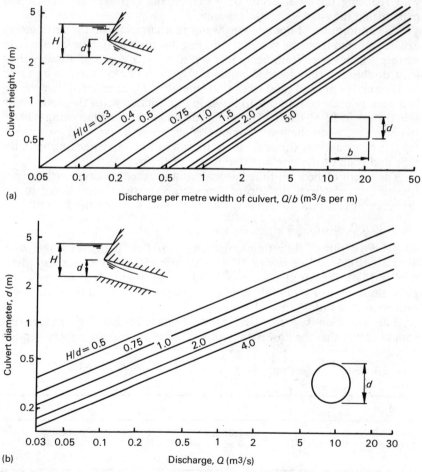

**Fig. 2.5**  Charts for estimating headwater depth on culverts with square-edged entrances, flowing partly full: (a) box culverts and (b) circular culverts

many hydraulic publications. These charts are applicable to problems involving culverts flowing partly full and having squared-edged entrances. When the culverts have rounded entrances under average conditions, the value of $H/d$ may be roughly estimated by the expressions given in Table 2.7; here $H/d$ refers to the ratio of headwater to barrel height for a culvert with a square-edged entrance.

## Drainage of carriageway surfaces

The development of multilane highways with wide carriageways has meant that the removal of rainwater from road surfaces has become increasingly difficult, whilst the use of relatively high speeds on many of these facilities has greatly increased the hazards faced by drivers on wet surfaces. When considering these problems, the highway engineer is basically concerned with reducing the total depth of water on the carriageway surface and maximizing the road–tyre contact-area.

The importance of not allowing water to accumulate on the carriageway can be gathered from the fact that stopping distances at 100 km/h, on a road surface which varies from being just wet to a water depth of 4 mm, can at least double for fully-treaded radial-ply tyres, and can increase by up to three times for normal road tyres[27]. Generally, it is considered that driving becomes quite dangerous due to losses in tyre friction when the water depth is in the range 2.5–5.0 mm. The critical depth at which aquaplaning is likely to occur (i.e. when the water completely supports the tyre and separates it from the carriageway surface) ranges from 4 to 10 mm, depending upon the type and state of the tyre and the nature of the road surface.

The depth of flow on rolled asphalt and brushed concrete surfaces has been measured (from the top of the surface texture) and related to the drainage length, rainfall intensity and flow path slope by the formula[28]:

$$d = 0.46(l_f I)^{0.5} n^{0.2}$$

where $d$ = depth of flow (mm), $l_f$ = length of flow path (m) = $W n_3/n_1$ = $W[1 + (n_2/n_1)^2]^{0.5}$, in which $W$ = width of carriageway under consideration (m), $n_1$ = crossfall (%), $n_2$ = longitudinal grade (%), and $n_3$ = flow path slope (%), $I$ = rainfall intensity (mm/h), and $n$ = flow path slope, expressed as a ratio 1 in $n$.

This equation suggests that good drainage design for carriageways should ensure that the flow path is kept as short as possible, i.e. the depth is

**Table 2.7** Estimating headwater depth on culverts with rounded entrances under average conditions

| $H/d$ range | Box culvert | Circular culvert |
|---|---|---|
| $H/d \leqslant 1.0$ | $1.00H/d$ | $0.87H/d$ |
| $1.0 < H/d \leqslant 1.5$ | $0.36 + 0.64H/d$ | $0.87H/d$ |
| $1.5 < H/d$ | $0.62 + 0.46H/d$ | $1.09 + 0.10H/d$ |

*Note*: These data give headwater heads which are as high as those likely to occur under adverse conditions; as such they are to a certain extent conservative.

proportional to the square root of the flow path. However, as the depth of flow also varies with the fifth root of the flow path slope, relatively little benefit can be gained in theory by increasing the slope; in fact, the major benefit to be gained from having a steep crossfall is a reduction in the amount of water which will pond in deformations in the surface. Furthermore, since the maximum depth occurs at the end of the flow path, it is important that runoff water be removed from the edge of the carriageway as quickly as possible.

In practical terms, the above equation also suggests that the major factor affecting the length and depth of flow is the width of the carriageway. Thus the use of a cambered surface with two-way crossfalls on wide one-way carriageways is a most effective way of decreasing the depth of flow, i.e. the length of the flow path is decreased by up to one-half on a straight alignment. On superelevated curved sections, particular care will need to be taken to ensure that the drainage from the high carriageway is collected in the central reservation, and does not cross over onto the lower carriageway.

Crossfall recommendations vary from country to country, and are mostly based on experience—and on the standard of construction capable of being achieved in relation to pavement surfacings. General practice in Britain is to use minimum crossfalls of 2 per cent with relatively smooth surfaces such as rolled asphalt and concrete, and 2.5–3.0 per cent for the rougher coated macadams.

For multilane carriageways without shoulders in urban areas, consideration should be given to having a steeper crossfall on the left-hand lane than on the adjacent lanes. This not only helps to remove water readily from the through lanes, but also allows the gully spacing to be increased (due to the higher channel capacity resulting from the steeper crossfall).

On carriageways with shoulders, the shoulder crossfall should normally be steeper than that on the adjacent through traffic lanes so as to increase the velocity of the escaping water. However, if the superelevated crossfall at bends is greater than the normal shoulder crossfall, then the shoulder crossfall should be made the same as in the adjacent lanes.

In the case of rural roads, water leaving the carriageway is often able to discharge through 'grips' into ditches parallel to the highway. In the case of roads in or adjacent to built-up areas, however, the water is normally directed to an underground system of pipe drains, and thence to convenient outfall points.

Figure 2.6 shows a typical stormwater drainage system for a high-quality dual carriageway in a built-up area. Note that it consists of roadside and median longitudinal drains, cross-drains, chute and toe-of-slope carrier drains and outfalls. With this particular design, water enters underground longitudinal drains either through gullies at the road edge or through filter media along the tops of these longitudinal drains; cross-drains are provided at appropriate intervals to convey water from the longitudinal drains to the carrier drains which are connected with the outfalls. Manholes for maintenance purposes are placed at intersections, changes in pipe size or slope, and at intervals along all drains subject to maximum spacing restrictions.

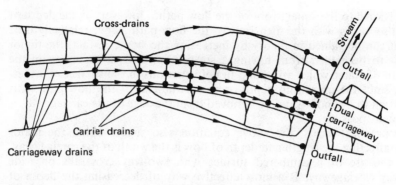

**Fig. 2.6**   Layout of a typical drainage system for a dual carriageway in a built-up area

(Dynamic programming procedures which may be utilized in the minimum-cost design of such drainage systems are described in the literature[29].)

*Road gulleys*   A road gulley is a waterway inlet designed to collect water which flows off the carriageway surface. It normally comprises a precast concrete or vitrified clay gulley pot (which acts as a trap for silt and small debris) connected by a pipe—usually about 150 mm in diameter—to an underground 'storm' drain or channel, and a steel frame fitted with a cover or grating which bridges the gulley pot.

The gratings/covers used on gulleys in Britain are as follows[30].

(1)   Heavy duty gratings—these are used for major carriageways carrying heavy wheel loads of up to 11.5 t.
(2)   Medium duty gratings and covers—these are used for minor carriageways carrying normal wheel loads up to 5 t.
(3)   A kerb inlet—this is normally made to fit in line with the road kerb so that water enters from the side.

In relation to the above, it may be noted that the kerb inlet is normally the most inefficient of all the gulley types, particularly on steep, longitudinal slopes. The reason for this is that the small hydraulic head acting at right-angles to the initial direction of flow is unable to move a significant amount of water over the side weir, and so much of the flow bypasses the gulley. The action of this gulley can, however, be greatly improved by shaping the approach channel so that the inlet is more directly in the path of the water flow. The other types of gulley can collect up to 95 per cent of the flowing water, provided that the width of flow does not exceed 1.5 times the width of the grating[31].

There is no simple general recommendation about where gulleys should be located. Generally, however, they are placed at low points or 'sags' on the roadway where water will naturally accumulate. They should also be inserted just prior to bus stops, laybys, and the upstream radii of corner kerbs so that they intercept the runoff water before it reaches carriageway locations used by pedestrians and turning vehicles.

A rough guide as to the locations of intermediate drains can be obtained by assuming that the impermeable area per gulley on housing estate roads should not exceed 200 m². Another similar rule-of-thumb is that gulleys on urban streets should not be more than 40–50 m apart. A more rational approach to the design of gulley spacings has been put forward by the Transport and Road Research Laboratory[31]; this makes use of tables incorporating data on the efficiencies of different inlets combined with data on the water flow over various widths of the road.

*Environmental issues*   The above discussion has been mainly concerned with hydrological considerations associated with the rapid removal of surface water in order to protect the highway pavement and carriageway. In recent years, however, attention has begun to be focussed upon the environmental impacts of some of these preventative measures.

For example, changing the alignment of a natural channel can be detrimental to fish and other aquatic life because of increased stream velocity, and the removal of boulders and irregularities in the channel. (This particular problem may be alleviated by placing boulders at random in the new channel to assist in restoring the fish habitat.)

Stormwater runoff from urban areas has long been recognized as a source of a wide variety of pollutants in surface waters. The runoff from major highways in rural areas has now been identified as also containing levels of vehicle-related pollutants, e.g. heavy metals, oil and polynuclear aromatic hydrocarbons, which have undesirable impacts on the quality of the receiving waters. Furthermore, the current wide usage of de-icing salts has raised environmental concerns related to chloride contamination of surface and subsurface waters and damage to roadside soil, trees and other vegetation.

Consequently, it can be expected that future years will see the runoff from these heavily-travelled highways being treated prior to discharge into receiving watercourses in order to reduce their pollution loadings. One study[32] of the effect of a shallow trapezoidal lagoon, sedimentation tank, and french drain in reducing the pollutants in the runoff from a section of the M1 motorway carrying between 25 000 and 40 000 vehicles per 24 h day, showed that the efficiency of removal of most of the unwanted materials followed the order

$$\text{lagoon} \geqslant \text{french drain} \gg \text{sedimentation tank}$$

## Subsurface moisture control

### Methods of control

As is discussed later in the text, all scientific pavement design procedures utilize measurements of the subgrade soil. The thickness design suggested by any procedure can only be validly utilized when the soil conditions assumed at the time of testing are similar to those that will actually pertain in the field. For instance, if the moisture content used in the test is exceeded in the field, then the design conditions no longer apply and the pavement may well fail. Thus good highway design seeks to ensure either that water is kept out of the pavement or that if water enters the pavement as a result of unavoidable circumstances, it is removed as safely and as quickly as possible.

An alternative to the above 'prevention' approach to pavement design is to construct a pavement structure which is capable of withstanding the anticipated traffic loads in the presence of *excess* water. The weakness in this approach, however, is that if the pavement is designed, for example, for saturated subgrade conditions (as is general practice in the USA), and if saturation is not likely to occur under natural conditions, then the pavement will be (expensively) over-designed. Furthermore, it is difficult to predict the exact stresses developed in a pavement when water is present, with the result that pavements designed for saturated conditions may in fact be structurally inadequate when subjected to continuous traffic loads.

It should be clear therefore that the subgrade conditions on which the thickness design is based should remain substantially unchanged throughout the design life of the pavement. From a drainage aspect this means that substantial moisture control installations may have to be incorporated into the roadway design. This is not always easy to do; in fact, it can be a major expense item for, as is illustrated in Fig. 2.7, there are very many ways in which moisture can enter and leave the subgrade of a highway.

**Seepage from high ground**
This condition is likely to occur in hilly topography and in highway cuttings below the water-table, where spring inflows and seepage from emerging groundwater can gain easy access to the pavement and subgrade.

The basic solution to this problem is to intercept the seepage water on the uphill side of the roadway. If the seepage zone is close to the surface, interception can sometimes be carried out by means of open ditches. Normally, however, surface drainage cannot be utilized since the seepage water must be kept at least 1.00–1.25 m below the formation level; this may require a deep drainage ditch which, if it is close to the edge of the pavement, will have to be relatively wide and have gentle slopes which can

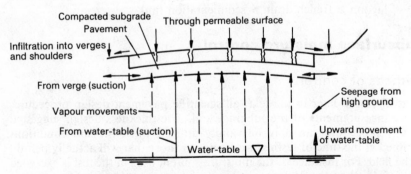

**Fig. 2.7**   Ways in which water can enter and leave road pavements and subgrades

be traversed by vehicles which accidentally leave the carriageway. In hilly country or in roadway cuttings this can result in construction costs that may often not be justified by the importance of the highway.

The more usual way of tackling the problem of seepage is to utilize a subsurface piped drain to intercept the water. If the seepage zone is not very deep, then ideally the subdrain should be installed to the depth of the underlying impervious stratum so that the entering water is completely cut off. This solution is illustrated in concept in Fig. 2.8(a). If, however, the seepage zone extends relatively deeply so that it is impractical to intercept all of the seepage water, then it should be sunk sufficiently deep to keep the free water at least 1.00–1.25 m below the bottom of the pavement.

When cuttings are made below a water-table in permeable materials or in alternate permeable and impermeable layers, so that excessive seepage results in erosion of the excavated face, then drainage can be achieved by several methods, or combinations of these methods[33], as follows.

(1) The slopes may be covered with a graded granular filter or porous fabric or artificial fibres under a free-draining blanket, both of which are used in conjunction with a subsoil drain at the toe.

(2) A system of slope drains may be laid as shown in Fig. 2.9. Note that they consist of perforated or porous pipes laid in trenches—the trench bottoms may be lined with plastic sheeting—which are backfilled with free-draining, non-plastic filter materials (see Table 2.8) of crushed rock, crushed slag or gravel. At least 15 per cent of the backfill material should be greater than the diameter of the perforation holes in the drainage pipe.

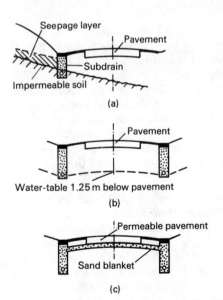

**Fig. 2.8** Diagrammatic illustration of the use of subdrains to prevent moisture intruding into the pavement and subgrade: (a) prevent seepage, (b) lower water-table, and (c) remove infiltrated moisture

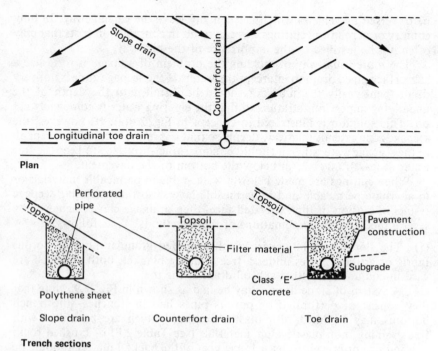

Plan

Trench sections

**Fig. 2.9**　Typical cutting slope drainage system

(3)　Cuttings through alternate permeable and impermeable layers, within groundwater not under artesian head, may be drained by sinking vertical stone-filled bores in advance of, or above, the cutting slopes to allow gravity drainage from upper aquifers to a lower one.

(4)　Where seepage in a cutting is confined to isolated permeable layers running horizontally or at a fairly shallow gradient, drainage may be achieved by drilling into them from the face of the excavation along the bedding to allow the insertion of a perforated pipe protected by a prefabricated filter[35]. (This process has also been successfully used to minimize the likelihood of landslides in highway cuttings through hilly terrain[36].)

In relation to Fig. 2.9 it might be noted that *trench* and *counterfort drains* (also known as *pillar drains*, *buttress drains*, and *batter drains*) are intercepting subdrains that are widely used in Britain as a remedy for slips in cuttings and embankments. Their function is to reduce pore-water pressures in the slope. Counterfort drains, which can be defined as intercepting trench drains which are carried into solid ground below a slip surface, provide some buttressing action in addition to the drainage function.

**High water-table**

Recommendations regarding the minimum acceptable depth to the free-

**Table 2.8** Recommended range of grading of filter material for drains[34]

| BS sieve (mm) | Percentage by mass passing | |
| | Type A | Type B |
| --- | --- | --- |
| 63 | — | 100 |
| 37.5 | — | 85–100 |
| 20 | 100 | 0–25 |
| 10 | — | 0–5 |
| 5 | 60–100 | — |
| 1.18 | 15–45 | — |
| 0.600 | 0–25 | — |
| 0.150 | 0–5 | — |

water-table vary from country to country[37] and, as might be expected, from soil type to soil type. In Britain, the water-table should preferably be kept at least 1.00–1.25 m below the formation also. Not only is it undesirable to have free water anywhere near the pavement, but the compacted subgrade must not lie within the zone through which the capillarity (suction) moisture is capable of rising. This is particularly important when the subgrade is composed of a fine-grained soil.

A high water-table can often be lowered by the installation of longitudinal drains on either side of the carriageway (see Fig. 2.8(b)). The depth to which the drains should be laid and the need for any particular type of system are functions of the width of the carriageway and the soil type. The most practical way of determining the effect of any particular system is to carry out simple field trials. For instance, for the installation illustrated in Fig. 2.8(b), two parallel trenches, each about 15 m long, should be dug to a depth of at least 0.6 m below the level to which it is desired to lower the water-table, along the line of the proposed drains. A transverse line of boreholes at intervals of 1.5–3.0 m are then sunk between the two ditches and extended on either side for a distance of about 4.5–6.0 m. Observations are then made of the levels of the water-table in the boreholes before and after pumping the water out of the trenches, allowing a sufficient period of time for equilibrium conditions to be established. By plotting the observations, an estimate can be made of the significance of the drawdown effects of the ditches, thereby enabling decisions to be made regarding the correct depth and spacing of the drains. The size of the drain pipes can be estimated on the basis of the rate of pumping necessary to keep the trenches free of water.

It must be pointed out that the level of the water-table will not normally be lowered to the level of the drains themselves, except immediately adjacent to the drains. As illustrated in Fig. 2.8(b), there is a natural tendency for the water-table to rise as the distance from the point of moisture release increases. The steepness of the water-table adjacent to the drain is dependent upon the soil type: if the soil is coarse grained the shape of the water-table will be relatively flat, whereas if the soil is fine grained it will be steep.

A further point to mention here is that a single longitudinal drain beneath the centre of the roadway may sometimes be sufficient. The most obvious examples of this are when the water-table is already relatively deep and/or when the subgrade soil is coarse grained.

Fine-grained soils cannot, however, be drained by means of gravity drains [38]. While sophisticated methods utilizing the theory of electro-osmosis are available to drain moisture that cannot be removed by ordinary means, they are expensive and require such specialized technical expertise that they are impracticable for use on most highway projects. Therefore, instead of attempting to lower the water-table in such soils, an embankment should be constructed so that the bottom of the pavement is raised the desired distance above the water level. The construction of an embankment is the usual remedy when the roadway crosses low-lying saturated soil (see Chapters 5 and 6). If the pavement is to be laid in permeable soil layers which have interspersed thin impermeable layers which trap water under sub-artesian head, adverse water pressure below formation level may be reduced by sinking bleeder wells vertically from the longitudinal drains to penetrate the impermeable layers, thereby allowing the free upward passage of water.

**Permeable surface**
A practical and economical method has yet to be invented that will keep highway pavements free of surface water for more than brief lengths of time after construction. Since pavements have wide, flat dimensions, they are, in general, highly vulnerable to inflows from many sources.

Overall, it can be said that each pavement has its own individual characteristics and that, at any given time in its life, certain amounts of water will inflow through its surface network of cracks, joints, porous areas, etc. For example, if the wearing course is composed of a soil–aggregate mixture or an open-graded coated macadam, it can be expected that rainwater (and water from road cleansers) will enter the pavement through the surface and eventually find its way to the subgrade. In concrete roads, water will intrude into pavements through joints and cracks which are not adequately sealed. Whilst the permeability of a rolled asphalt may decrease initially with time as a result of traffic compaction and the 'clogging' of surface pores by surface pollutants, it should also be appreciated that cracking defects are still likely to become a significant source of water entry through these surfacings as the pavement ages. If this inflow moisture is not removed immediately, it may cause the subgrade to soften or a surface layer to uplift, or some other detriment to happen which will eventually cause structural failure of the pavement.

As a general rule, it can be said that where it is expected that significant moisture will enter through the surface, a subbase of granular material designed to meet permeability requirements should be interposed between the subgrade and the roadbase. The purpose of this subbase is to act as a drainage layer to enable this infiltrated water to move freely and quickly to subdrains after it has penetrated through the roadbase. This concept is illustrated in Fig. 2.8(c).

One eminent authority on road drainage has stated [39] that 'if the total long-term costs of important pavements are to be kept to a minimum, design standards must be modified to produce structural sections capable of devoiding themselves of free water rapidly after its entry, rather than in days, weeks, or months'. Rapid drainage of these pavement structural sections can be most effectively accomplished by providing a layer of highly permeable macadam-type or open-graded material under the full width of the carriageway, in conjunction with collector pipes and outlet pipes which will ensure constant gravity drainage. Such systems will protect pavements not only from large surface inflows, but also from high groundwater inflows during wet periods, and from inflows from springs (or other such unknowns) which may not show up during the pre-testing and construction periods.

**Verge moisture movements**

Two problems are associated with the effect of roadside verges upon subgrade moisture. The first and more obvious is that which occurs in winter when the verges are much wetter than the subgrade. This sets up a suction potential which causes moisture to transfer to the subgrade, causing detrimental softening to take place. With a very expansive clayey subgrade this may cause the edge of the carriageway to be lifted sufficiently to initiate longitudinal cracking of the pavement. The second effect, which is just as important, occurs in very dry weather when the subgrade soil is significantly wetter than the verge soil. Moisture conditions such as are illustrated in Fig. 2.10 will cause soil shrinkage beneath the edges of the carriageway. If the subgrade soil is a fine-grained material, this in turn may lead to longitudinal cracking of the pavement.

Drying-out of the soil near the edges of the carriageway is accelerated if fast-growing trees and shrubs are allowed to grow adjacent to the roadway. This is accentuated in urban areas where much of the ground area is covered anyway, with the result that, especially in times of drought, the vegetation can have great difficulty in getting adequate moisture. It must be pointed out, however, that the removal of large trees from the sides of roads already

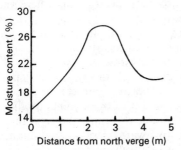

**Fig. 2.10** Variation across the width of a road of the average moisture content of the top 450 mm of the clay subgrade during a severe drought in Britain [40]

constructed has also been known to cause pavement trouble. Here the problems arose as a result of upsetting moisture conditions which had become stable over the course of time.

The movement of moisture to and from the verges can be prevented by interposing a waterproof membrane between the verges and the roadbase, subbase and compacted subgrade. Another approach, which from a stability aspect is most desirable, is to extend the roadbase, subbase and subgrade into the verge to form a continuous hardshoulder. This shoulder will then act as a buffer zone to absorb the most detrimental differential effects.

**Vapour movement**
The movement of moisture in vapour form is associated with differences in vapour pressure arising from differences in temperature and/or moisture contents in various vertical positions in the subgrade soil. Vapour movement resulting from temperature differences can assume considerable importance in climatic areas where there are substantial fluctuations in the daily temperature; because of the temperate climate prevalent in Britain, however, this form of moisture movement is not significant. Vapour movement because of moisture differences is not normally a problem in this country either. For it to occur to any large extent the soil must be relatively dry and again this is a moisture condition that is not very common in a temperate climate.

When moisture movement in the vapour phase does take place it will usually be in coarse- rather than fine-grained soils. For this reason the often advocated introduction of a coarse-grained cutoff layer between the subgrade and the roadbase will do little or nothing to protect either the roadbase or the subgrade. Perhaps the only effective method of combating vapour movement when it is expected to occur is to interpose a horizontal impermeable membrane between the compacted top 0.5 m of the subgrade soil and the underlying uncompacted soil.

## Subdrain design

As noted previously, the installation of a subdrainage system is economically justified when there is 'free' water to be collected and where the subdrains are properly designed and inserted.

Subdrain installations now used in highways contain pipes to remove the drainage moisture quickly. These pipes are placed in trenches containing carefully selected coarse-grained backfill material (see, for example, Table 2.8). Normally, the drainage pipes are of perforated metal, unplasticized polyvinylchloride, vitrified clay or concrete, of porous concrete, of plastic, or of unperforated concrete or vitrified clay laid with open joints to allow the water to enter. Perforated piping is less liable to silting and so is to be preferred. The perforations should be laid downwards in order to minimize clogging by soil fines. If the underlying soil is relatively impervious it will be necessary to bed the pipe in at least 50 mm of granular material to avoid plugging of the perforations; this bedding layer is usually not necessary if the soil is coarse grained.

In recent years there has been an increasing use of plastics in drainage systems both as pipes and as geotextiles. Perforated flexible plastic drain pipes, with the benefits of long length, light weight and flexibility, are now in common use. There have also been significant improvements in respect of glazed stoneware pipes, resulting in lighter pipes and better flexible joints. These improved pipe products have reduced maintenance costs as well as benefiting the initial construction.

In the past decade also satisfactory granular filter materials for sub-drains have become more difficult to obtain and more expensive to install. As a result, commercial plastic filter cloths—also known as geotextiles—have been developed[41] for use as a surround for filter media in subdrains. As is suggested by Fig. 2.11, such drains may not always need a drainage pipe since their coarse-graded aggregate–fabric structure is more permeable than a comparable cross-sectional area of conventional coarse- and fine-graded aggregates.

Geotextiles, of which those formed from polypropene and polyester are the most common, are normally classified as being knitted, woven or non-woven. Knitted materials are composed of loops of fibres or yarns connected by straight segments. With woven materials the yarns are oriented in two mutually perpendicular directions and overlapped. Non-woven geotextiles have pores which are formed by needle-punching through fabric, or by applying heat to bond filaments together at contact points, or by using resin to bond the fibres.

The use of geotextile filter cloth in relation to granular filter media has been so successful that it has led to the development and current use of prefabricated fin drains that are used as french drains and wall drains in their own right. The fin drain comprises a water-channelling fin which encapsulates a perforated pipe at its base. The fin is a sandwich of filter fabric on each side of a porous core. Water flows from the soil through the

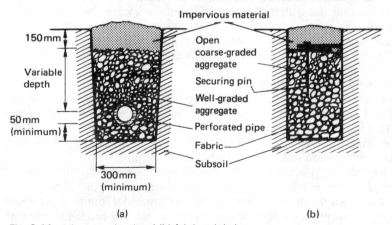

**Fig. 2.11**   (a) conventional and (b) fabric subdrains

filter and into the pipe—this is usually of perforated plastic—via the core system. Good performance is achieved by the use of filter fabrics with a specific mesh opening size and open area ratio that is related to the particle-size distribution of the soil into which it is installed. When water begins to drain into the system, the soil adjacent to the fabric is depleted of a specific controllable quantity of fines, thus creating a natural filter of higher permeability, and a beneficial permeability gradient towards the drain.

In many countries (including Britain) it is not uncommon to extend the filter material in longitudinal drainage ditches up to the surface, the theory being that the subdrain can serve both as a drain for the subgrade and as a means of removing the stormwater from the surface. While this may seem at first sight to be economic practice, it can in fact be poor engineering practice. If the surface catchment area contains much loose material, substantial amounts of fines will be washed from the surface down into the filter material and eventually they will clog the drain. In such instances, the end result will simply be that the surface water is provided with easy access to both the pavement and the subgrade. To prevent this happening, the top 150 mm of the subdrain should consist of a layer of an impervious covering, such as a layer of compacted clay.

Longitudinal subdrains are usually nearly parallel to the centreline of the roadway. If the intention is to intercept seepage water, then one drain between the roadway and the slope will usually be adequate. If the objective is to remove water infiltrating downwards through the pavement, then a granular subbase plus longitudinal subdrains will be required. If the water-table has to be lowered, then a subdrain on either side of the carriageway may be sufficient. If the soil is relatively pervious and if the amount that the water level has to be reduced is not too great, then a single drain beneath the centreline may be sufficient; in this case the subdrain should be beneath the compacted layer at the top of the subgrade if differential movement of the pavement is to be eliminated.

The longitudinal subdrains should be provided with outlets at regular intervals so that the collected moisture is able to escape. Normally, these outlets should be not more than about 90 m apart. The slope of the subdrain between the outlets should be as steep as possible, but certainly should never be less than 1 in 200 or 0.5 per cent.

**Conventional backfill criteria**
The purpose of the backfill is to improve the interception ability of the drain, and to provide an effective water-collecting space adjacent to the pipe. To fulfil this function, the backfill material must be sufficiently coarse to allow water to have easy access to the pipe, yet be fine enough to act as a filter to prevent base soil from intruding into the pipe.

Theoretically, the *permeability* required of a granular filter can be determined from considerations of groundwater flow; practicably, however, most recommendations are based on grain-size limits determined following comprehensive filter design investigations. An excellent review of the literature[42] on this subject concluded that a filter material interposed between a pipe and any type of granular soil should meet the following requirements to ensure that it will be sufficiently permeable at all times:

$$\frac{D_{15} \text{ (filter)}}{D_{15} \text{ (protected soil)}} \geqslant 5$$

where $D_{15}$ represents the 15 per cent size (mm) of either the filter material or the surrounding protected soil.

Many recommendations have been made with regard to *filtration* requirements for subdrains. The most reliable for granular soils is divided into four parts, as follows.

(1) $\quad \dfrac{D_{15} \text{ (filter)}}{D_{85} \text{ (protected soil)}}$ should be $\leqslant 5$

$\quad\quad \dfrac{D_{15} \text{ (filter)}}{D_{15} \text{ (protected soil)}}$ should be $\leqslant 20$

and $\quad \dfrac{D_{50} \text{ (filter)}}{D_{50} \text{ (protected soil)}}$ should be $\leqslant 25$

(2) If, however, the soil is uniform, i.e.

$$\frac{D_{60} \text{ (protected soil)}}{D_{10} \text{ (protected soil)}} \leqslant 1.5$$

then $\quad \dfrac{D_{15} \text{ (filter)}}{D_{85} \text{ (protected soil)}}$ should be $\leqslant 6$

instead of 5 as in (1) above.

(3) If the soil is well graded, i.e.

$$\frac{D_{60} \text{ (protected soil)}}{D_{10} \text{ (protected soil)}} \geqslant 4$$

then $\quad \dfrac{D_{15} \text{ (filter)}}{D_{15} \text{ (protected soil)}}$ should be $\leqslant 40$

instead of 20 as in (1) above.

(4) At no time should a filter material be used if it is gap graded (as it will tend to segregate during placement), nor should more than 5 per cent of its mass pass the 75 $\mu$m BS sieve (as otherwise the filter fines will migrate into the pipe). If the protected soil is gap graded, then the filter design (and, consequently, $D_{10}$, $D_{15}$, $D_{50}$ and $D_{85}$) should be based on the soil portion finer than the gap in the grading. If the protected soil contains layers of fine material, the filter design criteria should be selected to protect against the intrusion of the finest layer.

Many clay soils contain non-cohesive particles which are liable to migrate to the subdrain; however, the low water velocity and the natural cohesion of these soils will allow only groups or aggregates of clay particles about the drain to be washed away. For these reasons clay soils, and also silt soils, are best protected by a filter composed of a clean sand. Such a sand backfill will also normally be sufficiently permeable to allow easy transmission of all the water flow from the soils.

**Example of conventional filter design**
Design a subsurface filter material to protect a coarse-grained soil with a gradation as shown in Fig. 2.12.

*Solution*
Check first for filtration. In this case the uniformity coefficient of the protected soil is given by:

$$U_c = \frac{D_{60} \text{ (protected soil)}}{D_{10} \text{ (protected soil)}} = \frac{0.15}{0.075} = 2$$

The exceptions noted in (2) and (3) above do not therefore apply, so use the criteria in (1), thus:

$$\frac{D_{15} \text{ (filter)}}{D_{85} \text{ (protected soil)}} \leqslant 5 = \frac{D_{15} \text{ (filter)}}{0.21}$$

Therefore $D_{15}$ (filter) $\leqslant 1.05$ mm. Alternatively,

$$\frac{D_{15} \text{ (filter)}}{D_{15} \text{ (protected soil)}} \leqslant 20 = \frac{D_{15} \text{ (filter)}}{0.085}$$

Therefore $D_{15}$ (filter) $\leqslant 1.7$ mm.

*Decision*: use the lower $D_{15}$ (filter) value, i.e. 1.05 mm.

$$\frac{D_{50} \text{ (filter)}}{D_{50} \text{ (protected soil)}} \leqslant 25 = \frac{D_{50} \text{ (filter)}}{0.14}$$

Therefore $D_{50}$ (filter) $\leqslant 3.5$ mm.

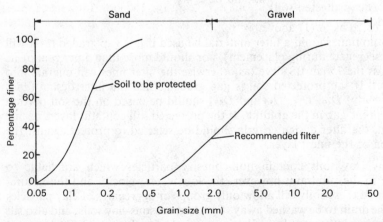

**Fig. 2.12**  Example of conventional filter design to protect a coarse-grained soil

A filter material should be chosen which will meet the above $D_{15}$ and $D_{50}$ criteria. In this instance a suitable backfill could well have a $D_{85}$ size of about 9.5 mm (see Fig. 2.12).

Now check that this filter material will meet the permeability requirements, thus:

$$\frac{D_{15} \text{ (filter)}}{D_{15} \text{ (protected soil)}} = \frac{1.05}{0.085} = 12.35$$

This value exceeds 5 and so the material will be sufficiently permeable.

**Geotextile criteria**

Filter design criteria for woven plastic filter cloth are also available. These are based[43] on the equivalent opening size (*EOS*) and percentage open area (*POA*) of the cloth. The *EOS* is defined as the size of the standard sieve with openings closest in size to the filter cloth openings, whilst the *POA* is defined as the summation of the open areas divided by the total area of the filter cloth.

Woven filter cloths are normally selected on the basis of the following criteria.

(1)  For filter cloth adjacent to granular materials containing 50 per cent or less by mass of fines $< 75\ \mu$m:

$$\frac{D_{85} \text{ (protected soil)}}{EOS} \text{ should be } \geqslant 1$$

and    *POA* should be $\leqslant 36\%$

(2)  For filter cloth adjacent to all other soil types:

$$EOS \text{ should be } \leqslant 210\ \mu\text{m}$$

and    *POA* should be $\leqslant 10\%$

To reduce the chance of clogging, no cloth should be specified which has a *POA* less than 4 per cent, or an *EOS* less than 100 $\mu$m. (In practice, most filter cloths commercially available have *EOS*-values in the range 150 to 600 $\mu$m.) When practicable, it is preferable to specify a cloth with openings as large as are allowed by the criteria.

When the gradation of the granular filter material used in the backfill is such that it satisfies requirements pertaining to materials adjacent to joint openings or pipe perforations, but is too coarse to satisfy the filter criteria pertaining to the protected soil, a single layer of filter cloth is normally used adjacent to the protected soil.

**Pipe criteria**

The length and diameter of a pipe should be selected so that the following criteria are satisfied.

(1)  The pipe will not run full near its outlet and flood the surrounding filter material.

(2)    The pipe must be able to intercept all of the water entering the drain without causing a high head in the filter material, as this, for example, will reduce both the depth to which a water-table can be lowered and its rate of lowering.

In the case of a perforated pipe, the holes must also be sufficiently small to prevent the filter material from being washed into the pipe and clogging it.

At this time no authoritative single recommendation can be made with regard to pipe diameters and length (although, in practice, 152 mm diameter pipes and outlet spacings of about 90 m are commonly used). However, the following criteria have been recommended[42] with regard to the size of the pipe perforations:

maximum size of circular holes = $D_{85}$ (filter)

and    maximum width of slotted holes = $0.83D_{85}$ (filter)

Special compaction of the backfill will not normally be required if these criteria are followed—although it is possible that the hole size limits could be increased if the filter material is compacted.

Although approaches based on various assumptions are suggested, there is, as yet, no definitive method of estimating the number of perforations per unit length of pipe.

**Example hole size calculation**
Determine the size of pipe perforations which can be used with the filter material shown in Fig. 2.12.

*Solution*
From this figure, $D_{85}$ (filter) = 9.5 mm. Therefore

maximum size of circular hole = 9.5 mm

and    maximum width of slot = $0.83 \times 9.5 = 7.9$ mm

If the only available pipes have perforations which are larger than the above, then an appropriate coarser material must be placed next to the pipe. In such a case, however, the gradation calculations for the new intervening filter material would have to be carried out with the old filter material (see Fig. 2.12) considered as the soil to be protected.

**Example calculation for the number of holes**
As noted above, there is no definitive procedure for determining the number of perforations per unit length of pipe. The following calculation[42] is simply one example of an approach towards determining the number of pipe perforations.

Consider the cross-section shown in Fig. 2.13 and assume that $D = 1$ m, $W = 12$ m, and $d = 0.06$ m at the time that drainage is started. Assume that the subgrade soil has a permeability of $1 \times 10^{-4}$ m/s (such as might occur in a saturated fine sand). Determine the order of magnitude of the water flow involved, and a probable number of 5 mm diameter circular perforations per metre length of pipe.

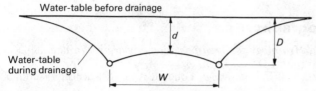

**Fig. 2.13** Example pipe perforation problem involving the use of McClelland's dimensionless ratios for drainage by two parallel pipes (as noted in reference 42)

**Dimensionless ratios**

| $tkD/yW^2$ | $d/D$ | $q/kD$ |
|---|---|---|
| 0.001 | 0.06 | 0.80 |
| 0.010 | 0.37 | 0.47 |
| 0.100 | 0.79 | 0.25 |

*Notes*: $q$ = discharge per unit length per unit time, $t$ = time since beginning of drainage, $k$ = coefficient of permeability, and $y$ = volume of drainable water per unit volume of soil

## Solution

The flow rate into the drains will be greatest just as drainage begins. Thus, using a $d/D$ ratio of 0.06, the flow into each pipe can be obtained from

$$0.8 = q/Dk = q/(1 \times 1 \times 10^{-4})$$

Therefore

$$q = 8 \times 10^{-5} \text{ m}^3/\text{s per metre length of pipe}$$

where $q$ = flow in the filter towards each metre length of pipe. However, the flow intercepted per metre length can also be approximated (from Bernoulli's equation) by

$$q = naC_d(2gh)^{1/2}$$

where $q$ = flow through perforations (assuming all water enters) (m$^3$/s), $n$ = number of perforations per metre length, $a$ = area of each perforation (m$^2$), $C_d$ = coefficient of discharge of each perforation (taken as 0.8 in this instance), $g$ = acceleration of free fall = 9.81 m/s$^2$, and $h$ = hydraulic head of each perforation (taken as 5 mm in this instance). Therefore

$$q = 8 \times 10^{-5} = na(0.8)(2 \times 9.81 \times 0.005)^{1/2}$$

Hence

$$na = 32 \times 10^{-5} \text{ m}^2 \text{ per metre length of pipe}$$

$$= 320 \text{ mm}^2 \text{ per metre length of pipe}$$

If the perforations are 5 mm diameter, then $a = \pi(2.5)^2$ mm$^2$. Therefore

$$n = 320/\pi(2.5)^2 = 16.3$$

Sixteen 5 mm diameter holes per metre length of pipe should be adequate for drainage purposes, since the permeability value used is significantly higher than that which would normally be encountered.

## Selected bibliography

(1) Sanders TG (Ed), *Hydrology for Transportation Engineers*, Washington DC, US Government Printing Office, 1980.

(2) Bartlett RE, *Surface Water Sewerage*, London, Applied Science, 1980 (2nd edition).

(3) Transport and Road Research Laboratory, *A Guide for Engineers to the Design of Storm Sewer Systems*, Road Note 35, London, HMSO, 1976 (2nd edition).

(4) Ackers P, *Charts for the Hydraulic Design of Channels and Pipes*, HRSP DE2, London, HMSO, 1969 (3rd edition).

(5) Young CP and Prudhoe J, *The Estimation of Floodflows from Natural Catchments*, TRRL Report LR565, Crowthorne, Berks., The Transport and Road Research Laboratory, 1973.

(6) Ministry of Health Departmental Committee on Rainfall and Runoff, *Journal of the Institution of Municipal and County Engineers*, 1929, **56**, No. 22, p. 1172.

(7) Lloyd-Davies DE, The elimination of storm water from sewerage systems, *Proc. Inst. Civ. Engrs*, 1906, **164**, pp. 41–67.

(8) Bilham EG, Classification of heavy rainfalls in short periods, *British Rainfall*, 1935, p. 262.

(9) Young CP, *Estimated Rainfall for Drainage Calculations in the United Kingdom*, TRRL Report LR595, Crowthorne, Berks., The Transport and Road Research Laboratory, 1973.

(10) Holland DJ, *Rainfall intensity–frequency relationships in Britain*, Appendix to Hydrological Memorandum No. 33, Bracknell, Berks., The Meteorological Office, August 1968.

(11) Colyer PJ, *Urban Drainage and Economic Evaluation*, Paper presented to the Yugoslav Association for Hydrology's Conference on Urban Hydrology, Novi Sad, June 1979 (available from the Institute of Hydrology, Wallingford, Oxon.).

(12) *Design of Urban Highway Drainage: The State-of-the-Art*, Washington DC, The Federal Highway Administration, August 1979.

(13) Task Force on Hydrology and Hydraulics, *Highway Drainage Guidelines*, Washington DC, The American Association of State Highway and Transportation Officials, 1979.

(14) AASHO Operating Subcommittee on Roadway Design, Guidelines for hydrology, in: *Drainage and Geological Considerations in Highway Location*, Transportation Technology Support for Developing Countries Compendium 2, Text 2, Washington DC, The Transportation Research Board, 1978.

(15) Escritt LB, *Sewerage and Sewerage Disposal*, London, CR Brooks, 1964.

(16) Colyer PJ and Pethick RW, *Storm Drainage Design Methods: A Literature Review*, Report No. INT 154, Wallingford, Oxon., The Institute of Hydrology, March 1976.

(17) Mulvaney TJ, On the use of self-registering rain and flood guages in making observations on the relation of rainfall and of flood discharges in a given catchment, *Trans. Inst. Civ. Engrs of Ireland*, 1850, **4**, No. 2, p. 18.

(18) Kuichling E, The relationship between the rainfall and the discharge of sewers in populous areas, *Trans. American Soc. Civ. Engrs*, 1889, **20**, No. 1, p. 60.

(19) Ackers P, *Tables for the Hydraulic Design of Storm Drains, Sewers and Pipelines*, Hydraulics Research Paper No. 4, London, HMSO, 1969 (2nd edition: metric units).

(20) *System of Drainage Design and Analysis Programs: Program HECB/R/7 DAPHNE and HECB/R/8–11 SAFRON*, Technical Memorandum H9/74, London, The Department of the Environment, September 1974.

(21) *Drainage of Asphalt Pavement Structures*, Manual Series No. 15, College Park, Maryland, The Asphalt Institute, September 1984.

(22) Watkins LH, *The Design of Urban Storm Sewers*, Road Research Technical Paper No. 55, London, DSIR, 1962.

(23) Searcy JK (Reporter), Design of roadside drainage channels, in: *Roadside Drainage*, Transportation Technology Support for Developing Countries Compendium 5, Text 1, Washington DC, The Transportation Research Board, 1979.

(24) Manning R, On the flow of water in open channels and pipes, *Trans. Inst. Civ. Engrs of Ireland*, 1891, **20**, pp. 161–207.

(25) US Corps of Engineers, *Planning, Site Selection and Design of Roads, Airfields and Heliports in the Theater of Operations*, US Army Technical Manual TM5-330, Washington DC, Department of the Army, 1963.

(26) Federal Highway Administration, *Design of Stable Channels with Flexible Linings*, Hydraulic Engineering Circular No. 15, Washington DC, US Government Printing Office, 1975.

(27) *Drainage of Wide Flat Pavements*, Sydney, NSW, The National Association of Australian State Road Authorities, 1974.

(28) Ross NF and Russam K, *The Depth of Rain Water on Road Surfaces*, RRL Report LR236, Crowthorne, Berks., The Road Research Laboratory, 1968.

(29) Templeman AB and Walters GA, Optimal design of stormwater drainage networks for roads, Part 2, *Proc. Inst. Civ. Engrs*, 1979, **67**, pp. 573–587.

(30) BS 497: Part 1: *Specification for Manhole Covers, Road Gulley Gratings and Frames for Drainage Purposes: Cast Iron and Cast Steel*, London, The British Standards Institution, 1976.

(31) Russam K, *The Hydraulic Efficiency and Spacing of BS Road Gulleys*, RRL Report LR277, Crowthorne, Berks., The Road Research Laboratory, 1969.

(32) Colwill DM, Peters CJ and Perry R, *Motorway Run-off: The Effect of Drainage Systems on Water Quality*, TRRL Research Report 37, Crowthorne, Berks., The Transport and Road Research Laboratory, 1985.

(33) Goodman RC and Jeremiah KBC, Groundwater investigation and control in highway construction, *Highways and Road Construction International*, 1976, **44**, No. 1798, pp. 4–7, and No. 1799, pp. 4–8.

(34) Department of Transport, *Specification for Highway Works*, London, HMSO, 1986 (6th edition).

(35) Royster DL, Horizontal drains and horizontal drillings: An overview, *Transportation Research Record 783*, 1980, pp. 16–20.

(36) Natarajan TK, Murty AVSR and Gokhale VL, Practical lessons on horizontal drain installations for landslide correction, *Journal of the Indian Road Congress*, 1986, **46**, No. 3, pp. 560–585.

(37) Ridgeway HH, *Pavement Subsurface Drainage Systems*, NCHRP Synthesis of Highway Practice No. 96, Washington DC, The Transportation Research Board, 1982.

(38) Russam K, *Sub-soil Drainage and the Structural Design of Roads*, RRL Report LR110, Crowthorne, Berks., The Road Research Laboratory, 1967.

(39) Cedergren HR, *Drainage of Highway and Airfield Pavements*, London, Wiley, 1974.

(40) Maclean DJ, The problem of clay in road construction, *Final Report of Public Works and Municipal Services Congress and Exhibition*, 1950, pp. 209–248.

(41) National report: Great Britain on Question 1: Earthworks—drainage—subgrade, *Proceedings of the XVII World Congress of the Permanent International Association of Road Congresses,* pp. 33–49, October 1983.
(42) Spaulding R, *Selection of Materials for Sub-surface Drains*, RRL Report LR346, Crowthorne, Berks., The Road Research Laboratory, 1967.
(43) Gerke RJ, *Subsurface Drainage Progress Report*, Nunawading, Victoria, The Australian Road Research Board, September 1979.

# 3
# Highway materials

The materials used in the construction of a highway are of intense interest to the highway engineer, in contrast to many other branches of civil engineering where the engineer need not be overly concerned with the properties of the materials being used. All highways have to be founded on the soil, and all require the efficient usage of locally available materials if economically constructed facilities are to be obtained. This requires a thorough understanding of not only the soil and aggregate properties which affect pavement stability and durability, but also the properties of the binding materials which may be added to improve these.

The most important highway materials are soil, rock and slag aggregates, bituminous binders, lime and cement, so these materials—with the exception of soil—are discussed in some detail in this chapter; because of the all-important role which soil plays in highway construction, it is discussed separately in Chapter 4. 'Waste' materials, such as shale, pulverized fuel ash, quarry byproducts, chalk and incinerated refuse, are discussed here also because of their potential for usage in highway construction instead of scarce high-quality aggregates.

## Bituminous binders

### Terminology

Readers of the scientific literature relating to bituminous road binders can come to the conclusion that there is confusion with regard to what is meant by the word 'bitumen', and to a certain extent they will be right. Chemically, it is accepted that all bituminous road binders are primarily hydrocarbons, i.e. combinations of hydrogen and carbon. Practically, however, there is some debate as to whether the term bitumen should be confined to naturally occurring materials, or whether it should include both the distillates of petroleum and the tars.

In a most authoritative treatise on bituminous binders[1], an analysis of the views concerning the scope of the term bitumen shows that the interpretations applied to it in different countries and by different bodies may be grouped into the four following classes.

(1) Bitumens as naturally occurring hydrocarbons—this tends to represent the layperson's interpretation of the word, and is based on the dictionary definition which for generations confirmed the term to the hydrocarbon

substances which occur in nature. This interpretation specifically *excludes* hydrocarbon substances which are produced artificially.

(2)   Bitumens as naturally occurring hydrocarbons, and the residues obtained from the distillation of petroleum—this is the view held by highway engineers in Britain.

(3)   Bitumens as naturally occurring hydrocarbons (which may be gaseous, liquid, semi-solid or solid), residues obtained from the distillation of petroleum, and artificial hydrocarbon substances, e.g. tars and pitches— this definition of bitumen is one which is now generally applied to a 'bituminous binder', i.e. a material which contains bitumens, or resembles bitumens, or constitutes the source of bitumens. Its particular difference from (2) above is that it accepts tars and pitches as being bitumens.

(4)   Bitumens as only those components of (3) above which are soluble in carbon disulphide ($CS_2$)—this interpretation is the one which is held in the appropriate standards and literature in the USA, and by the Association Internationale Permanente des Congrès de la Route (Paris).

To avoid any misinterpretation, the definition of the word bitumen used in this text will be that which is accepted in Britain, i.e. description (2) above. Thus tar is discussed as a substance which is different from bitumen. However, when the term 'bituminous binder' is used, it will refer to *both* bitumen and tar binders.

## Bitumen

Bitumen is a viscous liquid or solid material, black or dark brown in colour, having adhesive properties, consisting essentially of hydrocarbons, derived from petroleum or occurring in natural asphalt, and soluble in carbon disulphide $(CS_2)$[2]. It is substantially non-volatile, non-toxic, and softens gradually when heated. (It might be noted that the internationally agreed definition of bitumen relates its solubility to $CS_2$; however, in Britain trichloroethene is used as the test solvent as it is safer than carbon disulphide and has the same solvent power for all practical purposes.)

The two main categories of bitumens are, firstly, those which occur naturally and, secondly, those which are byproducts of the fractional distillation of petroleum at a refinery. Of the (literally) hundreds of possible types falling into these categories, the ones which historically have tended to be used for highway paving purposes in Britain are illustrated in Fig. 3.1.

### Natural bitumens

Bitumens are available in widely distributed natural asphalt deposits throughout the world. The term *asphalt*, as used in Britain, implies a mixture of bitumen and mineral particles. (It should be noted that in the American technical literature, the term asphalt is used to refer to what in Britain is simply called bitumen, i.e. the binder without any additional mineral matter.)

Whilst there is a great variety in the compositions and properties of these

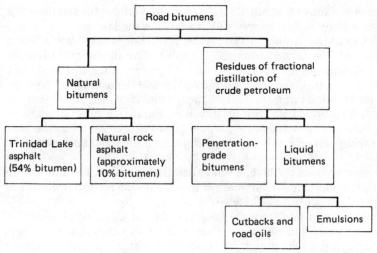

Fig. 3.1   Road bitumens traditionally used in Britain

natural deposits, for convenience they can be divided into three groups, viz.:

(1)  asphalts occurring in a fairly pure state, i.e. generally small deposits consisting of hydrocarbons with little or no mineral matter,

(2)  asphalts with an appreciable proportion of mineral matter, e.g. Trinidad Lake asphalt in the West Indies and Bermudez Lake asphalt found in Venezuela,

(3)  mineral matter associated with small proportions of asphalt, e.g. natural rock asphalts found in France, Switzerland and Colombia[3].

*Trinidad Lake asphalt*   The largest natural deposit of lake asphalt in the world occurs on the island of Trinidad, off the north coast of South America. The first commercial shipment of Trinidad asphalt came to England about 1840. The material continued to be widely used for well over a century because of its good durability, stability and skid-resistance qualities. However, the introduction of pitch–bitumen in the 1960s led to a marked decline in the use of lake asphalt, i.e. the new binder had adequate wearing properties whilst at the same time it was cheaper, easier to store, and not subject to international haulage problems. In recent years, however, the price of Trinidad Lake asphalt relative to that of conventional refinery bitumen has closed to near-parity (from being about 80 per cent higher), and should international oil prices increase again—as is most likely in the long term—usage of this material in Britain could increase.

The asphalt lake in Trinidad covers an approximately circular area of about 44.5 ha, and it is located in a shallow crater in the south of the island, at the crest of a hill 42 m above sea level. The lake has a diameter of about 600 m, and is at least 41 m deep at its centre, becoming shallower towards the edges. Since records were first kept in the late 1800s, some ten-million tonnes of asphalt have been extracted from the lake, during which time the surface level has sunk by about 1.5 m. At a conservative estimate, there is a further ten-million-tonnes supply still available in the lake.

The origin of the Trinidad Lake asphalt is still not exactly known, but it is believed that it is derived from the remnants of an oil deposit originally present in an anticline of cretaceous rocks. Lowering of the earth's surface led to an incursion of the sea, and a considerable deposit of sedimentary material covered the bitumen. Part of the silt and clay then penetrated the bitumen and saturated it, forming the now familiar asphalt mixture of bitumen, silt, clay, gas and water. Upon subsequent elevation of the land surface, the asphalt probably ascended along fault lines and flowed into the present lake.

As excavated from the lake, Trinidad asphalt is remarkably uniform in composition, and Table 3.1 summarizes average results for specimens taken from various portions of the lake's surface.

Following excavation from the lake, the asphalt is heated to 160 °C to drive out the gases and moisture, after which it is run through strainers to remove vegetable debris and then poured into light wooden barrels for export under the name of Trinidad Epure or Refined Trinidad Lake Asphalt. Bulk transport is not utilized due to the likelihood of the coarser mineral particles settling out in transit. Some of the asphalt is blended in the stills with a heavy petroleum oil to obtain a penetration-grade asphalt that is suitable for direct road use.

In Britain it is considered more convenient to import the Epure and to flux it at the paving plant as required. This is usually done by melting the

**Table 3.1**  Trinidad Lake asphalt: (a) asphalt composition and properties and (b) bitumen properties[4]

| Asphalt composition and properties | Crude (%) | Refined (%) |
| --- | --- | --- |
| Water and gas | 29.0 | — |
| Bitumen soluble in $CS_2$ | 39.0 | 55.1 |
| Bitumen adsorbed by mineral matter | 0.3 | 0.5 |
| Mineral matter on ignition | 27.2 | 36.5 |
| Water of hydration of mineral matter | 2.1 | 4.3 |
| Organic material insoluble in $CS_2$ | 1.5 | 3.2 |
| Penetration at 25 °C | — | 1.2 |
| Softening point (R and B) | — | 95 °C |

(a)

| Bitumen properties | Value |
| --- | --- |
| Relative density at 15.5 °C | 1.05 |
| Softening point (R and B) | 65 °C |
| Softening point (K and S) | 55 °C |
| Viscosity (°Engler) at 200 °C | 168 s |
| Volatilization loss after 5 h at 163 °C | 1% |
| Volatilization loss at 204.5 °C | 6.0% |
| Flash point (open cup) | 238 °C |

(b)

hard Epure (it has a penetration of about one at this stage) in tanks of up to 9000-litre capacity and adding to it an appropriate proportion of refinery bitumen of, most usually, nominal 200 penetration grade (200 pen). (Reference 5 gives details of standard 35, 50 and 70 pen Lake asphalt and bitumen mixtures.) The actual amount of refinery material added in any particular situation depends upon the penetration desired of the mixture; typically, however, the final product used in most road surfacings includes 20 to 50 per cent Epure. For rolled asphalt surfacings a 50 : 50 mixture of Epure and a 200 pen refinery bitumen tends to give near-optimum results for most normal roads, city bus stops and footpaths[6]; a 50 : 50 mixture of Epure and 50 pen refinery bitumen will also produce a resistance to deformation in a rolled asphalt that is comparable with that of a heavy duty bitumen that has a softening point of $63\,^\circ C \pm 5\,^\circ C$[7].

Details regarding the use of Trinidad Lake asphalt and bitumen mixtures in road surfacings are included in three British Standards[8-10].

*Natural rock asphalt*    Rock asphalts are usually limestones or sandstones that are impregnated with natural bitumen. The proportion of bitumen is less than that in lake asphalt, i.e. it usually varies between 5 and 15 per cent, but can be as high as 40 per cent. Rock asphalts found to be most suitable for commercial use are generally limestones impregnated with 6–10 per cent of soluble bitumen.

In the past few decades the use of natural rock asphalts as road surfacings in developed countries has been largely superseded by products prepared from petroleum bitumens. Should the substantial increases in the world prices of petroleum products which occurred in the 1970s be sustained into the long-term future, it is not unlikely that circumstances could occur where the use of this natural material would again become economically attractive.

Historically, the natural rock asphalt used in Britain was imported from France and Switzerland. The Swiss deposit, which is located in the Val de Travers region, is believed to have been produced by the decomposition of marine animal and vegetable matter. The bitumen content of the material obtained from France, mined in the Gard region, was probably introduced into the rock as a bituminous petroleum, the lighter fractions of which evaporated with time, leaving the bitumen behind. Both the French and Swiss deposits contain about 10 per cent bitumen. The composition of a typical road material from the Val de Travers region is shown in Table 3.2; this material has a solubility in $CS_2$ of 10.50 per cent.

Natural rock asphalts are now extremely rarely used in Britain. However, details regarding possible usage are given in a British Standard[9].

**Refinery bitumens**
Bitumens artificially produced by the industrial refining of crude petroleum oils are known under a number of names such as residual bitumens, straight-run bitumens, steam-refined bitumens and—as is now most commonly accepted—refinery bitumens. Not all petroleum crudes contain a sufficient quantity of bitumen to enable straight reduction to specification

**Table 3.2**   Composition of crude rock asphalt obtained from the Val de Travers region[1]

| Constituent | Percentage |
| --- | --- |
| Calcium oxide | 54.98 |
| Magnesium oxide | 0.15 |
| Carbon dioxide | 42.85 |
| Iron and aluminium oxides | 0.23 |
| Silica | 0.32 |
| Alkali, sulphates and loss | 1.47 |

road bitumen. Those which do are known as naphtenic- or asphaltic-base crudes. Crudes which contain high proportions of simpler paraffinic compounds, with little or no bituminous bodies present, are known as paraffinic-base crudes. Some petroleum crudes exhibit characteristics of both the previous categories, and these are known as mixed-base crudes. North Sea petroleum crudes are mainly of the light-paraffinic- or mixed-base types, and are generally considered unsuitable for bitumen production at this time. As a result, bitumens are still mainly derived from petroleum crudes obtained from the oilfields of the Middle East.

Both the source of the parent oil and the method of manufacture affect the physical properties of refinery bitumens[11, 12]. However, because of the wide variation in manufacturing conditions, it is difficult to separate the effects of each of these two factors. In practice, this is not normally a problem that need concern the highway engineer as (a) bitumens from crude oils from one geographical area tend to be very similar, and (b) when major changes in crude origin do occur, current refinery technology is well capable of producing road bitumens to the required specifications.

The composition of an asphaltic-base petroleum crude is shown in Fig. 3.2. It should be clear that this is a schematic diagram, and that the proportions in any particular instance will vary with the crude. Bitumen is obtained from the crude by a refinery distillation process which involves

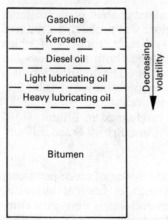

**Fig. 3.2**   Schematic illustration of the components of an asphaltic-base petroleum crude

condensation in a fractionating column. For bitumens utilized in Britain the first distillation is normally carried out in refineries at the oilfields; there the crude is heated to temperatures not greater than 350 °C at atmospheric pressure in order to drive off the light gasoline and kerosene fractions. The 'topped' oil is then shipped to Britain for further refining to remove additional fractions as required.

*Penetration-grade bitumens*   On arrival at the refinery, the topped oil is heated with the aid of reduced pressures and steam injection in the fractionating columns. Heating under atmospheric conditions is not possible as the temperatures required to drive off the heavier oils would be so high that 'cracking' or chemical change of the vapours would take place; this would impart undesirable paving properties to the bitumen residue.

Bitumens obtained by fractionating are mostly what are called penetration-grade bitumens. These are also known by the names 'asphaltic bitumens' and 'asphalt cements'. Depending upon the amount of distillate removed, they vary in consistency from semi-solid at room temperature to semi-liquid under the same conditions. These bitumens are classified according to hardness as indicated by the depth to which a specified needle is able to enter the samples when standard penetration tests are carried out. Details of the grades and properties of the asphaltic bitumens manufactured in Britain are given in Table 3.3. Note that the penetration number reflects the hardness of the bitumen; thus the 15 penetration-grade (15 pen) bitumen is the hardest and the 450 pen bitumen the softest of those shown. The penetration-grade bitumens most commonly used in rolled asphalt surfacings on high-quality roads in Britain are the medium ones, i.e. 35–70 pen. The softer 100–450 pen bitumens tend to be used with macadam-type pavements, whereas the very hard (15–25 pen) bitumens are rarely used in roads and are more usually associated with industrial usages, e.g. in paints and adhesives.

In a particular refinery, a bitumen of a desired penetration may be obtained either by controlled refining such as has been described, or by fluxing a harder grade with an oil of high boiling range such as is produced at the lower end of the fractionating column during distillation of the topped crude oil. Quite often a refinery will not manufacture all the penetration grades shown in Table 3.3 because of the large tankage which this would require. Instead, it is common practice to prepare and stock large quantities of two asphaltic bitumens, one of a low penetration and the other of a high one. All intermediate penetration grades are then prepared by blending appropriate quantities of the two stock grades.

Several British Standards for highway surfacing materials include specifications regarding the properties of the penetration-grade bitumens to be used in specific situations [8–10, 13].

All of the above refinery bitumens undergo approximately the same proportional change in viscosity per degree of temperature change. In certain instances, however, it can be desirable to lay a bitumen in a pavement which is less sensitive to temperature variations. It is appropriate to note here that in recent years a *heavy duty bitumen* (HD40) has been

**Table 3.3** Penetration-grade bitumens used for road purposes in Britain[14]

| Property | Grade | | | | | | | | | |
|---|---|---|---|---|---|---|---|---|---|---|
| | 15 pen | 25 pen | 35 pen | 40 pen HD | 50 pen | 70 pen | 100 pen | 200 pen | 300 pen | 450 pen |
| Penetration at 25 °C (0.1 mm) | 15 ± 5 | 25 ± 5 | 35 ± 7 | 40 ± 10 | 50 ± 10 | 70 ± 10 | 100 ± 20 | 200 ± 30 | 300 ± 45 | 450 ± 65 |
| Softening point ( °C) | | | | | | | | | | |
| minimum | 63 | 57 | 52 | 58 | 47 | 44 | 41 | 33 | 30 | 25 |
| maximum | 76 | 69 | 64 | 68 | 58 | 54 | 51 | 42 | 39 | 34 |
| Loss on heating for 5 h at 163 °C (%, maximum) | | | | | | | | | | |
| loss by mass | 0.1 | 0.2 | 0.2 | 0.2 | 0.2 | 0.2 | 0.5 | 0.5 | 1.0 | 1.0 |
| drop in penetration | 20 | 20 | 20 | 20 | 20 | 20 | 20 | 20 | 25 | 25 |
| Solubility in trichloroethene (% by mass, minimum) | 99.5 | 99.5 | 99.5 | 99.5 | 99.5 | 99.5 | 99.5 | 99.5 | 99.5 | 99.5 |
| Relative permittivity at 25 °C and 1592 Hz (minimum) | — | — | 2.630 | 2.650 | 2.650 | 2.650 | — | — | — | — |

developed for this purpose. This is a 40 pen 'blown' bitumen—it is produced by passing air through hot bitumen in a blowing column—with a softening point about 10 °C higher than that of a normal 40 pen refinery bitumen. This binder, which is most appropriately used when a reduced temperature-sensitivity is required, not only is characterized by a higher softening point but also gives a stiffer rolled asphalt with a consequent reduction in deformation under traffic; for best results, however, it requires that all mixing, laying and rolling operations be carried out at temperatures at least 10 °C higher than those for normal bitumen of the same penetration.

*Cutback bitumens*  The penetration-grade bitumens range from being very viscous to semi-solid in consistency at ambient air temperatures, so it is normal for them to be heated to quite high temperatures (140–180 °C, depending upon the grade) before use in road construction. There are many instances, however, where it is neither desirable nor necessary to use a hard bitumen and preference can be given to the use of liquid binders such as cutback bitumens which, depending upon the grade and the ambient temperature, may require little or no heating before usage—thereby also saving upon heating costs.

Cutbacks differ from penetration-grade bitumens in that the bitumen is dissolved in a liquid solvent which makes it suitable for direct application and manipulation in road construction. While the solvent is primarily a substitute for heat, in many instances it is more useful than heat since its liquifying effect lasts over a longer period of time.

After a cutback bitumen has been spread on the particles it is intended to bind, the solvent will dissipate itself by evaporation and/or photo-oxidation, leaving behind the cementitious bitumen to tie the particles together. Thus the character and behaviour of a cutback bitumen in any particular situation is largely dependent upon the character and amount of solvent present. The more volatile the solvent, the shorter will be the curing period necessary after using the cutback before the cohesive properties of the binder are utilized. The less volatile the solvent, the greater will be the quantity required to bring the bitumen to a given degree of fluidity.

As indicated by Fig. 3.3, cutback bitumens can be divided into three main types, depending upon the type of solvent used to dilute the bitumen. These are commonly designated as slow-curing, medium-curing, and rapid-curing cutback bitumens.

*Slow-curing cutback bitumens* may be manufactured in either of two ways. In the first, the cutbacks may be obtained entirely by direct distillation of the petroleum crude, in a manner similar to that by which penetration-grade bitumens are obtained. In the case of cutbacks, however, many of the volatile oils are left in the mixture and so the liquid bitumens are usually much more fluid than the penetration-grade ones. In the second method, penetration-grade bitumen is directly fluxed with slowly volatile oils to obtain particular cutbacks of the desired fluidity.

Whichever method is used, the slow-curing cutbacks are liable to remain liquid in or on the roadway for a relatively long time and so the binding

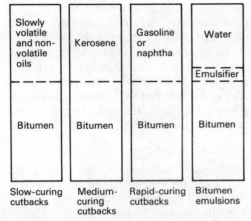

Fig. 3.3    Schematic illustration of the components of liquid bitumens. *Note:* These diagrams are not proportional to composition

strength is developed correspondingly slowly. For this reason, these cutbacks are, in theory, best used with well-graded aggregates which provide a strong interlocking framework and which do not require immediate, strong, cementing action from the binder. For the same reason, a slow-curing cutback should never be used as a binder for poorly-graded road surfacings. In practice, because of their slow-curing qualities, these cutbacks are mostly used directly onto the surfaces of soil–aggregate roads in warm climates, in order to keep the dry soil particles from creating a dust nuisance under traffic.

No slow-curing bitumens are included at this time in any British Standards dealing with road surfacings.

*Medium-curing cutback bitumens* are the variety mostly used in Britain. They are manufactured by combining 100/300 penetration-grade bitumens with a petroleum distillate, such as kerosene, or with a coal-tar creosote oil or anthracene oil, or with a mixture of these.

The grades and properties of the medium-curing cutback bitumens commonly supplied in Britain are shown in Table 3.4. The grades are designated in terms of viscosity limits expressed in seconds of flow when tested in the *standard tar viscometer* (STV) at 40 °C[15]. Even though the solvents in these cutbacks evaporate more rapidly than the oils used in slow-curing cutbacks, it can be a considerable time before the consistency of the base asphaltic bitumen is reached; for this reason, British practice is for them to be used in open-textured bitumen macadams[13] and surface dressings[16], i.e. in bituminous systems that are sufficiently porous to allow the flux solvent to evaporate fairly quickly. In both instances, the 100 s grade is most commonly used. Whilst the flux material is gradually escaping, the coated aggregates are open to stripping if the surfacing is subjected to water action in the early days of its life; to minimize this likelihood, it is usual to include an adhesion agent, e.g. tar acids or an amine salt, in the cutback bitumen during its manufacture.

**Table 3.4** Cutback bitumens used for road purposes in Britain[14]

| Property | Grade | | |
| --- | --- | --- | --- |
| | 50 (seconds of flow) | 100 (seconds of flow) | 200 (seconds of flow) |
| Viscosity (STV) at 40 °C, 10 mm cup | 50 ± 10 | 100 ± 20 | 200 ± 40 |
| Distillation | | | |
| (a) distillate to 225 °C (% by volume, maximum) | 1 | 1 | 1 |
| distillate to 360 °C (% by volume) | 8–14 | 6–12 | 4–10 |
| (b) penetration at 25 °C of residue from distillation to 360 °C | 100–350 | 100–350 | 100–350 |
| Solubility in trichloroethene (% by mass, minimum) | 99.5 | 99.5 | 99.5 |

In general, it can be said that medium-curing cutbacks have good aggregate coating properties, and are very useful when finely-graded, dusty materials are to be incorporated in a road surface, and it is desired to use a bituminous binder which is less viscous at the time of processing than after the mixture has cured for some time. In warm climates, medium-curing cutbacks are generally considered the most practical for use in the bituminous stabilization of soil for low-cost road construction.

*Rapid-curing cutback bitumens* are prepared by diluting a suitable penetration-grade bitumen with a very volatile petroleum distillate, such as gasoline or naphtha. Since the volatile constituents of these cutbacks quickly evaporate, they are used when a quick change back to the residual semi-solid binding agent is desired. Rapid-curing cutbacks are not used in Britain, preference being given to the medium-curing types. The volatility of the distillate, i.e. it has a relatively low flash point, can render the usage of rapid-curing cutbacks hazardous, particularly when the very viscous grades—which may have to be warmed before admixing—are used in road construction.

**Bitumen emulsions**  An emulsion is a relatively stable suspension of one liquid in a state of minute subdivision, dispersed throughout another liquid in which it is not soluble. The liquid which is dispersed is often called the internal phase, while the surrounding liquid is known as the continuous or external phase. Common examples of emulsion products in daily use are paints, hair dyes, mayonnaise and ice cream.

The viscosity, and temperature of application, of a bitumen can be reduced by emulsifying it in water. Bitumen emulsions can be of two types: inverted emulsions and conventional emulsions. An *inverted emulsion* consists of a bitumen–water mixture in which up to about 10 per cent water forms the dispersed phase and cutback bitumen is the continuous phase; whilst this type of emulsion has been used successfully in the USA (for cold-mix road surfacings and mix-in-place soil stabilization), it is not used in Britain and so will not be further discussed here. With *conventional emulsions*, which are the only type manufactured in Britain, minute globules of bitumen, typically 10 $\mu$m or less, are dispersed in water so that; the resulting emulsion has a 'viscosity' that is only slightly higher than that of the continuous water phase.

*Preparation of bitumen emulsions*  Many factors affect the production, storage, use and performance of a conventional bitumen emulsion, of which the following are probably the most significant[17]:

(1)    chemical properties of the base asphaltic bitumen,
(2)    hardness and quantity of the base asphaltic bitumen,
(3)    bitumen particle size in the emulsion,
(4)    type and concentration of the emulsifying agent,
(5)    manufacturing conditions such as temperatures, pressures, and shear,
(6)    the ionic charge on the emulsion particles,
(7)    the order of addition of the ingredients,

(8)   the type of equipment used in manufacturing the emulsion,
(9)   the property of the emulsifying agent,
(10)  the addition of chemical modifiers.

Bitumen emulsions can be divided into three categories: anionic, cationic, and nonionic. The anionic and cationic terms refer to the negative and positive electrical charges, respectively, imparted to the bitumen particles by emulsifying agents. With nonionic emulsions, the bitumen particles are neutral. In practice, the anionic and cationic emulsions are the two categories normally used in highway construction and maintenance throughout the world; however, nonionic emulsions may be more widely used in future as emulsion technology advances.

Many important properties of an emulsion are dependent upon the amount and type of emulsifying agent used to promote the dispersal and stability of the bitumen–water mixture. Were it not for the emulsifier, the bitumen, after dispersal (which may be brought about by rapid stirring), would quickly re-form into a separate layer once agitation is stopped. When a suitable emulsifier is added, it forms an adsorbed film about each dispersed droplet of bitumen and gives to each a protective coating which provides resistance to coalescence.

The structure of an anionic emulsifying agent may be represented by the formula for sodium stearate, $CH_3(CH_2)_{16}COONa$. When this is dissolved, it dissociates into the long-chain stearate anion $CH_3(CH_2)_{16}COO^-$ and the sodium cation $Na^+$. The long-chain anions are soluble in bitumen and so they attach themselves to the droplets in such a way that each bitumen globule is coated with a negatively-charged stearate film which causes the individual globules to repel each other when they come into contact.

The cationic emulsifiers, which have only relatively recently been developed, generally consist of amine salts made by reacting hydrochloric acid or acetic acid with an organic amine or diamine. When added to water, the emulsifying compounds dissociate in such a way that the long-chain amines—which in this case are the cations—attach themselves to the bitumen droplets so that each individual globule is coated with a protective positively-charged layer of amines. As with the anionic coatings, the result is that the positively-charged droplets tend to repel each other when they come into contact, which prevents coalescence.

These two types of emulsion can generally be distinguished by the fact that the anionics are normally mildly alkaline whilst the cationics are mildly acidic. It is vitally important that the two types are never mixed, even in small quantities, as breakdown of both will then occur[18].

The actual emulsification process involves mixing water, bitumen and the emulsifying agent in either a colloid mill disintegrator or a high-speed mixer. A colloid mill is composed of a conical disc which very rapidly revolves within a stationary part called the stator, the clearance between the two usually being within the range 25–50 $\mu$m. When the concurrent streams of hot bitumen and hot water and emulsifier are forced through this minute clearance, they are subjected to very large shearing stresses which cause disintegration of the bitumen into small globules; these subsequently become surrounded by a protective layer of the emulsifier, and an emulsion is formed. With the high-speed mixer manufacturing process, the emulsion is formed by adding the hot bitumen to the hot mixture of water and emulsifier and then using a high-speed propeller-type agitator to achieve dispersion as the bitumen is admixed; emulsion batches of about 900 litres per time can be prepared by this process. Whereas colloid mill emulsions can be produced as a continuous process with usual outputs of about 11 350 litres/hour, the high-speed mixer emulsions are output at the rate of 6000–9100 litres/hour.

All grades of bitumens can be emulsified, but the 70 to 300 pen bitumens are specified[19] for use in Britain.

The quality of the aggregate coating by an emulsion increases as the consistency of its contained bitumen is increased; this is particularly important in the case of emulsions to be premixed with finely-graded aggregates. It is common practice in such instances to add fluxing agents—these range from light, volatile distillates to heavy oils—to the bitumen before emulsification to ensure a good coating. The proportion of volatile oils added, however, must be sufficiently low to provide a resultant binder of adequate consistency; thus the additional amount of fluxing agent is normally not more than 5 per cent by mass of bitumen for anionic emulsions, and 10 per cent for cationic emulsions. Coated aggregates so obtained normally can be stockpiled for future use if desired.

*Classification and usage*   Table 3.5 summarizes the properties of the road emulsions used in Britain. Note that these are classified according to category, stability and binder content, and that a three-part code is used to designate each. Thus the prefix letter A is used to designate an anionic emulsion, and K a cationic one. Each emulsion is further designated by two sets of numbers separated by a hyphen. To the left is a number which signifies the general stability of the emulsion against breakdown, i.e. the higher the number, the greater is the stability; the number to the right indicates the nominal bitumen content. Thus a K1-70 emulsion is a cationic emulsion of low stability with a nominal bitumen content of 70 per cent.

Anionic emulsions are also designated as labile (class A1), semi-stable (class A2), and stable (class A3) in order of their stability; similarly, cationic emulsions are designated as rapid acting (class K1), medium acting (class K2), and slow acting (class K3).

*Labile anionic emulsions* are characterized by a rapid breakdown upon application, as they contain only a minimal amount of emulsifier. The ease with which labile emulsions break normally makes such emulsions unsuitable for mixing with aggregates; instead, they are used for surface dressing, tack-coating, patching, formation and subbase sealing, and concrete curing. Labile emulsions (as with semi-stable ones) are used cold and cannot be stored out of doors in very cold weather as they will usually break on freezing and will not redisperse on thawing.

*Semi-stable anionic emulsions* have sufficient emulsifier present to permit mixing with certain grades of aggregate before breakdown occurs. Premature breakdown most usually occurs when the aggregate contains too many fine particles; in any particular instance, however, this can only be

**Table 3.5** Properties of anionic and cationic road emulsions used in Britain[19]

| Property | Anionic class | | | | | | | Cationic class | | | | |
|---|---|---|---|---|---|---|---|---|---|---|---|---|
| | AI-60 | AI-55 | AI-40 | A2-57 | A2-50 | A3 | A4 | KI-70 | KI-60 | KI-40 | K2 | K3 |
| Residue on 710 μm BS sieve (% m/m, maximum) | 0.05 | 0.05 | 0.05 | 0.05 | 0.05 | 0.05 | 0.05 | — | 0.05 | 0.05 | 0.05 | 0.05 |
| Residue on 150 μm BS sieve (g/100 ml, maximum) | 0.15 | 0.15 | 0.15 | 0.15 | 0.15 | 0.15 | 0.15 | — | 0.15 | 0.15 | 0.15 | 0.15 |
| Stability to mixing with coarse aggregates (% coagulation) | 20–80 | 20–80 | 20–80 | <40 | <40 | <5 | <5 | — | — | — | — | — |
| Stability to mixing with cement (% coagulation) | — | — | — | >2 | >2 | <2 | — | — | — | — | — | — |
| Binder content (% m/m, minimum) | 58 | 53 | 38 | 55 | 48 | 55 | 56 | 67 | 57 | 38 | 57 | 56 |
| Viscosity [°Engler at 20°C (s)] | 6–9 | 5–8 | 4 (max.) | 8 (max.) | 5 (max.) | 9 (max.) | 8 (max.) | — | 6–9 | 4 (max.) | 10 (max.) | 10 (max.) |
| Coagulation of emulsion at low temperature | Nil | Nil | Nil | Nil | Nil | Nil | Nil | — | Nil | Nil | Nil | Nil |
| Storage stability short period test (inversions to clear sediment, maximum) | 60 | 60 | 60 | 60 | 60 | 60 | 60 | — | 60 | 60 | 60 | 60 |
| long period test (% water content difference, maximum) | 2 | 2 | — | 2 | 2 | 2 | 2 | — | 2 | — | 2 | 2 |
| Particle charge | −ve | −ve | −ve | −ve | −ve | −ve | −ve | +ve | +ve | +ve | +ve | +ve |

*Note*: As a general guide, the KI-70 emulsion should also fall within the viscosity range (Redwood No. II) of 25–35 s at 85°C determined by trial and error. Semi-stable emulsions are mostly used in Britain in the preparation of premixed coated stone (provided that the passing 75 $\mu$m fraction is well below 5 per cent), and in the retreading, i.e. reconstitution, of the surfacings of old waterbound macadam, coated macadam, grouted and surface dressed pavements.

*Stable anionic emulsions* have sufficient mechanical and chemical stability for all purposes involving cold mixing with aggregates, including those containing large proportions of fines or chemically active materials such as cement or hydrated lime. As such they are suitable for a variety of uses, the most usual being in the production of bitumen-coated macadam (coarse and fine gradings), fine cold asphalt, and in the retreading process. Normally, fully-stable bitumen emulsions are the only ones that can be used to stabilize in-place fine-grained soils (normally in warmer climates). In contrast to labile emulsions, fully-stable emulsions are useful for winter roadworks where the binder has to be stored out of doors, as they are less vulnerable to detrimental cold temperatures.

The class A4 anionic emulsion is a specially formulated emulsion for use in the slurry seal process. When mixed with the aggregate specified, it forms a free-flowing slurry which is sufficiently stable to be sustained throughout the laying procedure adopted. This class of emulsion is subdivided according to whether the slurry seal is slow setting or rapid setting. A *slow-setting* emulsion has a setting time of about six hours; this means that the slurry can be made at central mixing plants and transported by truck to the site. A *rapid-setting* emulsion produces a slurry mix which will only remain fluid for as long as it is agitated; it sets within a short time of the cessation of mixing, and develops a cohesion sufficiently strong to enable the slurry to be trafficked within a few minutes of being laid.

*Rapid-acting cationic emulsions* are characterized by more rapid deposition of bitumen on aggregates and road surfaces, and the consequent early resistance to rain. Whilst generally unsuited for mixing with aggregates, they are used for grouting, patching, formation and subbase sealing, and surface dressing purposes. Whilst bitumen emulsions are normally fluid enough to be applied at atmospheric temperatures, the highest-bitumen-content rapid-acting cationic emulsion (K1-70) must be applied hot; however, for obvious reasons the application temperature cannot be greater than 100 $^\circ$C where emulsions are concerned, and so a temperature within the range 75 to 85 $^\circ$C is most usual.

*Medium-acting cationic emulsions* are those in which the rate of deposition is sufficiently delayed to permit mixing with certain clear, coarse aggregates, before breaking to form a continuous adhesive film without stripping. Applied cold, this emulsion is mostly used to prepare coated mixtures which need to be stockpiled before usage, e.g. for trench reinstatement and remedial patching.

*Slow-acting cationic emulsions*, whilst also applied cold, are different from the medium-acting ones in that the rate of deposition of the bitumen is sufficiently delayed to enable it to be mixed with certain fine aggregates. Cationic slurry seals are formed with these emulsions.

Further information regarding the use of emulsions for roadworks in

Britain is readily available in the literature (see, for example, references 16 and 18–22).

*Mechanism of action*  If a bitumen emulsion is to perform its ultimate function of binding and waterproofing, the bitumen globules must separate from the water phase, coalesce and produce a continuous film on the aggregate or road surfacing. The exact mechanism by which emulsions break when brought into contact with aggregates is not yet fully understood, although the factors which bring it about are well established. In actual use, breaking of a particular emulsion is a function of three main factors: evaporation, compaction, and absorption.

Both anionic and cationic emulsions depend upon the evaporation of water for the development of their adhesion and curing characteristics, although perhaps the principal advantage of cationics is their ability to give up water faster. Whilst evaporation begins immediately upon application, the rate at which breaking occurs is dependent upon the atmospheric temperature, relative humidity, wind velocity, and the rate and method of emulsion application. Thus water displacement can be fairly rapid under favourable weather conditions, whilst it will be retarded by low temperatures, high humidity, and calm air. Rainfall soon after application can result in dilution of the emulsion so that it is washed from the roadway.

Traditional theory holds that anionic emulsions—which have negative charges on the bitumen globules—perform best with aggregates having mostly positive surface charges, e.g. limestone and dolomite. Similarly, cationic emulsions—with positive charges on the bitumen globules—are considered to perform best with aggregates with mostly negative surface charges, e.g. siliceous or granitic aggregates. Recent studies have challenged the traditional theories and, at present, there is not complete agreement regarding the subject of electrical charges on aggregate surfaces. Generally, however, it can be said that the vast majority of road aggregates (except dolomite limestones) can be coated with cationic emulsions, and that the use of particular anionic emulsifiers (with or without the use of additives) makes it possible to produce satisfactorily-coated acidic aggregates which are resistant to later displacement of the bitumen by water.

Breaking is also related to the absorption qualities of the surface being covered. Thus the more porous and dry the road surface and/or aggregate surface being coated, the more rapidly water from the emulsion is removed by capillary action, and the more quickly breaking occurs under the given atmospheric conditions.

The aggregate grading is also important, with fine aggregates tending to break more quickly. As the surface area of an aggregate–emulsion mix is varied, the breaking characteristic of the medium also changes because of the changed adsorption of the emulsifier by the aggregate. Furthermore, dirty aggregates, or those with excessive fines, may accelerate the breaking process.

As evaporation and moisture absorption take place, the emulsified bitumen particles come closer together and eventually coalesce. This change, which is identifiable by a switch from the normal brownish colour of the emulsion to the black of the bitumen, usually happens with an anionic bitumen when the proportion of bitumen in the emulsion is about 80 per cent. At this stage, the breakdown can be accelerated by compaction under rollers (or traffic), i.e. the roller pressure forces more water from the mixture, thereby causing further coalescence of the bitumen.

*Comparison of emulsion and cutback bitumen binders*  The choice between these two binders is a matter of some debate among highway engineers, and this is reflected in their usage, e.g. in 1974, before the full effects of the 'energy crisis' were felt, roughly 60 per cent of the surface dressing market was shared equally between these two liquid bitumens (with the balance composed of 30 per cent tar–bitumen and 10 per cent conventional road tar). In practice, satisfactory results may be obtained with both types, and the performance of individual binders depends upon their formulation and proper usage.

Both types of binder are of a lower viscosity than the base bitumen which they contain. This makes it possible to use high-viscosity bitumens in certain types of roadwork, and the desired grade of binder is available to serve its purpose when the liquid has evaporated.

Generally, emulsions are more vulnerable than cutbacks during the early life of a surface dressing. However, emulsions also exhibit tolerance to damp chippings and, once set, produce a more stable system due to their higher residual viscosity and built-in wetting agent (the emulsifier).

Internationally, the 'energy crisis' of the 1970s has promoted conservation measures involving the use of less petroleum fuel. In contrast to cutback bitumens, emulsions normally do not require the addition of petroleum solvents which must be wasted through evaporation before the original viscosity of the base bitumen is achieved. With the exception of the K1-70 cationic emulsion, emulsions do not require any heating for their application, thus also saving energy.

Since emulsions have a low temperature of application, and of storage, the possibility of heat degradation of the essential binder is avoided when they are used. Furthermore, the low temperature of application of emulsions minimizes hazards from fuming, whilst the danger of fire is eliminated.

## Tar

Tar is a viscous liquid, black in colour, with adhesive properties, obtained by the destructive distillation of coal, wood, shale, etc. By destructive distillation is meant the subjecting of the raw material to heat alone, without access to air. This definition means that there are many forms of tar. In practice, however, the highway engineer is concerned only with tar produced from the destructive distillation of bituminous coal. Other tars have been used for road surfacing purposes, but generally they have been unsatisfactory in comparison with bituminous coal tars.

### Preparation of crude tars
The first step in the manufacture of a bituminous road tar is the production of crude tar by the carbonization of bituminous coal. Crude tar is actually a

byproduct of this destructive distillation process, the prime objectives being the production of coke for the steel industry, gas for municipal and industrial heating purposes, and smokeless fuel for home heating.

Crude tar produced by the coke industry is called coke-oven tar. The crude is normally obtained by heating coal to temperatures between 1100 and 1300 °C in narrow, carton-shaped, refractory brick-lined ovens, so that the volatile constituents of the coal are removed and only coke is left. The volatile products, which include tar, are collected and the tar removed with ammonia liquor; the tar is later separated from the liquor by decantation.

Crude tar manufactured in conjunction with the production of gas is called gasworks tar. In this case, a highly volatile bituminous coal is heated to between 900 and 1200 °C in comparatively small cylindrical fire-clay retorts which may be of the horizontal, inclined or vertical variety. Heat is provided by water–gas obtained by passing air and steam through incandescent coke derived from a previous charge of bituminous coal. The water–gas is burnt in flues surrounding the retorts, the process of combustion being controlled by the introduction of air in order to obtain a higher and more uniform temperature. Gases which are given off in the retort are collected, and the tar is removed in its crude form in a similar manner to that for the coke-oven crude.

In the case of smokeless-fuel crude tars, the coal is usually carbonized in retorts at temperatures in the range 600–750 °C. In the coalite process—coalite being the only crude currently accepted as suitable for road tar production—the coal is carbonized at 640 °C in small, tapered retorts that are heated externally, by burning the gas produced during the carbonization. These tars have significantly lower densities than either coke-oven or gasworks tar; they also contain a higher proportion of tar acids and yield lower amounts of pitch on distillation to 315 °C.

It should be noted that, with the discovery and exploitation of the natural gas fields under the North Sea from 1965 onwards, the use of coal-based town gas began to be phased out in Britain, so that today the tar industry relies almost entirely for its crude tar upon the coke ovens of the steel industry, supplemented by the foundry and domestic coke ovens of British Coal and the smokeless-fuel producers.

**Road tars**
While the crude tars obtained from the destructive distillation of bituminous coal are unsuitable for direct use on the roadway, they do contain many valuable ingredients. Figure 3.4 is a schematic illustration of the composition of a tar crude after it has been dehydrated and transported to a tar refinery. At the refinery, the distillation process by which the crude tar is refined is not only analogous to, but also similar to, the process of obtaining asphaltic bitumen from petroleum crude. In the distillation process the light oils such as benzene, toluene and xylene are first collected, and then the middle and heavy oils containing creosote oils and naphthalene are extracted. The residual material, called 'base tar' or 'pitch', is then fluxed back with tar oils to obtain road tars of the desired consistency and properties. Tar distillates of the creosote or anthracene oil types are most

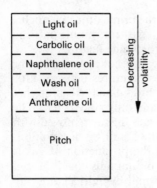

**Fig. 3.4** Schematic illustration of the components of a dehydrated crude tar

often used for this purpose. With both types, more viscous fluxing materials are used in winter than in summer.

Tars used in roadworks are defined as binders 'prepared entirely from crude tars produced wholly or substantially as a byproduct in the carbonization of coal at above 600 °C in externally-heated retorts or coke ovens'[23]. Within this definition, two types of road tar are recognized, viz. those produced at carbonization temperatures at or above 950 °C, i.e. high-temperature tars, and those produced below 950 °C, i.e. low-temperature tars.

Table 3.6 summarizes the main properties of the road tars manufactured in Britain. As can be seen, they are divided into two main groups, types S and C. The type S group is used for surface dressing purposes, whilst type C is used in coated macadam work. The number included in the designation of each grade refers to its nominal viscosity.

Advice regarding the use of these binders in road construction and maintenance is readily available in the literature[13, 16, 24, 25].

*Tar cutbacks and emulsions* As with the bitumen cutbacks and emulsions, tar cutbacks and emulsions may also be prepared. In practice, however, it has been found that these materials are comparatively difficult to handle, and as a result they are now rarely used for highway work in Britain.

## Comparison of bitumen and tar binders

There is some debate between engineers as to whether bitumen is 'better' than tar and vice versa. It is not intended to take sides in this controversy as, in fact, it can really be said with validity that each has particular advantages in certain situations.

Some obvious properties of equivalent tar and bitumen materials are as follows.

(1) Both binders appear blackish in colour when viewed in large masses, but make a brownish stain and appear brown in colour when viewed in thin films.

**Table 3.6** Properties of road tars[23]

| Grade | Surface dressing | | | | Coated macadam | | | | | | | |
|---|---|---|---|---|---|---|---|---|---|---|---|---|
| | S34 | S38 | S42 | S46 | C30 | C34 | C38 | C42 | C46 | C50 | C54 | C58 |
| Viscosity (°C evt) | 34.0±1.5 | 38.0±1.5 | 42.0±1.5 | 46.0±1.5 | 30.0±1.5 | 34.0±1.5 | 38.0±1.5 | 42.0±1.5 | 46.0±1.5 | 50.0±1.5 | 54.0±1.5 | 58.0±1.5 |
| Water (% by mass, maximum) | 0.5 | 0.5 | 0.5 | 0.5 | 0.5 | 0.5 | 0.5 | 0.5 | 0.5 | 0.5 | 0.5 | 0.5 |
| Distillation yield (% by mass, maximum) | | | | | | | | | | | | |
| oils below 200 °C | 1.0 | 0.5 | 0.5 | 0.5 | 0.5 | 0.5 | 0.5 | 0.5 | 0.5 | 0.5 | 0.5 | 0.5 |
| oils 200–270 °C | 4–13 | 3–10 | 2–8 | 2–7 | 4–11 | 3–10 | 1–8 | 1–6 | 1–5 | 0–4 | 0–3 | 0–3 |
| oils 270–300 °C | 4–9 | 4–9 | 3–8 | 2–7 | 4–9 | 4–9 | 4–9 | 3–8 | 2–7 | 2–7 | 2–7 | 1–6 |
| oils 200–300 °C | 18 | 16 | 14 | 12 | 16 | 15 | 13 | 12 | 11 | 10 | 10 | 8 |
| Softening point of residue (R and B) (%C) | | | | | | | | | | | | |
| high-temperature tars | 35–52 | 35–53 | 35–54 | 35–55 | 35–46 | 35–46 | 35–47 | 35–48 | 35–49 | 35–50 | 52 (max.) | 56 (max.) |
| low-temperature tars | 30–52 | 30–53 | 30–54 | 30–55 | — | — | — | — | — | — | — | — |
| SEGAS test (°C evt increase) | 20 ± 5 | 16 ± 5 | 12 ± 5 | 10 ± 4 | — | — | — | — | — | — | — | — |
| Beckton tray test (°C evt increase, maximum) | | | | | | | | | | | | |
| at 80 °C | — | — | — | — | 6 | 6 | 6 | 6 | — | — | — | — |
| at 100 °C | — | — | — | — | — | — | — | — | 8 | 8 | 8 | — |
| at 140 °C | — | — | — | — | — | — | — | — | — | — | — | 10 |
| Density at 20 °C (g/ml) | | | | | | | | | | | | |
| high-temperature tars | | | | | | | | | | | | |
| minimum | 1.110 | 1.115 | 1.120 | 1.125 | 1.105 | 1.110 | 1.115 | 1.120 | 1.125 | 1.130 | 1.130 | 1.135 |
| maximum | 1.250 | 1.255 | 1.260 | 1.265 | 1.245 | 1.250 | 1.255 | 1.260 | 1.265 | 1.270 | 1.275 | 1.275 |
| low-temperature tars | | | | | | | | | | | | |
| minimum | 1.060 | 1.063 | 1.067 | 1.070 | 1.060 | 1.060 | 1.063 | 1.067 | 1.070 | 1.073 | 1.077 | 1.080 |
| maximum | 1.250 | 1.255 | 1.260 | 1.265 | 1.245 | 1.250 | 1.255 | 1.260 | 1.265 | 1.270 | 1.275 | 1.275 |

(2)   Bitumen responds less readily than tar to small changes in temperature. Tar is liquid at lower temperatures and solidifies at comparatively higher ones.

(3)   Tar may be overheated and spoiled more easily than bitumen, but is much easier to get out of a road tanker.

(4)   Tar tends to penetrate more freely into open road surfaces.

(5)   Tar is not as susceptible as bitumen to the dissolving action of petroleum solvents or distillates. In parking areas where petrol and oil are likely to drip or spill from vehicles, a tar surfacing will usually have a longer life than a conventional bitumen one, e.g. a sample of dense tar surfacing made using a coalite low-temperature tar is reported[24] as having proved highly resistant to softening on complete immersion for up to eight days in kerosene.

(6)   Bitumen is less brittle at low temperatures. This is because tar contains a higher percentage of free carbon.

(7)   Historically, it is known that individuals engaged in specific occupations in the carbonizing and coal-tar byproduct industries have shown an abnormally high incidence of skin cancer. However, there is evidence[26] to show that the carcinogenic hydrocarbon concentrations emitted during tar-saving operations are so low as not to represent any health hazard.

(8)   Crude coal tar, after dehydration and cleaning, is now regarded as a suitable alternative fuel to petroleum fuel-oil in the iron and steel-making industry, and, as a result, changes in the price of road tar follow fairly closely those of road bitumen.

## Binder mixtures

Over the years many additives have been investigated with the aim of improving the rheological properties of bitumen and tar, but few have found a secure place in highway engineering practice. Often rheological improvements to the binder in the laboratory have not been reflected in pavement performance, and sometimes they have introduced construction problems which have discriminated against their proper usage and testing. However, the need for higher-quality bituminous materials to cope with increasing volumes of heavy traffic has ensured that the search is continued.

The following is a brief discussion on some of the materials examined.

### Rubber–bitumen/tar

Experiments involving rubber and bitumen or tar have been carried out for well over 100 years, and a wealth of literature exists on the subject. However, it is only since the development (in 1938) of rubber powders made from latex that any real progress has been made. Even so, real knowledge regarding the proper usage of rubber in bitumen or tar binders is still very limited.

At this time, the following forms of rubber latex are commercially available for use in bituminous road surfacings.

(1)   *Latex*   This, the natural product of the rubber tree, is a suspension of

rubber droplets in a watery serum concentrated and stabilized in such a way that the dry rubber content is between 60 and 70 per cent. Natural latex, concentrated by centrifuging to about 60 per cent of rubber and preserved with ammonia and other agents, is called *centrifugal latex*. *Evaporated latex* is that which is concentrated by evaporation to more than 60 per cent of rubber and preserved with potassium hydroxide.

(2)  *Unvulcanized powder*  This is a rubber powder containing 60 per cent latex rubber and 40 per cent by mass (19 per cent by volume) of inert earth to prevent caking. The powder is made by spray-drying the latex and then adding the inert earth.

(3)  *Vulcanized powder*  This is a powder containing about 95 per cent rubber. Vulcanization is the process of heating a mixture of the raw latex with sulphur compounds or other chemicals to produce cross-linking of the rubber molecules. The vulcanized rubber has improved strength and elastic properties.

(4)  *Sheet rubber*  Many forms of sheet rubber are made from coagulated latex. For use on the road, the sheet rubber must first be milled and then dissolved in a fluxing oil. As a result, sheet rubber is used only in the preparation of rubberized cutback bitumen.

(5)  *Graft rubber*  Used in the latex or powder form, this consists of a rubber to which is chemically grafted a proportion of a polymeric material (usually between 10 and 15 per cent of the natural rubber); this enables a stable mixture to be obtained with tar. Although considerable research work has been carried out, it has not yet been found possible to disperse an unmodified natural rubber directly into road tar and obtain a mixture that is sufficiently stable for road use.

Whilst specifications have been published [16,27] suggesting how rubber might be used in surface dressings for concrete pavements, and for rolled asphalt, bitumen macadam, and dense tar surfacings, there is little evidence to suggest that they are much applied in practice. Generally, it would appear that highway engineers have yet to be fully convinced of the economic benefits to be derived from rubber–bitumen surfacings.

A review of the literature [28] on the use of rubber in bituminous surfacings indicates the following points.

(1)  In the past, interest was centred on the addition of specially prepared natural and synthetic rubbers in bitumen. These additives have been relatively high in cost, and in order to keep the price of the modified binder within reasonable limits, the amount of additive has generally been less than 5 per cent by mass of bitumen. Also it was found that the use of higher concentrations of these additives led to difficulties in pumping and spraying with conventional bitumen-handling equipment.

(2)  More recently, attention has been directed towards the incorporation of larger amounts of pulverized scrap (vulcanized) rubber, prepared from comminuted motor vehicle tyres and rubber buffings from tyre retreaders. For spray-sealing work, scrap rubber up to 33 per cent by mass of bitumen has been added, whilst for plant-mix work, the corresponding figure is 40 per cent.

(3)   When comminuted scrap rubber is added to a hot bitumen, only a proportion of the rubber particles disperses in the bitumen and modifies its properties, whilst the remainder acts as a soft, elastic aggregate, or cushion, between stones in the total aggregate–binder structure.

(4)   The degree of dispersion of the rubber particles has a major effect upon the properties of the rubber–bitumen mix. For slightly vulcanized and unvulcanized natural rubber, the temperature and time of digestion are very important factors affecting the degree of dispersion, e.g. the optimum digestion time for a slightly vulcanized rubber powder was 30 minutes at 180 °C and 8 h at 140 °C.

(5)   The method of rubber addition is also important in respect of dispersion, e.g. powder rubber can be added directly to heated, agitated bitumen, whereas the addition of latex requires precautions to prevent foaming.

(6)   Rubber additives enhance the elastic responses of the bitumen at higher ambient temperatures, and tensile testing indicates increased toughness (i.e. energy absorption by specimens before fracture). Other laboratory tests have shown that the incorporation of rubber in bitumen produces a material which displays a marked increase in resistance to deformation simultaneously with reduced brittleness at low temperatures.

(7)   Whilst it is recognized that rubberized binders can improve the service performance of both plant-mix surfacings and spray seals, results from different field trials do not consistently show the same improvement, and it would appear that service performance is influenced by factors not yet recognized.

(8)   For bitumens containing dispersed rubbers, it could be desirable to use a softer grade of bitumen than is customary.

**Tar–bitumen**
Tar and bitumen each have their advantages and disadvantages, the relative importance of which depends upon the circumstances of usage. It is considered by many highway engineers that a significant advance in binder technology would be achieved if the favourable properties of both binders could be combined in one material, whilst at the same time minimizing their undesirable characteristics.

Most successful results to date have been obtained with tar–bitumen blends used for surface dressing purposes, and recommendations are available regarding their exact usage[16]. Individual blends normally fall within the composition ranges of 30–55 per cent by mass of road tar and 45–70 per cent of refinery bitumen, whilst the viscosity (STV) at 40 °C must be 100 s ± 20 s or 200 s ± 40 s[5]. The tar, which is most usually a low-temperature product as this has the advantage of being compatible with bitumen in almost all proportions, normally contains not less than 25 per cent pitch of softening point 80 °C (R and B). The main features of these blends are their good weathering characteristics, an improved 'wetting' of aggregate (with less tendency to strip) as compared with pure bitumen, and a less brittle product as compared with pure tar.

Tar–bitumen mixtures used in coated macadam surfacings have penetration values of 100 or 200; they normally contain 10 per cent refined tar and 90 per cent bitumen.

One analysis[29] has indicated the following points with regard to tar–bitumen blends.

(1) Tar–bitumen blends containing predominantly bitumen, but with a substantial proportion of tar, make highly satisfactory surface dressing binders.

(2) Tar–bitumen blends (65–70 per cent bitumen) can make satisfactory coated materials over a wide range of mixing temperatures. As with the blends used in surface dressing, a low brittle point similar to that of bitumen is a characteristic feature. The degree of hardening experienced by the blends during mixing and delivery of the coated materials depends upon the aggregate size and mixing temperature, and tends to be somewhat greater than that of bitumen. These blends will, however, readily withstand the high mixing temperatures often employed in cold weather. Fuming is at a low level also.

(3) The good compaction achieved at lower temperatures with tar–bitumen-coated materials indicates that considerable tolerance is available when laying during unfavourable weather conditions. A high resistance to deformation is exhibited on heavily-trafficked roads.

## Pitch–bitumen

When coal tar is distilled the final product is pitch. The dividing line between pitch and tar is fundamentally one of viscosity, so that a material that is below 60 °C evt (equivalent to an R and B softening point of 42 °C) is called tar, whilst anything more viscous is called pitch[30].

The use of tar on roads can be traced back to about 1832, whereas the use of pitch–bitumen mixtures in road surfacings dates only from 1950 when a patent was taken out which proposed the addition of coal-tar pitch to refinery bitumen in order to increase its susceptibility to oxidation, thereby producing a surfacing having a rougher surface texture and improved resistance to skidding. Research carried out at the (then) Road Research Laboratory showed that weathering due to oxidation of bitumen is the principal factor determining the skid-resistance of surfacings containing different bitumens. These experiments showed that the part played by the binder is primarily one of promoting a gradual wear of the sand-filler–bitumen mortar, as brought about by weather and traffic. The gradual erosion of the mortar—which still keeps a good microtexture—continually exposes fresh, unpolished aggregate, thereby maintaining a coarse, anti-skidding texture. Prior to the advent of pitch–bitumen, only rolled asphalt wearing courses containing a substantial Trinidad Lake asphalt content were permitted on motorways in Britain, i.e. the Trinidad material had the ability of constantly oxidizing where exposed to the atmosphere, so that the resultant thin film was removed progressively by vehicle wheels. It was then found that refinery bitumen could be made to oxidize at a rate equal to that of the Trinidad bitumen when modified by the addition of a certain amount of vertical retort pitch, with the result that the skid-resistance of the bituminous surfacing was considerably improved. Furthermore, the adhesion between the aggregate and the binder was improved by the addition of this pitch, while resistance to stripping by water was also increased.

At the present time, the pitch used in pitch–bitumen mixtures is almost exclusively that produced by the low-temperature carbonization process, because of the ease with which it can be blended with bitumen as compared with high-temperature pitch. The blend is included in the British Standard[8] for rolled asphalt, where it is now given equal status with refinery bitumen and lake asphalt/bitumen. The pitch–bitumen recommended is a mixture of 75–80 per cent by mass of bitumen with 20–25 per cent of coal-tar pitch of softening point (R and B) between 55 and 80 °C; it is normally either 50 or 70 penetration-grade[5].

### Sulphur–bitumen
Sulphur, which is one of the basic elements, is perhaps unique amongst the world's mineral resources in that it is one of the few elements that will be in abundant supply in the future, i.e. one conservative estimate[31] puts the world's mineable inventory of sulphur at about $10.3 \times 10^9$ t. Current projections indicate that the worldwide annual supply of sulphur is beginning to exceed the demand; this situation has existed in some producer countries for a number of years, and has encouraged the search for other uses for this relatively cheap material. One of the potentially important uses is as an additive in flexible pavements[32-34]. A major feature of sulphur–bitumen mixtures is that they have a lower temperature-susceptibility than conventional mixes, and they therefore offer the pavement designer increased flexibility with respect to low temperature and permanent deformation requirements[35].

In Britain, where the vast majority of sulphur for all uses has to be imported, there has been less interest shown in sulphur until fairly recently. However, as the need for more durable bituminous materials to cope with the demands of very heavy traffic has become more appreciated, a programme of research into the use of sulphur has been initiated at the Transport and Road Research Laboratory.

Sulphur exhibits a most interesting temperature–viscosity relationship. A yellow solid material at standard conditions of temperature and pressure, it melts at 116 °C, and exists as a very-low-viscosity liquid (compared with refinery bitumen) between 116 and 153 °C; its lowest viscosity is at 150 °C. At 154 °C, it becomes rapidly, and extremely, viscous.

Molten sulphur and hot bitumen react to release hydrogen sulphide ($H_2S$), which is a toxic gas and a health hazard. At temperatures above 150 °C, the rate of $H_2S$ evolution increases very rapidly.

*Sulphur-extended asphalt*   The use of sulphur as a partial binder substitute for bitumen has been experimentally tested in pavements in Britain, Canada, France, and the USA, and reported as having considerable potential. Known in the literature as sulphur-extended asphalt (SEA), the process can involve either pre-dispersing hot liquid elemental sulphur in bitumen to create a sulphur–bitumen binder that is then mixed with aggregate in the same way as penetration bitumen is used in conventional mixtures, or the simultaneous addition of the sulphur and bitumen to the aggregate as mixing takes place. Whilst both methods have been used successfully, the evidence would suggest that the preblend approach offers better control on the dispersion of the sulphur, and better mixture properties.

The conclusions drawn from the British laboratory and paving study[33] reflect the potential of sulphur-extended–asphalt pavements.

(1)   The resistance to permanent deformation of rolled asphalt should be improved substantially by the addition of sulphur. Mixes in which 25 to 30 per cent of the bitumen was replaced by sulphur produced about a five-fold improvement in wheel-tracking rate.

(2)   These sulphur–asphalts also had higher complex moduli than the equivalent unmodified asphalt. At $33\,^\circ C$ and a test frequency of 10 Hz, the sulphur–asphalt was approximately two to three times stiffer than the unmodified asphalt, indicating that load-spreading ability could also be improved by adding sulphur.

(3)   Initial measurements of laboratory fatigue-life indicated that improvements in load-spreading ability and resistance to permanent deformation are accompanied by some reduction in resistance to fatigue-cracking.

(4)   The mixing and laying temperatures for sulphur–asphalt must be controlled carefully to avoid any emission of hydrogen sulphide and to achieve optimum properties on compaction. Full-scale mixing and laying trials have shown that this can be done.

(5)   Although there is little doubt that sulphur can be used to improve the engineering properties of rolled asphalt, the practicality of its use under more normal contractual conditions has still to be established.

In respect of the above, it might be noted that in the early 1980s the price of liquid sulphur in Britain was approximately half that of bitumen. However, as its relative density is twice that of bitumen, their prices are similar per unit volume. Given that sufficient sulphur would be available for road purposes, its use should not, therefore, be uneconomic.

*Sand–asphalt–sulphur*   Another way of using sulphur in a pavement is as part of a sand–asphalt–sulphur mixture (SAS). With this method, hot liquid elemental sulphur is added, essentially as a filler, to a hot sand–bitumen mix during a second mixing cycle which occurs after the bitumen has been premixed with the aggregate. In this instance, the sulphur to bitumen mass ratio would normally exceed unity. In the secondary mixing process, a small portion of the sulphur becomes dissolved and dispersed in the bitumen, similar to SEA; the bulk of the sulphur, however, remains in a free form and occupies the void spaces between the bitumen-coated sand particles, conforming to the shape of the voids. Upon cooling, the sulphur in the void spaces solidifies, keying in the coated particles and imparting high mechanical stability to the mix.

The manner in which the sulphur is utilized in sand–asphalt–sulphur suggests that particular aggregate quality requirements might be relaxed, whilst still permitting the design of high-quality mixes using inexpensive materials (e.g. one-sized sands). Furthermore, the excess molten sulphur increases mix fluidity, producing a material which, it is reported, can be placed with little or no compaction effort. This last quality, whilst enabling pavement construction without roller compaction, should also give this material a considerable potential as a patching material in bituminous road maintenance operations.

Table 3.7 summarizes some factors relating to the use of sulphur in bituminous mixtures in road surfacings.

**Table 3.7**   Methods for using sulphur in bituminous mixtures (based on references 33 and 36)

| Basic method | Example sources | Features | Some concerns |
| --- | --- | --- | --- |
| Preblending of liquid sulphur and bitumen (SEA) | Gulf Canada SUDIC | Potential economy, extension of bitumen supply, use of conventional paving equipment, production of binder on site on demand, no additives required | Extra operators at plant, elemental sulphur vapour at paving site |
| Pugmill blending of liquid and bitumen with aggregate (SEA) | US Bureau of Mines | Potential economy, extension of bitumen supply, use of conventional paving equipment, no additives required | Elemental sulphur vapour at paving site, uniformity of dispersion, aggregate coating |
| Simultaneous mixing of powder sulphur, bitumen and aggregate (SEA) | TRRL | Potential economy, extension of bitumen supply, final properties (of rolled asphalt) largely independent of form in which sulphur added, use of conventional paving equipment | Elemental sulphur vapour at paving site, possibility of change in sulphur structure affecting long-term stability |
| Post-mix liquid sulphur addition to hot sand–bitumen mixes | Shell Canada | Use of marginal materials (unstable sands), no compaction requirements | Special equipment (insulated trucks), large quantities of sulphur, questionable economics (except for special situations) |
| Post-mix liquid sulphur addition to hot sand–bitumen mixes | Sociète Nationale des Petroles d'Aquitaine | Extension of bitumen supply, use of conventional paving equipment, no additives required | Storage (costs, formation of $H_2S$, need for inert cover gas), need for additives to maintain storage stability, extra operators at plant, elemental sulphur vapour at paving site |

**Other modified binders**

Over the years many additives to bitumen have been investigated with the aim of improving the life of bituminous surfacings and, in particular, the aggregate-retention performance of surface dressings at difficult sites subject to large volumes of turning movements and consequent high shearing stresses, e.g. at the approaches to roundabouts and junctions on major roads. These modifiers have included thermosetting resins, thermoplastics, and thermoplastic rubbers.

Commercial high-performance *epoxy-resin-modified bitumens* are now available that can cope easily with the above stresses. Unlike bituminous binders which are thermoplastic, these binders are thermosetting, i.e. they are a dispersion of bitumen in a continuous resin phase, and consequently they have the high-strength, resistance and non-temperature-susceptibility properties of the resin. In practice, because of their high additive content, and consequent high cost—about 20 times the cost of bitumen—epoxy-resin systems are used only at the most difficult sites. However, research[37] would suggest that it is possible to produce high-performance binders containing less resin (e.g. 31 per cent by mass of resin) than the currently available commercial epoxy-resin systems (with about 50 per cent resin).

Various *thermoplastic polymers*, e.g. polyethene, polypropene, polyvinylchloride, polystyrene, and ethyl vinyl acetate, have been examined in terms of their usage as modifiers to bituminous road binders. It has been found that these thermoplastics increase the viscosity and stiffness of the binder at normal service temperatures. Unfortunately, however, they also appear to lack elastic properties and tend to separate when heated with bitumen, giving rise to coarse dispersion upon cooling[38]. One laboratory study of the use of polymers in rolled asphalt[39] has suggested that ethyl vinyl acetate—at about seven times the cost of bitumen—has promise in improving resistance to permanent deformation and dynamic modulus at high temperatures without adversely affecting fatigue-life.

*Thermoplastic rubbers* are so called because they combine both elastic and thermoplastic properties. Introduced in the mid-1960s these modifiers, which consist of links of block copolymers of styrene and butadiene, coupled in pairs to give di-blocks or 'star' configurations, have been used widely with bitumen to provide high performance coatings for roofing membranes. Their unique properties are their thermoplastic behaviour at elevated temperatures coupled with vulcanized rubber type behaviour at ambient temperatures; thus modified binders can be prepared which exhibit enhanced elastic behaviour and still have normal bitumen viscosity characteristics at storage or mixing temperatures. Extensive laboratory testing and road trials have demonstrated that thermoplastic rubber–bitumen blends provide improved deformation resistance and fatigue-life when used in bituminous mixtures[38].

## Binder tests and their significance

The most careful specifications with regard to the design and construction of a bituminous road surfacing are of little value if the properties of the bituminous binder used in the design are not adequately controlled. To aid the engineer in ensuring that the material obtained has the desired qualities, a number of tests have been devised which attempt to measure various binder properties for particular reasons. As is unfortunately the case with so many highway engineering test specifications, there are variations from organization to organization with regard to how exactly these binder tests should be carried out, although there is general agreement as to their significance. Since detailed information on British practice in carrying out these tests is readily available in the literature (see references 23, 40–48), they will be only briefly described here, while more emphasis will be placed upon factors relating to *why* the tests are carried out. Particular properties of bituminous binders will also be discussed in relation to the significance of the tests.

It is most convenient to discuss tests on binders by dividing them into the following five categories:

(1)   consistency tests,
(2)   durability tests,
(3)   composition tests,
(4)   density test,
(5)   flash and fire point tests.

**Consistency tests**
By consistency is meant the resistance of a material to flow. Since this property varies as the temperature changes, from that required for processing at the construction site (i.e. up to about 177 °C) to the below zero temperatures to which a road surfacing may be subjected in service, and since the binders themselves may range from very thin liquids to semi-solids, it can be appreciated why there is no single method of test which can readily evaluate all bituminous binders for consistency over such a wide range. Instead, there are a number of tests, each of which has certain advantages under specific conditions. The ones of most importance are the penetration, viscosity and softening point tests.

*Penetration test*    This test consists of determining how far a standard steel needle will penetrate vertically into the binder under standard conditions of temperature, load and time (see Fig. 3.5 (a)). The standard test conditions are 25 °C, 100 g and 5 s. The results obtained are expressed in units of

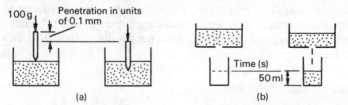

**Fig. 3.5**  Schematic illustration of: (a) the penetration test and (b) the standard tar viscometer test, for bituminous binders

penetration, where one unit is equal to 0.1 mm. The test is carried out on bitumens, rarely on tars.

*Significance of test* The penetration test measures the consistency of semi-solid bitumens so that they can be classified into standard grades. Since grade does not imply quality, the penetration test on its own has no relation to quality. However, penetration-grade refinery bitumens are known to reduce in penetration with age and some develop cracking tendencies.

Surfacings containing penetration-grade bitumens must be premixed and laid hot. Generally, the higher-penetration bitumens are preferred for use in colder climates to reduce cracking problems, whilst the lower-penetration ones should be used in warmer climates[49]. For normal roadworks in Britain, 50, 100 and 200 pen bitumens are in most common usage. Mastic asphalts containing 15 pen bitumens are used at such locations as bus stops, where traffic stresses are very high.

Although it is more difficult to get lower-penetration bitumens to adhere to aggregates, once adhesion has been established the bond is much stronger than if softer ones are used.

The penetration test, when carried out at different temperatures, can also determine the temperature-susceptibility of a bitumen. If a plot of penetration versus temperature is made on log-normal paper, the straight-line relationship established will be found to have the slope

$$m = \frac{\log \text{pen}_1 - \log \text{pen}_2}{T_1 - T_2}$$

where $\text{pen}_1$ and $\text{pen}_2$ are the penetration values measured at temperatures $T_1$ and $T_2$, respectively. From this it can be seen that the greater the slope, the more susceptible the bitumen is to softening under increased temperatures.

In practice, the slope ranges from 0.02 to about 0.05. In order to make the temperature-susceptibility a more easily appreciated factor, the concept of the *penetration index* has been devised, viz.:

$$\frac{20 - PI}{10 + PI} = \frac{50(\log \text{pen}_1 - \log \text{pen}_2)}{T_1 - T_2}$$

where $PI$ is the penetration index of the bitumen. The bitumen in most common usage at the time of the development of the $PI$ concept[50] had an index value of zero, and all bitumens with $PI < 0$ were regarded as inferior in terms of temperature-susceptibility. Nowadays, however, most acceptable road grades of bitumen have a penetration index of about $- 0.5$, heavy duty bitumen (HD grade) has a value of about $+ 1.5$, and blown bitumens are about $+ 5.0$.

The penetration index is also used to predict the stiffness modulus of bitumen at arbitrary times and temperatures. The deformation resistance of most engineering materials is usually expressed in terms of the modulus of elasticity, $E$, which for small deformations is defined by

$$E = \frac{\text{stress}}{\text{strain}} = \frac{\text{force/cross-sectional area}}{\text{increase in length/initial length}}$$

With a rigid material such as cement-concrete or steel, $E$ is (for all practical purposes) independent of the temperature and the time over which the force is applied. Bitumens, however, are viscoelastic materials, which means that their deformation increases with the length of time during which the force is applied, and the higher the temperature, the more rapidly this phenomenon occurs; as a result, the modulus has a lower value at longer loading times and at higher temperatures. To overcome this problem, the stiffness modulus, $S$, has been introduced for bitumen instead of the elasticity modulus, $E$.

An updated stiffness nomograph[51] is readily available in the literature which enables the modulus to be estimated under different conditions of loading time and temperature. In order to enter the nomograph two variables that are characteristic of the bitumen are required: these are the penetration index and the softening point (Ring and Ball).

A further use of the penetration test is as a measure of the effect of heating upon the hardening of a bitumen (see durability tests, p. 168).

*Viscosity tests*   In basic terms it can be said that the viscosity of a liquid is the property that retards flow so that when a force is applied to a liquid, the slower the movement of the liquid, the higher is its viscosity; in this sense viscosity is a 'pure' measure of consistency. The scientific definition of viscosity or, more correctly, the 'coefficient of viscosity' of a liquid may be explained as follows.

If the space between two parallel surfaces is filled with a liquid, and one of the surfaces is moved parallel to the other, a force which resists movement is set up as a result of the presence of the liquid. If the force of resistance is denoted by $F$, the area of the surface by $A$, the velocity of movement of one surface relative to the other by $v$, and the distance between the surfaces by $d$, then $F$ is proportional to $Av/d$. If a factor $\eta$, called the coefficient of viscosity, is introduced into the relationship, then the following equation can be written:

$$F = \eta A v/d$$

At a given temperature, $\eta$ has a constant value for any one liquid, but generally it is different for different liquids. If the variables are measured in centimetre–gramme–second (cgs) units, then the viscosity $\eta$ is equal to the resistance in dynes offered by the liquid to the movement of a surface 1 cm$^2$ in area moving with a velocity of 1 cm/s at a distance of 1 cm from another fixed surface. In this system the unit of viscosity is known as the poise; thus if $\eta = 200$, the liquid is said to have an absolute viscosity of 200 poises. The absolute viscosity of water at 30 $^\circ$C is 0.01 poise.

At this time, there are perhaps 60 instruments in use throughout the world for measuring 'viscosity'. They may be divided into three main groups, based on the following principles of operation:

(1)   the flow of a body through a liquid,
(2)   the flow of a liquid through a tube,
(3)   the rotation of one of two coaxial cylinders when the space between them is filled with a liquid.

While the truest measurements of viscosity are obtained with viscometers of the third group, they are relatively rarely used in highway engineering practice. Instead, most bitumen binder specifications for roadworks are based on the results obtained with industrial viscometers which utilize the second principle. The one in most common use in Britain is the *standard tar viscometer* (STV). Notwithstanding its name, this viscometer is used to evaluate both tar and cutback bitumen viscosities.

The STV test measures the time, in seconds, for a fixed quantity of the binder liquid (50 ml) to flow from a cup through a standard orifice under an initial standard head and at a known test temperature (see Fig. 3.5(b)). It is not practical with this viscometer to determine the viscosity of all bituminous binders at the same temperature because of the great variation in time required for a given amount of the different binders to flow through the orifice. Thus different temperatures are used for particular materials.

Since confusion can and does arise over employing several test temperatures, what is known as the *equiviscous temperature* (evt) system has been devised to overcome this source of error. In this system the temperature in degrees celsius is specified at which the time of flow of the binder is 50 s, as measured on the standard tar viscometer. A particular advantage of the evt system with respect to tars is that it provides a single scale on which can be accommodated the viscosities of all tar products, ranging from the very fluid ones to the hard pitches. As a result, the viscosities of tars—but not bitumens—are now commonly reported as equiviscous temperatures. This is possible with tars because the temperature-susceptibilities of all road tars are similar, irrespective of the source, whereas the temperature-susceptibilities of all bitumens are not.

If the viscosity of a tar as measured with the standard tar viscometer is known, and provided that it lies between 33 and 75 s, the evt of the tar can be determined by applying the appropriate correction factor given in Table 3.8 to the temperature at which the STV test was carried out. A more approximate translation may be carried out by using the relationships shown in Fig. 3.6.

*Significance of tests* The viscosity of a bituminous binder is its most important physical characteristic. Hence viscosity measurements are useful not only in ensuring that the material with the desired properties has been obtained, but also as a means of selecting binders for specific uses. If a binder with too low a viscosity is premixed with an aggregate, it may flow

**Table 3.8** Corrections, in °C, to be used in determining the equiviscous temperatures of road tars whose standard tar viscosities at known temperatures are already available[23]

| STV viscosity (s) | Corrections (°C) | | | | | | | | | |
|---|---|---|---|---|---|---|---|---|---|---|
| | 0 | 1 | 2 | 3 | 4 | 5 | 6 | 7 | 8 | 9 |
| 30 | — | — | — | − 2.5 | − 2.3 | − 2.2 | − 2.0 | − 1.9 | − 1.7 | − 1.5 |
| 40 | − 1.4 | − 1.2 | − 1.1 | − 0.9 | − 0.8 | − 0.6 | − 0.5 | − 0.4 | − 0.3 | − 0.1 |
| 50 | 0.0 | + 0.1 | + 0.2 | + 0.3 | + 0.5 | + 0.6 | + 0.7 | + 0.8 | + 0.9 | + 1.0 |
| 60 | + 1.1 | + 1.2 | + 1.3 | + 1.4 | + 1.5 | + 1.6 | + 1.7 | + 1.7 | + 1.8 | + 1.9 |
| 70 | + 2.0 | + 2.1 | + 2.2 | + 2.2 | + 2.3 | + 2.4 | — | — | — | — |

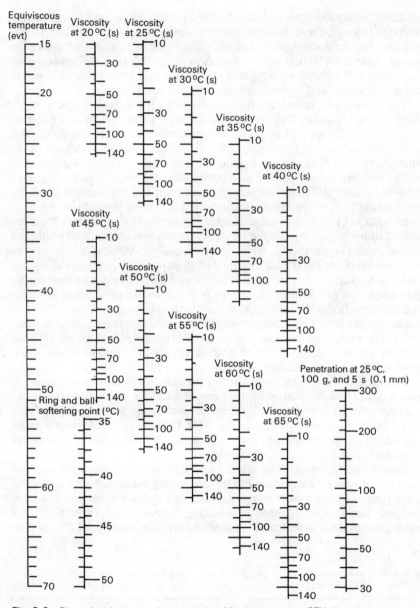

**Fig. 3.6**  Chart showing approximate relationships between evt, STV viscosity, ring and ball test, and penetration[23]. *Notes:* The graduations on the left of each column are evt units and correspond to the main evt scale. STV viscosities are by the 10 mm cup

off the stone while en route from the mixing plant. Conversely, if the viscosity is too high, the mixture may be unworkable by the time it reaches the site. If too low a viscosity is used for surface dressing purposes, the result may be 'bleeding' or a loss of chippings under traffic. With low-viscosity binders, there is generally less chance of pumping pipes becoming blocked, mixing and application temperatures can be kept lower, and aggregates are more easily coated.

Experience has shown that, for good mixing with aggregate, the viscosity of tar should preferably be about 2 poises, and should not exceed 4 poises, and that the compaction of coated tar macadams should take place at viscosities between 10 and 100 poises. The spraying of tar for use in surface dressing operations is best carried out at viscosities of 0.3–0.6 poise. In the case of cutback bitumens, the mixing and compaction of coated bitumen macadams are best carried out at viscosities of 2 and 200 poises, respectively, whilst spraying is most suitably carried out at about 0.5 poise for swirl jets and 0.8 poise for slot jets.

*Softening point test* The ring and ball (R and B) softening point test is also extensively used to evaluate the consistency of bituminous binders. In this test a 9.53 mm diameter steel ball (of mass 3.5 g) is placed on a binder sample held by a steel ring and immersed in a water bath (see Fig. 3.7). The water is heated until it reaches a temperature at which the test sample is sufficiently soft to allow the ball, enveloped in binder, to fall through a height of 2.5 cm. The water temperature at which this occurs is read to the nearest 0.5 °C and called the ring and ball softening point.

*Significance of test* The softening point is not a melting point; bituminous binders do not melt but instead gradually change from semi-solids to liquids on the application of heat. The method of test is entirely arbitrary and must be exactly carried out if the results are to be of value. As the practical significance of the test is limited, the specifications of many binders for particular purposes are now often written without softening point requirements.

The R and B test is included in the standard specifications for road tar; the softening point of the pitch residue is a means of characterizing its rate of setting. It is useful also for determining the temperature-susceptibilities of bitumens which are to be used in thick films, such as in crack fillers. When two bitumens have the same penetration value, the one with the higher softening point is normally less susceptible to temperature changes.

As noted previously in relation to the penetration test, the R and B softening point must be known before the stiffness modulus of a penetration-grade bitumen can be estimated from known properties of

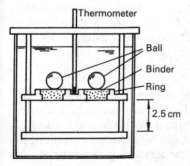

**Fig. 3.7** Diagrammatic representation of the apparatus for the ring and ball test

bitumen. For many bitumens (but not all), the R and B softening point corresponds to the temperature for 800 pen.

**Durability tests**
Bitumen and tar specifications contain criteria which relate to the control of hardening of the binders. For bitumens, tests used include the loss-on-heating and permittivity tests; for tars, they include the SEGAS and Beckton tray tests.

*Loss-on-heating test*    In this test, which is used on refinery bitumens, pitch–bitumens, and mixtures of Trinidad Lake asphalt and refinery bitumen, a 50 g sample of the binder is placed in a small container and left for 5 h in a revolving-shelf oven, the temperature of which is maintained at 165 °C. At the end of the heating period, the sample is cooled to room temperature and its mass is determined. The loss in mass is expressed as a percentage of the original mass.

The penetration test is also often carried out on the residue of the loss-on-heating test. The result obtained is then expressed as a percentage of the penetration of the bitumen before heating.

*Permittivity test*    For the purpose of the permittivity test, the permittivity or dielectric constant of a bitumen, which is a dimensionless value, is defined as the ratio of the capacitance of a capacitor with that bitumen as dielectric to the capacitance of the same capacitor with air as dielectric. Strictly, this is relative permittivity; however, for practical purposes the permittivity of air (1.000 59) can be taken as unity.

To measure permittivity, a rigid stainless steel cell composed of two cylindrical concentric-electrode capacitors, sharing a common central (voltage) electrode and guard cylinder, is filled with about 20 ml of bitumen at about 150 °C and allowed to cool; the capacitance $C_b$ is then determined at 25 °C, using a bridge frequency of 1592 Hz, for each capacitor. After emptying and cleaning, the air capacitance of the cell $C_a$ is inferred from a calibration procedure. The permittivity of the bitumen $E_b$ is then taken as the ratio of the mean $C_b$ to $C_a$.

The main value of the permittivity test lies in the fact that the permittivity of a bitumen has been correlated with the highway performance of mixes, even though the reason for the correlation is not clear. The Department of Transport now allows 50 pen refinery bitumens with a permittivity value of 2.650 or above at 25 °C to be used in rolled asphalt mixtures for roads designed to carry 0.5-million standard axles; previously, only the more expensive pitch–bitumens or mixtures of Trinidad Lake asphalt and refinery bitumen could be used in these roads.

*SEGAS test*    The SEGAS test, named after the South Eastern Gas Board where the test was developed, is applied only to road tars and tar–bitumen blends to be used in surface dressings. With the standard test a film of tar on a flat plate is exposed, at 45 °C, to a controlled current of air for 43 h and the increase in equiviscous temperature is determined. An accelerated version of the test may be carried out at 55 °C for 18 h; this gives similar numerical results but the precision is not as good as that for the standard test.

The basis of the test is that, regardless of its initial viscosity, the evt of a road tar after the test should generally lie between 50 and 60 °C. In the case of tar–bitumen blends, the range is about 55–67 °C.

*Beckton tray test* The Beckton tray test, which is named after the Beckton Laboratories of the North Thames Gas Board where the test was developed, can be applied to tars, cutback bitumens and tar–bitumen blends to be used in coated macadam mixtures; in practice, however, it is most commonly used with the tar-containing coating binders. As with the SEGAS test, the Beckton test is essentially a method whereby the rise in equiviscous temperature is determined which a film of binder undergoes during a specified time at a particular temperature; in this case the heating period is 1 h in a calibrated oven, and the test temperature varies according to the binder being considered, e.g. C30–C42 tars at 80 °C, 100 or 200 s (at 40 °C) tar–bitumens at 80 °C, C46–C54 tars at 100 °C, and C58 and 120 or 200 pen tar–bitumens at 140 °C.

In the original version of the test derived at Beckton, a film of tar contained in a brass tray was placed for 1 h in a specified oven at the same temperature as used at an adjacent commercial coating plant, and the evt increase measured.

*Significance of tests* There are ample performance data to show that the hardness of the binder is the one property most closely associated with the satisfactory continued performance of a bituminous pavement[52]. The hardness of a binder in a pavement depends upon the following factors:

(1)   the initial selection of the proper penetration or viscosity grade of binder to accommodate pavement design life and environmental and traffic-loading conditions,
(2)   the temperature-susceptibility characteristics of the binder,
(3)   the susceptibility of the binder to hardening during hot-plant mixing (coating) and the construction of the pavement,
(4)   the rate of hardening of the binder in the pavement in service,
(5)   binder–aggregate interactions such as adsorption or selective sorption of binder components.

All heated bitumen binders harden during storage and transportation, whilst all binders harden during mixing and laying, e.g. see Table 3.9 which shows the results of penetration tests on recovered binder from samples of rolled asphalt wearing course materials. During the subsequent life of the pavement, the binders further harden under the combined environmental effects of temperature, oxygen, sunlight, rainwater, oil deposition and traffic. Hard binders fracture more easily in cold weather, and weather more easily under heavy traffic.

The loss-on-heating test is essentially an accelerated volatilization test which has as its main aim the control of bitumen-hardening during storage.

**Table 3.9**   Hardening of bituminous binders during mixing and laying[53]

| Type of binder | Mixing temperature (°C) | Original pen | Pen of recovered binder | | |
|---|---|---|---|---|---|
| | | | After mixing | After laying | Surface of laid material |
| Refinery bitumen | 170 | 45 | 33 | 30 | 28 |
| | 142 | 45 | 37 | 34 | 32 |
| Pitch–bitumen | 180 | 44 | 30 | 27 | 24 |
| | 150 | 44 | 32 | 29 | 27 |

If the ratio of the surface area to the total size of sample is considered to be reflective of the conditions in a storage tank, then the test results may be considered as being representative of what might result from the heating conditions in the field tanks.

The permittivity test is intended to ensure that the high anti-skidding properties of rolled asphalt wearing courses are maintained. Whereas many bitumens promote the continuous development of good texture and a more skid-resistant surfacing, others produce a surfacing which becomes slippery under wet conditions, particularly in the presence of large amounts of oil droppings. Thus certain refinery bitumens which are incompatible with oil and precipitate resinous components which, under the high-volume, high-speed traffic conditions that exist on many trunk roads and motorways, can render their surfacings very slippery, are excluded by the permittivity test.

There is a close correlation between the SEGAS test results and the equiviscous temperature increases of tar binders in service after one year. The brittle points of surface dressing tars and tar–bitumens are about 65 and 75 °C below their evt values, respectively; they occur at road temperatures of − 15 to − 5 °C and − 20 to − 10 °C, respectively, after one year in the road pavement. The SEGAS result can thus be used to predict whether or not a loss of surface dressing chippings is likely to occur with either type of binder in the first year.

During the mixing of coated material, the binder is normally spread as a thin film about 0.1 mm thick on the aggregate particles. Now, all binders undergo some hardening when this process is carried out at elevated temperatures; however, binders containing volatile fluxing oils will harden most because of the evaporation of these oils. Overheating during mixing can lead to such high losses of oil that the binder becomes too hard to give satisfactory service, i.e. the binder is said to be 'burnt'. The application of the recommended Beckton tray test evt °C limits to tar-containing binders ensures that excessive hardening will not occur during coating, provided that the recommended aggregate coating temperatures are not exceeded.

**Composition tests**
As is clear from Tables 3.3–3.6, most binder specifications include criteria regarding composition. To ensure that these composition specifications are met, a number of tests have been developed to determine the proportions of the specific fractions and components of the bituminous binders.

*Distillation tests*   Distillation tests are used to determine the quantity and quality of the volatile constituents and the amount of non-volatile residues present in tar-containing binders, cutback bitumens, and binder emulsions. In emulsions, the volatile constituent is, of course, primarily water.

The distillation tests for cutbacks, tars and emulsions differ somewhat in procedure. Essentially, however, all involve heating a specified quantity of the binder in a standard flask or still at a specified rate, and then determining the amount of distillate removed at prescribed standard temperatures.

*Significance of tests*   The distillation tests are amongst the most valuable of the highway tests for bituminous binders in that they ensure the production of binders of consistent quality for use in road schemes.

Distillation tests carried out on tar-containing binders and cutback bitumens can also provide useful information both on the type of volatiles in the binder, and on the rate at which these volatiles will be lost under field conditions. For instance, if a given cutback is known to lose its volatiles too slowly under certain conditions, then under similar conditions a cutback with higher boiling range volatiles—as determined by the distillation test—can be expected to cure even more slowly.

The residue left from the distillation test can also provide useful information. While there is no guarantee that the residue is the same as either the base bitumen in the cutback or the material left in the road surfacing after curing, it is sufficiently similar to justify examination for characteristics measured by means of the standard consistency tests.

*Water content test*   While, of course, the moisture content of a binder is automatically determined when a distillation test is carried out, there are occasions when it is desirable to determine the moisture content alone, without carrying out a complete distillation procedure. In such instances, the moisture content may be determined 'directly' by mixing a specified amount of binder with a predetermined amount of petroleum spirit (for bitumens) or coal-tar solvent (for tar-containing binders) with which it is immiscible, and distilling in a flask or still which is attached to a glass watercooled reflux condenser and a graduated receiver. Distillation is continued until the volume of water in the receiver is constant. This volume is then expressed as a percentage by mass of the original material.

*Significance of test*   Bituminous binders should only contain extremely low moisture contents if they are to be heated beyond $100\,^{\circ}C$, i.e. if significant quantities of water are present, foaming of the binder will occur.

*Ash content test*   The ash content of a bitumen is the percentage by mass of inorganic residue left after ignition of the sample. In the course of the test, a known amount of the sample is gently heated until it begins to burn, and then it is fired until the ash is free from carbon.

*Significance of test*   This test is carried out on both penetration-grade and cutback bitumens. With refinery bitumens, the test is used to ensure that undesirable amounts of mineral matter are not present; this is particularly important with surface dressing materials. The presence of ash in a bitumen is not necessarily harmful in itself, as is evidenced by the use of lake asphalt in road surfacings either on its own or in blended mixtures. In such instances, the ash test can be useful in determining the composition of the binder.

*Solubility tests*   In determining the percentage of binder present in either bitumen or tar, different solvents are normally used. In the case of bitumens, the accepted solvent is trichloroethene, while in tars it is toluene. In either case, a specified quantity of binder—usually 2–5 g—is dissolved in a given quantity of solvent. After filtering the solution through a fine-porosity filter, the residue retained is determined and the percentage of soluble material is calculated by difference.

*Significance of test*   A solubility requirement of 99.5 per cent is found in all British specifications for refinery bitumens. Tars are not completely soluble in these or, indeed, in any other solvent, and so it is very important to be aware of how much of the binder is normally soluble in the solvent used. For instance, tar refined from a vertical-retort crude is between 90 and 95 per cent soluble in toluene, whereas tars manufactured from coke-oven or horizontal-retort crudes may only be 80 to 90 per cent soluble in toluene.

Insoluble material in refinery bitumens is normally dirt and similar material picked up in the course of storage, or else salt which was not removed during the refining process; those in natural bitumens are finely-divided mineral materials. Insolubles in tar may be measured in order to guard against an overheated or 'burnt' tar being used. Whichever binder is studied, solubility tests are most useful in establishing the amount of actual binder available for use in the road surfacing. Some authorities believe, however, that the ash content test is more reliable for this purpose as solvents fail to remove dust in colloidal suspension.

### Density test

The density of a bituminous binder is its mass per unit volume at a given temperature. Thus, for example, the density of tar-containing binders is normally determined at $20\,^{\circ}\text{C}$ using the following formula:

$$D_{20} = \frac{M_b \times m_5}{V_{20} - M_w \times m_1} + a_5$$

where $D_{20}$ = density of binder at $20\,^{\circ}\text{C}$ (g/ml), $M_b$ = mass of binder at the water bath temperature $t\,^{\circ}\text{C}$ (g), $M_w$ = mass of water at $t$ required to fill the bottle containing the binder (g), $V_{20}$ = volume of test bottle at $20\,^{\circ}\text{C}$ (ml), $m_1$ = multiplication factor to convert mass of water at $t$ to volume of vessel at $20\,^{\circ}\text{C}$, and $m_5$ and $a_5$ = multiplication and addition factors for conversions of mass/volume ratio at $t$ to density at $20\,^{\circ}\text{C}$.

*Significance of test*   The principal use of the density test is in establishing the relationship between binder mass and volume for invoicing and usage purposes. Specifications for binders in road surfacings are normally expressed as percentages by mass, whilst they are usually shipped and measured by volume.

**Table 3.10** Interrelationship between tar density, volume and temperature

| Density at 20 °C (g/ml) | Litres per tonne at different temperatures ( °C) | | | | | |
| --- | --- | --- | --- | --- | --- | --- |
| | 20 | 38 | 80 | 110 | 120 | 140 |
| 1.000 | 1000 | 1015 | 1049 | 1075 | 1084 | 1102 |
| 1.250 | 801 | 807 | 822 | 833 | 837 | 844 |

The importance of density is reflected in the data for tar given in Table 3.10; the temperatures given here approximate to atmospheric, to invoicing, and to those commonly used for spraying or coating.

Knowledge of the density can also be useful in differentiating between different types of binder. For example, the densities of refinery penetration-grade bitumens are normally less than tars, whilst coke-oven tars have higher densities than low-temperature tars.

As is discussed in Chapter 7, it is also necessary to know the relative density of the binder in order to determine the percentage of voids in mechanically-designed mixtures of bitumens and mineral aggregates.

**Flash and fire point tests**
The flash point test is carried out by heating a sample of the binder at a uniform rate, while periodically passing a small flame across the surface of the material. The temperature at which the vapours given off from the binder first burn with a brief flash of blue flame is called the flash point of the binder. If heating is maintained until the vapours continue to burn for a period of at least 5 seconds, the temperature at which this occurs is called the fire point.

*Significance of tests* The flash and fire point tests are primarily safety tests, although they may also be considered as indirect reflections of binder volatility. The flash point is the more important of the two, since it indicates the maximum temperature to which the binder can be safely heated. Safe practice requires special precautions when temperatures in excess of the flash point are being used. The flash points of most penetration-grade bitumens lie in the range 245–335 °C, while rapid-curing cutbacks may flash at temperatures as low as 27 °C. Medium-curing cutbacks usually flash between 52 and 99 °C, while slow-curing ones have flash points above 110 °C. The fire point is of little significance, and its use in specifications is negligible.

# Cement

A cement is a material which, if added in a suitable form to a non-coherent assemblage of particles, will subsequently harden by physical or chemical means and bind the particles into a coherent mass. This definition, which is very broad in scope, allows such diverse materials as bitumen, tar and lime to be grouped together under the umbrella of 'cement'. In general practice, however, the term is used to refer only to the Portland and high-alumina cement binders.

## Portland cement

This, the most commonly used cementing agent in the concrete building industry, was first made in England about 1825. The raw materials which constitute the various types of Portland cement now in use are calcium carbonate—found in the form of limestone or chalk—and alumina, silica and iron oxide—found combined in clay or shale. The first stage of the manufacturing process consists of mixing the clay or shale to a slurry with water, and then admixing the chalk or finely-ground limestone. The prepared slurry is then fed continuously through a long, gently-sloping, cylindrical kiln which is fired by burning pulverized coal blown into its lower end. As the slurry moves through the kiln, it is gradually heated and successive changes take place. First the water is evaporated, and then the calcium carbonate decomposes into calcium oxide (quicklime) and carbon dioxide. About three-quarters of the way down the kiln, when the temperature of the material is at about $1450\,^{\circ}C$, incipient fusion takes place and the components of the lime and the clay combine to form calcium silicates, calcium aluminates and the other compounds which constitute the burnt clinkers which leave the kiln. These clinkers, normally about 12.5 mm in diameter at this stage, are allowed to cool and then transported to ball-and-tube mills where they are ground to a fine powder. During grinding, a small amount—usually between 4 and 7 per cent—of calcium sulphate (gypsum) is added, to prevent the cement from setting too rapidly when hydrated and used.

By setting is meant the change in the cement paste which occurs when its liquid or plastic nature begins to disappear. The start of this change is called the initial set, and its completion is termed the final set. Hardening, which is the development of strength, does not begin until setting is complete. Gypsum has the effect of retarding setting and it is for this reason that a small amount is added to cement in the course of its production. The setting time and rate of setting are of vital importance in the construction of roads since, for good results to be obtained, concrete may have to be mixed, transported substantial distances, placed, and compacted before substantial setting can occur.

### Types of Portland cement

In essence, all types of Portland cement are manufactured as described above. The various types which are available differ only in that they are obtained by varying the proportions of the raw materials, the temperature of burning, and the fineness of grinding. The literature available on cement is literally legion and easily available, whilst the methods of testing cement are well established [54]. The following therefore is only a general description of the more important types of cement.

*Ordinary Portland cement* [55]   This might be termed the workhorse of the cement trade. Obtained by grinding a (mainly) calcium silicate Portland clinker—named after the colour and texture of the natural stone found on the Isle of Portland in the English Channel—it is this cement which is normally supplied by the manufacturer, unless another type is specifically called for. Having a medium rate of hardening, it is suitable for most kinds of concrete construction, including road construction.

*Rapid-hardening Portland cement*[55]   Also known as high-early-strength cement, rapid-hardening Portland cement was first developed about 1920 for use in circumstances where concrete of high early strength is required, e.g. when it is desired to allow traffic on a roadway as soon as possible. The principal difference between this and the ordinary cement is that the final cement clinker is much more finely ground. As a result, a much greater surface area is available for reaction with water, and so it is able to harden more rapidly.

Rapid-hardening cement is more expensive than ordinary cement, but this disadvantage is offset by the fact that the 7-day strengths of mixtures containing this material are approximately equal to the 28-day strengths of mixtures containing normal cement. Whilst the final strengths obtained with both cements are about the same, rapid-hardening cement is no longer permitted in new road construction in Britain, on the grounds that its high early strength requires low cement contents or high water to cement ratios to meet the normal 28-day strength, with a consequent loss of durability[56,57].

*Portland blastfurnace cement*[58]   This is a mixture of finely-ground cement clinker and blastfurnace slag, to which a little gypsum is added to retard the setting time. Granulated slag by itself is a relatively inert material; it reacts so slowly with water that it certainly cannot be regarded as a cementing agent. However, it has the important characteristic that it is pozzolanic, i.e. it will react with lime in the presence of water to form a cementitious product. The hardening of blastfurnace slag cement is characterized by the superposition of two processes. Firstly, there is the hydration of the ground Portland cement clinkers. Secondly, as this takes place, there is a release of free calcium hydroxide which reacts with the slag as it hydrates. Hence the properties of this type of cement are mainly dependent upon the ratio of the two constituent materials. A Portland blastfurnace cement that is low in slag behaves very much like an ordinary Portland cement, while one with a high slag content—this is rarely more than 65 per cent—reflects the influence of the slag ingredients.

As with ordinary and rapid-hardening Portland cement, the initial set of blastfurnace cement takes place after 45 minutes, and the final set may take up to 10 h. In general, slag cement hardens more slowly than ordinary cement, but in the long run there is little difference between the final strengths obtained with both types. The use of slag cement for road construction is more easily justified where economy is of primary importance and high initial strength is not. Usage of blastfurnace cement is mostly in Scotland, where a number of blastfurnaces produce slags suitable for the manufacturing process.

*Pozzolanic cements*   These are produced either by intergrinding the components of Portland cement and pulverized fuel ash or by dry blending

Portland cement and finely-divided pulverized fuel ash. Pulverized fuel ash (pfa) is a waste product obtained from burning pulverized coal in the generation of electricity; that which is used in cement, however, has to meet specified requirements[60]. The pfa content can range from a low of 15 per cent[61] to a high of 50 per cent[62].

As with slag cement, the hardening of the pozzolanic cement is characterized by the hydration of the ground cement clinkers and by the release of free calcium hydroxide which reacts with the pfa as it hydrates. It is slow hardening also, and its utilization is dependent upon a high initial strength not being required. Its main usage is as a low-heat cement to reduce the temperature rise in concrete, and where it is desired to impart a degree of resistance to the action of sulphates and weak acids.

Pozzolanic cement-concretes have a long-term increase in strength that is greater than ordinary Portland cement-concretes for the same 28-day strength, and provide greater durability and resistance to chemical attack. If pfa is included in the mix it permits lower water to cement ratios for a required workability, thereby providing a denser concrete of lower permeability and greater durability.

*Sulphate-resisting cement*[59]    In general, sulphate-resisting cement complies with the requirements for ordinary Portland cement. It is known that sulphates present in seawater, in some groundwaters, and in certain clay soils cause the disintegration of concrete or soil-cement pavements made with ordinary Portland cement. The advantage of sulphate-resisting cement is that this disintegration process, which is caused by the reaction between the sulphates and one of the compounds present in all Portland cements, is controlled to the extent that concrete or coarse-grained soil-cement can be protected against particular sulphate (sulphur trioxide, $SO_3$) concentrations.

## High-alumina cement

High-alumina cement is very different, both in composition and properties, from Portland cement. The British Standard[63] which governs the production of this cement specifies a minimum alumina content of 32 per cent and a ratio of lime to alumina of between 0.85 and 1.30; the cement is therefore composed mainly of these two constituents. It is manufactured by melting a mixture of limestone or chalk and bauxite in a reverberatory or electric furnace, allowing the clinker mass to cool, and then grinding it to a fine powder. The bauxite used in high-alumina cement production in Britain is imported from France and Greece; the cement manufactured is often known as 'Ciment Fondu'.

The principal feature of a high-alumina cement is its very-rapid-hardening property which enables it to attain a strength after 24 hours that would take ordinary Portland cement about 28 days to achieve. In the course of this very rapid hardening, a considerable amount of heat is generated and this enables the cement to be used at much lower air temperatures than ordinary Portland cement. Originally developed to provide concrete that was resistant to seawater and groundwaters, high-alumina cement has the advantage of being very resistant to the attacking action of sulphates. A drawback associated with high-alumina cement is that the aluminates which provide the high early strength are metastable at high temperatures and convert to other products, with a consequent loss of strength and durability; the rate of change, however, is critically dependent upon temperature, taking many years at $20\,^{\circ}C$ and only a few days at $50\,^{\circ}C$[64].

Although high-alumina cement hardens very rapidly, it is also relatively slow setting. The initial set requires at least 2 h, and the final set another 2 h, so there is normally more than adequate time to place the concrete in rigid roadway pavements. However, for the same (durability) reason as for rapid-hardening cement, high-alumina cement is no longer permitted in new concrete pavement work in Britain.

## Chemical composition of cements

The four main chemicals present in cement are quicklime (CaO), silica ($SiO_2$), alumina ($Al_2O_3$), and ferric oxide ($Fe_2O_3$). Some typical cement compositions are shown in Table 3.11.

From a practical point of view, however, the constituents of most importance in a cement are the mineralogical compounds formed during the fusion process in the kiln; it is these which, when hydrated, form the actual binding paste. The most important of these are as follows.

| | |
|---|---|
| Tricalcium silicate ($C_3S$) | $3CaO.SiO_2$ |
| Dicalcium silicate ($C_2S$) | $2CaO.SiO_2$ |
| Tricalcium aluminate ($C_3A$) | $3CaO.Al_2O_3$ |
| Calcium aluminoferrite ($C_4AF$) | $4CaO.Al_2O_3.Fe_2O_3$ |

It is customary in cement chemistry to denote the individual clinker minerals by short symbols such as $CaO = C$, $SiO_2 = S$, $Al_2O_3 = A$ and $Fe_2O_3 = F$, and this enables the above formulae to be abbreviated to $C_3S$, $C_2S$, $C_3A$ and $C_4AF$.

Much is still unknown about what happens when water is added to cement. As indicated by Table 3.12, the hydration of the $C_3A$ component takes place very quickly; in fact, whatever strength there is at the end of the

**Table 3.11** Main chemical constituents of cement (% by mass)

| | Type of cement | | |
|---|---|---|---|
| Chemical | Ordinary and rapid-hardening Portland cement | Portland blastfurnace cement | High-alumina cement |
| CaO | 59–66 | 45–55 | 35–40 |
| $SiO_2$ | 18–23 | 25–30 | 10–12 |
| $Al_2O_3$ | 4.5–8.0 | 10–20 | 40–45 |
| $Fe_2O_3$ | 2.5–4.5 | 3–5 | 1–20 |

**Table 3.12**   Comparison of effects of main Portland cement compounds

| Principal constituent compounds | Rate of chemical reaction and heat generation | Most active period | Contribution towards final strength |
| --- | --- | --- | --- |
| $C_3A$ | Fast | 1st day | Small |
| $C_3S$ | Moderate | 2nd to 7th day | Large |
| $C_2S$ | Slow | 7th day onwards | Moderate |

first day is a function of this hydrated product. It is suggested that this hydration takes place in the following manner, without any lime being picked up or released:

$$3CaO.Al_2O_3 + 6H_2O \rightarrow 3CaO.Al_2O_3.6H_2O$$

After the first day, the effect on strength of the hydrated $C_3A$ compound is negligible. In contrast to this, the principal contributor to the strength gain at this time is the $C_3S$ compound. The greatest $C_3S$ strength gain is observed within 28 days, after which hydration continues but at a much slower rate. The reaction that takes place is believed to take the following form:

$$2[3CaO.SiO_2] + 6H_2O \rightarrow 3CaO.2SiO_2.3H_2O + 3Ca(OH)_2$$

As can be seen, this reaction involves the evolution of lime. The tricalcium disilicate hydrate which is formed is the final product of cement hydration and is believed to be the principal binding material. A similar product is believed to be formed when the $C_2S$ compound is hydrated. Thus

$$2[2CaO.SiO_2] + 4H_2O \rightarrow 3CaO.2SiO_2.3H_2O + Ca(OH)_2$$

This compound's final contribution to the long-term strength may ultimately approach that of the $C_3S$ compound.

## Lime

The word *lime* is a much abused term, often loosely used to denote any calcareous material. Strictly defined, however, lime is calcium oxide (CaO). In highway engineering practice, the term is used to describe both the oxides and hydroxides of calcium and magnesium, i.e. quicklimes and hydrated limes formed from calcitic and dolomitic materials.

### Types of lime

Lime is most often produced by calcining limestones, but chalk and oyster shells are also calcined to make lime. If the limestone being treated is a pure or near-pure calcium carbonate ($CaCO_3$), the limes produced are described as *calcitic* or *high-calcium limes* or, more simply, 'white' limes. If the stone being calcined is a dolomitic limestone containing a high proportion of magnesium carbonate ($MgCO_3$), the lime products are termed *dolomitic* or *magnesian limes*.

Calcitic and dolomitic limes are available for use in road construction (most usually as soil modifiers or stabilizers) in both quicklime and hydrated lime forms. Whilst the standard British specification on building limes[65] does not differentiate in any major way between calcitic and dolomitic limes, it does accept that high-calcium hydrated limes and quicklimes contain not more than 4 and 5 per cent magnesium oxide (MgO), respectively, whilst dolomitic hydrated limes and quicklimes contain not less than 4 and 5 per cent MgO, respectively. In practice, however, most dolomitic limes contain much greater percentages of MgO.

A particular type of lime that is not much used in road construction at this time is hydraulic lime. Such limes, which may or may not be hydrated, can be considered as being intermediate between the above 'normal' limes and ordinary Portland cement. They are manufactured by calcining impure limestone containing up to about 35 per cent clay. If the lime produced contains more than 5 per cent soluble silica ($SiO_2$), it is termed a *semi-hydraulic lime*. If the clay content is greater than, say, 15 per cent, the lime may be termed an *eminently hydraulic lime* or, more simply, a *hydraulic lime*.

During the normal calcining of argillaceous or siliceous limestones, the calcium carbonate is caused to dissociate by heat, following which solid reactions take place between the calcium oxide which is formed and the silica, alumina and ferric oxide components of the clay. This leads primarily to the formation of the dicalcium silicate and tricalcium aluminate compounds which give to the hydraulic and semi-hydraulic limes their cement-like properties, whilst they still retain the plastic properties of conventional limes.

## Quicklimes

These, the most concentrated form of lime, are normally produced by direct calcination of crushed limestones in either shaft (vertical) kilns or rotary (near-horizontal) kilns. In the case of pure calcite, the following reaction takes place

$$CaCO_3 + heat \rightarrow CaO + CO_2$$

At atmospheric pressure and at a temperature of 900 °C, the lime product of the above reaction is termed calcitic or high-calcium quicklime.

If a dolomitic limestone is calcined, dolomitic quicklime is produced in the following manner. At atmospheric pressure and a temperature of 730 °C, the dolomitic rock decomposes to form magnesium oxide, carbon dioxide and calcium carbonate. At 900 °C, the $CaCO_3$ also decomposes and the end-product is a mixture of MgO and CaO, which is dolomitic quicklime.

A significant feature of quicklime which retards its usage is that its highly exothermic hydration reaction and causticity can make it a safety hazard; particularly in windy weather, construction workers can severely damage their eyes or skin if adequate precautions are not taken.

Bulk quicklime has a significant economic advantage over hydrated lime; as well as being cheaper, it also contains as much as 25 per cent more

CaO or MgO. This potential saving to the user may be, however, at least partially offset by an increased cost in the handling of the more active quicklime.

**Hydrated limes**

'Slaking' is a general term used in the lime industry to refer to the combining of quicklime and an excess amount of water in order to produce a slaked lime slurry or lime putty of varying degrees of consistency. A hydrated lime results from the addition of just sufficient water to the quicklime to satisfy its chemical affinity for moisture under the hydration conditions; the product is a dry, powdered lime.

Before quicklime is hydrated, the lumps are usually ground to particles less than 13 mm in size. The high-calcium quicklimes are then able to react readily with water to produce calcitic hydrated lime in which all the calcium oxide is converted to calcium hydroxide with the evolution of heat. The MgO component of dolomitic quicklime, however, does not hydrate so readily at the temperatures, atmospheric pressure and short retention times used in the ordinary lime hydration process. Thus dolomitic monohydrate lime is obtained after the following reaction has taken place:

$$CaO + MgO + H_2O \rightarrow Ca(OH)_2 + MgO$$

Since about 1940 it has been possible to hydrate dolomitic quicklime more fully under special conditions incorporating higher temperatures and pressures and longer retention times. With the MgO being hydrated to $Mg(OH)_2$, these pressure-hydrated limes are known as dolomitic dihydrate limes. These are not suitable for use in highway construction and so will not be discussed further here.

Whilst the hydrated limes are considerably less dangerous to handle than quicklime, they are still caustic and require some care in handling. Hydrated limes, as well as quicklimes, release heat upon contact with water; the heat given off by quicklimes, however, is much greater because of the highly exothermic hydration reactions.

Typically, hydrated lime contains about 30 per cent combined water. This makes it less economic than quicklime, particularly if large quantities and long haulage distances are involved.

# Natural rock aggregates

Mineral aggregates are the basic materials of highway pavement construction. Not only do they support the main stresses occurring within the pavement, but in addition the aggregates in the road surface must resist wear due to abrasion by traffic as well as the direct weathering effects of the natural elements. The manner in which they do so depends upon the inherent properties and qualities of the individual particles and upon the means by which they are held together, i.e. by interlocking, by cementitious binders, or by both.

Road aggregates may be used by themselves in road construction. In low-cost roads, where it is desired to make the most use of locally available materials, natural gravel aggregates or crushed aggregates mixed with soil frequently form the entire pavement structure. In such instances, the gradation of the soil–aggregate materials is most important and particular attention must be paid to ensuring that maximum plasticity criteria are not exceeded. Aggregates are also used by themselves to form the subbase beneath concrete pavements, and as roadbase and subbase materials in high-quality, flexible ones. In the former, the load-bearing capacity of the aggregate subbase is not of primary importance and emphasis is placed instead upon achieving a gradation which will prevent pumping of the subgrade or intrusion of frost-susceptible materials, while at the same time improving the subsurface drainage characteristics of the roadway. In a flexible pavement roadbase, the stress-carrying capacity is the factor of primary importance, so the aggregate must be selected to serve this purpose.

Aggregates may also be used with binders, of which the two most important are cement and the bituminous binders. In high-quality, bituminous road surfacings, aggregates may comprise up to 70–75 per cent by volume and 90–95 per cent by mass of the surfacing. It is the aggregate which is primarily responsible for any load-carrying capacity which the surfacing may have, while at the same time it provides the resistance to abrasion under traffic which is so important in preventing vehicles from skidding. Although there are very many types of bituminous surfacing, in general the ideal aggregates for their construction should have the following characteristics:

(1) strength and toughness,
(2) the ability to crush into chunky particles, and free from flakes, slivers and pieces that are unduly thin and elongated,
(3) low porosity,
(4) hydrophobic characteristics,
(5) a particle size and gradation appropriate to the type of construction.

Most specifications relating to aggregates tend to seek these properties.

The above criteria also apply to concrete pavements, particularly those relating to particle shape and size distribution, since they affect both water requirements and the workability of concrete mixes as well as other important concrete properties. Also of importance in concrete work are the textures and structures of the aggregates.

## Types of aggregate

One definition of an aggregate is that it is a material such as broken stone, slag, gravel or sand which, when held together by a binding agent, forms a substantial part of such materials as concrete, asphalt and coated macadam. This definition means that any hard material, whether it be natural or artificial, may be classified as an aggregate. In practice, however, the materials *suitable* for use as road aggregates may be limited in a particular area.

The following discussion is concerned with crushed rock aggregates. Gravels and sands are discussed separately in Chapters 4 and 5.

**Crushed rock aggregates**

By far the majority of pavement aggregates is formed from natural rock. As is indicated in Table 3.13, geologists have classified rocks into three main groups, based on their method of origin, viz. igneous, sedimentary and metamorphic rocks. It is of interest to make a brief examination of some of the components of these classification groups as it is the means by which they were formed which primarily determines the compositions and textures of the rock aggregates.

*Igneous rocks* were formed at or below the earth's surface by the cooling of molten material, called magma, which erupted from, or was trapped beneath, the earth's crust. Igneous rocks formed at the earth's surface when the magma came into contact with the atmosphere are called extrusive rocks, while those formed below the earth's surface are intrusive rocks. Extrusive magma cooled rapidly at the earth's surface and, as a result, the rocks formed are very often glassy or vitreous (without crystals) or partly crystalline and partly vitreous. This latter occurrence is due to the outer layers of the magma flow or lava cooling very rapidly and becoming vitreous, while the inner material cooled more slowly and became crystalline with the grain-sizes being very small indeed. As the magma escaped at the surface, the contained gases expanded, and hence an extrusive rock may contain cavities which give it a vesicular texture. In contrast to the extrusive rocks, the intrusive rocks are entirely crystalline, having been formed as a result of the magma cooling slowly under the protective cover of the earth's crust. In many instances, the rock crystals may be sufficiently large to be easily distinguished by the naked eye.

 The grain-size is most important in a road aggregate. If the grains are very coarse, i.e. > 1.250 mm, the particles are liable to be brittle and may break down beneath the crushing action of a compacting roller. However, if the grains are too fine, i.e. < 0.125 mm, and particularly if the rock is vesicular, they are also liable to be brittle and splintery. The best igneous roadstones normally contain medium grain-sizes between 0.125 and 1.250 mm.

Igneous rocks can also be separated on the basis of their being acidic or basic. Acidic rocks can be either extrusive or intrusive, depending upon their silica content. As used here, the term 'silica' is meant to refer to $SiO_2$, which may be either in combination with alumina, etc., to form feldspars and other minerals, or free as in the mineral quartz. When a rock contains more than about 66 per cent silica it is described as acidic, while it is a basic rock if it contains less than 55 per cent silica; those containing between 55 and 66 per cent total $SiO_2$ are called intermediate rocks. Acidic aggregates are considered by some authorities to be undesirable road-making materials as they are hydrophilic or 'water-loving'. In preparing bituminous mixtures, these aggregates can be difficult to coat with binder in contrast to the hydrophobic or 'water-hating' aggregates formed from a rock such as basalt.

Igneous rocks account for approximately 26 per cent of the rock (i.e. excluding gravel and sand) aggregates processed for all construction purposes in Britain.

*Sedimentary rocks* were formed when the products of disintegration and/or decomposition of any type of rock were transported and redeposited, and then consolidated or cemented into a new rock type. Sedimentary rocks also include those formed as a result of chemical precipitation or the deposition of organic remains in water. They were, as the name implies, laid down in stratified layers and so are easily distinguished from the massive structure of igneous rocks. The rock strata, at one time horizontal, may now be deformed and displaced through angles of up to 90 degrees as a result of upheavals which continually occurred throughout geologic history.

Sedimentary rocks may be subdivided by various means, but the most convenient one is that based on the predominant rock mineral. This allows three main rock subclassifications, the calcareous, siliceous and carbonaceous groups, of which the first two are mainly of interest to the highway engineer.

Calcareous rocks were formed as the result of great thicknesses of the remains of small marine animals being deposited on the ocean floors. The predominant mineral is calcite ($CaCO_3$), and this renders the rocks basic and, in general, most suitable as an aggregate for bituminous surfacings. Some types of calcareous rocks are, however, too porous to be used as road aggregates. Generally, the softer the rock, the more porous it is, and porosity can be expressed in terms of the rock's saturation moisture content, e.g. for soft chalks this may be as high as 25 to 30 per cent, while for hard limestone it will be less than 1 per cent. Tests[67] have shown that all crushed chalks are frost susceptible, with the magnitude of frost heave increasing linearly with the saturation moisture content of the chalk aggregate. Similarly, all oolitic and magnesian (dolomitic) limestones having an average saturation moisture content within the aggregate in excess of 3 per cent must be regarded as frost susceptible and should not be used within a highway pavement.

In contrast to the calcareous rocks, arenaceous siliceous rocks were formed from deposits of sand and silt which became lithified as a result of pressure by overlying strata, or by the deposition of cementing material between the grains. The predominant mineral in these rocks is either quartz or chalcedony (both $SiO_2$), and this may tend to make adhesion between these aggregates and bituminous binders relatively difficult. These rocks are also much harder than calcareous rocks, but some are so brittle as to be unusable in road pavements, particularly in bituminous surfacings.

Argillaceous siliceous rocks are those in which the clay minerals predominate. They were formed when fine-grained particles of soil were first deposited as clays or muds and then consolidated by pressure from overlying deposits. As a result, the argillaceous siliceous rocks are very fine grained, highly laminated, and very often are easily crushed into splinters. For these reasons, they are rarely used as pavement aggregates, and never in bituminous surfacings.

Limestone, one of the major (calcareous) sedimentary rocks, is the aggregate that is most widely used in Britain for all construction purposes, i.e. nearly 50 per cent of all crushed rock aggregates are crushed limestone.

**Table 3.13** Aid to identification of rocks for engineering purposes[66]

| Grain-size (mm) | Bedded rocks (mostly sedimentary) | | | | At least 50% of grains are of carbonate | At least 50% of grains are of fine-grained volcanic rock | |
|---|---|---|---|---|---|---|---|
| More than 20 | Grain-size description | | | | | | |
| 20 — 6 — 2 — | Rudaceous | | | **CONGLOMERATE** Rounded boulders, cobbles and gravel cemented in a finer matrix Breccia Irregular rock fragments in a finer matrix | Calcirudite | Fragments of volcanic ejecta in a finer matrix Rounded grains **AGGLOMERATE** Angular grains **VOLCANIC BRECCIA** | Saline rocks Halite Anhydrite |
| 0.6 — 0.2 — 0.06 | Arenaceous | | Coarse | **SANDSTONE** Angular or rounded grains, commonly cemented by clay, calcitic or iron minerals | LIMESTONE and DOLOMITE (undifferentiated) Calcarenite | Cemented volcanic ash **TUFF** | Gypsum |
| | | | Medium | Quartize Quartz grains and siliceous cement | | | |
| | | | Fine | Arkose Many feldspar grains Greywacke Many rock chips | | | |
| 0.002 — Less than 0.002 | Argillaceous | | | **MUDSTONE** | **SILTSTONE** Mostly silt | Calcareous mudstone — Calcis-iltite | Fine-grained **TUFF** |
| | | | | **SHALE** Fissile | **CLAYSTONE** Mostly clay | Calcil-utite — CHALK | Very-fine-grained **TUFF** |
| Amorphous or crypto-crystalline | | | | Flint Occurs as bands of nodules in the Chalk Chert Occurs as nodules and beds in limestone and calcareous sandstone | | | **COAL LIGNITE** |
| | Granular cemented, except amorphous rocks | | | | | | |
| | Siliceous | | | | Calcareous | Siliceous | Carbonaceous |

*Sedimentary rocks*
Granular cemented rocks vary greatly in strength, some sandstones are stronger than many igneous rocks. Bedding may not show in hand specimens and is best seen in outcrop. Only sedimentary rocks, and some metamorphic rocks derived from them, contain fossils.
  Calcareous rocks contain calcite (calcium carbonate) which effervesces with dilute hydrochloric acid

Notes
(1) Principal rock types (generally common) are shown in bold type in capitals, e.g. **GRANITE**; less common rock types are shown in medium type, e.g. Greywacke
(2) Granular rocks may be distinguished from crystalline rocks by scratching with a knife which should remove whole grains from the cement matrix in the granular rocks. The separate grains may also sometimes be distinguished by using a hand lens. Siliceous rocks are generally harder and more resistant to scratching than calcareous rocks
(3) In the table the boundaries of the heavy lined box describe the conditions to which the rock name applies

**Table 3.13**  (*cont.*)

| Obviously foliated rocks (mostly metamorphic) | | | Rocks with massive structure and crystalline texture (mostly igneous) | | | | |
|---|---|---|---|---|---|---|---|
| Grain-size description | | | Grain-size description | Pegmatite | | | |
| Coarse | **GNEISS** Well-developed but often widely spaced foliation, sometimes with schistose bands Migmatite Irregularly foliated: mixed schists and gneisses | **MARBLE** **QUARTZITE** Granulite **HORNFELS** Amphibolite Serpentine | Coarse | **GRANITE**[1]    Diorite[1,2]   **GABBRO**[3] These rocks are sometimes porphyritic and are then described, for example, as porphyritic granite | | | Pyroxenite Peridotite |
| Medium | **SCHIST** Well-developed undulose foliation; generally much mica | | Medium | Micro-granite[1]    Micro-diorite[1,2] These rocks are sometimes porphyritic and are then described as porphyries | | Dolerite[3,4] — | |
| Fine | **PHYLLITE** Slightly undulose foliation, some-times 'spotted' **SLATE** Well-developed plane cleavage (foliation) | | Fine | **RHYOLITE**[4,5]  **ANDESITE**[4,5]  **BASALT**[4,5] These rocks are sometimes porphyritic and are then described as porphyries — | | | |
| | Mylonite Found in fault zones, mainly in igneous and metamorphic areas | | | Obsidian[5]    Volcanic glass | | | |
| | Crystalline | | | Pale ←——— Colour ———→ Dark | | | |
| | Siliceous | Mainly Siliceous | | Acid Much quartz | Intermediate Some quartz | Basic Little or no quartz | Ultra-basic |

*Metamorphic rocks*
Most metamorphic rocks are distinguished by foliation which may impart fissility. Foliation in gneisses is best observed in out-crop. Non-foliated metamorphics are difficult to recognize except by association. Any rock baked by contact metamorphism is described as a 'hornfels' and is generally somewhat stronger than the parent rock.
   Most fresh metamorphic rocks are strong although perhaps fissile

*Igneous rocks*
Composed of closely interlocking mineral grains. Strong when fresh; not porous
   Mode of occurrence: 1, Batholiths; 2, Laccoliths; 3, Sills; 4, Dykes; 5, Lava flows; 6, Veins

Sandstone, another (arenaceous) sedimentary rock, contributes about 10 per cent to rock aggregate production.

*Metamorphic rocks* are igneous or sedimentary rocks which, as a result of being subjected to tremendous heat (thermal metamorphism), or heat and great pressure combined (regional metamorphism), were transformed into new types of rock by the recrystallization of their constituents. Metamorphism in any particular instance may have been aided by the presence of permeating solvents which worked through the rock and promoted new mineral growth.

Thermal metamorphic rocks are almost always harder than the rocks from which they were originally transformed. In addition, they often show an interlocking of mineral constituents that renders them more useful as aggregates. As a result, metamorphic rocks which were altered by heat alone are in considerable demand as road aggregates. In contrast to the thermally-formed rocks, the regional metamorphic rocks are relatively coarse grained and some are highly foliated, i.e. the minerals are arranged in parallel planes or layers along which the rock is much more easily split than in other directions. Examples of metamorphic rocks that exhibit this laminated structure are gneiss and schist (from igneous material) and slate (from shale, a sedimentary rock). Marble (from limestone) and quartzite (from sandstone) are examples of metamorphic rocks that are not foliated.

Aggregates from foliated metamorphic rocks are generally not desirable as a pavement material, as they can be quite fissile and liable to be crushed when compacted with rollers.

**Aggregate groups**
Within the broad geological classes shown in Table 3.13 and discussed above, geologists have identified literally hundreds of different types of rock. Many of these rocks differ little from each other with regard to their road-making qualities, and so it is convenient to gather them together into groupings with common characteristics. Figure 3.8 shows one such grouping, which is useful in describing the general suitability of aggregates for use in highway pavement construction. Included in this figure also is the 'artificial' aggregate group.

Rock included in these groups must be crushed and screened prior to usage in highway pavements. Crushing is necessary in order to reduce the rock fragments to the desired gradation of particle sizes. In the process, particles are made angular and surface textures are roughened.

The following is a brief description of the main rocks in each aggregate group.

(1)    *Basalt group*    The most important rocks in this group are basalt, dolerite, basic porphyrite and andesite. Members of the group are primarily basic and intermediate igneous rocks of medium and fine grain-size, but some of their metamorphic equivalents are also included. They are composed principally of feldspars and ferro-magnesian minerals, the latter giving the rocks their characteristic dark colouring and a relatively high

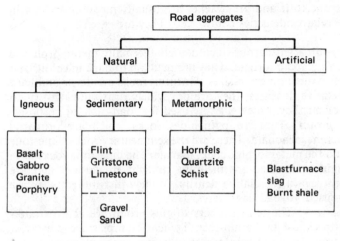

**Fig. 3.8**  Principal groups of road aggregates

relative density. They are widely distributed in Britain and are extensively used as road aggregates.

(2)  *Flint group*  This group has only two members, flint and chert, which are very-fine-grained sedimentary rocks consisting mainly of cryptocrystalline silica (chalcedony). These rocks vary from white to black in colour and have low relative densities. Flint is widely distributed as gravel material and, in eastern and southern England, this is the principal local source of road aggregate.

(3)  *Gabbro group*  There are eight members of this group, of which the most important are gabbro, basic diorite and basic gneiss. The gabbro group is composed primarily of basic igneous rocks, but some intermediate rocks of coarse grain-size—as well as their metamorphic equivalents—are included. The most common constituents are feldspars and ferro-magnesian minerals, and it is the latter which often predominate and give a dark colour and high relative density to the rocks. The rocks of this group are not widely distributed in Britain, but they are extensively used as roadstones where they occur.

(4)  *Granite group*  The members of this group are mostly acidic and intermediate igneous rocks of coarse grain-size, but also included are their metamorphic equivalents. Of the seven members of this group, the most important are granite, quartz–diorite, gneiss and syenite. The predominant minerals are feldspars and quartz, but micas, pyroxenes or amphiboles may also occur. These rocks, which are light in colour and have relative densities below 2.80, are widely distributed and extensively used for road aggregate purposes.

(5)  *Gritstone group*  This group is composed mainly of siliceous sedimentary rocks which are usually of medium or coarse grain-size; they are sometimes cemented with fine-grained material which may be siliceous, calcareous, argillaceous or ferruginous. These rocks, typical examples of

which are sandstone, tuff and greywacke, are usually medium or light in colour and have relative densities below 2.80. They are extensively used as road aggregates.

(6) *Hornfels group* This group includes all thermally-metamorphosed rocks, except marble and quartzite. They are medium to dark in colour and usually have fine to medium grain-sizes. Hornfels rocks are dense and hard and have high relative densities; they are not widely distributed in Britain but where they occur they are extensively used for road-making purposes.

(7) *Limestone group* This group includes rocks which are primarily composed of calcium carbonate. These are the sedimentary rocks, limestone and dolomite, and the metamorphic rock, marble. The limestone rocks have a medium to fine grain-size, are medium to light in colour, and are intermediate with regard to relative density. Widely distributed, they are most extensively used as road aggregates.

(8) *Porphyry group* The ten members of this group are acid or intermediate igneous rocks of fine grain-size. Typical examples are porphyry, granophyre, microgranite and felsite. Broadly similar to the rocks of the granite group, they are also widely distributed and much used as road aggregates.

(9) *Quartzite group* These are siliceous sedimentary or metamorphic rocks composed almost entirely of quartz. Members of this group, i.e. quartzite, quartzitic sandstone and ganister, are light in colour, have a grain-size which is medium to fine, and are intermediate in relative density. Quartzite rocks occur in Britain both as solid rock and as gravel, and are very much used as roadstones.

(10) *Schist group* This group is composed of laminated rocks such as schist, phyllite and slate. They are rarely used as road aggregates because of their general instability.

At the height of the motorway construction programme, the British construction industry used more than 300-million tonnes of aggregate per annum, of which at least 70–77-million tonnes were rock aggregate used directly in highway pavement construction[68]. Figure 3.9 shows the locations of all major quarries and gravel pits in Britain. It clearly shows that in particular parts of the country there is a shortage of suitable aggregates for road construction. The area most lacking in natural rock aggregate is South-east England; this region relies heavily upon natural sands and gravels plus imported rock aggregates for its construction needs. It has been estimated that by the early 1990s almost all of the gravel-bearing land in the South-east which is not agriculturally valuable or environmentally precious will have been worked out[70].

In particular localities it will be found that certain rock aggregates are known by traditional names which are very different from those recommended by the British Standard. This can be very confusing to those not familiar with local terminology, and it is strongly recommended that local names should not be used in official documents or scientific reports. Some of the more common traditional names and their proper group equivalents are given in Table 3.14.

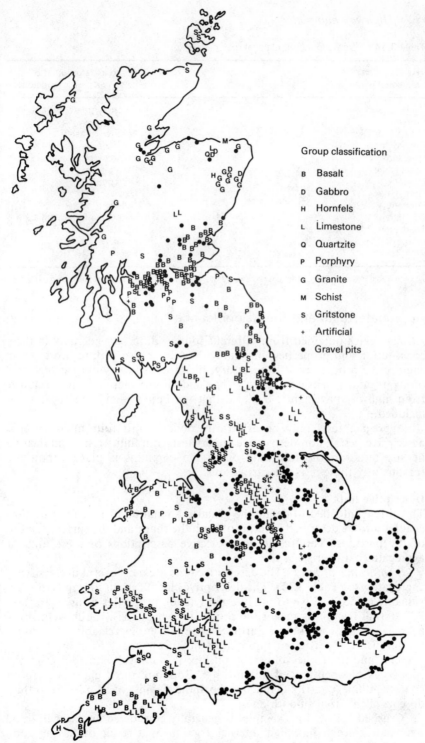

**Group classification**

B   Basalt
D   Gabbro
H   Hornfels
L   Limestone
Q   Quartzite
P   Porphyry
G   Granite
M   Schist
S   Gritstone
+   Artificial
•   Gravel pits

**Fig. 3.9** Distribution of road aggregate quarries and pits in Britain [69]

**Table 3.14**  Some common traditional rock names[71]

| Traditional name* | Appropriate group in BS classification for roadstone |
|---|---|
| Clinkstone | Porphyry (rarely basalt) |
| Cornstone | Limestone |
| Elvan (Blue Elvan) | Porphyry (basalt) |
| Flagstone | Gritstone |
| Freestone | Gritstone or limestone |
| Greenstone | Basalt |
| Hassock | Gritstone |
| Hornstone | Flint |
| Pennant | Gritstone |
| Rag (stone) | Limestone (rarely gritstone) |
| Toadstone | Basalt |
| Trap (rock) | Basalt |
| Whin (stone) | Basalt |

*As the traditional names are often applied loosely, the information in this table cannot be precise

## Aggregate tests and their significance

As aggregates obtained from different sources differ considerably in their constitution and properties, inevitably they differ also with regard to their engineering properties. It is necessary, therefore, to carry out various tests on aggregates to ensure not only that undesirable materials are excluded from highway pavements, but also that the best available aggregates are included. كاى كوا تـــــبادى

Aggregate tests may be arbitrarily divided into four main groups: descriptive 'tests', non-destructive quality tests, durability tests, and relative density tests. In the following discussion emphasis is placed upon the reasons why these tests are carried out.

**Descriptive tests**
This title is intended to define the visual examination of an aggregate that enables it to be described in terms of both the shape and the surface texture of the particles. This results in subjective descriptions of these mineral aggregate characteristics.

*Significance of tests*  The descriptive tests are most useful in classifying aggregates (see Table 3.15). The descriptive classifications are, in turn, very valuable guides relative to the internal friction properties of an aggregate. By internal friction is meant the properties which resist the movement of aggregates past each other. Particle shape has an appreciable effect upon the physical properties of bituminous mixtures, upon the proper binder content, and upon the voids relationship; it is critical with respect to the properties of open-graded mixtures[72]. Rough-textured aggregates (both coarse and fine) contribute much more to the stability of all pavements than do equivalent-sized smooth ones.

Crushed basalt, for example, is generally considered an excellent road aggregate since it has high internal friction as a result of having good interlocking qualities—because of the angular shapes of the particles—and a rough surface texture. In contrast to basalt, a rounded, smooth aggregate  such as gravel is relatively low in internal friction since particle interlock is not possible and surface friction is low. It is for this reason that very many gravel aggregate specifications require that the gravel be artificially crushed

**Table 3.15** Descriptive evaluations of mineral aggregates: (a) particle shape and (b) surface texture

| Classification | Description | Examples |
| --- | --- | --- |
| Rounded | Fully water-worn or completely shaped by attrition | River or seashore gravel; desert, seashore and wind-blown sand |
| Irregular | Naturally irregular, or partly shaped by attrition and having rounded edges | Other gravels; land or dug flint |
| Flaky | Material of which the thickness is small relative to the other two dimensions | Laminated rock |
| Angular | Possessing well-defined edges formed at the intersection of roughly planar faces | Crushed rocks of all types; talus; crushed slag |
| Elongated | Material, usually angular, in which the length is considerably larger than the other two dimensions | — |
| Flaky and elongated | Material having the length considerably larger than the width, and the width considerably larger than the thickness | — |

(a)

| Surface texture | Characteristics | Examples |
| --- | --- | --- |
| Glassy | Conchoidal fracture | Black flint, vitreous slag |
| Smooth | Water-worn, or smooth due to fracture of laminated or fine-grained rock | Gravels, chert, slate, marble, some rhyolites |
| Granular | Fracture showing more or less uniform rounded grains | Sandstone, oolite |
| Rough | Rough fracture of fine- or medium-grained rock containing no easily visible crystalline constituents | Basalt, felsite, porphyry, limestone |
| Crystalline | Containing easily visible crystal-line constituents | Granite, gabbro, gneiss |
| Honeycombed and porous | With visible pores and cavities | Brick, pumice, foamed slag, clinker, expanded clay |

(b)

to produce jagged edges and surfaces before being used in a highway pavement.

### Non-destructive quality tests

These non-destructive tests are carried out on the aggregate to determine its suitability for a specific use. The results obtained are normally compared with aggregate specifications to see whether they comply with the desired properties and characteristics. The tests of particular interest are the gradation[73], shape[74,75], and water absorption[76] tests.

*Gradation test*   Gradation, sieve analysis, screen analysis, and mechanical analysis are synonymous terms which refer to the quantities, expressed in percentages by mass, of the various particle sizes of which a sample of aggregate is composed. These quantities are determined by separating the aggregates into portions which are retained on a number of sieves or screens having specified openings which are suitably graded from coarse to fine. As with soils, the results obtained with aggregates may be expressed either as the total percentage passing or retained on each sieve or as the percentages retained between successive sieves. The total-percentage-passing method is very convenient for the graphical representation of a grading and is most widely used in graded-aggregate specifications. The individual-percentages-retained-on-particular-sieves procedure is, however, preferred in specifications for single-sized aggregates[77,78].

*Significance of test*   Gradation tests are quick and cheap, and provide information that can be useful to aggregate producers (for quality-control purposes) and to users (for checking compliance). As well as being the characteristic of a road aggregate on which the greatest stress is paid in specifications, gradation is probably the cause of the majority of controversies which arise between the aggregate supplier and the road builder. The proper grading of an aggregate is important because of its direct influence upon both the quality and the cost of a completed pavement.

Many aggregate specifications, based as they are on practical experience, include an allowance for sampling and testing errors. Even so, single gradation test results are not necessarily reliable indicators of compliance, especially if they lie close to the specified limits, i.e. some materials apparently outside the specification limits might truly comply, whilst others apparently within the limits may actually be outside them[79]. In such cases, it normally takes a large number of check tests to confirm the 'true' results; however, the cost of testing at high frequencies must always be balanced against the value of the information gained from the extra testing.

The limits placed upon a particular gradation depend upon the nature of the work in which the aggregate is to be employed. Thus, for instance, the grading of a material to be used in a dense, bituminous surfacing—which depends considerably upon gradation for its denseness and consequent stability—is more critical than the grading of an aggregate for use in macadam, in which stability is heavily dependent upon the interlocking of the aggregate particles. With well-graded aggregates—those having gradation curves resembling a parabola, which is a combination of a curve approaching an ellipse for the fines portion and a tangential straight line for the coarse portion—care should be taken to minimize the amount of handling or transporting to which they are subjected as segregation of sizes can easily occur, and this can be quite expensive to remedy.

When aggregate particles are to be bound together by cement, bitumen or tar, a variation in the gradation of the aggregate will result in a change in the amount of binder required to produce a mixture of given stability and quality. In addition to affecting the binder content, aggregate gradation and size range also have a considerable influence upon the strength and stiffness characteristics of a bituminous mixture, and upon its permeability, economy, workability, and skid-resistance.

*Shape tests*  There are two mechanical measures of particle shape which may be included in the specifications for aggregates for road construction. These are the flakiness index and the elongation index.

The *flakiness index* of an aggregate is the percentage by mass of particles whose least thickness is less than 0.6 times their mean dimension; the mean dimension as used in each instance is the average of two adjacent sieve aperture sizes between which the particle being measured is retained by sieving. The flakiness test, which is not applicable to particles greater than 63 mm or smaller than 6.3 mm in size, is carried out by first separating the aggregate into individual percentages retained on specified sieve sizes, and then passing the flaky particles from the individual percentages through special sieves or patterns having elongated slots whose widths are 0.6 times the individual mean dimensions. The flakiness index is then reported as the total mass of material passing the various thickness gauges or sieves, expressed as a percentage of the total mass of the sample gauged.

The *elongation index* of an aggregate is the percentage by mass of particles whose largest dimension is greater than 1.8 times their mean dimension. As with the flakiness test, the elongation test is not applicable to aggregate sizes smaller than 6.3 mm; it is also similar in that first the aggregate sample is fractionated and then the individual particles from the fractions are passed through openings on a special metal length-gauge. The elongation index is taken as the total mass of material retained on the length-gauge, expressed as a percentage of the total mass of the sample gauged.

*Significance of tests*  As noted previously, the internal friction of an aggregate is the property which, by means of the interlocking of particles and the surface friction between adjacent surfaces, resists particle movement under the action of an imposed load. Use of the shape tests in specifications is based on the view that internal friction is influenced by the shapes of the particles. Thus, for instance, the standards for single-sized aggregates have particular requirements relating to flakiness, since they cannot rely upon gradation to achieve high density and, consequently, high internal friction.

*Water absorption test*  This test is normally carried out in conjunction with the relative density test. The procedure consists of soaking the aggregate sample in distilled water for 24 hours, surface-drying and determining its mass in air, and then oven-drying and determining its mass in air again. The water absorption is obtained by expressing the difference between the masses of the saturated and the oven-dried sample in air as a percentage of the latter.

*Significance of test*    Knowledge of the absorption properties of an aggregate is useful when evaluating the results of durability tests carried out on marginal aggregates for use at particular locations, as some of the weaker aggregates would have their test values reduced if they were subjected to testing under saturated conditions. The test is also useful in giving an indication of the bitumen-absorption properties of an aggregate, i.e. the porosity of the aggregate affects the amount of binder required and additional binder material may have to be incorporated in the mixture to satisfy the absorption by the aggregate after the ingredients have been mixed. On the beneficial side, porous aggregates usually show better adhesion to a binder due to the mechanical interlock caused by the binder penetrating the particles.

The water absorption values allowed for road aggregates normally range from less than 0.1 per cent to about 2.0 per cent for materials used in road surfacings, while values of up to 4.0 per cent may be accepted in roadbases.

**Durability tests**

Two types of resistance test are carried out on road aggregates. These are the abrasion and toughness tests.

*Abrasion tests*    Many abrasion tests have been developed in order to evaluate the ease (or difficulty) with which aggregate particles are likely to wear under attrition from traffic. The aggregate abrasion test and the accelerated polishing test are the two such tests most widely accepted in Britain.

The *aggregate abrasion test* is carried out in a sample of aggregate of at least 24 particles, all passing the 14 mm test sieve and retained on the 20 to 14 mm flake-sorting sieve. The particles are mounted in, but project above, the surface of a setting compound contained in a small, shallow tray. The tray is up-ended and the aggregate pressed in contact with a 600 mm horizontal rotating steel disc; contact is maintained by a 2 kg load for 500 revolutions at a speed of 28–30 revolutions per minute. As the disc rotates, a standard abrasive sand is fed continuously to its surface just in front of the inverted tray. On completion of the 500 revolutions, the test sample is removed and the percentage loss in mass of the aggregate is calculated; this is called the abrasion value of the aggregate.

The *accelerated polishing test* is essentially a skid-resistance test which is carried out on aggregate particles subjected to accelerated attrition. In the course of the test, 35–50 particles passing the 10 mm test sieve and retained on the 14 to 10 mm flake-sorting sieve are set in a sand–cement mortar and clamped on to the flat periphery of a 406 mm diameter wheel which is then rotated at a speed of 320 revolutions per minute. A 200 mm diameter pneumatic-tyred wheel is brought to bear on the aggregate surfaces with a force of 390 N, and corn emery (for 3 h) and then emery flour (for 3 h) are fed continuously to the interacting surfaces. At the end of the six hours of attrition, the state of polish reached by the aggregate specimen is measured in terms of the coefficient of friction between its wet surface and a wet rubber slider in a standard pendulum-type, portable skid-resistance tester. The measurement on this tester is called the polished-stone value of the aggregate.

*Significance of tests*   For an aggregate to perform satisfactorily in the wearing course of a highway pavement, it must be sufficiently hard to resist the abrasive effects of traffic over a long period of time. For aggregates used in other layers of the pavement, the abrasion resistance should be such that the risk of production of fine material, caused by the movement of particles, is kept at an acceptable level. The abrasion tests are basically accelerated tests which attempt to eliminate aggregates which may be unsuitable from these points of view.

The *macrotexture* of a road surfacing (see Fig. 3.10) is dependent for its maintenance upon the resistance of its ingredient materials to deformation and abrasion under traffic. It is this macrotexture which facilitates the rapid drainage of water from the surface whilst it is in contact with high-speed-vehicle tyres, and which utilizes the hysteresis effects in the tyre-tread rubber to absorb some of the kinetic energy of the vehicle. Whether the aggregate abrasion test simulates abrasion under actual traffic conditions is, of course, highly debatable. Numerous testings have shown, however, that aggregates with abrasion values greater than about 16 are too soft for use in wearing courses carrying significant amounts of heavy traffic.

The accelerated polishing test is generally considered more representative of tyre–surfacing interaction on the *microtexture* of the aggregate in the road surfacing. It is this microtexture which provides the main friction with a vehicle's tyres; the basic mechanism by which a road surface becomes slippery is the loss of microtexture brought about by the smoothing of the exposed aggregate surfaces by the tyres of passing vehicles. Extensive research has shown that the microstructure of the aggregate at the end of the six-hour test approximates the state of polish reached after several months on a heavily-trafficked road or several years on a road carrying light traffic. Results indicate that an aggregate with a polished-stone value greater than 80 is likely to remain rough under any traffic conditions, whereas one with a value of 30 or lower will become so highly polished as to give rise to a dangerously slippery road surface when either wet or dry.

Table 3.16 shows the minimum polished-stone values for aggregates that are recommended at particular sites in Britain. (For comparison purposes, it

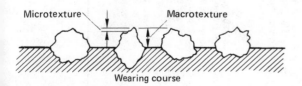

**Fig. 3.10**   Microtexture and macrotexture of a pavement surface

**Table 3.16** Recommended aggregate polished-stone values ($PSV_{min}$ values) for use in bituminous surfacings at different locations[80]

| Site | Definition | Traffic (commercial vehicles per lane per day) | $PSV_{min}$ | Comments |
|---|---|---|---|---|
| A1 (difficult) | Approaches to traffic signals on roads with 85th percentile speed of traffic >64 km/h; approaches to traffic signals, pedestrian crossings and similar hazards on main urban roads | <250<br>250–1000<br>1000–1750<br>>1750 | 60<br>65<br>70<br>75 | Applicable to <0.1 per cent of all roads in England; risk rating 6; values include +5 units for braking/turning |
| A2 (difficult) | Approaches to and across major priority junctions on roads with >250 commercial vehicles per lane per day on each approach; roundabouts and their approaches; bends with radius >150 m on roads with the 85th percentile traffic speed >64 km/h; gradients ≥5 per cent, and longer than 100 m | <1750<br>1750–2500<br>2500–3250<br>>3250 | 60<br>65<br>70<br>75 | Applicable to <4 per cent of all roads in England; risk rating 4; values include +5 units for braking/turning |
| B (average) | Generally straight sections of, and large radius curves on, motorways, trunk and principal roads, and other roads carrying >250 commercial vehicles per lane per day | <1750<br>1750–4000<br>>4000 | 55<br>60<br>65 | Applicable to <15 per cent of all roads in England; risk rating 2 |
| C (easy) | Generally straight sections of lightly-trafficked roads, i.e. <250 commercial vehicles per lane per day; other roads where wet skidding accidents are unlikely to be a problem | — | 45 | Applicable to <81 per cent of all roads in England; no risk rating applied; many local aggregates have $PSVs$ >45 and normally these are used |

might be noted that the artificial aggregate calcined bauxite typically has a polished-stone value of about 75, and an aggregate abrasion value of about 3.)

Table 3.17 shows results obtained from a comprehensive series of tests (including the abrasion and polishing tests) carried out on various aggregate groups during the 1950s. Whilst some of the tests (and consequently the results) have changed slightly since these data were determined, e.g. the polished-stone values are all about 10 per cent too high, the table usefully represents the comparative values to be obtained with each aggregate group.

*Toughness tests* If toughness is defined as the power possessed by an aggregate to resist fracture under an applied load, then the tests in common usage which are reflective of this quality are the aggregate crushing, ten per cent fines, and aggregate impact tests[82].

The *aggregate crushing value* is a measure of the resistance of an aggregate to crushing under a gradually applied compressive load. The test is normally carried out on material passing the 14 mm BS sieve and retained on the 10 mm BS sieve. The aggregate is placed in a standard mould using a specified procedure, and then a 400 kN load is gradually applied to the material over a period of ten minutes. The load is then released, and the amount of material passing the 2.36 mm BS sieve is determined. This mass, expressed as a percentage of the total mass of the sample, is termed the aggregate crushing value.

The *ten per cent fines test* is similar to the aggregate crushing test, except that the force (kN) is determined which causes 10 per cent fines (passing the 2.36 mm BS sieve) to be formed over a period of ten minutes. Preliminary estimates of this force are first obtained, e.g. from the formula:

$$\text{required force (kN)} = \frac{4000}{\text{aggregate impact value}}$$

and then after carrying out the test a simple formula is applied to the results obtained to determine the exact 10 per cent fines value.

The *aggregate impact value test* is carried out by subjecting aggregate which has passed the 14 mm BS sieve and is retained on the 10 mm BS sieve to 15 blows of a 13.5–14.0 kg hammer falling through a height of 380 mm. After impact, the material passing the 2.36 mm BS sieve is expressed as a percentage of the total mass of the original sample and termed the aggregate impact value.

*Significance of tests* In all forms of flexible pavement, the aggregate must be tough enough to support the weight of the rollers during construction and the repeated impact and crushing actions of traffic. Thus the aggregate must have a durable resistance to both crushing and impact. The toughness tests just described are empirical attempts to measure this resistance; however, since they are empirical, the results obtained have to be correlated with field experience for them to have any significance.

The aggregate crushing value gives a relative measure of the resistance of an aggregate to crushing under a gradually applied load. The results obtained with this suggest that materials with values greater than about

**Table 3.17** Summary of means and ranges of test values for natural roadstones in various aggregate groups[81]

| Group | Measure | Aggregate crushing value | Aggregate impact value | Aggregate abrasion value | Water absorption (%) | Relative density | Polished-stone value |
|---|---|---|---|---|---|---|---|
| Basalt | Mean | 14 | 15 | 6.1 | 1.1 | 2.80 | 62 |
| | Range | 7–25 | 7–25 | 2.0–12.0 | 0.0–2.3 | 2.60–3.00 | 45–81 |
| Flint | Mean | 18 | 23 | 1.1 | 1.0 | 2.54 | 39 |
| | Range | 7–25 | 19–27 | 1.0–2.0 | 0.3–2.4 | 2.40–2.60 | 30–53 |
| Granite | Mean | 20 | 19 | 4.8 | 0.4 | 2.69 | 59 |
| | Range | 9–35 | 9–35 | 3.0–9.0 | 0.2–0.9 | 2.60–3.00 | 45–70 |
| Gritstone | Mean | 17 | 19 | 7.0 | 0.6 | 2.69 | 72 |
| | Range | 7–29 | 9–35 | 2.0–16.0 | 0.1–1.6 | 2.60–2.90 | 60–80 |
| Hornfels | Mean | 13 | 12 | 2.2 | 0.4 | 2.82 | 45 |
| | Range | 5–15 | 9–17 | 1.0–4.0 | 0.2–0.8 | 2.70–3.00 | 40–50 |
| Limestone | Mean | 24 | 23 | 13.7 | 1.0 | 2.66 | 43 |
| | Range | 11–37 | 17–33 | 7.0–26.0 | 0.2–2.9 | 2.50–2.80 | 30–75 |
| Porphyry | Mean | 14 | 14 | 3.7 | 0.6 | 2.73 | 56 |
| | Range | 9–29 | 9–23 | 2.0–9.0 | 0.4–1.1 | 2.60–2.90 | 43–71 |
| Quartzite | Mean | 16 | 21 | 3.0 | 0.7 | 2.62 | 58 |
| | Range | 9–25 | 11–33 | 2.0–6.0 | 0.3–1.3 | 2.60–2.70 | 45–67 |

*Note:* Whilst some of the tests (and consequently the results) have changed slightly since these data were determined, the table usefully represents the comparative values to be obtained with each road group

25–30 are too weak to be utilized in a pavement. When aggregates with values greater than about 30 are evaluated, the crushing test begins to become insensitive due to the restricting cushioning effect which the fines formed in the early part of the test have on later aggregate breakdown. The 10 per cent fines test was developed to evaluate these weak aggregates. Values obtained with this test range from as low as 1 kN for chalk to over 40 kN for the hardest aggregates; normally, however, road aggregates should not show a fines value of less than about 8 kN.

As its name implies, the aggregate impact value provides a relative measure of the resistance of an aggregate to sudden shock, e.g. as might occur under vibratory compaction. Values obtained with this test are, in general, numerically similar to those obtained with the aggregate crushing test. As it is a simple test to carry out, and uses comparatively unsophisticated equipment, the impact test therefore tends to be used instead of the more complicated crushing test. However, care should be taken in translating the values from one test to another, especially when working with fine-grained, highly-siliceous aggregates such as flint and quartzite, i.e. these aggregates are quite brittle and sensitive to shock waves, so that their impact values are significantly different from their crushing values.

**Relative density test**

This test [76] is normally carried out in conjunction with the water absorption test. It consists of soaking a sample of aggregate in distilled water for 24 hours, determining its mass in water at the end of this period, surface-drying and determining its mass in air, and then, after oven-drying for 24 hours, determining its mass in air again. The *relative density on an oven-dried basis* is obtained by dividing the mass in air of the oven-dried sample by the difference between the saturated sample masses in air and in water. The *apparent relative density* is obtained by dividing the mass in air of the oven-dried sample by the difference between the oven-dried sample mass in air and the sample mass in water.

The formulae used in the relative density calculations are as follows:

$$\text{relative density on an oven-dried basis} = \frac{M}{A - (B - C)}$$

$$\text{and} \quad \text{apparent relative density} = \frac{M}{M - (B - C)}$$

where $A$ = mass in air of the saturated surface-dry aggregate, $B$ = mass in water of the container plus its sample of saturated aggregate, $C$ = mass in water of the empty container, and $M$ = mass in air of the oven-dried aggregate, all of which are measured in grammes.

*Significance of test*    As is illustrated in Fig. 3.11(a), the relative density on an oven-dried basis is the ratio of the mass in air of the total aggregate volume (including voids which are permeable and impermeable to water intrusion) to the mass in air of an equal volume of distilled water. It is this value of relative density which is used in most normal aggregate calculations.

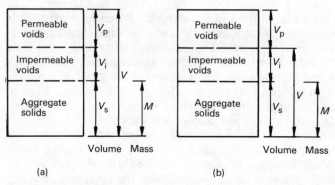

**Fig. 3.11** Diagrammatic illustration of the composition of an aggregate particle showing the mass and volumes used in relative density calculations: (a) relative density on an oven-dried basis and (b) apparent relative density

The apparent relative density (Fig. 3.11(b)) is the ratio of the mass in air of the solid aggregate volume (including the impermeable voids but excluding the permeable voids) to the mass in air of an equal volume of distilled water. By definition, therefore, the apparent relative density is always greater than the relative density on an oven-dried basis.

As will be discussed later (see Chapter 7), the apparent relative density is normally used in bituminous mixture design, as use of the relative density on an oven-dried basis would give a markedly different, indeed erroneous, result if the aggregate was very porous.

As road aggregates are normally proportioned by mass, the relative density on an oven-dried basis is of vital importance in determining the proper particle-size blend. Gradation specifications are valid only if the coarse and fine fractions have approximately the same relative densities. If the value for the fine fraction is much greater than that for the coarse, the result is a mixture which, because of a lack of fines, may be too harsh. However, if the relative density of the coarse fraction is the greater, a mixture which is too rich in fines may be obtained. When these conditions are encountered in practice, arbitrary gradations should not be used, but instead various gradation mixtures should be analysed carefully and evaluated on their merits.

The 'average' relative density of an aggregate composed of fractions of different relative densities can be calculated from the individual values. Figure 3.12 is a schematic illustration of such an aggregate; it is composed of three fractions of known masses, volumes and relative densities. From this diagram

$$R_{\text{ave}}\psi_M = M/V$$

However, the individual mass of each aggregate is always expressed as a percentage of the total mass, $M$. Thus taking $M$ as equal to 100,

$$R_{\text{ave}}\psi_M = 100 \bigg/ \left( \frac{M_1}{R_1\psi_M} + \frac{M_2}{R_2\psi_M} + \frac{M_3}{R_3\psi_M} \right)$$

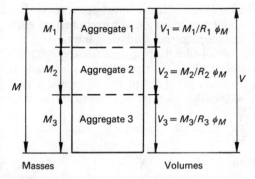

Masses               Volumes

**Fig. 3.12** Schematic representation of the components of an 'average' relative density calculation

Therefore

$$R_{ave} = 100 \bigg/ \left( \frac{M_1}{R_1} + \frac{M_2}{R_2} + \frac{M_3}{R_3} \right)$$

where $R_{ave}$ is the average relative density of the final aggregate and $M_1$, $M_2$ and $M_3$ are the mass percentages of the individual fractions.

## Aggregate gradation calculations

Most aggregate gradation problems are straightforward and require no special mathematical knowledge to solve them. A hypothetical gradation determination is shown in Table 3.18. This table shows that there are three ways of representing the grading of an aggregate: these are by an individual percentage which is retained on each sieve, by a cumulative percentage retained on each sieve, and by a total percentage passing each sieve.

As noted previously, most standard specifications are expressed as the total percentage passing each sieve. In certain instances, however, an

**Table 3.18** Laboratory determination of the gradation of an aggregate (sample size = 2000 g)

| BS sieve size (mm) | Individual mass retained on each sieve | | Cumulative mass retained on each sieve | | Total mass passing each sieve (%) |
|---|---|---|---|---|---|
| | g | % | g | % | |
| 28 | 0 | 0 | 0 | 0 | 100 |
| 14 | 160 | 8 | 160 | 8 | 92 |
| 3.35 | 240 | 12 | 400 | 20 | 80 |
| 2 | 200 | 10 | 600 | 30 | 70 |
| 1.18 | 300 | 15 | 900 | 45 | 55 |
| 0.600 | 180 | 9 | 1080 | 54 | 46 |
| 0.300 | 180 | 9 | 1260 | 63 | 37 |
| 0.150 | 340 | 17 | 1600 | 80 | 20 |
| 0.063 | 220 | 11 | 1820 | 91 | 9 |

aggregate gradation may be submitted in which the limits are expressed in terms of the individual maximum and minimum amounts retained on each sieve, and it is then necessary to compare the gradation limits with the percentage-passing specification; this can be troublesome for the inexperienced engineer and so one way in which the comparison can be made is briefly described here. Another troublesome problem also discussed is that which arises when two or more aggregates have to be blended in order to meet a specification.

**Comparing gradation specifications**

The simplest way of comparing two specifications is to plot them on a gradation chart and then to see the extent to which they are related to each other. Unfortunately, when one specification is given in terms of the individual amounts retained on each sieve, and the other is laid down in terms of the total percentage passing given sieve sizes, this direct comparison is not possible—except perhaps by the very experienced engineer who is able to determine instinctively by reading the two specifications just what exactly is the relationship between the two. There is, however, a very useful and simple method of translating specifications for individual contents retained into those based on total percentages passing[83] which enables the comparison to be made by even the most inexperienced; this is described here.

To demonstrate the translation procedure, the hypothetical individual passing-and-retained specification shown in Table 3.19(a) will be used. The derivation of the percentage-passing specification, which is shown analytically in Table 3.19(b), and graphically in Fig. 3.13, may be explained as follows.

*Step 1*   Calculate from Table 3.19(a) the cumulative percentages of material passing each sieve. First use the minimum limits throughout and then the maximum limits, starting with the smallest sieve size in each case. Enter the results in columns 1 and 2 of Table 3.19(b).

*Step 2*   Plot the minimum cumulative percentage passing as curve 1 in Fig. 3.13(a), and the maximum values as curve 2. Some of the calculated percentages are found to be greater than 100 per cent: they are disregarded as they are fictitious values. Thus curves 1 and 2 define the limits of the intended grading in the fine sizes but not in the coarse sizes.

*Step 3*   Calculate from Table 3.19(a) the cumulative percentages of aggregate retained on each sieve. First use the minimum limits throughout and then the maximum limits, starting with the maximum sieve size in each case. Enter the results in columns 1R and 2R of Table 3.19(b).

*Step 4*   Using the data in columns 1R and 2R, calculate the percentage passing each sieve by subtracting the percentage retained from 100. Enter the results in columns 3 and 4 of Table 3.19(b).

*Step 5*   Plot the maximum cumulative percentage-passing values from column 3 as curve 3 in Fig. 3.13(a) and the minimum values from column 4 as curve 4. Some of the calculated minimum values are found to be negative

**Table 3.19** Translating an aggregate specification written in terms of percentage passing and retained into one of percentage passing: (a) assumed aggregate gradation requirements and (b) calculations

BS sieve size (mm)

| Passing | Retained | Percentage of material |
|---|---|---|
| — | 28 | 0 |
| 28 | 14 | 25–45 |
| 14 | 5 | 10–25 |
| 5 | 2 | 6–15 |
| 2 | 1.18 | 6–9 |
| 1.18 | 0.425 | 8–13 |
| 0.425 | 0.150 | 7–13 |
| 0.150 | 0.063 | 7–12 |
| 0.063 | | 2–8 |

(a)

| | 1 | 2 | 1R | 2R | 3 | 4 | 5 |
|---|---|---|---|---|---|---|---|
| BS sieve size (mm) | Cumulative percentage passing, by simple addition | | Cumulative percentage retained | | Cumulative percentage passing, by subtraction | | Derived specification on a percentage-passing basis |
| | Minimum | Maximum | Minimum | Maximum | Maximum | Minimum | |
| 28 | 71 | 140 | 0 | 0 | 100 | 100 | 100 |
| 14 | 46 | 95 | 25 | 45 | 75 | 55 | 55–75 |
| 5 | 36 | 70 | 35 | 70 | 65 | 30 | 36–65 |
| 2 | 30 | 55 | 41 | 85 | 59 | 15 | 30–55 |
| 1.18 | 24 | 46 | 47 | 94 | 53 | 6 | 24–46 |
| 0.425 | 16 | 33 | 55 | 107 | 45 | -7 | 16–33 |
| 0.150 | 9 | 20 | 62 | 120 | 38 | -20 | 9–20 |
| 0.063 | 2 | 8 | 69 | 132 | 31 | -32 | 2–8 |

(b)

and so they are disregarded since they are fictitious. These two curves define the limits of grading in the coarse sizes but not in the fine sizes.

*Step 6*   Select the lower values of curves 2 and 3 and connect these with a solid line as illustrated in Fig. 3.13(b). Similarly, the higher values of curves 1 and 4 are selected and connected by a solid line. These curves define the

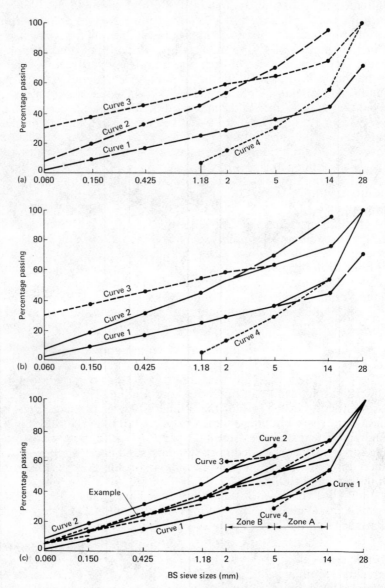

**Fig. 3.13**   Graphical translation of an aggregate specification written in terms of percentage passing and retained into one of percentage passing: (a) limiting curves of grading, (b) desired grading band, and (c) example grading passes both types of specification

limits of the intended grading band. The percentage-passing values—also shown in column 5 of Table 3.19(b)—enclose an area identical in shape and size with that representing the passing-and-retained specification from which they are derived.

The two specifications are not yet completely identical however. There is a requirement in the passing-and-retained specification in Table 3.19(a) that for each fraction defined there is a definite control over the amount which passes any particular sieve and which must be retained on the next smallest sieve in the named series. This has the effect of placing maximum and minimum limits on the slope of each segment of any particular gradation curve that might be drawn within the outlines of the grading band. These maximum and minimum slopes vary as the grading limits pass from zone to zone, but they may be fixed in the manner described in the following steps.

*Step 7* Minimum slopes are fixed by curves 1 and 3 in Fig. 3.13(b); these are parallel to each other throughout. Therefore each of the solid lines in the envelope curve that represents a segment of either curve 1 or curve 3 establishes the minimum slope for its zone.

*Step 8* Maximum slopes are fixed by curves 2 and 4 in Fig. 3.13(b); they are also parallel to each other throughout (including the fictitious segments not shown).

*Step 9* In the transition zone A, no segment of curves 1 and 4 was used as a part of the envelope curve; similarly, in zone B, no segment of curves 2 and 3 was used as a part of the envelope curve. In these zones, proper control can be obtained by using the dashed segment of curve 1 to set the minimum permissible slope in zone A, and the dashed segment of curve 4 to set the maximum permissible slope in that zone. Likewise, the dashed segments of curves 3 and 2 established the minimum and maximum slopes, respectively, in zone B.

It may be noted that the number of different gradation curves which may be drawn within the boundaries of the grading band illustrated in Fig. 3.13(b) is greatly reduced by the slope limitations that are imposed in each zone by the passing-and-retained type of specification. There is, of course, no such restriction in the case of the ordinary type of percentage-passing specification. As a result, unless some slope limit criterion is included in the grading requirements of the percentage-passing type, a great many more grading curves may be included in the grading band under discussion than will meet the requirements of the passing-and-retained specification on which the grading band is based.

The solid line contained within the grading band limits of Fig. 3.13(c) represents a gradation curve that meets both the fractional and slope limits of the passing-and-retained grading specification of Table 3.19(a).

**Combining aggregates**
The grading required in a road aggregate for a given pavement layer depends very much upon the form of construction which will be used. It is common practice therefore for the aggregate to be sorted beforehand into a number of closely-graded 'single sizes' which may be subsequently remixed

**Table 3.20**   Hypothetical gradations to be combined to meet specification limits

| BS sieve size (mm) | Percentage passing given sieve size | | | Specifications | |
| | Fine aggregate (A) | Intermediate aggregate (B) | Coarse aggregate (C) | Limits | Midpoint |
|---|---|---|---|---|---|
| 28 | 100.0 | 100.0 | 100.0 | 100.0 | 100.0 |
| 14 | 100.0 | 100.0 | 94.0 | 90.0–100.0 | 95.0 |
| 5 | 100.0 | 100.0 | 54.0 | 60.0–75.0 | 67.5 |
| 1.18 | 100.0 | 66.4 | 31.3 | 40.0–55.0 | 47.5 |
| 0.300 | 100.0 | 26.0 | 22.8 | 20.0–35.0 | 27.5 |
| 0.150 | 73.6 | 17.6 | 9.0 | 12.0–22.0 | 17.0 |
| 0.063 | 40.1 | 5.0 | 3.1 | 5.0–10.0 | 7.5 |

in desired proportions in order to meet the gradation specified for use. The blending of aggregates to obtain a desired gradation is a relatively simple exercise to the experienced engineer. To the inexperienced engineer, however, this can be a most complicated problem, particularly when more than two aggregates are to be combined and their gradations overlap. While in the long run the blending of aggregates to meet a particular specification resolves itself into a trial-and-error procedure, the initial decision of 'where to start' can be made by using either of the following two methods, one mathematical and the other graphical. To illustrate these methods, it will be assumed that three aggregates are to be combined and that their gradations, and the required specification, are as listed in Table 3.20. It should be understood that neither the gradations nor the specification shown in Table 3.20 are in any sense typical or recommended values; they are simply hypothetical working data.

*Mathematical method*   Before proceeding to the solution, a consideration of the following general mathematical relationships will help to clarify the method.

(1)   An equation of the general form:

$$aA + bB + cC = T$$

can be obtained for each sieve size. In this equation, the lower-case letters are decimal values representing the proportions of the blend to be taken from each aggregate. When their values have been determined they may be expressed as percentages by multiplying each by 100. The capital letters represent the percentages either passing or retained on a particular sieve. For example, using the percentages passing the 5 mm sieve, the following is a valid equation:

$$100.0a + 100.0b + 54.0c = 67.5$$

Or, using the percentages retained on the same sieve, the equation becomes

$$0a + 0b + 46.0c = 32.5$$

(2)   Equations obtained from any particular sieve can be combined either

by addition or by subtraction with equations obtained from one or more other sieves to produce other equations which are equally valid. Thus, combining equations obtained from the 1.18 mm and 300 $\mu$m sieves

$$100.0a + 66.4b + 31.3c = 47.5 \quad \text{(for 1.18 mm sieve)}$$

and

$$100.0a + 26.0b + 22.8c = 27.5 \quad \text{(for 300 } \mu\text{m sieve)}$$

by addition

$$200.0a + 92.4b + 54.1c = 75$$

and by subtraction

$$0a + 40.4b + 8.5c = 20$$

(3)  A valid equation can also be obtained by summing the proportions of the individual aggregates. Thus

$$a + b + c = 1$$

Proceeding now to the solution of the problem, it is seen that all the material larger than the 5 mm sieve is contained in the coarse aggregate. Using the percentages retained on that sieve, the following equation is obtained:

$$0a + 0b + 46.0c = 32.5$$

Therefore

$$c = 0.71$$

By subtracting the equation for the 300 $\mu$m sieve from that for the 1.18 mm sieve, the following equation is obtained:

$$0a + 40.4b + 8.5c = 20$$

Therefore

$$40.4b + 8.5(0.71) = 20$$

and

$$b = 0.35$$

However,

$$a + b + c = 1$$

Therefore

$$a + 0.35 + 0.71 = 1$$

and

$$a = -0.06$$

Obviously a negative value cannot be accepted; it simply indicates that the midpoint specification values used in the calculation are exactly unobtainable. The computation is repeated using specifications of 70 per cent passing for the 5 mm sieve, and 45 per cent passing for the 1.18 mm sieve. Then

$$0a + 0b + 46.0c = 30$$

and

$$c = 0.65$$

Now

$$0a + 40.4b + 8.5c = 17.5$$

Therefore

$$40.4b + 8.5(0.65) = 17.5$$

and

$$b = 0.30$$

However,

$$a + b + c = 1$$

Therefore

$$a + 0.30 + 0.65 = 1$$

and

$$a = 0.05$$

It is now necessary to check whether the proportioning values obtained are applicable to all the sieves. If they are, the specification will be met. This check is illustrated in Table 3.21 and, as can be seen, the assumed proportions are satisfactory since the combination in all respects lies within the specification limits. It is to be noted, however, that the amounts passing both the 150 and 63 $\mu$m BS sieves tend to be on the low side of the specification, so that it is advisable to adjust the proportion to increase

**Table 3.21** Example of results of mathematical method of combining aggregates to obtain a desired gradation

| BS sieve size (mm) | Aggregate | | | Combined aggregates |
|---|---|---|---|---|
| | $A \times 5\%$ | $B \times 30\%$ | $C \times 65\%$ | |
| 28 | $100.0 \times 0.05 = 5.0$ | $100.0 \times 0.30 = 30.0$ | $100.0 \times 0.65 = 65.0$ | 100.0 |
| 14 | $100.0 \times 0.05 = 5.0$ | $100.0 \times 0.30 = 30.0$ | $94.0 \times 0.65 = 61.0$ | 96.0 |
| 5 | $100.0 \times 0.05 = 5.0$ | $100.0 \times 0.30 = 30.0$ | $54.0 \times 0.65 = 35.1$ | 70.1 |
| 1.18 | $100.0 \times 0.05 = 5.0$ | $66.4 \times 0.30 = 19.8$ | $31.3 \times 0.65 = 20.4$ | 45.2 |
| 0.300 | $100.0 \times 0.05 = 5.0$ | $26.0 \times 0.30 = 7.8$ | $22.8 \times 0.65 = 14.8$ | 27.6 |
| 0.150 | $73.6 \times 0.05 = 3.7$ | $17.6 \times 0.30 = 5.3$ | $9.0 \times 0.65 = 5.9$ | 14.9 |
| 0.063 | $40.1 \times 0.05 = 2.0$ | $5.0 \times 0.30 = 1.5$ | $3.1 \times 0.65 = 2.0$ | 5.5 |

these values. In this example, this can be best done by increasing the proportion of fine aggregate at the expense of the intermediate aggregate.

*Graphical method* The use of simultaneous equations can be a very suitable method when it is necessary to combine two or perhaps three aggregates. Beyond this number, the method can be quite cumbersome due to the number of adjustment checks which may have to be made. In such instances, the following graphical procedure can be most useful. This is best explained by referring to Fig. 3.14 and outlining the graphical procedure in a series of steps.

*Step 1* Plot the percentage passing of fine material on scale A and the percentage passing of intermediate aggregate on scale B.

*Step 2* Connect by a straight line the percentage passing for each sieve size. Note that the intersections of each sieve line with any vertical gradation line will define the composite gradation of the fine and intermediate aggregates for the blend proportions shown on the top and bottom horizontal scales.

*Step 3* Lay off the specification limits as intercepts on each sieve line; these are the solid portions of the sieve lines shown in the right-hand block of Fig. 3.14. Note that the intercepts for any particular sieve line represent the range of proportions that will meet the specification limits.

*Step 4* Select a vertical line that will strike the 'best average' through all of the specification intercepts shown. In this example, the vertical line selected represents 8 per cent fine material and 92 per cent intermediate aggregate. This is the line *XY* indicated in the figure.

*Step 5* Project horizontally onto the vertical scale C the intersections of each sieve line with the gradation line *XY*. The numerical values obtained

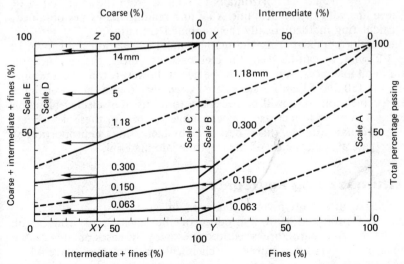

**Fig. 3.14** Graphical method of combining aggregates to obtain a desired gradation. *Note:* The data used are from Table 3.20

**Table 3.22**   Example of results of graphical method of combining aggregates to obtain a desired gradation

| BS sieve size (mm) | Aggregate A = 3.2% | B = 36.8% | C = 60.0% | Combined aggregates |
|---|---|---|---|---|
| 28 | 100.0 × 0.032 = 3.2 | 100.0 × 0.368 = 36.8 | 100.0 × 0.600 = 60.0 | 100.0 |
| 14 | 100.0 × 0.032 = 3.2 | 100.0 × 0.368 = 36.8 | 94.0 × 0.600 = 56.4 | 96.4 |
| 5 | 100.0 × 0.032 = 3.2 | 100.0 × 0.368 = 36.8 | 54.0 × 0.600 = 32.4 | 72.4 |
| 1.18 | 100.0 × 0.032 = 3.2 | 66.4 × 0.368 = 24.4 | 31.3 × 0.600 = 18.8 | 46.4 |
| 0.300 | 100.0 × 0.032 = 3.2 | 26.0 × 0.368 = 9.6 | 22.8 × 0.600 = 13.7 | 26.5 |
| 0.150 | 73.6 × 0.032 = 2.4 | 17.6 × 0.368 = 6.5 | 9.0 × 0.600 = 5.4 | 14.3 |
| 0.063 | 40.1 × 0.032 = 1.3 | 5.0 × 0.368 = 1.8 | 3.1 × 0.600 = 1.9 | 5.0 |

on scale C represent the percentages passing the respective sieve sizes for the combined gradation of the fine and intermediate aggregates.

*Step 6*   Plot the percentage passing of coarse aggregate on scale D, and repeat the process as outlined in steps 1 to 4 in order to determine the blend proportions of coarse with the mixture of intermediate plus fines. In this example, the vertical line *XYZ* is selected; it represents 60.0 per cent coarse aggregate and 40.0 per cent intermediate plus fine aggregate, or

coarse aggregate = 60.0%

intermediate aggregate = 40.0 × 0.92 = 36.8%

and   fine aggregate = 40.0 × 0.08 = 3.2%

*Step 7*   Determine the gradation of the combined materials. This can be done either by projecting horizontally to scale E from the intersection of each sieve line with the vertical line *XYZ* and reading the values obtained, or by calculating mathematically the combined gradation.

The results obtained from the mathematical calculation are shown in Table 3.22 and, as can be seen, the blend selected meets the specification criteria in all instances. Again it is to be noted, however, that the amounts passing the 150 and 63 $\mu$m BS sieves are extremely close to the lower limits of the specification, so it will be necessary to adjust the selected blending percentages in order to increase the percentage passing for these sieve sizes. In this particular instance, this is best done by increasing the proportion of fine aggregate at the expense of the intermediate material.

## Blastfurnace slag aggregates

The principal artificially-formed slag used in road construction is blast-furnace slag produced as a byproduct of the smelting of iron ore in blastfurnaces. As the iron ore is reduced to iron by the gases obtained when the coke in the furnace is burned, a chemical reaction takes place which causes the silica and alumina compounds present in the ore to combine with the limestone and dolomite of the fluxing stone to form slag. At combustion temperatures between 1300 and 1600 °C, the slag is in a molten form and floats as a separate layer on top of the liquid iron. The slag is drawn off at intervals throughout the smelting process and is either run into huge ladles for transmission to a remote cooling bed, run straight to an adjacent cooling bed, or allowed to solidify in the ladle.

Slag can take on various forms, depending upon the cooling conditions imposed after leaving the blastfurnace. If it is left to cool slowly in the open air, a crystallized slag suitable for crushing is obtained that is known as *aircooled blastfurnace slag*. If the hot slag is subjected to sudden cooling by using water or water and air, vitrified slags are obtained which are known as *granulated slag* and *pelletized slag*, respectively. The hot slag may also be cooled under controlled conditions where the steam produced gives rise to a type of slag known as *expanded blastfurnace slag*.

For practical purposes, it can be assumed that the aircooled slag is the only one produced in Britain in sufficient quantities to be used in roadworks to a significant extent.

For many years, aircooled blastfurnace slag was regarded as a nuisance material. Nowadays, however, it is no longer considered a waste material; indeed, it is not incorrect to say that the quality of the crushed slag is nearly controlled as much as that of the iron itself. Whilst road-making is but one of the uses to which aircooled slag is put, it is known that about ten-million tonnes are used in highway construction each year. Most of this slag aggregate is taken from current production as the bulk of the slag accumulations created during the past century has been utilized over the years.

When produced under the proper controlled conditions, aircooled slag is reasonably uniform in density and quality, and contains few glassy fragments. Its internal porosity makes it an excellent non-frost-susceptible road aggregate. In general, this slag's quality is such that it is normally regarded as uneconomic to use it as bulk fill.

Specifications controlling the use of crushed aircooled slag in pavements usually state that it must meet the normal requirements relating to gradation, shape, durability and toughness that are applied to natural aggregates. Table 3.23 gives the results of various tests carried out on a range of slags. If these values are compared with those for the natural aggregates shown in Table 3.16—both sets of data were obtained as part of the same study and are therefore subject to the same qualifications in respect of their current validity—the relative quality of this artificial aggregate vis-à-vis the natural aggregates can be seen.

Aircooled slag used in coated macadams[13] is normally also required to have a bulk density greater than 1100 kg/m$^3$, a 10 per cent fines value of less than 50 kN, and a sulphur content of less than 2.75 per cent; in addition, the porosity of the aggregate (as reflected by water absorption) cannot be greater than 10 per cent. In the case of slag used in concrete[84], the density, 10 per cent fines, and porosity figures are as given above, but the maximum sulphur content is reduced to 2 per cent.

Due to its vesicular structure, aircooled blastfurnace slag has very good anti-skid properties and, hence, is widely used in surface dressings. The high

**Table 3.23**    Means and ranges of test values for aircooled blastfurnace slag[81]

| Measure | Aggregate crushing value | Aggregate impact value | Aggregate abrasion value | Water absorption (%) | Relative density | Polished-stone value |
|---------|--------------------------|------------------------|--------------------------|----------------------|------------------|----------------------|
| Mean  | 28    | 27    | 8.3      | 0.7     | 2.71      | 59    |
| Range | 15–39 | 17–33 | 3.0–15.0 | 0.2–1.8 | 2.60–3.40 | 35–74 |

angularity and irregular shapes of slag particles mean that pavements incorporating this aggregate have high internal friction. Bituminous surfacings using slag are normally very stable; however, an additional amount of binder will normally be required (as compared with natural aggregates) to compensate for what is absorbed by the slag pores.

## Colliery shale

Colliery shale is the waste product of coal mining which is either removed to gain access to the coalface, or unavoidably brought out of the pit with the coal and has to be separated out at the coal-cleaning plant. It is available in two forms in coal-mining areas: *unburnt shale*, also known as *minestone*, which is the normal shale found as dumped in the conical-shaped spoil heaps adjacent to the mines, and *burnt shale* which is derived from unburnt shale by spontaneous combustion in the spoil heaps.

Very large quantities of shale are available in coal-mining areas. In Britain alone, it is estimated[85] that there are over 3000-million tonnes accumulated in tips as a result of past coal mining, whilst about 50-million tonnes are produced additionally each year from existing coal mines. These heaps occupy some 80 km$^2$ of land in mining areas in, mainly, England and Wales.

The results of chemical and physical analyses of some burnt and unburnt colliery shales are given in Table 3.24. These suggest that shales, which are composed mostly of silica, alumina and iron, can differ considerably in their road-making properties.

At the present time, about six-million tonnes of shale are used in highway construction every year, mostly as bulk fill material in embankments. Burnt shale, in particular, has been used as a fill material for many years in locales close to the spoil tips; in many such areas, usage for this purpose has been so successful that little burnt material now remains and so attention has been turned towards the usage of unburnt shale. Until fairly recently, the fear of spontaneous combustion has been a major restriction on the use of unburnt shale in embankments. It is now known, however, that spontaneous combustion in embankments is determined not only by the percentage of carbon remains present in the shale but also by the shale particle size, the distribution of carbonaceous material and the proportion of volatile constituents contained within it, the pyrite content and, particularly, the ease with which oxygen can penetrate into and through the fill[86]. Furthermore, experience has shown that spontaneous ignition does not

**Table 3.24** Burnt and unburnt colliery shales from various sources: (a) chemical and (b) physical analyses[85]

| Component | Burnt colliery shale sources | | | | | | Unburnt colliery shale source |
| --- | --- | --- | --- | --- | --- | --- | --- |
| | A | B | C | D | E | F | S |
| $SiO_2$ | 57.6 | 56.2 | 60.2 | 55.6 | 56.4 | 45.5 | 51.9 |
| $Al_2O_3$ | 31.3 | 31.1 | 21.2 | 26.5 | 23.3 | 21.5 | 19.4 |
| $Fe_2O_3$ | 3.9 | 4.3 | 8.0 | 4.6 | 6.1 | 13.4 | 6.1 |
| $K_2O$ | 2.5 | 2.1 | 3.3 | 3.5 | 2.6 | 2.8 | 3.0 |
| $SO_3$ | 0.1 | 1.4 | 0.9 | 1.9 | 2.8 | 4.7 | 0.4 |
| Other | 4.6 | 4.9 | 6.4 | 7.9 | 8.8 | 12.2 | 19.2 |
| Loss on ignition | 1.9 | 2.2 | 3.8 | 6.3 | 5.5 | 2.6 | 16.1 |
| $SO_3$, as percentage content of 1:1 shale–water suspensions | 0.06 | 0.14 | 0.16 | 0.70 | 0.69 | 0.15 | na |

(a)

| Property | Burnt colliery shale sources | | | | | | Unburnt colliery shale sources | | | | |
| --- | --- | --- | --- | --- | --- | --- | --- | --- | --- | --- | --- |
| | A | B | C | D | E | F | S | T | U | V | W |
| Gradation analysis, as percentage of shale in the following sizes (mm): | | | | | | | | | | | |
| >40 | 2 | 0 | 6 | 0 | 3 | 0 | 7 | 5 | 6 | 12 | 15 |
| 20–40 | 81 | 69 | 72 | 75 | 71 | 68 | 82 | 82 | 49 | 58 | 73 |
| <20 | 17 | 31 | 22 | 25 | 26 | 32 | 11 | 13 | 45 | 30 | 12 |
| Relative density | 2.65 | 2.69 | 2.71 | 2.72 | 2.76 | 2.90 | 2.60 | 2.51 | na | na | na |

(b)

occur if the unburnt shale is properly compacted as it is placed in the embankment. As a result, increasing amounts of unburnt shale are now being permitted and used in roadworks.

Some of the older shale tips may contain significant amounts of intermixed low-grade coal. Notwithstanding the above comments, this coal represents an additional combustion hazard, and these shales should be avoided where possible.

Sulphate present in shale can cause damage to concrete and cement-bound materials if the conditions are such that the sulphate is able to leach out of the shale into the concrete. Research has shown that where shale is used as bulk fill in an embankment, no limitations need normally be imposed with regard to the sulphate content of the material. If, however, the shale is to be used within 0.5 m of a bridge abutment, rigid pavement or concrete pipe, etc., the sulphate content of a 1 : 1 shale–water extract should not exceed 2.5 g sulphate (as $SO_3$) per litre.

## Spent oil shale

The commercial exploitation of oil-producing shale in Europe has tended to be concentrated in Scotland, Italy and Spain. At its peak (in 1913), the West Lothian area of Scotland produced about 3.3-million tonnes of shale oil per annum, and roadside petrol stations throughout Scotland supplied significant quantities of refined shale oil—otherwise known as 'Scotch'—to motorists. However, the average oil yield per tonne of shale declined steadily over the years, e.g. from 160 litres per tonne in 1890 to 90 litres per tonne in 1947, despite improved retort efficiency. As a result, the industry declined until the production of oil shale was finally halted in 1962.

In Scotland, the mined oil shale was passed through a vertical retort whose gradually increasing temperatures (up to 700 °C) resulted in the removal of naphtha and other crude oils. The spent oil shale, together with other waste shales brought to the surface which were considered unsuitable for processing, was dumped in heaps on land adjacent to the refineries and mines. Spontaneous combustion sometimes occurred in the heaps and this caused further changes to take place to the material deposited.

The amount of spent oil shale located in the West Lothian area of Scotland is estimated at 100–150-million tonnes[87]. In addition, there is probably about another 50–100-million tonnes of unmined shale oil in the area.

Table 3.25 shows the chemical composition of a typical spent oil shale; as can be seen, it is generally similar in composition to colliery shale. As would be expected, the loss-on-ignition value for spent oil shale is normally low, and there is no risk of spontaneous combustion taking place if the material is properly compacted as it is placed in an embankment. The sulphate-content values for spent oil shale tend to be relatively high and, for similar reasons as for colliery shale, care should be taken when using this material in the proximity of cement-bound materials such as bridge abutments, concrete pipes, etc.

**Table 3.25** Chemical composition of a typical spent oil shale[87]

| Component | % |
| --- | --- |
| $SiO_2$ | 48.5 |
| $Al_2O_3$ | 25.2 |
| $Fe_2O_3$ | 12.1 |
| CaO | 5.3 |
| MgO | 2.2 |
| $SO_3$ | 3.2 |
| Loss on ignition | 3.0 |

The gradations of spent oil shale accumulations appear to be such that they can be readily used as bulk fill in embankments within economical haul distances of the source. However, water absorption tests give an average absorption value of about 15 per cent, whilst the shale particles are relatively soft and tend to break down under compaction. Frost heave tests indicate that spent oil shale particles normally exhibit heaves well in excess of 18 mm in 250 h, which is the maximum permissible for Scotland; this means that the material normally cannot be used in pavements or in subgrades within 450 mm of the road surface.

Estimates suggest that only about 20–25-million tonnes of spent oil shale have been used in highway construction in Scotland since the 1960s.

## Pulverized fuel ash

Pulverized fuel ash (pfa) may be described as the solid fine material carried out in the flue gases of power-station boilers that are fired with pulverized coal. The ash itself is a fine powder, which is why, in the technical literature, it is also referred to as *fly ash*.

Fly ash is a waste product which accounts for more than three-quarters of the residue obtained from burning pulverized coal in the generation of electricity. The finer component of the ash—which is a light brown to dark grey colour, depending upon the amount of unburnt coal present—is removed from the flue gases with the aid of mechanical and electrical precipitators, and initially collected in hoppers; this fly ash material, known as *hopper ash*, can be obtained as a dry white powder. If the hopper ash is deliberately passed through a mixer-conveyor plant so that a measured amount of water can be added to it prior to stockpiling, it is described as *conditioned pfa*. At some power stations the pfa is mixed to a slurry and transported hydraulically to storage ponds or lagoons; this material is known as *lagoon ash*.

The coarser component of the residual ash is not carried over with the flue gases in the course of the burning process, but instead falls to the bottom of the furnace; this material is called *furnace-bottom ash*. At some power stations the furnace-bottom ash is sluiced out to lagoons in conjunction with the hopper ash; separation of the coarse from the fine particles of the mixed material takes place during settlement in the lagoons, with the result that the lagoon ash at these stations is both coarser and more variable than that obtained at other stations.

In the early 1970s, it was estimated[88] that the residues produced each year at Britain's pulverized-fuel-burning power stations amounted to about 7.41-million tonnes of fly ash and 2.46-million tonnes of furnace-bottom ash. These were produced in Central England (69 per cent), London and South-east England (14 per cent), North-east England (9 per cent), and South Wales and Bristol (8 per cent).

## Pfa properties

As would be expected, pulverized fuel ash obtained at different stations can vary considerably. Table 3.26 lists the main chemical components of a range of pfas. The main ingredients of pfa are finely-divided, glassy spheres of silica and alumina. Residual unburnt carbon is usually present, together with inclusions of unfused ash. Magnetic and non-magnetic iron compounds, some alkali, and limited amounts (2–3 per cent) of water-soluble materials are also present. Calcium oxide derived from the burning of limestone present in the original coal may occur alone or in combination with the other ingredients in the ash.

Fly ashes are pozzolans, i.e. in the presence of lime and water a reaction takes place which results in the formation of hydrous calcium aluminates and silicates which are similar to the reaction products of hydrated cement. Thus pfas which contain significant quantities of water-soluble lime ($CaO$ and $MgO$) and calcium sulphate can become involved in pozzolanic reactions, and thus are said to have self-hardening capabilities.

The quantity of unburnt carbon present in a pfa (determined as loss on ignition) depends upon the efficiency with which the pulverized coal is burned in the furnace. Thus older power stations (e.g. the Croydon Power Station) have ignition losses well in excess of 10 per cent, whilst the more modern stations (e.g. Hams Hall) produce pfas with carbon contents of less than 2 per cent. This carbon exists in the fly ash as irregular, porous, coke-like particles. A high carbon content increases the moisture content

**Table 3.26**  Chemical composition of pulverized fuel ash[88]

| Component | Typical (%) | Range (%) |
|---|---|---|
| $SiO_2$ | 48.0 | 45.0–51.0 |
| $Al_2O_3$ | 27.0 | 24.0–32.0 |
| $Fe_2O_3$ | 9.0 | 7.0–11.0 |
| $CaO$ | 3.3 | 1.1–5.4 |
| $MgO$ | 2.0 | 1.5–4.4 |
| $K_2O$ | 3.8 | 2.8–4.5 |
| $SO_3$ | 0.6 | 0.3–1.3 |
| Other | 2.2 | 1.7–2.9 |

requirement of any mixture in which the pfa is used; it also results in lower dry densities, reduces the proportion of reactive surface area available to enter into pozzolanic reactions, and physically limits the contacts of cementitious materials. Hence it is generally accepted that the fly ashes with high carbon contents tend to be poorer-quality construction materials.

Figure 3.15 shows the particle-size compositions of various hopper and lagoon fly ashes from some of the major power stations in Britain. Particle size is important from two aspects. Firstly, from a frost-action viewpoint, fly ash is a very vulnerable material; thus Fig. 3.15 shows that the hopper ashes in particular are predominantly silt-size, uniformly-graded materials, and as such are liable to be frost susceptible if located within 450 mm of a road surface. Secondly, analysis of the different size-fractions indicates that the chemically-reactive, non-combustible materials, i.e. silica, alumina, and haematite, tend to be concentrated in the finer fractions of the pfa; as a result, it is now accepted by many highway authorities, as a rule-of-thumb, that a good-quality reactive fly ash will have at least 80 per cent by mass of its particles smaller than 42 $\mu$m.

Sometimes a hopper ash can be obtained which has retained latent electrical charges which cause the individual ash particles to repel each other, thereby causing bulking of the massed material. These charges are difficult to dispel, and so pfa retaining them normally should be rejected for use in highway construction, due to the difficulty in achieving adequate compaction.

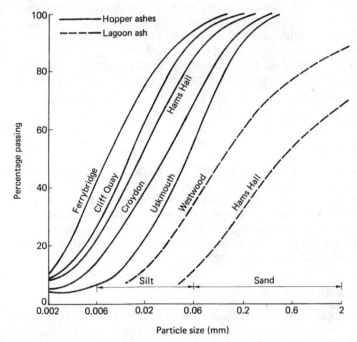

**Fig. 3.15**   Particle-size distribution of samples of pulverized fuel ash[88]

## Fly ash usage

Of the current total annual output of about ten-million tonnes of pulverized fuel ash and furnace-bottom ash, about 60 per cent overall is put into productive use. In South-east England the utilization is close to 80 per cent. The main outlets in Britain are as a partial replacement for ordinary Portland cement in the production of less expensive concrete, as a component of cement[61,62], in patented processes for the manufacture of lightweight sintered aggregates and building blocks, and as a fill material in highway construction. In 1971–72, about 3.5-million tonnes of pfa were utilized for this last purpose.

When compacted, pfa has a low dry density (typically about 1.28 Mg/m$^3$) compared with most other materials that might be used in embankments, and this lightweight property is particularly advantageous when mass filling is required on highly-compressible soils. The self-hardening properties of some fly ashes are especially useful when selected fill is required behind bridge abutments, where settlement problems can be very troublesome, i.e. the result of hardening is that settlement within the pfa fill is less than that which would occur with conventional materials that might otherwise be used.

Although not normally used for this purpose in Britain, pfa can be combined with lime and soil, and cement and soil, to produce highway pavements of a high quality (see Chapter 5).

The frost-susceptibility of fine pfa is not usually an important restriction on its usage as a bulk fill material, provided that no vulnerable material is within 450 mm of the carriageway surface. As a general guide, it can be assumed that ashes with less than 40 per cent of particles passing the 75 $\mu$m BS sieve are unlikely to be frost susceptible in Britain.

Detailed advice regarding the compaction requirements of pfa when used as a fill material in roadworks is readily available in the technical literature[88].

## Quarry wastes

Most quarry operations produce waste and low-grade materials which must be removed and disposed of in order to utilize valuable material. In many instances, the amount of waste produced may exceed the quantity of good-quality material mined. Often regarded as a costly nuisance, these quarry wastes can sometimes be put to valuable usage. Some quarry wastes that have been put to good usage in highway construction at particular locations in Britain are china-clay wastes and slate waste.

### China-clay wastes

The china-clay (kaolin) industry is concentrated in the Devon and Cornwall region, which is one of the most environmentally attractive areas of Britain. In the mining operation, kaolinized granite is extracted from steep-sided open pits by washing the faces with high-pressure jets of water. The broken-up rock is collected in a slurry and first processed to remove the sand waste; the residual slurry is then de-watered and a second separating process is carried out to remove the fine clayey sand and mica residue. Thus, for each tonne of china clay finally extracted, nearly 9 t of waste is produced; this is typically composed of 3.7 t of coarse sand, 2 t of waste rock, 2 t of overburden, and 0.9 t of micaceous residue.

The wastes are usually tipped on adjacent land that is less suitable for china-clay workings, often in mounds up to 45 m high. It is reported[89] that these tips cover about 800 ha of land, and contain at least 280-million tonnes; about 125-million tonnes of this accumulation is coarse sand which is increasing at the rate of 10–15-million tonnes per annum.

All of the waste materials—with the exception of the micaceous residue—have potential for use in road construction. Relatively little is used, however, because of the concentration of the tips in a locale which is away from potential markets. The material with the greatest potential for 'export'—because of its desirable engineering properties—is the sand waste; this potential is limited, however, by the constraint imposed by transport costs.

Most china-clay sands are not very frost susceptible, and thus can be used in highway pavements and as a bulk fill in embankments. Other uses include back-filling pipe trenches and trench drains, and applications such as permeable backings to earth-retaining structures and as free-draining materials.

The sand wastes have also been used extensively in concrete. However, they require more cement than river sands to achieve the same strength, probably because of the angularity or harshness of the waste sand mixes; the additional cement requirement is normally about 15–20 per cent (by mass) of the cement content.

A synthetic surface dressing aggregate, utilizing china-clay sand, has been developed which is highly resistant to wear and to the polishing action of heavy traffic.

**Effect of mica**
A feature of china-clay wastes is the obvious presence of mica in the coarse sand. This initially gave rise to serious suspicions about its real value as a road-making material, i.e. micaceous materials have a dubious reputation amongst engineers, and the technical literature contains many reports of compaction difficulties associated with materials containing mica.

All micas—*muscovite* $(K_2O.3Al_2O_3.6SiO_2.2H_2O)$ being the most common one—have a layered structure in which successive sheets are able to part easily in the plane parallel to their larger surfaces, and to form very thin flakes. These flakes are extremely resilient when subjected to pressure on their larger surfaces, behaving somewhat like the leaves of a leaf-spring. Muscovite is silvery white in colour and its flakes glitter strongly in the light, due to the high sheen parallel to its cleavage plane.

Most troubles associated with the presence of mica in soils are encountered in fine-grained materials as opposed to coarse-grained ones.

Studies have shown[90] that the proportion of mica normally present in china-clay sand is too low to cause problems in most road construction usages. In fact, the main detrimental effect is that its resilience reduces the degree of compaction achievable for a given compactive effort, by about 0.007 and 0.012 Mg/m$^3$ for each one per cent of fine ( $< 75 \mu$m) and coarse (mostly 212–600 $\mu$m) mica, respectively. Further tests on three waste sands[89] have shown that their maximum dry densities varied from 1.92 to 2.15 Mg/m$^3$, with corresponding air voids of 6 per cent or less, and that the mica present had no deleterious effect upon compaction.

## Slate waste

About 1.2-million tonnes of slate waste is currently produced each year from slate quarries in Wales, and in England in the Lake District, Devon and Cornwall. This quantity is much reduced from that generated in the late 19th century when the slate industry was at its peak. When it is appreciated that, for every tonne of slate produced, an additional 20 tonnes of waste material is produced as a byproduct, then it can be understood why the amount of slate waste available from past production is reported[91] as about 300–500-million tonnes in Wales, 15–20-million tonnes in the Lake District, and about 15-million tonnes in Cornwall.

From an environmental viewpoint, it is perhaps fortunate that most slate waste accumulations are located in relatively remote parts of Britain. From a road-making viewpoint, however, it has meant that little research has been carried out to determine its potential as an engineering material, since its usage would be relatively low anyway, due to the high cost of transport to points of highway construction.

Generally, the nature of slate waste varies according to its origin. Thus *mill waste* consists mainly of the slate blocks and chippings from the dressings of the slate. Rocks such as cherts, which are sometimes interbedded with the slate, and igneous rocks, may also be found in slate waste accumulations.

Experience to date would suggest that slate waste is best used as a bulk fill material. The flaky nature of the waste particles causes problems in compaction, and grid rollers have been found to be most suitable in overcoming these, i.e. they break the longer, needle-shaped pieces of slate into short pieces.

## Chalk

The difficulties often encountered in the course of highway construction with chalk have tended to encourage some engineers to treat chalk as a material of little use for this purpose, and to import more expensive alternative materials when constructing embankments and making pavements in chalk areas.

Typically, fills constructed from soft, fresh chalk with high moisture contents become unstable during the formation of embankments; their high, positive pore-water pressures make compaction impractical, and work sometimes has to be stopped due to the inability of compaction plant to operate efficiently on the spread material. Conversely, with less serious results, very hard chalk can be difficult to excavate and the resulting coarse particles may also be the cause of compaction problems. Chalks with physical properties between these two extremes pose relatively few problems in roadworks.

## Chalk geology

Chalk represents about 15 per cent of the major geological formations of England. As its occurrence at ground level is mainly south of a line between the Wash and Lynne Bay, the proportion in South-east England accounts for more than 50 per cent.

Chalk is a soft, white, porous limestone which was laid down as an ooze on the sea-bed when most of north-western Europe was covered by sea. This sediment was composed almost entirely of organic skeletons of two different origins. The finer fraction of the ooze, which usually comprised about 70–80 per cent of the whole, was composed of microscopic calcareous bodies known as coccoliths, and these yielded particles in the size range 0.5–4.0 $\mu$m. A coarser fraction, composed of skeletal remains of microorganisms known as foraminifera and the broken-down remains of large-shelled organisms such as molluscs and sea urchins, yielded particles in the size range 10–100 $\mu$m. The finer fraction formed a matrix for the coarser particles during the settlement process, and it is most likely that the proportion in which these quite separate ranges of particle sizes became mixed is the main cause of the variations in physical properties exhibited by chalk.

Relatively thin layers of very hard chalk are found at intervals in the chalk mass. Where the layers of ooze became mixed with clay muds, a greyish or buff-coloured chalk marl was formed; this marl is sometimes found as separate layers or is homogeneously distributed throughout the chalk in varying proportions, e.g. non-chalk constituents as high as 40 per cent have been measured. The horizon between the chalk and the overlying deposits is often sharply undulating, and solution holes in the chalk also allowed intrusion of these overlying deposits.

## Classification

The natural moisture content of fresh chalk is normally at, or very close to, its saturation moisture content. These saturation values can range from as low as 8 per cent to as high as 36 per cent.

Chalk fill in embankments typically consists of a mixture of chalk lumps and chalk fines, and at high moisture contents these fines can form a slurry that is known as *putty chalk*, i.e. in the excavation and construction processes the natural rock structure of the chalk is partly broken down and some of the contained water is released. A temporarily weak and unstable embankment results if the proportion of putty chalk present in the fill is high enough to control the behaviour of the whole.

Since the stability of a freshly-placed fill depends upon its moisture content and upon the degree of crushing it has experienced (as reflected in its fines content), a classification system based on these two parameters has been proposed[92] to aid in the use of chalk as a fill material.

Figure 3.16 shows critical saturation moisture contents and chalk crushing values at which the onset of unstable conditions is likely when each of the four indicated types of excavation plant is in use. The critical values are based on the assumption that the moisture content of the compacted fill in winter will be at the saturation moisture content, whilst in summer it will be equal to 85 per cent of the saturation content. Unstable conditions do not normally occur with class A chalk. However, class B and class C chalk—especially when they have high saturation moisture contents—can produce unstable conditions occasionally, even when the recommended type of excavation plant is used. Unstable conditions can be frequently expected with class D chalk.

To predict the probable behaviour of freshly-placed chalk using Fig. 3.16, it is first necessary to determine its saturation moisture content using an extension of the British Standard test for determining the dry density of soil by the *immersion in water method*[93]. From the value of dry density obtained, and assuming a relative density for chalk solids of 2.70, the saturation moisture content is then given by the following formula:

$$\text{saturation moisture content (\%)} = \left( \frac{1}{\varphi_d} - \frac{1}{2.7} \right) \times 100$$

where $\varphi_d$ = dry density $(\text{Mg/m}^3)$.

If the saturation moisture content is less than 23 per cent, the chalk belongs to class A and no further classification tests are necessary.

If a chalk with a saturation moisture content greater than 23 per cent is encountered, then the impact crushing value of the material must be determined using a simple test[92]. The *impact crushing value* is the rate at which a 1 kg sample of single-sized chalk lumps—they must all pass the 20 mm BS sieve and be retained on the 10 mm BS sieve—contained in a mould 100 mm in diameter, crushes under a series of impacts delivered by a 7 kg rammer falling freely through a height of 250 mm. The amount of crushing is determined by measuring the penetration of the rammer into the mould by means of a scale attached to its side. The rate of crushing, i.e. the impact crushing value, is then determined as one-tenth of the slope of the straight section of the relationship between penetration (mm) and the logarithm of the number of blows. A steep slope indicates a fast rate of crushing and, therefore, a soft chalk. Crushing values vary from about 4.2 for a very soft chalk to about 2.4 for a very hard chalk.

At least six tests should be carried out on samples of chalk obtained at any given location. This number of tests should ensure that the mean value for samples of the same chalk will be accurate to ± 1.7 per cent of the saturation moisture content, at the 95 per cent confidence level. If the range

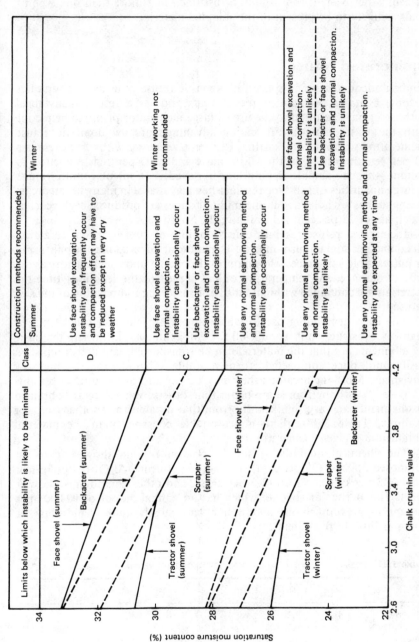

**Fig. 3.16** Suggested chalk classification system, with measures required to avoid or minimize instability[192]

of crushing values exceeds 0.7, or the range of saturation moisture contents exceeds 8 per cent, it can usually be assumed that more than one type of chalk is likely to be present in the sampled material.

## Incinerated refuse

Finding adequate tipping space for domestic refuse near major towns has become a major problem in recent years and, as a result, many local authorities have resorted to the use of large incinerator plants to help cope with the waste material. A major advantage of raw domestic refuse incineration without prior sorting, i.e. *direct incineration*, is that there is a 60 per cent reduction in the waste mass and a 90 per cent reduction in volume—hence valuable tipping land is saved. It also, of course, results in large quantities of ash-type residues being available in many urban areas; in England as a whole, about one-million tonnes are produced each year, of which about 25 per cent is located in the South-east.

Incinerated refuse residues consist mainly of clinker, glass, ceramics, metal and residual unburnt matter. The unburnt material may be paper, rag or putrescible substances, the amounts depending upon such factors as the type of furnace, the temperature of the firebed or the length of time the materials are contained within it, and, of course, the composition of the raw refuse itself.

The least demanding use to which any waste material can be put in highway construction is as bulk fill for embankments, i.e. where the basic requirements are that the material can be transported, laid and compacted easily and, once compacted, form a stable subgrade for the highway pavement. Most incinerator ashes may be considered as suitable for this purpose[94], although some are better than others. Whilst the ash obtained at one plant can vary significantly from that obtained at another (see, for example, Table 3.27), there is reasonable consistency in the material obtained at a given incinerator.

The chemical analysis of the Edmonton residue showed it to be composed of $SiO_2$ (35 per cent), $Fe_2O_3$ (26 per cent), $Al_2O_3$ (23 per cent), CaO (6.3 per cent), $Na_2O_3$ (2.5 per cent), and other compounds (4.5 per cent). This particular residue, which has an annual output of 90 000 t per annum, is grey in colour and well burnt; mostly clinker and glass, it contains little ferrous metal.

**Table 3.27**  Loss-on-ignition and sulphate content data for various incinerator ashes[94]

| Source of ash | Loss in mass on ignition (%) | Soluble sulphate, $SO_3$ (g/l) |
| --- | --- | --- |
| Edmonton (London) | 2.6 | 2.32 |
| Nottingham | 5.7 | 3.15 |
| Derby | 4.2 | 2.70 |
| Birmingham | 6.4 | 5.51 |
| Sunderland | 15.2 | 4.32 |

The presence of significant amounts of tin cans in an incinerator ash can create problems if they are not flattened, because in time the metal cans will rust away and leave large voids in compacted material. This is not normally a major problem with incinerated refuse in general, however, as plants now usually remove most ferrous metals with magnetic separators before discharging residue to waste tips.

The soluble sulphate figures shown in Table 3.27 usually reflect the presence in the raw rubbish of gypsum plaster or similar material from builders' rubble. Since concrete and cemented products are attacked by sulphates dissolved in water, incinerated refuse in which the soluble sulphate content exceeds 2 g/l should not be used within 0.5 m of a concrete structure, unless the structure is adequately protected through the use of such binders as supersulphated cement or sulphate-resisting Portland cement.

## Demolition wastes

It has been reported[91] that about one-million tonnes of concrete and three-million tonnes of brick become available every year from the demolition of dwelling houses. These figures can be augmented with the materials available from the demolition of other buildings and structures, and estimates as high as 21-million tonnes per annum have been made. Thus demolition wastes represent a significant potential construction material, particularly as they are mostly available in urban areas where there is often a shortage of conventional aggregates.

Unfortunately, most demolition debris is produced spasmodically and in relatively small quantities, so that advanced planning for its usage is generally impracticable. Furthermore, it is very variable, and the major components (brick, building stone and concrete) are very often hopelessly intermixed with such minor components as plaster, wood, glass, etc. In fact, the resultant mixture can be so heterogeneous that it is unsuitable for use in highway construction even as bulk fill.

Debris that is relatively free from contamination can be obtained, however; this is composed predominantly of brick, building stone, unreinforced concrete, and reinforced concrete. In practice, waste reinforced concrete is rarely used in roadworks because of the difficulty in separating out the reinforcement, whilst building stone is not widely available. Thus brick and unreinforced concrete have the greatest potential for highway construction, and are sometimes included in specifications as *hardcore* for use in both bulk fill and highway pavements.

## Selected bibliography

(1) Abraham H, *Asphalts and Allied Substances*, Volumes 1–5, New York and London, Van Nostrand, 1960.
(2) BS 892: *Glossary of Highway Engineering Terms*, London, The British Standards Institution, 1967.

(3) Dowling JWF, Franco RL, and Russell RBC, *Natural Asphalts: Their Occurrence, Properties and Use in Road Construction in Colombia*, TRRL Report SR729, Crowthorne, Berks., The Transport and Road Research Laboratory, 1982.

(4) Dussek I, Trinidad Lake asphalt has a future in paving, not just a history, *Highways and Public Works*, 1979, **47**, No. 1834, pp. 10–14.

(5) BS 3690: Part 3: *Bitumens for Building and Civil Engineering Purposes: Bitumen Mixtures*, London, The British Standards Institution, 1983.

(6) Anon, The modern use of Trinidad Lake asphalt, *Highways and Road Construction*, 1975, **43**, No. 1786, pp. 18–20.

(7) Jacobs FA, *A Study of Blends of Trinidad Lake Asphalt and Bitumen in Rolled Asphalt*, TRRL Report SR561, Crowthorne, Berks., The Transport and Road Research Laboratory, 1980.

(8) BS 594: Part 1: *Hot Rolled Asphalt: Constituent Materials and Asphalt Mixtures For Roads and Other Paved Areas*, London, The British Standards Institution, 1985.

(9) BS 1446: *Mastic Asphalt (Natural Rock Asphalt Fine Aggregate) for Roads and Footways*, London, The British Standards Institution, 1973.

(10) BS 1447: *Mastic Asphalt (Limestone Fine Aggregate) for Roads and Footways*, London, The British Standards Institution, 1973.

(11) Puzinauskas VP, Properties of asphalt cements, *Asphalt Paving Technology*, 1979, **48**, pp. 646–697.

(12) Epps JA, Button JW and Galloway BM, *Paving with Asphalt Cements Produced in the 1980s*, NCHRP Report 269, Washington DC, The Transportation Research Board, 1983.

(13) BS 4987, *Coated Macadam for Roads and Other Paved Areas*, London, The British Standards Institution, 1973.

(14) BS 3690: Part 1: *Bitumens for Building and Civil Engineering Purposes: Bitumens for Road Purposes*, London, The British Standards Institution, 1982.

(15) BS 2000: Part 2: *Viscosity of Cutback Bitumen and Road Oil*, London, The British Standards Institution, 1982.

(16) Transport and Road Research Laboratory, *Recommendations for Road Surface Dressing*, Road Note No. 39, London, HMSO, 1981 (2nd edition).

(17) Asphalt Institute, *A Basic Asphalt Emulsion Manual*, Manual Series No. 19, Maryland, The Asphalt Institute, 1979.

(18) Hoad L, Bitumen road emulsions: road binders for the 1980s, *The Highway Engineer*, 1980, **27**, No. 10.

(19) BS 434: Parts 1 and 2: *Bitumen Road Emulsions (Anionic and Cationic)*, London, The British Standards Institution, 1984.

(20) Bradshaw LC, Bitumen emulsions in road mixes, *Shell Bitumen Review*, 1974, **45**, pp. 8–11.

(21) Korn AJ, Bitumen emulsions for road maintenance and construction, *The Highway Engineer*, 1981, **28**, No. 3, pp. 22–27.

(22) Gillespie I, Surface dressing with K1-70 bitumen, *The Highway Engineer*, 1981, **28**, No. 1, pp. 19–23.

(23) BS 76: *Tars for Road Purposes*, London, The British Standards Institution, 1974.

(24) Nicholas JH, Recent developments in the use of tar for highways in the United Kingdom: Parts 1 and 2, *Road Tar and Allied Binders*, 1977, **31**, No. 1, pp. 4–8, and No. 2, pp. 4–8.

(25) BS 5273: *Dense Tar Surfacing for Roads and Other Paved Areas*, London, The British Standards Institution, 1985.

(26) Jamieson IL, *The Carcinogenic Potency of Tar in Road Construction*, Technical Report RB/2/78, South Africa, National Institute for Transport and Road Research, 1978.

(27) Road Research Laboratory, *Specification for the Manufacture and Use of Rubberized Bituminous Road Materials and Binders*, Road Note No. 36, London, HMSO, 1967 (2nd edition).

(28) Dickinson EJ, A critical review of the use of rubbers and polymers in bitumen bound pavement surfacing materials, *Australian Road Research*, 1977, **7**, No. 2, pp. 45–52.

(29) Liversedge F, Tar–bitumen blends in road construction and maintenance, *Road Tar*, 1972, **26**, No. 3, pp. 4–7.

(30) Shoop S, Pitch, *Road Tar and Allied Binders*, 1978, **32**, No. 2, pp. 4–6.

(31) Love GD, Sulphur: Potential pavement binder of the future, *Transportation Engineering Jl of ASCE*, 1979, **105**, No. TE5, pp. 525–533.

(32) McBee WC, Sullivan TA and Izatt JO, *State-of-the-Art Guideline Manual for Design, Quality Control and Construction of Sulphur-Extended-Asphalt (SEA) Pavements*, Washington DC, US Government Printing Office, 1980.

(33) Denning JH and Carswell J, *Improvements in Rolled Asphalt Surfacings by the Addition of Sulphur*, TRRL Report LR963, Crowthorne, Berks., The Transport and Road Research Laboratory, 1981.

(34) Deme I, Shell sulphur–asphalt products and processes, *Shell Bitumen Review*, 1981, **59**, pp. 1–7.

(35) Kennepohl GJ, Bean DC, Miller LJ and Haas RCG, A summary of sulphur–asphalt design technology, *Proceedings of the 5th International Conference on the Structural Design of Asphalt Pavements*, 1982, **5(1)**, pp. 864–877.

(36) Kennedy TW and Haas R, Sulphur–asphalt pavement technology: A review of progress, *Transportation Research Record 741*, 1980, pp. 42–49.

(37) Denning JH, *High-performance Surface Dressing: (2) Road Experiments with New Thermosetting Binders*, TRRL Report SR416, Crowthorne, Berks., The Transport and Road Research Laboratory, 1978.

(38) Downes MJW, Modified binders in the year 2000, *Proceedings of the 6th International Asphalt Conference*, pp. 35–39, Sydney, The Australian Asphalt Pavement Association, 1986.

(39) Denning JH, *Improvements in Rolled Asphalt Surfacings by the Addition of Organic Polymers*, TRRL Report LR989, Crowthorne, Berks., The Transport and Road Research Laboratory, 1981.

(40) BS 2000: Part 45: *Petroleum and Its Products: Loss on Heating of Bitumen and Flux Oil*, London, The British Standards Institution, 1982.

(41) BS 2000: Part 72: *Petroleum and Its Products: Viscosity of Cutback Bitumen and Road Oils*, London, The British Standards Institution, 1982.

(42) BS 2000: Part 49: *Petroleum and Its Products: Penetration of Bituminous Materials*, London, The British Standards Institution, 1983.

(43) BS 2000: Part 58: *Petroleum and Its Products: Softening Point of Bitumen (Ring and Ball)*, London, The British Standards Institution, 1983.

(44) BS 2000: Part 47: *Petroleum and Its Products: Solubility of Bituminous Binders*, London, The British Standards Institution, 1983.

(45) BS 2000: Part 27: *Petroleum and Its Products: Distillation of Cut-back Asphaltic (Bituminous) Products*, London, The British Standards Institution, 1982.

(46) BS 2000: Part 113: *Petroleum and Its Products: Flash Point (Closed) of Cut-back Bitumen*, London, The British Standards Institution, 1982.

(47) BS 2000: Part 35: *Petroleum and Its Products: Flash Point (Open) and Fire*

*Point of Petroleum Products by the Pensky-Martens Apparatus*, London, The British Standards Institution, 1982.

(48) BS 2000: Part 357: *Petroleum and Its Products: Permittivity of Bitumen*, London, The British Standards Institution, 1983.

(49) Committee on Significance of Tests for Highway Materials, Significance of tests for highway materials—Basic tests, *Amer. Soc. Civil Engrs, Journal of the Highway Division*, September 1957, **83**, No. HW4.

(50) Pfeiffer JPH and van Doormaal PM, Rheological properties of asphaltic bitumen, *Jl Inst. Petrol. Technol*, 1936, **22**, No. 154, pp. 414–440.

(51) Heukelom W, Improved nomographs for bitumen, *Shell Bitumen Review*, 1973, **43**, pp. 8–9.

(52) *Relationship of Asphalt Cement Properties to Pavement Durability*, NCHRP Report 59, Washington DC, The Transportation Research Board, June 1979.

(53) ACMA Final report on pitch/bitumen, *Road Tar and Allied Binders*, 1973, **27**, No. 1, pp. 4–7.

(54) BS 4550: Parts 0–6: *Methods of Testing Cement*, London, The British Standards Institution, 1970 and 1978.

(55) BS 12: *Ordinary and Rapid-hardening Portland Cement*, London, The British Standards Institution, 1978.

(56) Department of Transport, *Specification for Highway Works*, London, HMSO, 1986 (6th edition).

(57) Department of Transport, *Notes for Guidance on the Specification for Highway Works*, London, HMSO, 1986.

(58) BS 146: Part 2: *Portland-blastfurnace Cement*, London, The British Standards Institution, 1973.

(59) BS 4027: *Sulphate-resisting Portland Cement*, London, The British Standards Institution, 1980.

(60) BS 3892: Part 1: *Pulverized-fuel Ash*: *Pulverized-fuel Ash for Use as a Cementitious Component in Structural Concrete*, London, The British Standards Institution, 1982.

(61) BS 6588: *Portland Pulverized-fuel Ash Cement*, London, The British Standards Institution, 1985.

(62) BS 6610: *Pozzolanic Cement With Pulverized-fuel Ash as Pozzolana*, London, The British Standards Institution, 1985.

(63) BS 915: Part 2: *High Alumina Cement*, London, The British Standards Institution, 1984.

(64) Bate SCC, High alumina cement concrete—An assessment from laboratory and field studies, *The Structural Engineer*, 1980, **58A**, No. 12, pp. 388–393.

(65) BS 890: *Building Limes*, London, The British Standards Institution, 1972.

(66) BS 5930: *Site Investigations*, London, The British Standards Institution, 1981.

(67) Croney D and Jacobs J, *The Frost Susceptibility of Soils and Road Materials*, RRL Report LR90, Crowthorne, Berks., The Road Research Laboratory, 1967.

(68) Shane BA, *Estimating the Demand for Aggregate in Great Britain*, TRRL Report SR414, Crowthorne, Berks., The Transport and Road Research Laboratory, 1978.

(69) Road Research Laboratory and Geological Survey and Museum, *Sources of Road Aggregate in Great Britain*, London, HMSO, 1960.

(70) *Aggregates: The Way Ahead: Report of the Advisory Committee on Aggregates*, London, The Department of the Environment, 1975.

(71) Sherfold FA, The classification, production, and testing of road-making aggregates, *Quarry Managers Jl*, 1960, **44**, No. 2, pp. 47–54.

(72) Benson FJ, *Effects of Aggregate Size, Shape, and Surface Texture on the Properties of Bituminous Mixtures—A Literature Survey*, HRB Special Report 109, 1970, pp. 12–21.

(73) BS 812: Part 103: *Testing Aggregates: Determination of Particle Size Distribution*, London, The British Standards Institution, 1985.

(74) BS 812: Section 105.1: *Testing Aggregates: Flakiness Index*, London, The British Standards Institution, 1985.

(75) BS 5835: Part 1: *Testing of Aggregates: Compactibility Test for Graded Aggregates*, London, The British Standards Institution, 1980.

(76) BS 812: Part 2: *Sampling and Testing of Mineral Aggregates, Sands and Fillers: Physical Tests*, London, The British Standards Institution, 1975.

(77) BS 63: Part 2: *Single-sized Roadstone and Chippings*, London, The British Standards Institution, 1971.

(78) BS 1984: *Gravel Aggregates for Surface Treatment (Including Surface Dressing) on Roads*, London, The British Standards Institution, 1967.

(79) Pike DC, *Variability in Grading Results Caused by Standard Sample-reduction Techniques*, TRRL Report SR489, Crowthorne, Berks., The Transport and Road Research Laboratory, 1979.

(80) *Specification Requirements for Aggregate Properties and Texture Depth for Bituminous Surfacings in New Roads*, Technical Memorandum H16/76, London, The Department of Transport, 1976.

(81) Road Research Laboratory, *Roadstone Test Data Presented in Tabular Form*, Road Note No. 24, London, HMSO, 1959.

(82) BS 812: Part 3: *Sampling and Testing of Mineral Aggregates, Sands and Fillers: Mechanical Properties*, London, The British Standards Institution, 1975.

(83) Dalhouse JB, Plotting aggregate gradation specifications for bituminous concrete, *Public Roads*, 1953, **27**, No. 7, pp. 155–158.

(84) BS 1047: *Air-cooled Blastfurnace Slag Aggregate for Use in Construction*, London, The British Standards Institution, 1983.

(85) Sherwood PT, *The Use of Waste and Low-grade Materials in Road Construction: (2) Colliery Shale*, TRRL Report LR649, Crowthorne, Berks., The Transport and Road Research Laboratory, 1975.

(86) OECD Research Group C12, *Use of Waste Materials and By-products in Road Construction*, Final Report RR/C12/77.1, Paris, OECD, March 1977.

(87) Burns J, *The Use of Waste and Low-grade Materials in Road Construction: (6) Spent Oil Shale*, TRRL Report LR818, Crowthorne, Berks., The Transport and Road Research Laboratory, 1978.

(88) Sherwood PT, *The Use of Waste and Low-grade Materials in Road Construction: (3) Pulverized Fuel Ash*, TRRL Report LR686, Crowthorne, Berks., The Transport and Road Research Laboratory, 1975.

(89) Tubey LW, *The Use of Waste and Low-grade Materials in Road Construction: (5) China Clay Sand*, TRRL Report LR817, Crowthorne, Berks., The Transport and Road Research Laboratory, 1978.

(90) Tubey LW and Webster DC, *The Effects of Mica on the Roadmaking Properties of Materials*, TRRL Report SR408, Crowthorne, Berks., The Transport and Road Research Laboratory, 1977.

(91) Sherwood PT, Tubey LW and Roe PG, *The Use of Waste and Low-grade Materials in Road Construction: (7) Miscellaneous Wastes*, TRRL Report LR819, Crowthorne, Berks., The Transport and Road Research Laboratory, 1977.

(92) Ingoldby HC and Parsons AW, *The Classification of Chalk for Use as a Fill*

*Material*, TRRL Report LR806, Crowthorne, Berks., The Transport and Road Research Laboratory, 1977.

(93) BS 1377: *Methods of Test for Soils for Civil Engineering Purposes*, London, The British Standards Institution, 1975.

(94) Roe PG, *The Use of Waste and Low-grade Materials in Road Construction*: (*4*) *Incinerated Refuse*, TRRL Report LR728, Crowthorne, Berks., The Transport and Road Research Laboratory, 1976.

# 4
# Soil engineering for highways

Soil is the foundation material for all highways, whether it be in the form of undisturbed in situ subgrade material or transported and reworked embankment material. In addition, the highway pavement itself, as well as the flanking shoulders, is very often composed of the cheapest raw material available, soil.

Soil deposits are rarely homogeneous; they can vary from loose to dense, from uncemented to highly cemented, and the particle distribution can range from poorly graded (highly sorted) to well graded (little or no sorting). Basically, they must be dealt with as they are met, as it is not normally economic to attempt to make major modifications to their physical properties. It is axiomatic therefore that the highway engineer should have a thorough understanding of soils and how they behave.

## Origin of soil

### Definition of soil

The term soil stems from the Latin word 'solum' and this designation is still very much used by the agricultural scientist. Whereas, in older times, only the agriculturalist's view of soil as a material was accepted, developments in other professional fields have resulted in the term now having various meanings and connotations.

According to the pedologist, soil is a natural body, differentiated into horizons of mineral and organic constituents, usually unconsolidated, of variable depths, which differs from the parent material below in morphology, physical properties and composition, and biological characteristics. Soil, as used in this context, is rarely considered as extending to more than 1.0–1.5 m below ground level. This definition is a natural one from the agricultural viewpoint, since applications of soil science in this area are mainly concerned with understanding and improving the material in which crops are grown.

To the geologist, the earth's crust is composed of rocks and the unconsolidated sediments which make up the regolith. As these sediments are exposed to the weather and biological activity, the uppermost part becomes considerably modified. This upper plant-growing stratum is given the designation soil by the geologist to distinguish it from unmodified sediments beneath.

To the engineer, soil means any naturally occurring loose or soft deposit resulting from weathering or breakdown of rock formations or from the decay of vegetation. This definition includes many materials of varied origin that are movable by normal earthmoving equipment, viz. detrital sediments such as gravels, sands, silts and clays, organic deposits such as peats, calcareous deposits such as shell and coral sands, pyroclastics such as uncemented volcanic dust, and residual soils such as the laterites. In other words, to the engineer the term soil means all unconsolidated materials above bedrock with which and upon which structures are to be built. The engineer also uses the term *topsoil* to describe the upper humic, or plant-growing, portion of the soil profile.

## Soil formation and types

The earth's crust is composed of in-place rock and unconsolidated sediments. These sediments were themselves derived from rock formations through physical disintegration and chemical decomposition processes, and deposited through gravity, ice, water action or wind. As soils were moved and reworked, further weathering, abrasion, mixing with organic materials and soluble minerals, and leaching took place—all in varying degrees— until eventually the material was formed that concerns the highway engineer at a given location.

Figure 4.1 summarizes how various types of soils are developed from parent rocks, and indicates factors which influence the type of soil formed: the nature and extent of weathering as controlled by climatic conditions are of particular importance. For example, in arid and semi-arid regions, solution by percolating water is of less importance than water drawn to the surface by capillary action; here the concentration and deposition of calcium and magnesium have considerable influence upon soil formation. In moist, temperate climates with marked seasonal changes, percolating water is most important in soil formation; in this instance, solution and decomposition are dominant, and acid soils of the iron and aluminate varieties are developed. In humid, hot climates, chemical processes are very active, and organic influences are pronounced; the result is that the decomposition and removal of silica take place, iron and alumina are concentrated, and lateritic soils are formed. Organic materials have a significant influence upon the formation of soils in both humid, cold climates and cold climates.

Given that the mechanical forces of nature have been instrumental in moving most soils from place to place, it is possible to speak of soils according to the means by which they were naturally transported and/or deposited in their present locations.

### Residual soils
These are inorganic soils which have been formed from the underlying bedrock and which, as the name implies, have never been moved.

The climate, i.e. temperature and rainfall, mainly determines the type of residual soil formed. Mechanical weathering (disintegration) predominates in northern cold climates and in arid regions; thus, for example, a soil formed in a cold climate from a granite parent material is normally granular and the various mineral components that constitute the granite are chemically unaltered. By contrast, chemical weathering dominates the soil forming process in tropical regions with high year-round temperatures and rainfall; thus a granite in the wet tropics would be so affected by chemical weathering that, except for its quartz mineral component, all of its other constituents would be chemically altered as it decomposed into clay-type soils.

Typically, residual soils found in Britain are relatively finely grained near the surface but become more coarsely grained, since they contain angular fragments of rock, with increasing depth. Residual soils are very rarely found in glaciated areas as either they have been removed or they are buried beneath other overlying glacial soils.

**Colluvial soils**
These are simply accumulations of rock debris, scree, or talus which become detached from the heights above and are carried down the slopes by the force of gravity. Soils formed from these accumulations are usually poorly sorted and composed of coarse, angular particles. Bedding, if present, is poorly developed and the upper and lower surfaces of the soil deposits are rarely horizontal. Some colluvial soils are very thin and may be mistaken for topsoil; however, thicknesses in excess of 15 m are found in non-glaciated areas of Britain in valley bottoms and in concave parts of hill slopes.

In Britain, colluvial soils are known as *head deposits*. One of the oldest and most widespread of these soils is the clay-with-flints which caps many of the chalk areas; these soils are believed to have been derived by solifluction from earlier deposits that have since been eroded.

**Cumulose soils**
These are *organic* soils such as peats or mucks which have been formed in place as a result of the accumulation of chemically decomposed plant residues in shallow, ponded areas. Although easily noted when on the surface, they are often encountered in glacial areas at considerable depths below the surface. Both peat and muck are highly organic, but muck is considerably older. While the fibres of unoxidized plant remains are obviously visible in peat, they are largely oxidized in muck soil.

**Glacial drift**
Soils of the glacial drift are those which have been transported and deposited by great glaciers of ice. During the Ice Ages—these ended approximately 10 000 years ago after spanning a period of about two-million years—glaciers, several kilometres thick, covered vast areas of the northern hemisphere. When they retreated, deposits composed of boulders, rock fragments, gravel, sand, silt and clay were left behind. These deposits are commonly called glacial drift, irrespective of their method of deposition. Such glacial deposits cover large areas of Britain north of a line passing through the Thames and Severn estuaries; this line roughly marks the southern limit reached by the ice sheets.

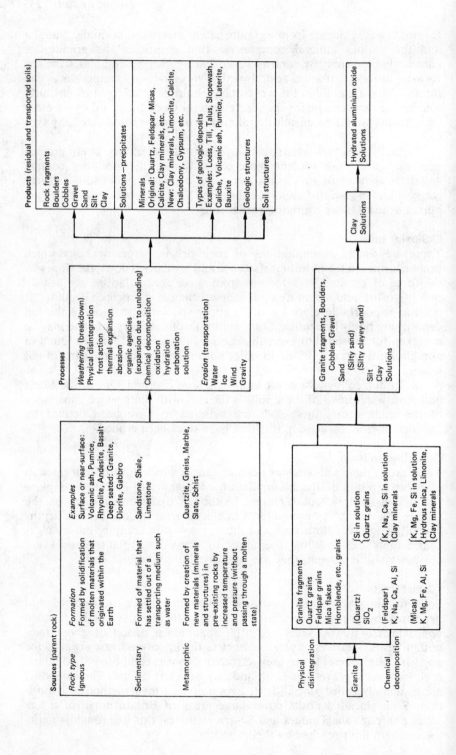

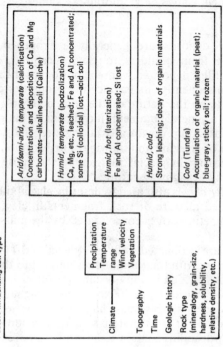

**Factors influencing soil type**

Climate ── Precipitation
            Temperature
            range
            Wind velocity
            Vegetation

*Arid/semi-arid, temperate* (calcification)
Concentration and deposition of Ca and Mg
carbonates—alkaline soil (Caliche)

*Humid, temperate* (podzolization)
Ca, Mg, etc., leached; Fe and Al concentrated;
some Si (colloidal) lost—acid soil

*Humid, hot* (laterization)
Fe and Al concentrated; Si lost

*Humid, cold*
Strong leaching; decay of organic materials

*Cold* (Tundra)
Accumulation of organic material (peat);
blue-gray, sticky soil; frozen

Topography

Time

Geologic history

Rock type
(mineralogy, grain-size,
hardness, solubility,
relative density, etc.)

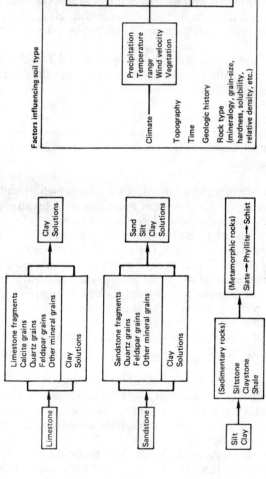

Limestone → Limestone fragments
            Calcite grains
            Quartz grains
            Feldspar grains
            Other mineral grains
            Clay
            Solutions
            → Clay
              Solutions

Sandstone → Sandstone fragments
            Quartz grains
            Feldspar grains
            Other mineral grains
            Clay
            Solutions
            → Sand
              Silt
              Clay
              Solutions

Silt → (Sedimentary rocks)
Clay    Siltstone
        Claystone
        Shale
        → (Metamorphic rocks)
          Slate → Phyllite → Schist

**Fig. 4.1** The soil forming processes

Glacial drift can be subdivided into two classes: (a) deposits laid down directly by the glacial ice, e.g. glacial till and drumlins, and (b) deposits laid down by glacial melt waters, e.g. moraines, kames, eskers, and glacial outwash deposits.

*Glacial till*   These deposits are generally heterogeneous in grain-size (sometimes varying from boulders to clay), unsorted, and variable in composition. Most till is deposited from the bottom of the ice sheet whilst it is still moving. Consequently, its engineering properties can vary considerably, depending upon the nature of the rock outcrops upstream of the deposition area. As a general comment, it can be said that glacial till has the tendency to creep or slump downwards along steep hillsides (solifluction) under the influence of freezing and thawing. Furthermore, saturated lenses of sandy soil occurring in glacial till can be the cause of erosion and slumping and sliding in highway cuttings.

The term *boulder clay* is also used to describe glacial till composed of an unsorted, unstratified mixture of rock fragments in clay, which has been compressed and sometimes over-consolidated by the mass of the ice.

*Drumlins*   These are elongated hills of glacial drift with ellipse-type contour lines, oriented with their major axes parallel to the direction of ice movement. Drumlins, which usually occur in groups, may be as much as 2 km long, over 400 m wide, and 100 m or more high. It is believed that their smoothly-rounded shapes may have been formed as a result of irregular accumulations of drift material being overridden by the moving ice. Although many drumlins contain some sand, they are usually composed of materials very rich in clay.

*Moraines*   These are irregular, hummocky hills which usually contain assorted glacial materials. Four types of moraines are generally recognized, viz. terminal, lateral, recessional and ground moraines.

Terminal moraines are those long, low hills, perhaps 1.5–3.0 km wide and up to 30 m high, which mark the southernmost limit of the glacial advance. Roughly perpendicular to the direction of glacial movement, they are believed to have occurred as the ice sheet started to melt as it reached a warm climate. As the front of the ice sheet melted, the material carried was dropped by the melting waters. At the same time the ice front was continually forced forward by the pressures from the colder regions, so that more drift material became added to that which had already accumulated. These irregular ridge accumulations are known as terminal moraines or end-moraines.

Lateral moraines are similar to terminal moraines. They were formed along the lateral edges of the ice sheet as glacial material was dropped by the melting ice, and as a result they are roughly parallel to the direction of ice movement. Lateral moraines are most clearly defined along the edges of valleys in mountainous terrain.

As the temperature increased, the ice front melted faster than its rate of advance, with the result that the glaciers began to 'recede'. This recession was constantly interrupted of course, with the result that minor 'terminal' moraines were formed at irregular intervals. These crescent-shaped hills are known as recessional moraines. When the topography is characterized by a series of recessional moraines interspersed with many depressions containing small lakes, it is sometimes called a 'knob-and-kettle' topography.

When the ice sheet melted rapidly, material continually dropped at the edges of the receding ice sheet; this material is referred to as ground moraine.

*Kames* Of particular interest to the highway engineer are the hummocky-shaped hills or mounds known as kames; these are believed to have been formed where glacial streams emerged from an ice front. These hills mainly contain poorly-stratified accumulations of gravel and sand, but some clay is also usually present. The materials found in kames are generally quite suitable for road-building purposes.

*Eskers* These are long, sinusoidal ridges, usually with flat tops and steep sides, which contain highly-stratified gravel and sand eminently suitable for highway construction. Eskers are relatively low, usually not more than about 18 m in height, but may be many kilometres in length. They are the end-products of accumulations of glacial material which were deposited at crevices or tunnels within the thin wasting ice as the ice front retreated. The lack of fine-grained materials in eskers is explained by the fact that they were washed away by streams flowing rapidly from the edge of the ice front.

*Glacial outwash deposits* At the time of the northern hemisphere's Ice Age, the weather was obviously warmer at particular times of the year than at others, just as it is today. When this occurred, huge volumes of ice melted and streams rushed out from the wasting ice field. These streams were charged with large quantities of glacial materials which spread out over the uncovered land away from the glaciers. In narrow valleys, through which these waters were able to flow rapidly and freely, the materials deposited tended to be coarsely grained, whereas on plains they were extremely varied.

In many instances, the outwash waters fed into enclosed valleys within which lakes were formed. Great quantities of debris were deposited in these lakes, ranging from coarse to fine in content. The different rates of settlement of the various materials carried by the waters led to extreme stratification taking place and, particularly towards the middle of the lakes, uniform horizontal and alternating layers of silt and clay were laid down. Over the centuries, these layers accumulated and formed lacustrine deposits now given the name of *varved deposits*. The thickness of each varve or layer can vary from being infinitesimally small to perhaps 10 mm thick, each layer corresponding to one year's deposit. Varved soils can give rise to troublesome foundation problems and should be avoided when locating a highway.

**Alluvial stream deposits**
Alluvial soils are ones which have been deposited by river waters that are no longer moving fast enough to keep their loads in suspension. They are

generally regarded as falling into the following three categories: floodplain soils, alluvial fans, and deltas.

*Floodplain soils*　These are found to a certain extent alongside every river, but are most evident along mature streams. Older rivers are usually on gently-inclined beds and, as a result, they tend to use up their energies in horizontal meandering rather than in cutting deeper channels. In the course of a stream's meanders, coarse-grained material is deposited at the inside of the meander curves, while the moving waters cut into the opposite banks. These deposits at the insides of bends can be very valuable as construction materials and may influence the location of a highway as well as its pavement design.

With time, the mature river continually changed its path, with the result that old meanders were cut off and the now-familiar half-moon shaped *ox-bows* were formed. In other words, these ox-bows are simply old meander beds which were left as depressions after the river changed its course. Over the years, these depressions became filled with water during wet weather and dried out again during fine weather. As moisture ran into the ox-bow lakes, fine-grained material was carried in also, so that, with the passage of time, the depressions became full of silty and clayey materials. Since they are not continuous but rather occur as pockets of clay-like materials, ox-bows should be avoided when locating a highway as they are liable to cause differential heaving and/or settlement of the pavement.

When a stream is carrying an excess of water, due to heavy rainfalls or perhaps sudden snow melting, it will very often burst its banks and the water will spread out over the adjacent land—this is particularly true of the more mature rivers. If the land is wide and flat it becomes a *floodplain* over which the velocity of the flooding water decreases the further it gets from the river bed. This decrease in velocity results in sand and gravel being deposited adjacent to the river banks, silt further out, and the finest materials still further away. Thus natural levees or ridges of coarse-grained materials may be found adjacent to rivers in floodplains, while poor-draining, swampy lands are to be found further back. The coarse-grained materials can be used for construction purposes on highway projects, but usually they must be washed beforehand to remove excess fines.

In many instances, it has happened that, for some geological reason, an old meandering river suddenly becomes 'rejuvenated' and begins to incise a new channel in the old formed alluvium, leaving so-called *terraces* on either side. A number of these raised horizontal terraces can be seen along the sides of river-bearing valleys, indicating that there were periods when the streams were at these heights. Again, these terraces can be good sources of construction materials. In addition, they very often provide good locations for highways through valleys, as they reduce the need for expensive excavation into the sides of the valley, while at the same time keeping the highway well above the possible floodwaters of the river.

*Alluvial fans*　Other good sources of highway construction materials are alluvial fans. This is a landform which is to be found at the foot of a stream which emerges suddenly from high land onto a plain. As the stream rushes onto the flat ground, the rapid change in gradient causes it to spread out in the shape of a fan. Sediment carried in the water is deposited in this characteristic shape also. Since the water has a higher velocity as it enters the plain, fan material is generally coarsely grained and well drained, and contains little or no fines.

*Delta deposits* Although much of the material carried by a river is deposited over its floodplains, a considerable amount obviously still reaches the mouth of the stream, where it is discharged into the body of water such as an ocean or lake to which it is a tributary. By this time, the sediment carried may be mostly fine-grained material which has not had the opportunity to settle previously. If the stream flows into a standing body of water, where currents or wave action are minor, much of the suspended sediment drops to the bottom to form a fan-shaped promontory known as a delta. The most-highly-developed deltas are generally to be found where large rivers enter the ocean. When the body of water into which the stream discharges is a lake, the deposits are known as *lacustrine* soils.

### Marine soils
In addition to the material carried to the sea by rivers and streams, the ocean itself is continually eroding the shoreline at one location and depositing the eroded material at another. These processes have been going on for millions of years with the result that, as oceans have receded from old land areas, great areas of new land surface became exposed to the weathering elements. These exposed deposits very often consist of clay, silt and fine sand-sized materials that were deposited in salt marsh and inter-tidal flat environments. The coarser materials are usually largely derived by longshore drift, and the finer materials from stream sources. In many British coastal areas, marine clays are interbedded with freshwater alluvium and peat, giving rise to very soft organic clays.

It is difficult to make more definite comments about marine soils, except that their usage for highway location or construction purposes should be treated with considerable care, especially if they contain much fine-grained material.

### Aeolian soils
Aeolian soils are those which have been transported and laid down by the wind. The wind-blown soils are usually subdivided into two groups: dune sands and loess silts.

*Dune sands* These soils are to be found both in arid regions and in temperate zones adjacent to large bodies of water where large quantities of beach sand are deposited. When the wind blows consistently from one direction in these areas, the coarse sand particles move by *saltation*, i.e. by skipping across open ground with little vegetative cover, until eventually they lodge together and dunes begin to form. These dunes have a relatively gentle slope on the windward side, whereas the leeward slopes are at the very much steeper angle of repose of the sand. Although highly vulnerable to wind or water erosion, sand dunes are not susceptible to sliding unless the angle of repose of the sand particles is exceeded.

It is because of their tendency to shift that sand dunes can become a problem for the highway engineer. When a sand dune is sufficiently formed for the amount of sand deposited on it by the wind to balance the amount taken away from the leeward side by the same wind, the dune is caused to migrate as sand particles are blown up and over the top. Highways which pass through migrating dune sand areas that are not stabilized by vegetation can be continually covered and uncovered by sands and, in some instances—particularly when the roads are low cost and unsurfaced—rendered impassable.

*Loess silts* Loesses can be defined as porous aeolian silts of uniform grading, which are usually calcareous. They occur extensively in eastern Europe and in the USA, but are relatively unknown in Britain.

Loess soils are to be found further away from the beaches on which they draw for their resources. They are composed primarily of silt-sized particles which have been picked up from the beaches by the wind and transported through the air to their ultimate destinations. As found at particular locations in the field, loess soils are composed of very uniform particles which get smaller and smaller the further the distance from the beach source.

Loess soils are both free draining and rich in calcium carbonate, and this combination makes it possible to excavate highway cuttings with near-vertical sides. The cementing action of the calcium carbonate is lost, however, with manipulation of the loess, and hence embankments formed from loessial soils must have similar side slopes to those formed from other soils.

## Composition of soil

As found in nature, soil can be considered as an assemblage of solid particles interspersed with void or pore spaces which may or may not contain water. This concept of soil is a very important one since the highway engineer is most often concerned with obtaining a soil condition *where the void spaces are kept to a minimum and the volume occupied by the mineral particles is at the maximum possible.*

### Soil phase relationships

It is easiest to visualize the various soil phases, and the relationships which exist between them, by representing in graphical form a soil sample in which the solid, liquid and gaseous phases are segregated. Figure 4.2 is a schematic diagram in which it is assumed that a sample of soil is placed in an equivolume cylinder of unit cross-section. Such an arrangement makes it possible to consider the component volumes as represented by their heights, so that it is a simple matter to develop some important relationships.

**Moisture content**
The moisture content of a soil is its mass of water expressed as a percentage

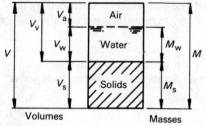

**Fig. 4.2** Diagrammatic illustration of the three phases of a soil

of the mass of dry solids in the soil. Thus

$$m = (M_w/M_s) \times 100$$

where $m$ = moisture content of the soil (%), $M_s$ = mass of solids, and $M_w$ = mass of water.

### Voids ratio
The voids ratio of a soil is the ratio of the volume of voids to the volume of solids present in the soil. This relationship pays no regard to the proportions of water, air or other gases which may constitute the pore spaces. Thus

$$e = V_v/V_s$$

where $e$ = voids ratio, $V_s$ = volume of solids, and $V_v$ = volume of voids.

In a saturated soil, the voids ratio is, of course, directly proportional to the moisture content. In this case, the volume of voids, $V_v$, is equal to the volume of water, $V_w$. Then

$$e_s = V_w/V_s = (M_w/M_s) \times (\psi_s/\psi_w) = m \times \psi_s/\psi_w$$

where $e_s$ = voids ratio when the soil is saturated, $\psi_s$ = mass per unit volume of solids, and $\psi_w$ = mass per unit volume of water.

### Porosity
The porosity of a soil is defined as the ratio of the volume of the voids to the total volume of the soil. As with the voids ratio, the porosity pays no regard to the constituent volumes of the pore spaces. In contrast to the voids ratio, porosity is usually expressed as a percentage value. Thus

$$n = (V_v/V) \times 100$$

where $n$ = porosity (%) and $V$ = total volume of the soil mass.

The porosity of a soil can also be expressed by the formula

$$n = [e/(1 + e)] \times 100$$

### Percentage voids
The percentage of the total volume of the soil which is occupied by the air in the voids is referred to as the percentage air voids. Thus

$$n_a = (V_a/V) \times 100$$

where $n_a$ = percentage air voids and $V_a$ = volume of air voids.

The percentage of the total volume of the soil which is occupied by the water in the voids is referred to as the percentage water voids. Thus

$$n_w = (V_w/V) \times 100$$

where $n_w$ = percentage water voids and $V_w$ = volume of water voids.

Obviously, the sum of the percentage air voids and the percentage water voids is equal to the porosity. Thus

$$n = n_a + n_w$$

## Degree of saturation

The extent to which the voids present in a soil are filled with water is termed the degree of saturation. It is the ratio of the volume of water to the volume of voids, expressed as a percentage. Thus

$$S = (V_w/V_v) \times 100$$

where $S$ = degree of saturation (%).

## Dry density

The mass of the dry solid particles per unit volume of soil is defined as the dry density. Thus

$$\psi_d = \frac{M_s}{V} = \frac{M_s}{V_s + V_w + V_a}$$

where $\psi_d$ = dry density of the soil.

The mass of the wet solids plus the water contained in the pore spaces of a soil per unit volume is called the wet (or bulk) density. Thus

$$\psi = \frac{M}{V} = \frac{M_s + M_w}{V_s + V_w + V_a}$$

where $\psi$ = wet (or bulk) density of the soil.

## Relationships between dry density, wet density, moisture content, and percentage air voids

The relationship between the wet, $\psi$, and dry, $\psi_d$, densities of a soil follow from their definitions. Thus

$$\frac{\psi}{\psi_d} = \frac{M}{V} \times \frac{V}{M_s} = \frac{M_s + M_w}{M_s} = 1 + \frac{m}{100}$$

therefore

$$\psi_d = \frac{100\psi}{100 + m}$$

The relationship between dry density, $\psi_d$, moisture content, $m$, and percentage air voids, $n_a$, is deduced as follows:

$$\psi_d = \frac{M_s}{V_s + V_w + V_a}$$

thus

$$\frac{1}{\psi_d} = \frac{V_s}{M_s} + \frac{V_w}{M_s} + \frac{V_a}{M_s} = \frac{1}{\psi_s} + \frac{m}{100\psi_w} + \frac{V_a}{V\psi_d}$$

hence

$$\frac{1}{\psi_d} \times \left(100 - \frac{100 V_a}{V}\right) = \frac{100}{\psi_s} + \frac{m}{\psi_w}$$

$$\frac{1}{\psi_d} \times (100 - n_a) = \frac{100}{\psi_s} + \frac{m}{\psi_w}$$

and

$$\psi_d = \psi_w\left(1 - \frac{n_a}{100}\right)\Big/\left(\frac{\psi_w}{\psi_s} + \frac{m}{100}\right) = \psi_w\left(1 - \frac{n_a}{100}\right)\Big/\left(\frac{1}{r_s} + \frac{m}{100}\right)$$

where $r_s$ = relative density of the soil solids and $\psi_w$ = density of water.

This particular relationship shows that if any two of the factors dry density, moisture content, and percentage air voids are known for a soil of a particular relative density, then the third can be very easily established.

## Soil solids

Soil is a porous mixture of inorganic particles, decaying organic matter, air and water. The solid phase consists of particles of varying degrees of subdivision, ranging in size from boulders to colloids. The coarseness or fineness of a soil is reflected in terms of the relative fractions of the different separates present; those most commonly used are gravel, sand, silt and clay.

These terms have different meanings to different scientific organizations, and it is necessary to be aware of these differences when reading and interpreting the technical literature on soils. All organizations accept that the most convenient way to define the separates is on the basis of particle size; the differences arise over what exactly these sizes should be.

To the Swedish soil scientist Atterberg can be given the credit for what is perhaps the most important early attempt to put on a scientific basis the choice of the limiting sizes of the various soil fractions. It is his 1908 classification system which was essentially adopted by the International Society of Soil Science.

Atterberg classified gravel particles as those which were between 2 and 20 mm in size. He suggested that these were the limits within which no water is held in the pore spaces between the particles and where water is weakly held in the pores. Sand was stated to be between 0.2 and 2 mm in size, the lower limit being set at the point where water is held in the pores by capillary action. The lower limit of Atterberg's silt group was given the theoretical significance of being the size beyond which smaller particles could not be seen with the naked eye, did not have the usual properties of sand, and could be coagulated to form 'crumbs'. Thus silt was visualized as being the material which ranges from where sand begins to assume clay-like features to the upper limit of clay itself. The choice of 0.002 mm as the upper limit

**Table 4.1**   Particle-size range limits and scales of fines used in practice in various countries[3]

| Country | System | Particle-size range limits | | | |
|---|---|---|---|---|---|
| | | Upper gravel (mm) | Lower gravel/ upper sand (mm) | Lower sand/ upper fines ($\mu$m) | Dividing percentage between coarse and fine soils |
| UK | BSCS: 1981 | 63 | 2 | 63 | 35 |
| Germany | DIN 18196: 1970 | 63 | 2 | 63 | 40 |
| Switzerland | SNV 70005 and 8: 1959 | 60 | 2 | 60 | 50 |
| France | LCPC: 1965 | 60 | 2 | 80 | 50 |
| Japan | Japanese USCS M1-1973(79) | 75 | 2 | 74 | 50 |
| USA | USCS (ASTM: 1969) | 75 | 4.75 | 75 | 50 |

of the clay fraction was based on the premise that particles smaller than this exhibited Brownian movement when in aqueous suspension.

Table 4.1 shows the limiting sizes adopted by various international organizations which set standards. It should be noted that the British Soil Classification System for Engineering Purposes[2-4] actually defines gravel as material within the size range 2–60 mm, sand 0.06–2 mm, silt 0.02–0.06 mm, and clay < 0.002 mm; in practice, however, the nearest available sieve sizes, e.g. 63 mm and 63 $\mu$m, are generally used for sizing purposes. In Britain also, the sands and silts are further subdivided into coarse sand 0.6–2 mm, medium sand 0.2–0.6 mm, fine sand 0.06–0.2 mm, coarse silt 0.02–0.06 mm, medium silt 0.006–0.02 mm, and fine silt 0.002–0.006 mm.

For completeness, it should be noted that material greater than 60 mm is defined as very coarse in Britain, with *cobbles* being 60–200 mm and *boulders* > 200 mm. Furthermore, the term *soil fines* is sometimes used to describe all material smaller than 0.06 mm; thus if the percentage of soil fines is equal to or greater than 35 per cent, the soil is described as a 'fine soil'; correspondingly, a soil with less than 35 per cent by mass smaller than 0.06 mm is termed a 'coarse soil'.

**Physical and mineralogical characteristics**
The inorganic soil solids are composed of primary mineral fragments in conjunction with the secondary mineral products of weathering. The term 'secondary mineral', as used here, refers to any mineral created after the original rock was formed from which the soil was derived. The primary mineral quartz dominates the soil fraction derived by physical weathering, i.e. the sand and coarse silt fraction. Quantities of other primary silicate minerals such as feldspars, hornblende and the micas are also present at this stage. The primary minerals become of less significance in the fine silt particles until, with the clay fraction, it is found that the secondary minerals are the dominant ones.

*Sand*  Since sand is primarily composed of quartz particles, it is quite inactive chemically, so its physical characteristics are of most interest. In contrast to clay particles which are flat or flake shaped, sand particles are generally bulky in shape. The individual grains may be further classified as angular, subangular, rounded or subrounded, depending upon the degree of abrasion received prior to final deposition. For instance, residual sands are usually angular, whereas river and beach sands are generally rounded. Wind-blown sands are usually very fine and well rounded, while ice-worn sand particles may have flat faces which have been scoured by the ice.

Table 4.2 shows that the stability potential of a sandy soil is significantly influenced by its state of compaction, gradation, and particle shape, i.e. the shearing resistance increases with the degree of compaction, and with the angularity and size of particle. Not shown here is the effect of moisture content upon stability.

Clean sand particles do not exhibit any cohesive properties and so are little influenced by changes in moisture content. Since the particles are generally bulky in shape, the pores between them are relatively large; thus sandy soils are very permeable and well drained, and consolidation effects are small.

*Silt*  Silt particles can be considered as transitional between sand and clays. Physically they are similar to sands in that they derive much of their stability from the mechanical interaction between the particles. Coarse silt particles are essentially miniature sand particles and so tend to have similar bulky shapes as well as the same dominant mineral. Unlike sands, silts possess a certain limited amount of cohesion due to interparticle water films. Although they are generally classed as permeable, moisture can only move through the (small) pore spaces relatively slowly. Where the smaller-sized particles predominate, silts exhibit strong clay-like tendencies and may undergo considerable shrinkage and expansion when exposed to changes in moisture content.

**Table 4.2**  Some approximate shearing resistance results for coarse-grained soils [5]

| Grain-size | Degree of compaction | Angle of internal friction (degrees) | |
|---|---|---|---|
| | | Rounded grains, uniform gradation | Angular grains, well graded |
| Medium sand | Very loose | 28–30 | 32–34 |
| | Moderately dense | 32–34 | 36–40 |
| | Very dense | 35–38 | 44–46 |
| Sand and gravel | | | |
| 65% G + 35% S | Loose | — | 39 |
| | Moderately dense | 37 | 41 |
| 80% G + 20% S | Dense | — | 45 |
| | Loose | 34 | — |

*Note:* For comparative purposes, blasted rock fragments have an angle of internal friction of 40–55 degrees

*Clay*   The particles in the clay fraction differ from the sand and silt particles both in their chemical make-up and in their physical properties. Physically they are different in that they are flat and elongated, or lamellar, and thus have a much larger surface area per unit mass than the bulky-shaped silts and sands. A crude measure of the effect of the differences in external surface areas exposed by the various soil fractions can be obtained by assuming that individual separates are spherical in shape and then calculating the surface areas involved. Table 4.3 presents a summary of one such calculation. Since the intensity of the physico-chemical phenomena associated with soils is a function of the exposed surface area, this table illustrates why the clay fraction exerts an influence on a soil's behaviour which can appear to be very much out of proportion to its mass or volume in the soil.

Any study of the clay fraction of a soil is to a large extent a study of its colloidal ingredient. It is the soil colloids that are primarily responsible for the cohesiveness of a plastic soil, its shrinking and swelling characteristics, and its ability to solidify into a hard mass upon drying. In addition, the drainage characteristics of a soil are considerably influenced by the amount and form of its colloidal content.

There is no uniform designation as to what constitutes a *soil colloid*. In theory, it can be said that a colloid is any particle which exhibits Brownian movement when in an aqueous suspension. In practice, however, the term is usually applied to particles smaller than 1 $\mu$m, even though it is known that the Brownian phenomenon is applicable to particles up to 4 $\mu$m in size.

The importance attached to the colloidal fraction is associated with the electrical charges which the colloids carry on their surfaces.

The reasons for these charges can perhaps be briefly explained by considering the manner in which ions, atoms or molecules are combined to form a crystalline solid. These chemical units tend to combine in a definite pattern so as to accomplish the greatest possible degree of electrical neutralization. The simplest grouping of these atoms is called a unit cell, while the term 'crystal' is applied to a three-dimensional repetition of unit cells. Within the structural arrangement of a crystal—this is called a space lattice—the electrostatic bonds or valencies of the atoms are completely

**Table 4.3**   Some physical characteristics of soil separates[6]

| Name | Diameter (mm) | Number of particles per gramme | Surface area of 1 gramme of each separate (cm²) |
|---|---|---|---|
| Fine gravel | 1.00−2.00 | 90 | 11.3 |
| Coarse sand | 0.50−1.00 | 722 | 22.7 |
| Medium sand | 0.25−0.50 | 5 777 | 45.2 |
| Fine sand | 0.10−0.25 | 46 213 | 90.7 |
| Very fine sand | 0.05−0.10 | 722 074 | 226.9 |
| Silt | 0.002−0.05 | 5 776 674 | 453.7 |
| Clay | <0.002 | 90 260 853 860 | 11 343.5 |

*Note:* Each particle is assumed to be a sphere having the maximum diameter of each group

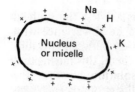

**Fig. 4.3**  Schematic representation of a colloidal particle

neutralized, whereas those at the edges, corners and surfaces are not. The net result is the unbalanced negative charge associated with a colloidal particle.

A second major cause of the electrical charge carried by a soil colloid is the substitution of one ion for another within the crystal lattice. This phenomenon, which is known as *isomorphous substitution*, is the main source of the electrical charges associated with montmorillonitic and illitic soil colloids; this is in contrast to kaolinitic colloids, where the unsatisfied valency phenomenon is the main cause. In montmorillonite, for instance, the substitution of magnesium ($Mg^{2+}$) for aluminium ($Al^{3+}$) on the basis of one $Mg^{2+}$ for one $Al^{3+}$ results in an unsatisfied valency.

As a result of the electrical charges that they carry, colloidal silicate–clay particles also attract to, or adsorb on, their surfaces positively-charged cations such as hydrogen and the base metals sodium, calcium, potassium and magnesium. Figure 4.3 illustrates what is known as the Helmholtz double-layer concept of the make-up of a colloidal particle. As can be seen, the inner part consists of an insoluble nucleus or micelle—the inner sheath of negative charges is part of the wall of the nucleus—surrounded by a swarm of positively-charged cations. These cations are in equilibrium at different but infinitesimally small distances from the surfaces of the colloid.

A clay in which the principal adsorbed ion is hydrogen is called a hydrogen clay; a calcium clay is one in which the adsorbed ions are mostly calcium. If a clay having adsorbed ions of one particular type is brought into contact with ions of another kind, some of the first type of ions may be released and some of the second type adsorbed in their place. This exchange of positively-charged ions, i.e. *cation exchange*, is at the basis of the stabilization of soils with certain chemicals and by electro-osmotic phenomena.

The efficiency with which ions can replace each other is dependent upon the following factors.

(1)  *Relative concentration or numbers of ions*  This is an application of the chemical law of mass action, whereby the larger the number of ions in the solution, the greater is the probability of exchanges taking place.

(2)  *Number of charges on the ions*  The higher the valency, the greater is the number of charges on an ion and, other things being equal, the greater is its replacing power and the more difficult it is to displace when already attached to the colloidal particle. The exception to the rule is hydrogen which behaves similarly to a divalent or trivalent ion.

(3)  *Speed of movement or activity of the different ions*  With ions of the same valency, the replacing power tends to increase as the effective diameter

of the ion increases. In other words, the smaller ions are less tightly held than the larger ones. This may seem at first sight to be at variance with Coulomb's law, which states that the force of attraction between two ions varies inversely as the square of the distance between them; this means that the smaller ions should be held more tightly. In a soil solution, however, the ions are all hydrated, with the result that a water hull surrounds each ion. By Coulomb's law, the smaller ions will have the thickest water hulls and larger effective sizes than the more weakly hydrated but initially larger ions. The greater effective size reduces the ease of movement (migration velocity) of the hydrated ion, as well as the degree of tightness with which it is held to the colloidal particle.

(4) *Type of clay mineral*    Clay minerals differ considerably in the amount of surface area exposed. Thus montmorillonites, which have expandable lattice structures, have high exchange capacities, whereas kaolinites have relatively low ones.

The actual manner in which the cations are exchanged can be explained by considering colloidal particles in a solution. Owing to heat movement and Brownian motion, the adsorbed ions are never at rest but are in fact continually moving back and forth within a limited range from the surfaces of the particles. If electrolytes are added to the solution, cations are set in random motion because of the Brownian effect, and numbers of them may slip between the negative wall of the nucleus and the adsorbed but oscillating ions. These electrolytic cations then become preferentially adsorbed, while some surface ions are released and remain in the solution as exchanged ions. Obviously, the more loosely the surface ions are held, the greater is the average distance of oscillation and hence the greater is the possibility of ion adsorption and/or replacement.

The ease with which cations may be exchanged and adsorbed is expressed in terms of the *cation-exchange capacity* of a soil. This is the number of milli-equivalents (meq) of ions that 100 grammes of the soil can adsorb. By definition, one milli-equivalent is one milligramme of hydrogen, or the amount of any other ion that will combine with or displace it. Thus, if the cation-exchange capacity of a soil is 1 meq it means that every 100 g of dry material is capable of absorbing and holding 1 mg of hydrogen or its equivalent of other ions.

*Clay minerals*    Not so many years ago, clays were believed to be amorphous materials having no definite recurring patterns of atoms, ions or molecules. Research on clay minerals started about 1925 and since then it has been clearly established that clay minerals have overwhelmingly crystalline structures. Thus clay particles are now seen as essentially composed of minute flakes and in these flakes, as with all crystalline substances, the atoms are arranged in a series of units to form clay minerals.

The atomic structure of most clay minerals consists of two fundamental building blocks, viz. tetrahedrons of silica and octahedrons of alumina.

As is illustrated in Fig. 4.4(a), a silica tetrahedron has one silicon atom equidistant from four oxygens or hydroxyls. Figure 4.4(b) shows that the tetrahedrons are arranged in a sheet-like hexagonal structure so that the

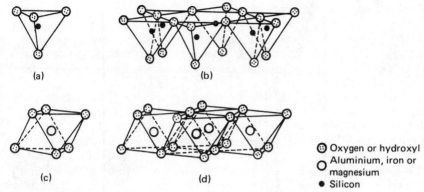

(a)  (b)

(c)  (d)

⊕ Oxygen or hydroxyl
○ Aluminium, iron or magnesium
● Silicon

**Fig. 4.4**  Basic building blocks of the clay minerals

oxygen atoms at the basal corners of the tetrahedrons are in a common plane, with each shared between two tetrahedrons. Thus the silica tetrahedron sheet may be viewed as a layer of silicon atoms located between a layer of oxygens in the base and a layer of hydroxyls at the tips of the tetrahedrons.

The second fundamental building block is an octahedral unit (see Fig. 4.4(c)) in which an atom of aluminium, iron or magnesium is equidistant from six oxygens or hydroxyls. Again, as is illustrated in Fig. 4.4(d), these units also form sheet-like layers in which each oxygen is common to three octahedral units. In this case, the sheet can be viewed as two layers of densely-packed oxygens/hydroxyls with the aluminium between the layers in octahedral coordination.

The different clay mineral groups—of which seven are generally recognized—are formed as a result of the bonding together of two or more of these molecular sheets. Six of the seven groups are composed of layered phyllosilicates, whilst in the seventh group the minerals take the form of laths. From an engineering point of view, the ones which are of most interest are the kaolinite, smectite, and hydrous mica groups. Table 4.4 summarizes some typical characteristics of the three most important clay minerals in these groups.

The kaolin group is named after a hill in China where white clay used in the making of chinaware was extracted for centuries. The most common, as well as important, of the ten clay minerals in this group is *kaolinite* which is one of the layered silicates. The chemical formula of kaolinite is $2SiO_2.Al_2O_3.2H_2O$ which indicates that it is exclusively silico-aluminous.

As indicated schematically in Fig. 4.5, the kaolinite structural unit is composed of an aluminium octahedral layer with a parallel superimposed silica tetrahedral layer intergrown in such a way that the tips of the superimposed silica sheet and one of the layers of the aluminia unit form a common sheet. Thus the kaolin unit can be viewed as a succession of layers of oxygens, silicons, oxygens and hydroxyls, and aluminiums and hydroxyls, which is about 0.7 nm thick, and—in theory—extends infinitely in the other two directions. The kaolinite mineral is composed of a stacking of these

**Table 4.4** Typical characteristics of the more important clay minerals[7]

| Clay mineral | Sheet thickness (nm) | Micelle thickness (nm) | Specific surface (m$^2$/g) | Cation-exchange capacity (meq/100 g) | Hydro-scopicity (%) | | PL (%) | LL (%) | PI | Activity and swelling | Main occurrence |
|---|---|---|---|---|---|---|---|---|---|---|---|
| Kaolinite | 0.71 | 100 | 15 | 5–15 | 0.5 | Na | 26 | 52 | 26 | Low | Hydrothermal deposits; products of strong leaching and weathering, especially on acid rocks |
| | | | | | | Ca | 36 | 73 | 37 | | |
| Illite | 1.00 | 20 | 80 | 20–40 | 3.0 | Na | 34 | 61 | 27 | Medium | Marine clays and shales; products of intermediate weathering with adequate potassium |
| | | | | | | Ca | 40 | 90 | 50 | | |
| Montmorillonite | Variable | 2 | 800 | 80–100 | 17.0 | Na | 97 | 700 | 603 | High | Some marine clays; weathered volcanic ashes; products of restricted weathering (dry conditions or impeded drainage) |
| | | | | | | Ca | 63 | 177 | 114 | | |

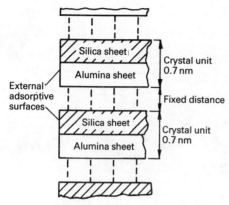

**Fig. 4.5** Schematic diagram of the structure of typical kaolin crystals

0.7 nm thick sheets such that its structure might be considered akin to a book in which each leaf is 0.7 nm thick. Successive layers are held together by hydrogen bonds which allow the mineral to cleave fairly easily into very thin platelets.

The kaolinites are considered to be very stable clays from an engineering aspect. The hydrogen bonds between the elemental sheets are sufficiently strong to prevent water molecules and other ions from penetrating, and hence the lattice is considered to be restricted or non-expanding. As with the other clay minerals, the kaolinite platelets carry negative electrical charges on their surfaces which attract thick layers of adsorbed water. Since the lattice is non-expanding, the effective surface area to which the water molecules can be attracted is restricted to the outer faces, and for this reason the plasticity, cohesion, and shrinkage and swelling properties of kaolinite are very low when compared with other silicate clays.

The second important clay mineral group was, until fairly recently, called the montmorillonite group, after the town of Montmorillon in France; it is now also known as the smectite group, the term smectite being descriptive of a layered structure. The smectite group contains five clay minerals of which *montmorillonite* is by far the most important.

As is illustrated in Fig. 4.6, each montmorillonite crystal unit is composed of two silica tetrahedral sheets and one octahedral sheet, giving a 2:1 type of lattice structure. The octahedral sheet is between the silica sheets, with the tips of each tetrahedral sheet and a hydroxyl layer of the octahedral sheet intergrown to form a single layer. The minimum thickness of each crystal unit is about 0.95 nm and the dimensions in the other two directions are indefinite. These sheets are stacked one above the other, like the leaves of a book. There is very little bonding between successive crystal units and, as a result, water molecules and other cations can readily enter between the sheets. In the presence of an abundance of water, the mineral can be split into individual unit layers.

The facility with which water can enter between the montmorillonite's

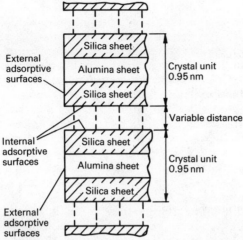

**Fig. 4.6**   Schematic diagram of the lattice structure of typical montmorillonite crystals

crystal units makes these clays a matter of critical concern to highway engineers. The considerable area of charged surfaces which are exposed means that substantial amounts of dissolved ions/water can be attracted to these soils, and this facility gives to montmorillonite its high plasticity and cohesion, its marked shrinkage on drying, and a ready dispersion of its fine flaky particles. (The effect of the nature of the predominant adsorbed cation upon the plasticity characteristics is particularly well illustrated in Table 4.4.) In connection with this, it might be mentioned that each thin platelet of montmorillonite has the power to attract a layer of adsorbed water approximately 20 nm thick to each flat surface. Thus, assuming zero pressure between the surfaces, the platelets may be separated by a distance of 40 nm and still be 'joined' together.

The most important clay mineral in the hydrous mica group is *illite*, which is named after the State of Illinois, USA. Amongst clay minerals in their natural state, illite is possibly the most common. Like montmorillonite, illite has a 2 : 1 lattice structure. The thickness of each crystal unit is 1 nm.

The illite clay mineral differs from that of montmorillonite in that there is always a substantial (about 20 per cent) replacement of silicons by aluminiums in the tetrahedral layers. The valencies vacated by this substitution are satisfied by positively-charged potassium ions which lie between the structural units and tie them together. The strength of this potassium bond is intermediate between the hydrogen bond of kaolinite and the water linkage of montmorillonite, and the net result is that illites have properties intermediate between those of the two other clay minerals.

## Soil water

There are many ways by which soil water can be classified or described. One of the more practical ways is to divide it into three main groups: gravitational water, groundwater, and held water.

**Gravitational water**

By definition, gravitational water is that part of the precipitation which does not evaporate or flow away in the form of surface runoff but penetrates the ground and percolates downwards under the action of gravity. The downward infiltration of gravitational water continues until a depth is reached below which the soil pores are completely saturated with water; the upper surface of this saturated zone is called the *water-table*.

The zone between the water-table and the ground surface is often described as the zone of aeration; its thickness may range from (exceptionally) more than 100 m to (commonly in Britain) less than 1 m. The soil voids in this zone are normally not entirely filled with water, e.g. the gravitational water content of this zone will vary from a near-saturated state near the ground surface soon after precipitation to a minimum after a lengthy period without replenishment.

The rate at which gravitational water migrates downwards is mainly dependent upon the texture and structure of the soil(s) within the zone of aeration. In general, however, the more coarsely grained the soil, the more quickly the water infiltrates down. Fine-grained soils, while they may have considerable porosity, are noted for the slow rate at which gravitational water moves through them; this is mainly due to the resistance to flow (resulting from the percolating passages and high sidewall frictions) encountered by the water as it attempts to infiltrate downwards.

Sometimes the zone of aeration will contain a coarse-grained soil lying on top of an inclined layer of fine-grained soil, e.g. in glacial till. In such instances, gravitational water may infiltrate more quickly laterally than vertically, and may appear as seepage water at hillsides, in road cuttings, beneath highway pavements, etc., following precipitation.

Since air is present in the soil pores within the zone of aeration, Darcy's law of saturated flow cannot be properly applied to estimate gravitational water seepage.

**Groundwater**

Below the water-table the soil pores are completely saturated; the moisture in this zone of saturation is known as groundwater.

Contrary to what is often believed by the layperson, the water-table is not a horizontal plane, but in reality is a surface that is as constantly changing as the topography above it. Therefore, as a result of elevation differences in the water-table, groundwater is rarely at rest but tends to flow laterally and emerge as ground seepage water or to feed lakes, streams and swamps.

The water-table also rises or falls, depending upon climatic conditions and changes in elevation of streams and lakes. In dry weather the water-table may be considerably lowered, whereas in wet weather it will normally rise considerably as precipitation adds to the moisture in the soil, and lakes and streams are replenished. For this reason, it is important to make a formal note of the date at which any measurement of the water-table is taken in the course of survey work; if necessary, a seasonal correction can be applied at a later time.

Since the soil pores below the water-table are saturated, Darcy's law can be used to estimate the water flow through the soil in the event that it is required in an attempt to lower the water-table, e.g. by pumping. Developed in 1856, Darcy's law states that the average velocity of flow at atmospheric pressure through the voids in a column of saturated soil is proportional to the hydraulic gradient, which is the difference in pressure (or headloss) divided by the distance travelled by the water. It follows from this that the quantity of water flowing through such a column in unit time is proportional to the cross-sectional area of the column and the hydraulic gradient. Thus

$$Q = kiA = khA/l$$

where $Q$ = water flow in unit time, $i$ = hydraulic gradient, $h$ = headloss due to flow through the soil, $l$ = length of flowpath through the soil, $A$ = cross-sectional area of the flowpath, and $k$ = coefficient of permeability or average velocity of the water through the soil.

Gravel and sand soils have good groundwater drainage properties, e.g. clean gravels typically have $k$-values between 1 and 10 cm/s, whilst clean sands and sand–gravel mixtures have $k$-values ranging from $10^{-3}$ to 1 cm/s. In contrast, homogeneous clays are practically impervious ($k < 10^{-7}$ cm/s), whilst sand–silt–clay mixtures such as are found in glacial tills often have $k$-values between $10^{-7}$ and $10^{-4}$ cm/s. As might be expected, fine sands and silts tend to have $k$-values ranging from $10^{-5}$ to $10^{-3}$ cm/s.

If a laboratory test is to be used to determine the coefficient of permeability of a soil, it should be carried out on undisturbed soil samples cut in the direction of the anticipated moisture flow. This is important since, for instance, the coefficient of permeability in the horizontal plane of a sand–gravel material may be as much as ten times greater than the vertical value, whilst in uniformly-graded sand soils the coefficient of permeability in the horizontal direction may be up to four times greater than the vertical one.

**Held water**
If gravity were the only force acting on the water in the aeration zone, then the pores in the material above the water-table would be dry at all times other than when gravitational water is in the process of infiltrating downwards. In fact, this is far from being the case. For example, if a cross-section were to be taken through the zone of aeration, it would be found that a layer exists above the water-table within which the pores are wholly or partially filled with moisture. The thickness of this layer, which is often termed the *capillary fringe*, is typically about 2–5 cm in coarse soils, 12–35 cm in medium sands, 35–70 cm in fine sands, 70–150 cm in silts, and 200–400 cm or greater (after considerable periods of time) in clays.

Water held within the capillary fringe (excluding water vapour) can be subdivided as follows: (a) water which is chemically combined within the crystal structure of the individual soil particles, (b) adsorbed water, and (c) water held by capillarity and surface-tension forces between the particles.

From a practical point of view, the water combined within the structure of a soil particle can be considered as an integral part of the soil solid. Certainly most soil particles will not lose this internal moisture within the range of temperatures to which soils are normally subjected in the course of testing for highway purposes, or in use thereafter. Hence this component of the held water can be normally disregarded in the context of moisture content measurements of soil samples from the capillary fringe.

As has been already discussed in this chapter in relation to clays, colloids, and clay minerals, the adsorbed water component of the held water is particularly important in fine-grained soils, e.g. swelling and shrinkage are dependent upon the thickness of the water films about the particles. Some of the adsorbed water, but not all, will be removed during the normal heating (at $105-110\,^{\circ}C$) applied to a soil sample in the course of determining its moisture content; however, much of the removed moisture will be returned to the particles if the soil sample is exposed to a surrounding atmosphere of a higher relative humidity.

No discussion of the adsorption phenomenon in respect of held water can avoid mentioning its effect in relation to organic matter or humus present in the soil. Since they are predominantly negatively charged, the humus particles display adsorptive properties similar to, but greater than, clay minerals. Humus has an extremely high adsorptive capacity and is therefore capable of attracting and holding very thick films of water—which is why the humic topsoil is normally removed prior to the construction of a highway pavement or low embankment.

The finer the soil, the more important adsorbed moisture becomes in terms of its contribution to the moisture content of soil within the capillary fringe. However, with the more coarse types of fine-grained soils, a greater proportion of the held water can be attributed to moisture which is held by surface-tension forces about the points of contact of soil particles and by capillarity in the pores between the particles.

If the pores present in a soil are considered to form an interrelated mass of irregular 'capillary tubes', then the movement and retention of water within the fringe can be simply and qualitatively explained in relation to the rise and retention of water in a capillary tube. Consider the situation where the lower end of a capillary tube of uniform diameter is immersed in water. It will be found that the level of water in the tube will continue to rise above the free-water level until the upward component of the surface-tension force, i.e. that force which is in operation at the interface of the water meniscus at the top of the column and the inside surface of the tube, is in equilibrium with the gravitational force acting on the volume of water raised. The height of this capillary rise is given by the well-known formula:

$$h = (2T \cos \alpha)/r\rho_w g$$

where $h$ = height of rise of water, $T$ = surface tension, $r$ = radius of the circular capillary tube (i.e. of the meniscus), $\rho_w$ = density of water, $g$ = acceleration of free fall, and $\alpha$ = angle of contact between the water meniscus and the wall of the tube.

From this equation it follows that the capillary rise in the tube is increased as the radius of the tube is decreased. Similarly, the capillary rise in the capillary fringe of a soil is increased as the sizes of the soil pores are decreased; thus the more finely grained the soil, the greater is the potential for moisture to rise through capillary action. Since the pore-sizes in a soil are never uniform in practice, the water will rise to a different height in each capillary channel; the net result therefore is that there is a decrease in soil moisture content due to surface tension and capillarity, as the distance above the water-table increases.

There are several important features associated with the presence of capillary moisture in a soil.

For instance, although the capillary fringe is usually considered in terms of being vertically above the water-table, capillary flow can and does occur in any direction. The main feature is that the moisture finds its way from a zone of saturation to one with a low degree of saturation, irrespective of whether the movement is in a lateral or vertical direction.

The stability of a fine-grained soil, particularly a clay, is very heavily dependent upon the moisture content. Thus, if a clayey soil is within the capillary fringe, it will be found that its cohesion is heavily dependent upon the amount of capillary water present.

Sands and silts located within the capillary fringe can exhibit a phenomenon known as *apparent cohesion* as a result of surface tension which tends to pull the damp particles together. This cohesion is termed apparent because immersion *or* drying will destroy the films, thereby eliminating the tendency for the particles to stick together.

When soil is compacted, the soil particles are pushed together under the influence of the compaction forces. If particles which are bound together by capillary moisture are compacted, the water will tend to be pushed out from between them and the radii of the water menisci will increase. If too much compaction is applied, the soil pores will become filled with water, the menisci radii will become infinite, and the cohesion between the particles will disappear.

It might be noted that the capillary movement concept is also associated with what highway engineers call *embankment pumping*. This refers to the phenomenon observed in embankment construction when a fine-grained soil is over-compacted. In this case, and even though the water-table may be at some considerable depth, the repeated kneading of the soil has the effect of stimulating the upward capillary movement of water.

*Soil moisture suction*   Whilst the capillary-tube analogy (and the capillary-rise formula) are most useful qualitatively in explaining why moisture is present in a fine-grained soil above the water-table, it is of little quantitative use to the engineer interested in predicting the probable distribution of moisture in the soil beneath a highway pavement—and thus, indirectly, the probable stability of the pavement. This particular need can be overcome by recognizing the relationship between soil suction and moisture content.

If a sample of soil that is sufficiently small for self-loading to be neglected, is removed from the capillary fringe, it can be shown that the water contained within it has a pressure less than that of the free atmosphere. If a standard test is carried out on the soil sample and the negative gauge pressure is determined which, through a porous membrane, will hold a column of water in equilibrium with the water within the sample, it is termed the soil moisture suction or, more commonly, the *soil suction*. This suction can be described as a macroscopic property of the soil that indicates the intensity with which it is able to attract moisture. It results from the interplay of charged clay particles and polar water molecules, the surface-tension forces of water, solution potentials caused by dissolved ions, and soil density. As distinct from pore-water pressure, suction represents total head, i.e. it includes pore-water pressure, osmotic pressure, and adsorptive pressure.

There is ample empirical evidence (see, for example, reference 8 for an excellent treatise) to show that for a given soil there is an increase in soil suction with decreasing moisture content, and that this relationship is continuous over the entire moisture range, e.g. the suction value may range from up to $10^9$ N/m$^2$ for oven-dry soils down to zero for soils which will take up no more water. As a result of this large variation, the soil suction is usually expressed in terms of the common logarithm of the length in centimetres of an equivalent suspended water column; this logarithmic value is termed the pF-value of the soil moisture.

Table 4.5 shows the relationship between the pF-scale and the soil suction. Note that, as a result of the logarithmic nature of the scale, pF = 0 does not relate exactly to zero suction. Oven-dryness corresponds closely to pF = 7.

*Hygroscopic moisture* When soil is allowed to dry 'naturally' in the air, e.g. in a laboratory, moisture will be removed by evaporation until the remaining held water in the soil is in equilibrium with the moisture vapour in the air. If a sample of the air-dry material is then placed in an oven and dried at 105 to 110 °C (as is the standard practice[9, 10] when determining moisture contents for engineering purposes), and the moisture content driven off is determined, the value obtained is called the hygroscopic moisture content.

Knowledge of the hygroscopic content is necessary when laboratory studies are being carried out which involve the addition of controlled amounts of moisture to soil. In such studies, however, it has to be

**Table 4.5** Relationship between pF and soil moisture suction

| pF | Equivalent suction | |
|---|---|---|
| | Centimetres of water | N/m$^2$ |
| 0 | $10^0$ | $97.9 \times 10^0$ |
| 1 | $10^1$ | $97.9 \times 10^1$ |
| 2 | $10^2$ | $97.9 \times 10^2$ |
| 3 | $10^3$ | $97.9 \times 10^3$ |
| 4 | $10^4$ | $97.9 \times 10^4$ |
| 5 | $10^5$ | $97.9 \times 10^5$ |
| 6 | $10^6$ | $97.9 \times 10^6$ |
| 7 | $10^7$ | $97.9 \times 10^7$ |

remembered that the hygroscopic content can be a variable value for a given soil, i.e. its value depends upon the temperature and humidity of the air over the soil at the time the determination is carried out.

## Soil structure

The engineering behaviour of an in situ soil is a function of its structure or fabric, which in turn is a result of the geological conditions governing the deposition and subsequent history of stressing and weathering of the soil. Soil structure is a complex concept that is very difficult to quantify, since it can exist at a number of levels from micro to macro. Soils in which microstructure dominates engineering behaviour in the mass include sensitive and quick clays, collapsing sands, loesses and clays, compressible creep-prone clays and peats, expansive clays, clays and shales, and residual and lateritic clays. Soils in which macrostructure predominates include such features as horizontal layering, laminations and varves, vertical root channels and tension cracks, and random fissuring and jointing[11].

Historically, two types of soil structure have been differentiated for engineering purposes, viz. primary structure and secondary structure.

### Primary structure

This refers to the manner in which the sand, silt and clay particles in the soil mass are arranged into compound aggregates or peds. Karl Terzaghi, the founder of modern soil engineering, has classified undisturbed soils with regard to primary structure as single grained, honeycomb, and flocculent. This classification recognizes that structure is dependent upon particle size and shape, as well as upon the minerals composing the individual grains.

#### Single-grained structure

In a single-grained structure, each individual soil particle can be considered as being in direct point-to-point contact with several adjacent particles, or, by analogy, as having come to rest as might a mixture of marbles poured into a container. In other words, the arrangement of particles is entirely accidental and has no particular pattern. In addition, there is virtually no

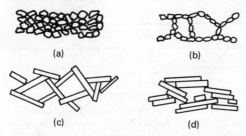

(a)          (b)

(c)          (d)

**Fig. 4.7**  Types of structure found in natural soils: (a) single-grained, (b) honeycomb, (c) flocculated, and (d) oriented

tendency for the particles to form aggregates, but each particle functions as an individual (see Fig. 4.7(a)).

Although found to a lesser extent with the fine-grained soils, a single-grained structure is usually associated with the coarse-grained sands and gravels. The individual mineral particles may be deposited in a loose state having a high voids ratio, or in a dense state having a low voids ratio; whichever it is, the structural designation is the same.

From an engineering viewpoint, an important characteristic associated with single-grained soils is their ability to deform. Dense soils increase in volume when caused to deform, whereas loose soils decrease in volume when deformed by, for example, vibration which causes the particles to slide or roll into a more dense state. Fine-grained, cohesionless particles that are deposited in a loose state, say in an embankment, and then saturated, form a particularly unstable construction. When the material is deformed by a sudden vibration, the voids ratio decreases; because of the lower permeability of the denser material, the water cannot escape from the soil quickly, with the result that the water has to carry the load and liquefaction takes place.

**Honeycomb structure**
As illustrated in Fig. 4.7(b), a honeycomb structure is composed of particles which touch each other at only a few points. The configuration would obviously be unstable were it not for the binding action of the molecular forces which occur at the points of contact of the particles.

Honeycomb structure is most often associated with water-deposited, silt-sized soil particles. The structure was created by the silt particles settling out of suspension as individual grains. When the grains came together, however, the molecular forces at the contact points were sufficiently strong to prevent the particles from rolling down over each other under the gravitational influence of the submerged mass. In this way, several adjacent particles formed chains or strings which became miniature beams or arches capable of bridging relatively large void spaces.

Honeycomb soils have high voids ratios and so have to be treated with respect when engineering loads are to be placed upon them. In general, they tend to have a critical loading below which excessive volume changes will not occur. When, however, the applied load is sufficient to break down the honeycomb structure, considerable settlement can occur, since the material then acts as if it were single grained and deposited in a loose state.

**Flocculent structure**
This type of structure is generally associated with clay soils formed in large bodies of water.

When a clay soil is formed as a result of individual particles coming into contact whilst still in suspension and prior to deposition, e.g. in salty water, then the soil is said to have a *flocculated-type* structure in which particles are arranged in an edge-to-edge or 'card-house' manner (see Fig. 4.7(c)). If, however, the individual particles settle independently from a dispersed suspension, the sediment will have a *dispersed-type* or *oriented* structure in which the platelets tend towards face-to-face contact (see Fig. 4.7(d)). In reality, clay soils tend to be composed of a more random mixture of the above two idealized forms of flocculent structure, i.e. some particles are face-to-face, some are edge-to-edge, and others have intermediate orientations.

The individual particles can also combine into aggregates or 'clusters' within which they may be, for example, randomly in contact with each other. If these clusters then form cementitious bonds with each other—these are much weaker than the bonds within each cluster—a flocculent-honeycomb-type soil structure will be formed. This is termed a cluster-type structure. Since there is a relatively large volume of interaggregate pores in cluster-type clays, they tend to be more permeable than the other flocculent clays.

Clay soils with flocculent structures can also have relatively high voids ratios. When a heavy load is placed on such a deposit, the high pressures experienced at the points of contact can cause the edges of the platelet particles to slide along the flat surfaces with which they are in contact; this results in a more dense arrangement of particles with a consequent reduction in the voids ratio. Remoulding a clay soil similarly breaks down its structure and makes it possible to obtain a considerably reduced voids ratio when the reworked soil is compacted.

## Secondary structure

Systems of secondary structure found in undisturbed soil masses which are of particular interest to the highway engineer (but which have not been discussed previously in this chapter) include fissures and cracks, slickensides, concretions, and other discontinuities that sometimes develop subsequent to a soil's formation or deposition. Their formation is generally associated with a modification of the primary structure during prolonged consolidation, followed by a stress relief and swelling process caused by erosion of overburden and chemical and physical weathering.

Over-consolidated *fissured clays*, and normally consolidated clays which have become fissured by desiccation, are widely distributed in Britain. Fissured clays are also found which were formed as a result of the surface swelling and softening of shales and mudstones which are much stronger at depth.

*Slickensides* are smooth (almost characteristic), polished, shear surfaces found in clays as a result of differential movements or expansions. The original movements frequently occurred on low-angle slip surfaces, and were often associated with the climatic conditions of the glacial or immediate post-glacial periods. Sidelong cuttings in clay can be a particular source of trouble involving slickensides.

*Concretions* are accumulations of carbonates and iron compounds which further disrupt the continuity of the soil mass, thereby significantly affecting the properties of the soil.

# Forces in soil systems

The forces operating in soils which exert major influences upon their stability are, as can be surmised from the previous discussions, quite complex. For the sake of simplicity, such forces can be grouped under the following headings: adsorption, cohesion, surface tension, internal friction and, of course, inertia. Soil stability is the product of these forces acting in unison, but their relative importance in any given instance will vary with the kind of soil.

*Adsorption* is the phenomenon responsible for the attraction of water molecules and ions to the surfaces of soil particles. As has been previously mentioned, this attractive force is chemical in nature; the soil surfaces are predominantly negatively charged, the water molecules are dipolar, and the ions in the soil water that are attracted to the particle surfaces are predominantly positively charged. All soils have adsorptive powers which increase with decreasing particle size and increasing soil surface area. The mineralogical/chemical composition of a particle also influences its adsorptive capacity.

Adsorption plays its most important role in clay and colloidal-sized particles. It is in this size range that the conditions of surface area and mineralogical/chemical composition that foster high adsorptive forces are usually present. As a result, clay particles never exist in nature without adsorbed films of water. In fact, an individual colloidal particle may be capable of attracting and holding a water film that is much thicker than its own diameter. However, the thickness of an adsorbed film on a soil particle can vary considerably, depending upon such factors as the availability of soil water, soil temperature, and the nature of the adsorbed cation. In this last respect, it should be remembered that positively-charged ions have their own adsorptive capabilities, and can carry their own films of water. This adsorptive attraction of cations for water molecules generally increases with decreasing cation size; this is reflected in the fact that calcium ions, which are actually much larger than sodium ions, carry thinner films so that the effective diameter of a 'free' calcium ion is much smaller than that of a sodium ion. When the calcium ions are then adsorbed onto a colloidal particle, for example, the particle will tend to have an adsorbed water film that is much thinner than when sodium ions are adsorbed.

*Cohesion* can be defined as the attraction between like molecules, and in the soil system it is exemplified by the attraction of one water molecule for another. In ordinary tap water placed in a container and apparently at rest, the individual water molecules are actually moving too fast to be able to cohere or stick together. However, when they are present in a soil, the water molecules come under the influence of strong particle surface charges and are considerably slowed down so that they become more or less oriented in the force fields of the soil particles. Under such conditions, the dipolar molecules of water are attracted to each other through their oppositely-charged ends, in much the same manner as tiny bar magnets are attracted to each other.

Cohesion plays a most important role in cementing clay particles together in soil. An over-simplified way of picturing the mechanism of this cementation is to visualize the oriented water molecules as links in a chain connecting up the soil-particle–cation–soil-particle system. When soil particles are connected by films of water which are only a few molecules thick, the cementation is very strong—in fact, it may be stronger than the cementation in Portland cement concrete. However, as the films become thicker, due to additional water being allowed into the soil, the forces of cohesion decrease, since the water molecules which are most distant from the charged surfaces are less strongly oriented and their attraction for each other is accordingly weakened. At the point where the forces of cohesion disappear, the soil–water system takes on the properties of a liquid.

From this, and the preceding discussion, it is apparent that cohesion is the principal cementitious force operating in clayey soils, and that conditions are most favourable for strong interparticle cementation when the particles are flaky in shape and the water films between the flat surfaces are very thin.

Water exhibits the force of *surface tension* due to the molecular attraction which exists between its molecules at the air–water interface. When surface tension combines with the attraction between water and the surfaces of soil particles (adsorption) to constitute a force that is opposed to gravity and tends to draw or retain water above the water-table, the combination of forces is called capillarity. As noted previously, capillarity has an important effect upon soil stability since it contributes to excess moisture in soils and also to frost action.

As the name implies, *internal friction* in soils is reflected in the resistance to displacement caused by the interlocking of bulky-shaped particles. The factors which have important effects upon internal friction are particle shape and texture, the gradation of particle sizes, and the pressure of particles against each other. The more angular the particles, the greater is the frictional resistance of the soil. Similarly, the better the gradation and the greater the dry density of a soil, the greater is the internal friction.

Generally speaking, soils such as gravels, sands and silts have grains that are spherical or cubical in shape, and thus derive their shear strengths almost entirely from intergranular friction. As noted previously, clay particles tend to have flat, plate-shaped particles; thus their shearing resistances are due to the forces of adhesion/cohesion. Many soils, however, obviously derive their shear strength from a combination of these forces.

## Frost action in soils

Frost action can be defined as any action resulting from freezing and thawing which alters the moisture content, porosity or structure of a soil, or alters its capacity to support loads. In order to take these factors into account in highway pavement design, it is important to have an understanding of how frost action occurs and its consequences. Accordingly, this discussion will be confined to the mechanics of frost action and its consequences, and to the recognition of frost-susceptible soils. Methods to alleviate the effects of frost action from the standpoint of initial prevention and protection of frost-susceptible roads are discussed in Chapter 6.

## Mechanism of frost heaving

By frost heaving is meant the process whereby a portion of a soil (or pavement above it) is raised as a direct result of ice formation in a frost-susceptible material. In Britain, significant frost heaving is most usually associated with severe winters, i.e. those having forty or more days of continuous frost.

Most cases of severe frost heave are attributed to the formation of ice lenses, and not only—as some of the pre-1900 technical literature suggested—to volume increases of soil water upon freezing. The densities of ice and water at $0\,^{\circ}C$ are 0.916 74 and 0.999 87 $g/cm^3$, respectively, which means that the increase in volume when water changes to ice is only about 0.907 $cm^3$, or just over 9 per cent; this increase is normally well exceeded in practice.

Although much basic research has been carried out in the complex field of ice lens formation, the exact mechanism by which it occurs is still not completely understood. It is well recognized that, for ice lenses to develop, three conditions must be met: (a) sufficiently cold temperatures to freeze *some* of the soil water, (b) a supply of water available to the freezing zone, and (c) the means by which the moisture supply can be readily moved to the freezing zone, i.e. a frost-susceptible soil. Ice lensing does not occur when any of these three conditions is missing.

Figure 4.8 illustrates generally the manner in which layers of segregated ice are formed in a soil in which heaving occurs. These ice lenses, which normally grow parallel to the ground surface and perpendicular to the direction of the heat flow, can vary from being of hairline thickness to many centimetres thick.

Under conditions favourable to ice lens growth, the moisture necessary for an individual lens to grow can theoretically be supplied by capillary action and by vapour movement from the water-table. The amount of

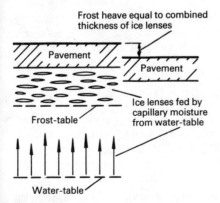

**Fig. 4.8** Ice lens formation in a soil

moisture capable of being transferred upward in the vapour phase towards the freezing ice lens is negligible however; furthermore, moisture diffusion in the vapour phase takes place more readily in soils with large pore spaces rather than in fine soils. Thus the vapour movement of moisture in frost-susceptible soils can be ignored for all practical purposes[12]. It being clear, therefore, that the significant moisture contributions are fed to the ice lens via the capillary (suction) process, it is now possible to discuss the means by which this may occur.

Figure 4.9 is an enlarged schematic diagram showing a section through an ice lens, fine-grained soil particles, and a soil pore. Surrounding each particle is an adsorbed layer of water, and this separates the growing ice crystal from the mineral particle. When the water temperature decreases below $0\,^\circ$C, the outermost part of the adsorbed water begins to freeze and to attach itself to the bottom of the ice crystal, so that the water films about the particles become thinner, i.e. when a water molecule in a film becomes linked with an ice crystal, it loses its dipolar character and, concurrently, the attraction between the molecule and the particle disappears, and the thickness of the adsorbed layer is reduced. The adsorbed layer, in turn, seeks to maintain equilibrium thickness and, consequently, supercooled water begins to flow from the soil pores to the points where the water films have become thinner. As equilibrium thickness is restored, the ice lens and the soil above it are pushed upwards and the result is 'frost heave'. The pore moisture, in turn, is replaced by water taken from the water-table. In other words, this concept envisages ice lens growth in fine-grained soils as being really no more than the result of moisture film adjustment about the particle which continues until the temperature drops sufficiently for the ice front to propagate through the soil pore[13].

Capillary theory can be used to explain the growth of the ice lens in an idealized fine-grained soil in which adsorbed moisture is assumed to be negligible. This theory (see, for example, reference 14) postulates that to pass through the neck of a water-filled pore, the radius of curvature at the face of the penetrating ice crystal must be reduced to a critical value that is less than the effective radius of the pore. The required reduction is

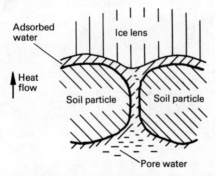

**Fig. 4.9** Enlarged schematic diagram showing a section of the ice lens with respect to the soil particle and soil pore

associated with both a pressure difference and a freezing point depression according to the equation:

$$p_i - p_w = 2\sigma_{iw}/r_{iw} = L\Delta T/V_w T_0$$

where $p_i$, $p_w$ = ice and water pressures, respectively (N/m$^2$), $\sigma_{iw}$ = ice–water interfacial energy (J/m$^2$), $r_{iw}$ = radius of the ice–water interface at a particular instant (m), $L$ = latent heat of fusion (J/kg), $\Delta T$ = freezing point depression (K), $V_w$ = specific volume of water (m$^3$), and $T_0$ = 273 K.

In the absence of special restraint, $p_i$ (which is usually about the overburden pressure) will not be significantly above the atmospheric pressure, whilst $p_w$ will be less than atmospheric; this negative pressure differential gives rise to a suction which draws water continuously towards the freezing front. If the suction is not sufficiently large, the radius of the ice–water interface will be greater than the radius of the underlying pore neck so that ice penetration is prevented. Growth of the ice lens will then continue until the temperature drops sufficiently to produce an ice crystal curvature which is less than or equal to the neck of the pore. (If the soil is non-idealized, and a part of the neck of the pore is occupied by the adsorbed moisture phase, this places additional size limitations upon the penetration of the ice crystal.) In other words, the advance of the ice–water interface in a soil containing mostly small pores will occur at a lower temperature than in one in which large pores predominate.

The above outline emphasizes the importance of the suction characteristics, which reflect (amongst other factors) the pore-size distribution and the permeability in the development of the ice lens. It explains why soils of intermediate pore-size, e.g. silty soils, which give rise to both adequate suction and permeability, are the most susceptible to frost action.

The *rate* of frost heaving is, for all practical purposes, independent of the rate of frost penetration[15]. If freezing occurs rapidly, the water sucked up is frozen into many thin layers; if it occurs slowly, the layers are thick. Thus the ice stratification of the frozen soil is an index of the rate of freezing, with thick ice indicating slow, and thin ice fast, frost penetration. From the highway engineer's point of view, it is more desirable to have a rapid, early freeze than a slow one since, by influencing the thickness of the ice lenses, both the distribution of the extra moisture and the consequent reduction in capacity are also influenced. This rapid, early freezing leaves the critical upper layers relatively barren of ice and thus, when the thaw begins, there is less moisture accumulation in the soil at a given instance and this benefits stability at that vulnerable time.

## Depth of frost penetration

The engineer is very much interested in the depth to which the freezing temperatures will penetrate into the soil beneath the highway pavement. The importance of this determination can be gauged from the fact that the most complete protection is afforded to a pavement by providing non-frost-susceptible material to a depth below that of the frost penetration, and thus preventing any underlying frost-susceptible soil from freezing.

Great care should be taken when estimating the depth of frost penetration in the case of a new road, as it is not always advisable to base the prediction on records of previously observed frost depths in the raw soil, new road pavement surface temperatures usually being lower than the temperatures of the surrounding natural surfaces in the winter months. In addition, since the pavement itself will probably be well drained, it is likely to exist at a lower moisture content than the natural soil in the surrounding area, and this can also contribute towards a relatively large temperature differential.

The depth of frost penetration at any given location, and the nature and severity of the freezing to which the various elements of the road structure are subjected, therefore depends primarily upon the thickness of the layers and the ingredient material in each layer, as well as upon the prevailing air temperature. Nevertheless, it can be said that it is rarely that the freezing isotherm would ever penetrate more than 51 cm beneath the carriageway surface in Britain[16].

## Moisture and frost action

The greatest potential trouble from frost heave arises when the water-table is relatively close to the ground surface and just below the freezing zone. It may, however, be concluded that a potentially troublesome water supply for ice segregation is present when the highest water-table level at any time of the year is within, say, 1.0–1.5 m of the proposed subgrade surface or the bottom of any frost-susceptible material used in the roadway. When the depth to the water-table is in excess of 3 m throughout the year, a source of water for substantial ice segregation is usually not present.

The existence of a deep water-table does not necessarily ensure that the detrimental effects associated with frost action will not occur. For instance, the equilibrium moisture content which a homogeneous clay subgrade will develop under the road pavement after its construction is usually sufficient to provide water for at least limited ice lens formation, even though the water-table be at great depth. It can be assumed, however, that appreciable ice lensing will not normally occur in frost-susceptible soils with a remote water-table when the degree of saturation of soils in the zone subject to freezing is less than about 70 per cent.

For a given water-table position, heaving tends to be less for heavy clays than for lean clays and silt soils. This is due to moisture being able to move only relatively slowly over short distances during the freezing process because of the much lower permeability of the heavy clays. However, in relatively pervious but frost-susceptible dirty sands and gravels, differential frost heave may be more intense than in clay subgrades. In such cases, water may move to the growing ice lenses from substantial distances, both laterally and vertically.

## Frost-susceptible soils

Investigators of frost problems in soils discovered early that certain types of soil are more susceptible to frost action than others. The most expedient rule-of-thumb means of identifying, without the benefit of laboratory testing procedures, soils in which damaging frost action may occur were suggested by Casagrande in 1932[17]. He stated that, under natural freezing conditions and with a sufficient water supply, considerable ice lensing could be expected in any non-uniform soil with more than 3 per cent of its particles smaller than 0.02 mm and in very uniform soils with more than 10 per cent smaller than 0.02 mm. According to the study on which these recommendations are based, no significant ice lensing need be expected in soils containing less than one per cent of particles smaller than 0.02 mm, even if the groundwater level is as high as the frost-table. In using these recommendations, it should be realized that the values of 3 and 10 per cent were not intended to represent points at which no ice lensing would take place, but rather levels below which frost heave would not usually exceed tolerable limits in ordinary roadway applications.

The Casagrande recommendations cannot be expected to cover all soils and materials or be applicable to all situations because of their extreme simplification. It is important to realize that the intensity of ice lens formation is dependent not only upon the percentage finer than 0.02 mm, but also upon the particle-size distribution and/or the physico-chemical properties of these fines. Other practical contributing factors are density, initial moisture content, and, of course, permeability. The influence of density, for example, is indicated in Fig. 4.10, where it can be seen that, for a given increase in dry density, the rate of frost heave may increase or decrease depending upon the soil. This figure is indeed a reminder that the most obvious solution to guaranteeing the built-in stability of high-density roadbases and subbases is to use only free-draining, non-frost-susceptible materials within the freezing zone.

The soils shown in Fig. 4.10 are classified according to the American

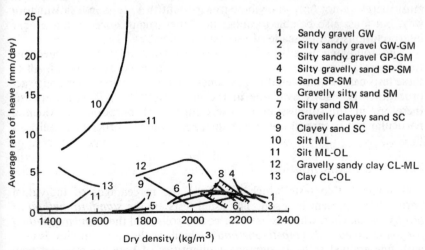

| | |
|---|---|
| 1 | Sandy gravel GW |
| 2 | Silty sandy gravel GW-GM |
| 3 | Silty sandy gravel GP-GM |
| 4 | Silty gravelly sand SP-SM |
| 5 | Sand SP-SM |
| 6 | Gravelly silty sand SM |
| 7 | Silty sand SM |
| 8 | Gravelly clayey sand SC |
| 9 | Clayey sand SC |
| 10 | Silt ML |
| 11 | Silt ML-OL |
| 12 | Gravelly sandy clay CL-ML |
| 13 | Clay CL-OL |

**Fig. 4.10** Effect of dry density upon average rate of frost heave[18]. *Note:* Soils are grouped according to the American Unified System

Unified Soil Classification System, which is very similar to the British Soil Classification System.

British experience[16] is that *cohesive soils* can be regarded as non-frost-susceptible soils when the plasticity index is greater than 15 per cent for well-drained soils, or 20 per cent when the soils are poorly drained, i.e. when the water-table is within about 0.6 m of the bottom of the pavement resting upon it; the natural permeability of these soils is generally too low to allow significant migration of water to the freezing front during the relatively short periods of freezing associated with British winters. Furthermore, the liability of these soils to frost heave decreases with decreasing state of compaction.

*Non-cohesive soils* (except limestone gravels) can be regarded as non-frost-susceptible soils if the mass of material passing the 75 μm BS sieve is less than or equal to 10 per cent; limestone gravels with an average particle saturation moisture content in excess of 2 per cent are normally considered as potentially susceptible to frost action. The state of compaction of these non-cohesive soils is not generally considered to have any significant effect upon their liability to frost heave.

All *chalk soils* (and crushed chalks) are susceptible to frost action and their usage should be avoided in highway construction in locales subject to freezing temperatures. Degree of compaction also has little influence upon the frost-susceptibility of this material.

## Basic methods for testing soils

The sensible highway engineer uses soil tests for guidance purposes when locating, designing and constructing roadways. If the results of these tests are to be of optimum value, then the tests must be carried out correctly and the data obtained from them analysed intelligently. The highway engineer must therefore not only know how to carry out these tests in a satisfactory way, but must also be able to understand their significance so that proper interpretations can be made of the data obtained.

The following is a brief discussion of what might be termed the fundamental physical tests carried out on soils for highway purposes. All of these tests can be considered routine ones, and information regarding exact procedures is readily available in the literature[9, 10, 19, 20]. The emphasis therefore in this discussion is placed upon the purpose for which a particular test is carried out rather than upon the test procedure itself.

### Particle-size distribution

This involves two tests which determine the percentages of individual particle sizes present in a soil. The usual tests are the *standard method of test by wet sieving*, which is used for coarse soils, and the *standard method for fine-grained soils* (*pipette method*), which, as the name implies, is used with fine-grained soils. If significant quantities of both coarse- and fine-grained particles are present in the given soil, then the results of both tests may have to be combined to give the particle-size distribution.

The wet sieving test covers the quantitative determination of the particle-size distribution in a soil down to the fine-sand size; the combined clay and silt fraction in the soil is obtained by difference. The procedure given involves the preparation of a measured quantity of soil and the removal of all silt and clay by wet sieving through a 63 $\mu$m test sieve; the retained coarser material is then dry sieved through a series of successively smaller sieves, and the mass retained on each sieve, as well as the material passing the 63 $\mu$m sieve, is expressed as a percentage of the total sample.

A reliable procedure, which allows the process of washing the sample free of clay and silt and the process of sieving the coarser fractions to be combined in a single wet sieving operation, is also available in the literature[21]. This procedure is, however, only suitable for soils which contain little gravel-sized material (say less than 10 per cent retained on the 10 mm sieve), as the reduction of the sample mass by riffling at intermediate stages in the process, which is necessary to avoid sieve overloading, is not possible in this combined wet method.

The standard fine-grained soil test covers the quantitative determination of the particle-size distribution in a soil from the coarse-sand size down. The test, which is not applicable to soils in which less than 10 per cent of the sample material passes the 63 $\mu$m sieve, is divided into two parts, viz. a conventional sieve test which is carried out on material retained on the 63 $\mu$m sieve, and a sedimentation test (pipette method) which is carried out on particles passing the 63 $\mu$m sieve.

All sedimentation tests are based on the assumption that the particles being considered are spherical in shape, can be dispersed uniformly throughout a constant-temperature liquid without being close enough to influence each other, and that the particles of different size have settling velocities in accordance with Stoke's law. This law, postulated in 1891, states that the terminal velocity, $v$, of a spherical particle settling in a liquid is proportional to the square of its diameter, $d$. Whilst clay particles, for example, cannot by any means be considered as spherical, the results obtained are sufficiently realistic for practical soil testing purposes.

In a typical sedimentation test, a suspension of a known mass of fine particles of various sizes is made up in a known volume of water. The mixture is shaken thoroughly and the particles are then allowed to settle under gravity. With the sedimentation test (pipette method) (which is generally the more reliable procedure, requiring quite sophisticated and expensive equipment), the mixture is sampled at a fixed depth after predetermined periods of time, and the distribution of particle sizes is then determined by mass differences. With the older hydrometer procedure (which is still widely used overseas, as well as in field laboratories in Britain), the density of the soil–water mixture is determined at fixed time intervals using a relative density hydrometer of special design, and the distribution of particle sizes is then determined by formula calculation or nomograph. The results are first expressed as a percentage of the fine-grained sand and then, if there is a coarse-grained fraction, converted to percentages of the total soil sample.

*Typical test results*  The results of a particle-size analysis can be presented in either of two ways. The first of these is a table in which is listed the percentage of the total sample that passes a given sieve size or is smaller than a specified particle diameter. The second way is to make a plot of the sieve or particle size versus the percentage passing the given sieve (or percentage smaller than the given diameter). Since there is a wide range of possible values, the usual procedure is to plot the particle size on a logarithmic scale whilst the percentages finer are plotted on an arithmetic scale.

Some typical particle-size distributions for different soils are shown in Fig. 4.11. Apart from being examples of different soils, some other very interesting factors are illustrated. For instance, the sandy, gravelly fine soil is relatively flat, indicating that this soil contains a wide range of particle sizes; this could be therefore termed a fairly-well-graded soil. However, the steepness of the estuarine sand shows that this soil contains a large number of particles of the same size; this soil would be therefore described as a uniform soil or a poorly-graded one. A gradation curve having a near-horizontal 'hump' in it, e.g. the gap-graded moraine soil, suggests that either the soil has had a large amount of its intermediate sizes removed or it is composed of a mixture of two soils of near-normal particle distribution.

*Significance of test*    The results of this test are of most value when used for soil classification purposes, and further use of the gradation should be discouraged unless verification by studies of performance or experience permit empirical relationships to be formulated[22]. Although it is often found that the larger the particle size, the better will be the engineering properties of the soil, nevertheless only rough approximations of strength or resistance properties should ever be attempted. It is a known fact that detrimental capillarity and frost damage are not a problem when a soil is coarsely grained, whereas fine-grained silts and clays can be very dangerous. As discussed elsewhere (pp. 267–268, 287), empirical relationships based on particle size have been developed for determining the frost-susceptibility of a soil. Highway specifications for roadbase and subbase construction use the particle-size analysis in the quality control of soil materials.

When stabilizing soils by mechanical or chemical means, use is frequently made of particle-size analyses for mix design or control purposes. For instance, one American design procedure allows the percentage of cement to be used in coarse-grained soil-cement mixtures to be estimated on the basis of particle size. For mechanical stabilization, the results of gradation analyses are used to determine the size and percentage of coarse or fine materials that need to be added to obtain a dense, impermeable road pavement.

On occasions, it is possible to make general estimates of the permeability of a soil on the basis of its gradation. Broadly, it can be said that coarse-grained soils will more readily permit the flow of water than will fine-grained ones, e.g. sands are more permeable than silts, and silts are more permeable than clays. An example of the variation from this generality is a well-graded, compact, granular material which can be virtually impermeable.

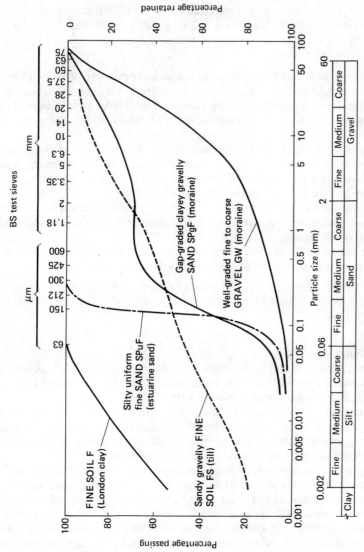

**Fig. 4.11** Typical particle-size distribution curves for different British soils[2]

## Consistency tests

By consistency is meant that property of a soil which is manifested by its resistance to flow. As such it is a reflection of the cohesive resistance properties of the soil rather than of the intergranular ones. These properties are considerably affected by the moisture content of the soil.

About 1910, Atterberg suggested that soil consistency should be described by arbitrarily dividing a soil's cohesive range into six stages and expressing the limits of each range in terms of moisture content. The limits he chose are as follows:

(1)   upper limit of viscous flow, above which the mixture of soil and water flows like a liquid,
(2)   liquid limit, or lower limit of viscous flow, above which the soil and water mixture flows as a viscous liquid and below which the mixture is plastic,
(3)   sticky limit, above which the mixture of soil and water will adhere or stick to a steel spatula or other such object that is wetted by water,
(4)   cohesion limit, which is at the water content at which crumbs of the soil cease to adhere when placed in contact with each other,
(5)   plastic limit, or lower limit of the plastic range, which is at the water content at which the soil starts to crumble when rolled into a thread under the palm of the hand,
(6)   shrinkage limit, or lower limit of volume change, at which there is no further decrease in volume as water is evaporated from the soil.

Two of these limits, the liquid limit ($LL$) and the plastic limit ($PL$) have won wide acceptance by highway and soil engineers and so they are briefly discussed here.

### Liquid limit

The liquid limit of a soil is the moisture content, expressed as a percentage by mass of the oven-dry soil, at the boundary between the liquid and solid states. This boundary was arbitrarily defined by Atterberg as being the moisture content which caused the soil to begin to flow when lightly jarred against the heel of the hand. Obviously, this procedure involves considerable possibility of human error, so mechanical liquid limit instruments have been devised in order to eliminate the personal factor.

The device most widely used internationally is that developed by Casagrande at Harvard University in 1932. The *Casagrande apparatus* consists of a shallow, circular brass cup resting on a hard rubber or bakelite base. In the course of the test, a soil pat consisting of a mixture of water and soil passing the 425 $\mu$m BS sieve is placed in the cup and divided with a special wedge-shaped cutting tool. By means of a cam on a shaft turned by a handcrank, the brass cup is raised through a height of 1 cm and then dropped sharply onto the hard base. The device has been calibrated so that twenty-five drops of the cup at the rate of two drops per second are equivalent to ten light jars as specified by the Atterberg hand method. The liquid limit of the soil is then taken as the moisture content at which the groove cut in the soil pat closes for a length of 13 mm after twenty-five blows.

In the standard Casagrande method of test, at least three moisture contents are determined: below the liquid limit, at or near the liquid limit, and above the liquid limit. A 'flow curve' such as is illustrated in Fig. 4.12 is then plotted on log-normal paper, with the moisture contents on the arithmetical scale and the number of impacts on the logarithmic scale. The results should approximate a straight line and from this the liquid limit can be taken as the moisture content corresponding to the intersection of the flow curve with the twenty-five-shock point on the ordinate scale.

Common sources of error in carrying out the liquid test using the Casagrande apparatus are: (a) inaccurate height of drop of cup, (b) cup worn due to scratching the bottom with the grooving tool, (c) too thick a soil pat, (d) variation in the rate of dropping the cup, and (e) the human element in deciding when the groove has closed exactly 13 mm.

Since the early 1970s, the *cone penetrometer test* has been the preferred liquid limit test in Britain, since it is easier to carry out, is less dependent upon the judgement of the operator, and is capable of giving more reproducible results. Basically, this test consists of measuring the penetration of an 80 g standardized cone into a soil pat, at various moisture contents. A moisture content versus depth of penetration relationship (similar to that illustrated in Fig. 4.12) is established, and the moisture content corresponding to a cone penetration of 20 mm is taken as the liquid limit.

*Typical test results* The results obtained with the cone penetrometer may differ very slightly from those with the Casagrande apparatus. In most cases, however, these differences will not be significant, i.e. they will be less than the normal variation obtained with the Casagrande equipment.

Table 4.6 shows some liquid limit test results for various soils. Generally, liquid limits vary widely, but values of 40–60 per cent and above are typical for clay soils. Clays in which montmorillonite is the predominant clay mineral have even higher liquid limit values (see, for example, Table 4.4). For silty soils, values of 25 to 50 can be expected. Sandy soils do not have liquid limits and are reported as non-plastic.

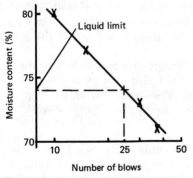

**Fig. 4.12** Casagrande liquid limit flow curve

**Table 4.6**   Clay content, particle relative density and plasticity test results for various British soils (extracted from Table 6.2 of reference 8)

| Soil description | Place of origin | Clay content (%) | PL (%) | LL (%) | PI | Relative density |
|---|---|---|---|---|---|---|
| Gault clay | Aylesbury, Bucks. | 69 | 34 | 102 | 68 | 2.70 |
| Kimmeridge clay | Sunningwell, Berks. | 67 | 24 | 77 | 53 | 2.74 |
| Weald clay | Ditchling, Sussex | 62 | 25 | 68 | 43 | 2.74 |
| Gault clay | Shaves Wood, Sussex | 60 | 32 | 121 | 89 | 2.65 |
| London clay | Heathrow, Middx | 60 | 26 | 78 | 52 | 2.73 |
| Gault clay | Stoke Mandeville, Bucks. | 57 | 29 | 81 | 52 | 2.68 |
| Oxford clay | Cumnor, Berks. | 56 | 24 | 72 | 48 | 2.74 |
| Gault clay | Steyning, Sussex | 56 | 25 | 70 | 45 | 2.68 |
| Lias clay | Shipton, Oxon | 39 | 24 | 60 | 36 | 2.71 |
| Silty clay | | 34 | 24 | 43 | 19 | 2.70 |
| Silty clay | Harmondsworth, Middx. | 33 | 10 | 43 | 24 | 2.72 |
| Sandy clay | | 24 | 19 | 27 | 8 | 2.70 |
| Clay silt | Ripon, Yorkshire | 19 | 17 | 28 | 11 | 2.67 |
| Clay silt | Wellington, Somerset | 12 | 19 | 33 | 14 | 2.75 |

The liquid limit test is usually carried out on material which has been air-dried only. Whereas the values obtained from oven-dried, inorganic soil samples are little different from those obtained with air-dried samples, the liquid (and plastic) limits of organic clays determined from oven-dried samples are much lower than the limits obtained when the same soils have not been oven-dried before testing.

**Plastic limit**
The plastic limit of a soil may be defined as the moisture content of the soil at the boundary between the plastic and semi-solid states. This boundary was originally defined by Atterberg as the moisture content at which a sample soil begins to crumble when rolled into a thread under the palm of the hand. As now arbitrarily defined, the plastic limit of a soil is the moisture content, expressed as a percentage of the oven-dried sample, of the air-dried material passing the 425 $\mu$m BS sieve at the time that the soil–water mixture has been rolled into a thread 3 mm in diameter and it begins to crumble at this size.

*Typical test results*   Pure sands cannot be rolled into a thread and so these soils are termed 'non-plastic'. The plastic limits of silts and clays do not vary too widely; the normal values range from 5 to 30, with the silty soils having the lower plastic limits.

When carrying out the test, it is left to the operator to decide how much pressure to apply to the soil thread when it is rolled on a glass plate. This means that there is a tendency for a heavy-handed operator to get a consistently higher value than would an operator with a lighter touch.

**Significance of consistency tests**
A value usually used in conjunction with the liquid and plastic limits is the plasticity index. The *plasticity index* (*PI*) of a soil is the arithmetic difference between the liquid and plastic limits; in other words, it is the range of moisture content over which the soil is in the plastic state.

**Table 4.7** Soil plasticity ranges and characteristics

| Plasticity | *PI* range | Characteristics |
|---|---|---|
| Highly plastic | >35 | High dry strengths; impossible to crush with the fingers |
| Plastic | 16–35 | Medium to high dry strengths; difficult to crush with the fingers when dry |
| Moderately plastic | 7–15 | Low to medium dry strengths; require only a slight pressure to be crushed |
| Slightly plastic | 4–6 | Low dry strengths; easily crushed by the fingers |
| Non-plastic | 0–3 | Little cohesion; a very low dry strength; falls apart when handled |

**Table 4.8** Some overall soil characteristics indicated by the consistency tests

| Characteristic | Comparing soils of equal *LL*, with *PI* increasing | Comparing soils of equal *PI*, with *LL* increasing |
|---|---|---|
| Compressibility | About the same | Increases |
| Permeability | Decreases | Increases |
| Rate of volume change | Increases | — |
| Dry strength | Increases | Decreases |

The most common application of the plasticity test results is for the purpose of soil classification. Both the liquid limit and the plasticity index can be used to a certain extent as a quality-measuring device for pavement materials, in order to exclude granular materials with too many fine-grained particles that have cohesive plastic qualities. The *PI* can also be used (in Britain) to estimate directly the strength of a subgrade soil, as reflected by its California Bearing Ratio value.

If the plasticity index of a soil is known, it can be used to give a rough approximation of the clay content; Table 4.6 shows results which reflect clay content similarities and differences for some important British soils. Table 4.7 gives the dry strength characteristics of soils of various degrees of plasticity. Some overall soil characteristics indicated directly by the consistency tests are summarized in Table 4.8.

## Relative density test

The relative density of a soil is the ratio of the mass in air of a given volume of soil particles to the mass in air of an equal volume of water.

The relative density test most commonly used in Britain today for soils is the *gas jar method*. This test is applicable to all fine-, medium-, and coarse-grained soils, provided that they do not have more than 10 per cent of stones retained on a 37.5 mm BS sieve. It requires a series of mass determinations to be carried out after the soil has been placed in a gas jar with a one-litre capacity, and the relative density, *r*, of the material is then calculated from the following formula:

$$r = \frac{M_2 - M_1}{(M_4 - M_1) - (M_3 - M_2)}$$

where $M_1$ = mass of gas jar, $M_2$ = mass of gas jar and dry soil, $M_3$ = mass of gas jar, soil and water, and $M_4$ = mass of gas jar when full of water only.

*Typical test results*   The true relative density of a soil is actually the weighted average of the relative densities of all the mineral particles present in the soil. Since about 1000 minerals have been identified as present in rocks, and since soil is derived from rocks, very many of these minerals will normally be present in any given soil. The clay minerals normally will also be present; their relative densities vary from 2.20–2.70 for mortmorillonites, 2.60–2.68 for illites, and 2.64–3.00 for kaolinites. In practice, however, it is found that, because of the natural preponderance of quartz and quartz-like minerals ($2.60 < r < 2.70$), the relative densities of soils in Britain are most often between 2.55 and 2.75, with the lower values generally indicating the presence of organic matter and the higher values metallic ores.

*Significance of test*   The relative density is used in the computations of many laboratory tests on soils. In particular, it is required in the calculation of the voids ratios of soil specimens, and in the determination of the moisture content of a soil by the pycnometer method, and in the particle-size analysis (sedimentation) test. The density of moist soil, which is needed in most pressure, settlement, and stability problems, can be computed with known values for relative density, degree of saturation, and voids ratio.

## Moisture–density test

Most highway engineering projects utilize soil as fill material in embankments, whilst many rural roads are constructed with soil as a pavement construction material. Wherever soil is used for such construction purposes, it is placed in a loose state and then compacted by rolling or vibrating until the desired degree of compaction is achieved. Laboratory moisture–density tests provide a means by which compaction of the soil is controlled on site.

In 1933, R R Proctor of the Los Angeles Bureau of Waterworks and Supply published what might be described as one of the first scientific approaches to the study of soil compaction; his work was carried out during the construction of several large earth dams in the USA. He devised a laboratory method of test, now commonly known as the *Proctor test*, in order to ensure that soil compaction would be carried out in such a way that dry densities would be attained which would give the desired impermeability and stability to the earth dams. By compacting over 200 different soils at various moisture contents, and using laboratory compacting energies which were considered equivalent to those produced by field compaction, he discovered that, as moisture contents were increased, the densities increased to maximum values, after which they decreased. The moisture content at which the *maximum dry* density was attained under a given compactive effort was termed the *optimum moisture content*. Following these early studies of Proctor, standardized laboratory procedures were developed and it is these which are in use today.

The moisture–density test is normally carried out by compacting a prepared air-dried soil sample in a given number of layers into a metal cylindrical mould of volume equal to 944 cm$^3$. In the *standard* Proctor test, a 2.5 kg metal rammer is dropped from a height of 30.5 cm onto each layer of soil in the mould; a total of twenty-five blows is used to compact each of three layers. In the *modified* Proctor test, a 4.5 kg rammer falls 45.8 cm, and a total of twenty-five blows is applied to each of five layers. Following compaction, the mass of the soil in the mould is determined and, with the volume of the mould known, the wet density is calculated by dividing the mass by the volume. A determination is then made of the moisture present in the soil sample in the mould, after which the soil is removed from the mould. A new air-dried soil sample is then prepared, a higher increment of water added, and the procedure repeated. The test is continued until the mass of a compacted sample in the mould is less than that obtained in the preceding measurement.

As stated above, it is necessary to carry out a moisture content determination on every sample prepared in the course of the test. The moisture content referred to in this case is the total amount of water contained in the compacted sample. It is obtained by determining the mass of a representative sample of the soil before and after drying in an oven at a temperature between 105 and 110 °C. The difference in the masses represents the amount of water in the sample and, when this is expressed as a percentage of the dried sample, the moisture content of the soil is given.

Knowing the wet density and moisture content of each sample, it is then possible to calculate the dry densities. The following formula is used for this purpose:

$$\psi_d = 100\psi/(100 + m)$$

where $\psi_d$ = dry density and $\psi$ = wet density (both measured in Mg/m$^3$), and $m$ = moisture content (%).

When the dry densities are plotted against their corresponding moisture contents, and a smooth curve is drawn through the data points, a curve similar to those shown in Fig. 4.13 is obtained.

Both of the Proctor tests can be criticized as providing only a poor guide for specifications relating to the compaction of highly-permeable soils, e.g. fine-grained, clean gravels or uniformly-graded, coarse, clean sands, and so the *vibrating hammer test*[23] has been developed in Britain for use with these soils. With this test, a 3 kg electric-powered vibrating hammer is used to compact three layers of moist soil (each layer for 60 seconds) in a California Bearing Ratio test mould; the total downward force during compaction, including that resulting from the mass of the hammer and tamper, is 300 to 400 N. The wet or bulk density, $\psi$ Mg/m$^3$, for the compacted soil can be calculated from the formula:

$$\psi = M/18.1h$$

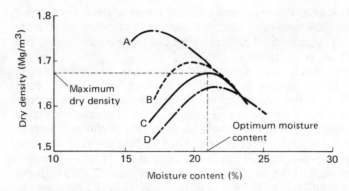

A    Oven dried
B    Air dried, wetted, air dried
C    Air dried
D    Natural moisture

**Fig. 4.13**   Moisture-content–dry-density curves, showing effect of drying and wetting sequences. The air-dried raw soil had *LL* and *PI* values of 34 per cent and 14, respectively

where $M$ = wet mass of the soil (g) and $h$ = height of the compacted specimen (mm).

The dry density is then easily calculated using the same formula as for the Proctor tests. By varying the moisture content of the soil, a moisture-content–dry-density relationship can be derived as before.

Care should be taken at all times to ensure that the moisture–density test is carried out according to the appropriate prescribed procedure[9], as otherwise misleading results can be obtained. For example, with soils containing granular material such as soft limestone or sandstone, particle breakdown during compaction can result in misleading data. The use of an incorrect soil condition at the start of the test can also result in variations in compaction test data (see Fig. 4.13), i.e. the test should always be carried out on air-dried soil samples.

*Typical test results*   The maximum dry densities that can theoretically be attained with a soil having a relative density of 2.65 is 2.65 Mg/m$^3$. In fact, this density could only be obtained if all the soil particles were fitted against each other exactly. Since soil particles come in various shapes and sizes, there are always air voids in the soil and so this theoretical figure can never be achieved. The dry density of soils in situ is often about 50 to 60 per cent of the theoretical maximum value. Soils such as peat and muck have natural densities of about 15 per cent of the theoretically possible value. However, well-graded, dense gravel mixtures can be compacted to dry densities of perhaps 90 per cent of the theoretical limit.

Using the standard Proctor method of compaction, Table 4.9 gives a range of values that may be anticipated for the moisture–density test[22].

Changing the amount of energy applied to a soil by varying the number of blows and/or the mass of the compaction hammer also has considerable influence upon the dry density. The net effect of increasing the amount of

**Table 4.9**  Range of values that may be anticipated for the moisture–density test

| Type of soil | Maximum dry density (Mg/m³) | Optimum moisture content (%) |
|---|---|---|
| Clays | 1.440–1.685 | 20–30 |
| Silty clays | 1.600–1.845 | 15–25 |
| Sandy clays | 1.760–2.165 | 8–15 |

compactive energy is to increase the maximum density and decrease the optimum moisture content of a given soil. If a number of such curves are compared, it is seen that, when the air voids content is small, the effect of increasing the compaction is negligible; when the air voids content is large, the effect of increasing the compaction is considerable.

The two laboratory methods of test most commonly used in Britain are the standard Proctor test (2.5 kg rammer) and the modified Proctor test (4.5 kg rammer). A constant relationship does exist between the standard and modified maximum dry densities, i.e. the standard maximum dry density typically corresponds to about 95 per cent of the modified density for sands and gravels, whereas it may be less than 90 per cent for clays.

The results obtained when both Proctor tests were carried out on five soils ranging from a well-graded gravel–sand–clay mixture to a heavy clay are summarized in Table 4.10. Note that the increase in the amount of compaction had the greatest effect upon the heavy silty clays, resulting in large increases in the maximum dry densities and correspondingly large decreases in the optimum moisture contents. This table also illustrates that, for a given compaction effort, the particle size and gradation of the soil are of considerable importance (see also Fuller's law in Chapter 5).

*Significance of test*  The moisture–density test is designed specifically to aid in the field compaction of soils. The assumption is that the stability of a given soil increases with increasing dry density. It is therefore common practice to specify the compaction required for a soil or soil–aggregate mixture as a percentage of that achieved in the laboratory when compacted at the moisture content which produced the maximum density for the applied effort.

The compactive efforts used in the laboratory tests are generally assumed to be similar in effect to that of the construction equipment available in the field. This assumption is, of course, one which is very much open to criticism.

A most important factor to be noted about this test is that the presence of a certain amount of water is needed in order to achieve the desired dry densities. For simplicity, this water can be regarded as acting as a lubricant which enables the soil particles to slide over each other freely in the course of compaction. However, as the moisture content is increased, a point is reached at which only a small amount of air remains trapped in the soil; this is the point at which maximum density is achieved. Any increase in moisture content above this level simply results in soil being replaced by water, with a consequent reduction in dry density. Thus the laboratory test not only

**Table 4.10**   Comparison of results of the standard and modified Proctor tests[20]

| Type of soil | Mean results of standard Proctor compaction test | | Mean effect of modified Proctor compaction test | |
|---|---|---|---|---|
| | Maximum dry density (Mg/m³) | Optimum moisture content (%) | Maximum dry density (Mg/m³) | Optimum moisture content (%) |
| Heavy clay | 1.555 | 28 | +0.320 | -10 |
| Silty clay | 1.670 | 21 | +0.275 | - 9 |
| Sandy clay | 1.845 | 14 | +0.210 | - 3 |
| Sand | 1.940 | 11 | +0.145 | - 2 |
| Gravel–sand–clay | 2.070 | 9 | +0.130 | - 1 |

defines the maximum dry density but also suggests how much water should be used during the compaction if this density is to be achieved.

Given the maximum dry density and the optimum moisture content of a soil, the construction forces can compact the soil to the desired design condition. As a check, the field engineer carries out a density test to determine the density obtained by the construction equipment; if the result obtained is lower than the value permitted by the specifications, the contractor is required to recompact the soil. Normally, relative compaction specifications require that a certain percentage of the maximum dry density be achieved. This percentage varies from 90 to 95 per cent for the more granular materials, and 95 to 100 per cent for the fine-grained silts and clays.

## Unconfined compressive strength test

This test can only be carried out on cohesive soils or soils stabilized with an additive which binds the particles together. With raw soil samples[9], the test is best carried out on cylindrical specimens having a diameter of about 38 mm and a height to diameter ratio of 2 : 1. Cylindrical specimens are also used to test all stabilized soils in many countries, although in Britain it is recommended[10] that 150 mm cubes be used for coarse-grained soils (i.e. passing the 37.5 mm BS sieve) and medium-grained soils (i.e. passing the 20 mm BS sieve); for medium-grained soils (alternatively) and fine-grained soils (passing the 5 mm BS sieve), cylindrical specimens 100 mm diameter by 200 mm high and 50 mm diameter by 100 mm high, respectively, are recommended.

Stabilized specimens compacted to a predetermined dry density (the preferred method in Britain) may be prepared by static (fine- and medium-grained soils) or dynamic (medium- and coarse-grained soils) compaction methods. Stabilized specimens compacted with a constant compactive effort are prepared by dynamic compaction. In either case, the final dry densities achieved may be the maximum values obtained during the moisture–density compaction test.

In the course of the compression test, the load is applied at a predetermined, uniform rate of increase of stress in the cube test specimen of

3.5 MN/m$^2$ per minute for coarse- and medium-grained stabilized soils; for fine- and medium-grained stabilized soils, the load is applied at a uniform rate of deformation in the cylindrical test specimen of 1 mm per minute. In the case of raw, cohesive soil specimens, the load is applied at about 8 mm per minute, the aim being to achieve a test time of about 2 minutes for a specimen failing at 20 per cent strain. In all cases, the maximum load exerted by the compression machine at the time of specimen failure is recorded as the unconfined compressive strength.

*Typical test results*   Although a load versus deflection curve can be plotted, it is the ultimate compressive strength which is most frequently used in highway engineering studies, particularly those relating to soil stabilization. For mixtures that produce a reasonably rigid material, the load–deflection curve may be a straight line over a relatively long range, indicating fairly elastic materials.

The ultimate compressive strengths of soils and stabilized soil mixtures vary over a wide range. Results obtained are considerably influenced by such factors as the amount and type of stabilizing additive, the method and length of curing of the test specimens, and whether or not the specimens are saturated before testing.

*Significance of test*   The unconfined compressive strength test of a natural soil may be classed as a shear test, since it is essentially a triaxial shear test with zero lateral pressure. Reference is made to the discussion on shear tests for further details on this aspect.

For soil stabilization work, the test serves much the same purpose as for concrete work. Particular uses of the test are to determine the suitability of the soil for treatment with a given additive and to compare different mixtures to specify the additive content to be used in construction, and to provide a standard by which the quality of the field processing can be assessed. The measured strength value is not used for design purposes, nor is the modulus of the elasticity that is available from the load–deflection curve. Rather, the unconfined compressive strength data are principally significant for control purposes.

## Shear tests

All laboratory shear tests seek to evaluate specimens in a way that is as similar as possible to that anticipated under field conditions, as a multitude of test values can be otherwise obtained. Here it is extremely important to follow closely a testing programme that is deliberately designed to duplicate natural, construction, and operational conditions so that the results can be translated into reliable predictions of soil responses in terms of the parameters needed for the particular type of design analysis contemplated.

The selection of truly representative samples for testing is particularly important. In the case of natural soil which is unworked, this requires an 'undisturbed' sample which must be carefully removed from the ground with as little disruption to its structure as possible. When the soil has to undergo compaction or other manipulation, the sample for laboratory testing should be prepared in anticipation of the expected future condition of the soil.

Shear tests may be described as 'quick', 'consolidated quick', and 'slow' tests, depending upon the loading conditions expected and desired. For quick tests, the sample is loaded relatively rapidly and the moisture content does not change during the test. In the slow tests, however, water is permitted to drain freely from the samples during all stages of testing. For the consolidated quick test, the specimen is preloaded and allowed to drain freely prior to the actual shearing test being carried out. The variations in these three types of test arise from the need to approximate the actual conditions to which the soil will be subjected.

The principal types of *laboratory* shear tests are the direct shear and triaxial shear tests. The vane test [9] is a *field* shear test whereby a cruciform vane on the end of a solid rod is forced into the soil below the bottom of a borehole, and then rotated. The torque required to rotate the vane can be related to the shear strength of the soil, provided that use of the test is confined to uniform, saturated, cohesive soils having undrained shear strengths up to about 100 kN/m$^2$, i.e. the results are questionable in stronger clays, or if the soils tend to dilate on shearing or are fissured; the presence of thin layers of laminations of sand or silt, or of rootlets or coarse particles, can also lead to erroneously high torques.

British practice with respect to laboratory shear testing is to carry out the direct shear test [24] on coarse-grained soils, whilst an undrained triaxial shear test [9] is applied to clays and fine-grained materials. The following is a summary description of each of these laboratory tests.

### Direct shear test

Specimens used in the direct shear test may be saturated prior to testing if it is desired to represent the most critical condition for the given soil structure. To carry out the test, the specimen is placed in the lower (holding) place of the shear-box testing device, the upper plate is then placed in position, and a shearing load is applied perpendicular to the axis of the sample. Measurements are made of the incremental loads applied and the lateral displacements as a result of these loads. The test is conducted on a minimum of two samples, for each of which a normal or compressive load is applied in a direction parallel to the axis of the soil cylinder; this normal force is different for each sample.

### Triaxial shear test

In this test, the specimen is subjected to three compressive stresses at right-angles to each other, and one of these stresses is increased until the specimen fails in shear. The triaxial test differs from the direct shear test in that the plane of shear failure is not predetermined. It is similar, however, in that a number of identical specimens must be tested, and the test conditions are selected to correspond as closely as possible with the field conditions.

The triaxial cell consists of a transparent plastic cylinder which is much larger than the soil sample; this enables the specimen to be observed during the test. The cylinder is capped at the top and bottom with removable metal plates. The soil sample is placed inside a very thin rubber membrane which is slightly smaller than the specimen, capped at the top and bottom, and placed in the cylindrical cell. In the course of the test, a compressive load is applied by a piston arrangement through the top metal plate, while at the same time a uniform lateral pressure is obtained by means of a liquid placed in the cell and about the rubber-enclosed specimen.

A series of tests is run, using a different lateral pressure for each test. Measurements are made in each case of the compressive loads applied and of the deformations of the samples in the direction parallel to the axis of the cylinder.

*Typical test results*  Whatever the type of laboratory test, the shear test results are analysed in a similar fashion. Load–displacement curves are plotted, and a critical point on each curve is determined; this point is related to the allowable displacement, the slope of the load–displacement curve, and other factors.

The shearing resistance of the soil is generally assumed to result from two components, friction and cohesion, and so the test is aimed at determining the value of these two constituent characteristics. Since frictional resistance is increased by normal or compressive loads, the shearing resistance of a soil in the field at any instant is influenced by the loads perpendicular to the plane of shear. Therefore laboratory shear tests determine the 'angle of internal friction', commonly designated by $\phi$, and cohesion, usually termed $c$. These two values are considered constant for both laboratory and field conditions, and the actual shearing resistance can then be calculated.

Typical values for friction and cohesion are as follows:

(1) sandy soils

$\phi = 28$–45 degrees  and  $c = 0$–2.06 MN/m$^2$

(2) clay soils

$\phi = 0$–15 degrees  and  $c = 0.7$–13.8 MN/m$^2$

Generally, sandy soils develop their shearing resistance through friction, with little or no cohesion. The opposite is true for clay soils, the bulk of their resistance coming from cohesion associated with water bonds between the particles. When an unconfined compression test is carried out on a clay soil, $\phi$ can be assumed to be zero, and then the value of $c$ is one-half of the compressive strength.

Internal friction is greatly affected by the shape of the coarse particles in the soil, whereas cohesion is mainly influenced by the properties of the soil fines. Internal friction is little affected by moisture content, but increases rapidly with an increase of density; in contrast, cohesion is greatly influenced by moisture content, i.e. it decreases with increasing moisture to reach a low level at the plastic limit and almost zero at the liquid limit.

*Significance of tests*  Shear tests are used in highway engineering to determine experimentally the shear characteristics of the soil. Normally, the test values obtained are applied in the form of a stability equation which attempts to determine the probability of a soil failing in shear under the loads and conditions imposed in the field.

The shearing resistance offered by a soil is a very important factor in the design of earth slopes for highway cuttings and embankments. Shearing of the foundation soil can result in complete pavement disintegration, collapse of a bridge, or the loss of an embankment through sliding. While the prediction of the unit shearing resistance is the objective of laboratory shear tests, the application of these results requires extensive soil mechanics' experience.

## Consolidation test

The consolidation test (see, for example, reference 9) is used to estimate both the rate of settlement and the total amount of settlement of a soil layer under an applied load. The procedure and analysis are restricted to problems involving saturated soil masses, principally clays, fine silts, and other such soils of low permeability. Prediction of the settlement of a structure by the use of a laboratory consolidation test requires that the sample used should be as nearly identical and representative of the soil mass as possible.

To carry out the test, a soil sample is cut and trimmed so as to fit into a special metal ring provided for the test; this sample is normally a disc 75–100 mm in diameter by about 25 mm thick. Porous discs are placed on top and beneath the specimen, and the assembled sample discs and ring are placed in a loading unit. A compressive load is applied and the changes in thickness of the sample are read at set time intervals. After settlement is complete—this is usually taken as having occurred after 24 hours—the applied unit load is increased and a series of readings is taken as before. This procedure is generally followed through four to six loading increments, with the magnitude of the final increment depending upon the actual loadings expected in the field.

*Typical test results*  The two principal values obtained from the consolidation test are the compressibility index, $C_c$, and the coefficient of consolidation, $C_v$. These values are calculated from the test data and are used to estimate the rate as well as the total settlement under a given load condition.

The compressibility index is used in the analysis of total settlement. It is a dimensionless factor which normally ranges in value from 0.1 to 0.3 for silty clays, and from 0.2 to 1.0 for clays[22]. The total amount of settlement is also related to the thickness of the layer under consolidation and the applied load. Settlements of 150–450 mm are not at all unusual beneath large structures.

The values for the coefficient of consolidation range from 0.2–2.0 cm²/s for silty clays, and 0.02–0.10 cm²/s for clays[22]. The coefficient is used to estimate the amount of settlement for a given period of time under a given increment of load.

The settlement for the time period is compared with the total settlement for the load, and the ratio of the two, usually expressed as a percentage, is called the degree of consolidation. Thus, in the construction of a 10 m embankment, if the work is discontinued after a height of 3 m is reached, a time lapse of three weeks may produce a degree of consolidation of 90 per cent. Subsequently, another 3 m may be added, and time for settlement again allowed, and so on. Stage construction of this form permits the underlying, saturated soil mass to eliminate pore water in safety and develop shearing resistance.

*Significance of test* When a load is applied to a soil mass, the immediate tendency is for the soil particles to be pushed closer together. However, when the soil mass is saturated, the water, being incompressible, must initially carry part of the applied load. This results in the production of an initial pressure, commonly termed the pore-water pressure, which continues as water proceeds to drain from the soil. During the drainage period, which in very impermeable soils may require many years to complete, the soil particles are forced closer together, thereby producing the volume change known as settlement.

The laboratory consolidation test attempts to determine in an accelerated manner both the rate of settlement and the total amount to be expected under the total load applied. These values can be most important for analyses of highway embankment settlements and slope stabilities during construction stages. In the field, however, actual settlements may take place more rapidly than might be predicted by settlement theory, e.g. 50–75 per cent of the total settlement under an embankment is likely to occur during the construction period[8].

As is described in Chapter 6, drains can be used to accelerate settlement by providing readily available passageways for the escape of pore water. Settlement can then proceed more quickly because of the shorter distance which the water has to travel in getting out of the soil. Thus the road pavement can be placed in safety on the embankment when it is known that the bulk of the settlement is complete.

It is important to remember that the shearing resistance of a soil is lower during periods of high pore pressures. Thus the consolidation test can also be used to determine how rapidly the height of an embankment can be increased during construction without a shear failure being produced in the soil.

## Frost heave test

The Transport and Road Research Laboratory has developed a test[25] to establish the degree of frost-susceptibility of materials used in highway pavements and subgrades. Originally developed in 1967 as a research tool, the test has been modified to make it more usable to the materials engineer and pavement designer.

The test involves the preparation of 101 mm diameter by 152 mm high specimens. The sample of material to be tested is first sieved to remove material greater than 37.5 mm and then oven-dried. In the case of granular materials and non-cohesive soils, the optimum moisture content and maximum dry density to be used for testing are determined using the vibrating hammer test[23]. In the case of cohesive soils, the moisture content used is equivalent to the plastic limit plus two ($PL + 2$) per cent; the compacted density corresponds to an air voids content of 5 per cent at this moisture content, and is determined from the equation

$$\psi_d = \psi_w \left(1 - \frac{n_a}{100}\right) \bigg/ \left(\frac{1}{r_s} + \frac{m}{100}\right)$$

where $\psi_d$ = dry density of the soil ($Mg/m^3$), $\psi_w$ = density of water = 1 $Mg/m^3$, $n_a$ = air voids content = 5%, $r_s$ = relative density of the soil particles, and $m$ = moisture content expressed as a percentage of the mass of the dry soil = ($PL + 2$)%.

With either type of material, each test specimen is prepared in a specified manner, using a vibrating hammer for compaction, and placed on a porous disc in water (so that the water level is just in contact with the bottom of the specimen) in a self-refrigerated unit in which the air temperature is maintained at $-17\,^\circ C$ and the water temperature at $+4\,^\circ C$ for four days. The maximum vertical heave measured within 96 h is then termed the frost heave of the specimen.

*Typical test results*   As discussed previously, different soils have considerably different frost heaving capabilities (see, for example, Fig. 4.10). Various frost tests also provide different results, as might be expected. With the TRRL test, soils in which the mean heave is reported as being less than 9.0 mm after four days are classed as non-frost-susceptible soils; if the mean heave is greater than 15.0 mm, the soil is classed as a frost-susceptible one. Materials with heaves between 9.1 and 14.9 mm are classed as 'not proven' and require further testing.

*Significance of test*   As discussed previously, frost damage can result from the formation of ice lenses in frost-susceptible materials in the lower pavement/soil subgrade layers from water drawn up from the water-table. The ice lenses cause the whole road structure to heave; then when warmer weather comes the lenses melt from the top down, and the free water is trapped within the pavement to form 'soft spots' which cause the bearing capacity to be reduced and the pavement to break up under traffic.

The TRRL test is used in Britain as a compliance criterion[26] to ensure that unbound granular materials that the test demonstrates to be susceptible to frost action, are not used within 450 mm of the road surface. Its practical value therefore is, on the whole, limited to British environmental and design conditions.

It should be appreciated that there are currently at least 125 different frost-susceptibility tests and criteria in use throughout the world[27]. These tests can be divided into direct and indirect tests.

Direct tests (22 in number) are frost heave tests where a test specimen in the laboratory is exposed to an environment that is supposed to simulate that of the highway. Different freezing principles are used, for example:

(1)  constant freezing temperature of the air measured at some distance above the surface of the specimen (Britain),

(2)  constant freezing temperature at the surface of the specimen (France),
(3)  decreasing temperature at the surface and constant rate of frost penetration in the specimen (USA),
(4)  constant rate of heat removal from the specimen (Sweden).

As a consequence of the different approaches, different countries have different susceptibility criteria.

Indirect tests (103 in number) can be divided into four categories, as follows:

(1)  tests based on particle-size characteristics,
(2)  tests based on pore-size characteristics,
(3)  tests based on soil–water interaction,
(4)  tests based on soil–water–ice interaction.

Of those, the tests based on particle-size characteristics (90) are by far the most extensively used, albeit the criteria applied can vary from country to country.

# Soil classification

Whereas a full soil *description* provides detailed information regarding a soil as it occurs in situ, soil *classification* is concerned with placing a soil within a limited number of soil groups on the basis of the grading and plasticity of a disturbed sample. These characteristics, which are independent of the particular condition in which the soil occurs and pay no regard to the influence of the structure or fabric of the soil mass, are quite useful as guides as to how a disturbed soil will behave when used as a highway construction material.

Three soil classification systems are of particular interest to the highway engineer, viz. the British Soil Classification System (BSCS) for Engineering Purposes, the American Association of State Highway and Transportation Officials (AASHTO) System, and the Textural Classification System.

## British Soil Classification System (BSCS)

Undoubtedly the most widely used engineering classification systems are those based on common soil characteristics as developed by Casagrande in the early 1940s. The original Casagrande system was developed as a result of difficulties experienced in the use of the other systems then in existence for the design and construction of military airfields during World War II, and hence it was first known as the Airfield Classification System[28]. Subsequently this system was modified and today there are a number of 'outgrowth' systems in use which have many common characteristics. One of the most well known of these is the Unified Soil Classification System, which is used extensively in the USA; another is the British Soil Classification System (BSCS), which is primarily used in Britain. The following is a summary description of the British system[4].

Soil classification is carried out on material nominally finer than 60 mm (i.e. passing the 63 mm sieve). Thus, if the soil contains any very coarse material, it must be picked out and its proportion recorded. The removed material may be described as follows:

### BOULDERS or BOULDER GRAVELS B
these have more boulder- than cobble-sized material

### COBBLES or COBBLE GRAVELS Cb
these have more cobble- than boulder-sized material

The grading and plasticity characteristics of the material passing the 63 mm sieve are divided into a number of clearly defined ranges, each of which is referred to by a descriptive name and letter as shown in Table 4.11.

Table 4.12 shows the manner in which soil groups are formed from combinations of the ranges of grading and plastic characteristics, and lists the names of the groups and the symbols used to represent them. Note that the letter describing the dominant size fraction is placed first in the group symbol, e.g. Sandy CLAY CS or Clayey SAND S-C. The soil group symbol is enclosed in brackets if laboratory test methods were not used in the classification process.

Laboratory classification of a soil can be easily carried out by following the procedure suggested in Fig. 4.14.

### Description of soil groups
The following summarily describes some particular features of the soils in the major groups.

**Table 4.11** Names and descriptive letters for grading and plasticity characteristics

| Components | Terms | Descriptive name | Letter |
|---|---|---|---|
| Coarse | Main | GRAVEL | G |
| | | SAND | S |
| | Qualifying | Well graded | W |
| | | Poorly graded | P |
| | | —may be differentiated into Pu or Pg | |
| | | Uniform | Pu |
| | | Gap graded | Pg |
| Fine | Main | FINE SOIL, FINES | F |
| | | —may be differentiated into M or C | |
| | | SILT or M-SOIL | M |
| | | of restricted plastic range (plots below the A-line) | |
| | | CLAY | C |
| | | fully plastic (plots above the A-line) | |
| | Qualifying | Of low plasticity | L |
| | | Of intermediate plasticity | I |
| | | Of high plasticity | H |
| | | Of very high plasticity | V |
| | | Of extremely high plasticity | E |
| | | Of upper plasticity range | U |
| | | —incorporating groups I, H, V and E (e.g. during rapid assessment of soils) | |
| Organic | Main | PEAT | Pt |
| | Qualifying | Organic | O |
| | | —may be suffixed to any group | |

*Coarse-grained soils* The determination of the classification groupings of the coarse-grained soils is primarily based on particle-size distribution, i.e. coarse soils have less than 35 per cent by mass of silt- and clay-size particles.

A soil designated as GRAVEL G contains more material of gravel- than of sand-size, whereas the reverse is true for SAND S. Gravels and sands can be qualified according to the *proportion of sand or gravel* material present in the soil, as follows.

| | |
|---|---|
| Slightly sandy GRAVEL | <5% sand |
| Sandy GRAVEL | 5–20% sand |
| Very sandy GRAVEL | >20% sand |
| GRAVEL/SAND | About equal proportions |
| Slightly gravelly SAND | <5% gravel |
| Gravelly SAND | 5–20% gravel |
| Very gravelly SAND | >20% gravel |

The *amount of fine material* present in the soil can also be used to qualify sands and gravels, as follows for gravels (and similarly for sands).

| | |
|---|---|
| Slightly silty GRAVEL G | <5% silt |
| Silty GRAVEL G-M | 5–15% silt |
| Very silty GRAVEL GM | 15–35% silt |
| Slightly clayey GRAVEL G | <5% clay |
| Clayey GRAVEL G-C | 5–15% clay |
| Very clayey GRAVEL GC | 15–35% clay |

When gravels and sands have up to 15 per cent of fines, the *type of grading* can be indicated as follows.

Well-graded W
with a wide range of grain-sizes present and well distributed, e.g. Well-graded GRAVEL GW

Poorly-graded P
not well graded, e.g. Poorly-graded SAND SP

Poorly-graded soils with up to 5 per cent of fines can be further subdivided as follows.

Uniform Pu
size of most particles lies between narrow limits, e.g. Uniform SAND SPu

Gap-graded Pg
an intermediate size of particle is markedly under-represented, e.g. Gap-graded GRAVEL GPg

For very silty or very clayey gravels and sands, the *plasticity of the fine fractions* (i.e. material finer than 425 $\mu$m) can be used to qualify coarse soils using Fig. 4.14, e.g. Very clayey GRAVEL (clay with high plasticity) GCH.

*Fine-grained soils* These soils contain more than 35 per cent of silt- and clay-size particles; by definition, therefore, they contain up to 65 per cent of coarse-size particles.

**Table 4.12** British Soil Classification System for Engineering Purposes and Field Identification[4]

First remove material coarser than 60 mm and record as cobbles (60 to 200 mm) or boulders (over 200 mm).

| Soil groups* | Description | Group symbol | Subgroup symbol | Subgroup symbol | Fines (% less than 0.06 mm) | Subgroup name | Casagrande group symbol | Field identification |
|---|---|---|---|---|---|---|---|---|
| COARSE SOILS (less than 35% finer than 0.06 mm)<br><br>GRAVELS [more than 50% of coarse material is of gravel size (coarser than 2 mm)] | Slightly silty or clayey GRAVEL | G | GW | GW | 0–5 | Well-graded GRAVEL | GW | Particles easily visible to naked eye. Particle shape and grading can be described |
| | | | GP | GP / GPu / GPg | | Poorly/uniformly/gap-graded GRAVEL | GP/GU | |
| | Silty GRAVEL | G-F | G-M | GWM / GPM | 5–15 | Well/poorly-graded, silty (clayey) GRAVEL | GC/GF | Particles easily visible to naked eye. Particle shape and grading can be described. A medium to high dry strength indicates that some clay is present. A negligible dry strength indicates the absence of clay |
| | Clayey GRAVEL | | G-C | GWC / GPC | | | GF | |
| | Very silty GRAVEL | GF | GM | GM | 15–35 | Very silty GRAVEL: subdivide like GC | GF | |
| | Very clayey GRAVEL | | GC | GCL / GCI / GCH / GCV | | Very clayey GRAVEL (clay of low/intermediate/high/very high plasticity) | GF | |
| SANDS [more than 50% of coarse material is of sand size (finer than 2 mm)] | Slightly silty or clayey SAND | S | SW | SW | 0–5 | Well-graded SAND | SW | Majority of the particles visible to naked eye. Feels gritty when rubbed between the fingers. A medium to high dry strength indicates that some clay is present. A negligible dry strength indicates the absence of clay |
| | | | SP | SP / SPu / SPg | | Poorly/uniformly/gap-graded SAND | SP/SU | |
| | Silty SAND | S-F | S-M | SWM / SPM | 5–15 | Well/poorly-graded silty (clayey) SAND | SC/SF | |
| | Clayey SAND | | S-C | SWC / SPC | | | SF | |
| | Very silty SAND | SF | SM | SM | 15–35 | Very silty SAND: subdivide like SC | SF | |
| | Very clayey SAND | | SC | SCL / SCI / SCH / SCV | | Very clayey SAND (clay of low/intermediate/high/very high plasticity) | SF | |

Subgroups and laboratory identification

| Soil groups* | Description | Group symbol | Subgroup symbol | Liquid limit (%) | Subgroup name | Casagrande group symbol | Field identification |
|---|---|---|---|---|---|---|---|
| **FINE SOILS** (more than 35% finer than 0.06 mm) | | | | | | | |
| Gravelly or sandy SILTS and CLAYS (35–65% fines) | Gravelly SILT | FG | MG | | Gravelly SILT: subdivide like CG | — | Coarse particles visible to naked eye. Silt fraction dries moderately quickly and can be dusted off the fingers. Clay fraction can be rolled into threads when moist, smooth to touch and plastic, sticks to fingers and dries slowly |
| | Gravelly CLAY | CG | CLG | 35 | Gravelly CLAY of low plasticity | | |
| | | | CIG | 35–50 | Gravelly CLAY of intermediate plasticity | | |
| | | | CHG | 50–70 | Gravelly CLAY of high plasticity | | |
| | | | CVG | 70–90 | Gravelly CLAY of very high plasticity | | |
| | Sandy SILT | FS | MS | | Sandy SILT | ML | Sandy silts and sandy clays feel gritty when rubbed between the fingers. Silts and sandy silts dry quickly and can be dusted off the fingers, exhibit marked dilatancy. Dry lumps have some cohesion but can be powdered easily in the fingers |
| | Sandy CLAY | CS | CLS etc. | | Sandy CLAY: subdivide like CG | MI | |
| SILTS and CLAYS (65–100% fines) | SILT (M-SOIL) | F | M | | SILT: subdivide like C | ML/MI | Clays, silty clays and sandy clays are plastic and can be readily rolled into threads when moist. Dry lumps can be broken but not powdered, but they disintegrate under water. They stick to fingers and dry slowly. Clays feel smooth to touch |
| | CLAY | | CL | 35 | CLAY of low plasticity | CL | |
| | | | CI | 35–50 | CLAY of intermediate plasticity | CI | |
| | | | CH | 50–70 | CLAY of high plasticity | CH | |
| | | | VC | 70–90 | CLAY of very high plasticity | — | |
| ORGANIC SOILS | Descriptive letter O suffixed to any group or subgroup symbol. Organic matter suspected to be a significant constituent. Example MHO: Organic SILT of high plasticity | | | | | — | Usually dark in colour, plant remains may be visible, often with distinctive smell |
| PEAT Pt | Peat soils consist predominantly of plant remains which may be fibrous or amorphous | | | | | Pt | Usually black or brown in colour. Very compressible. Easily identifiable visually |

*Gravel and sand may be qualified as Sandy GRAVEL and Gravelly SAND where appropriate

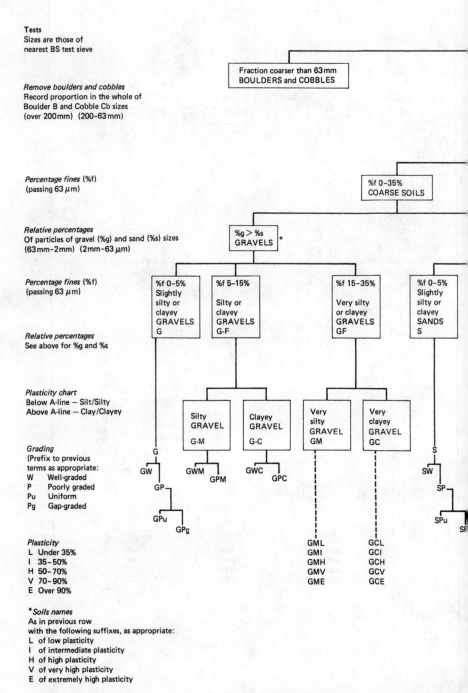

**Fig. 4.14** Outline of laboratory procedure for classifying soils within the British Soil Classification System[3]

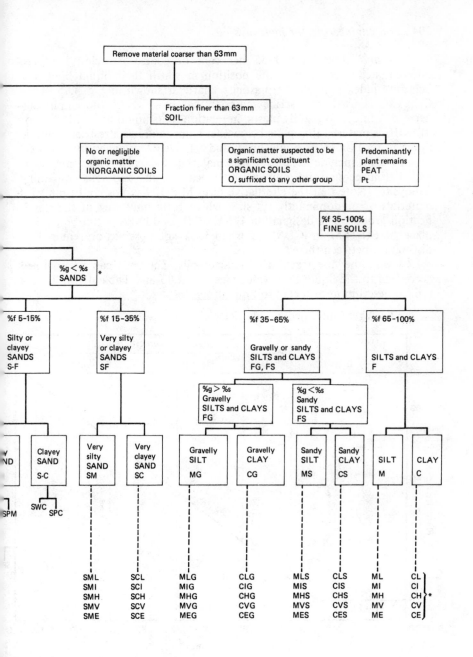

*Silts and clays* have 0–35 per cent of coarse particles; they are differentiated according to the position in which their liquid limit and plasticity index plot on the plasticity chart, as shown in Fig. 4.15. Thus CLAY C is used to describe material that plots above the empirically derived A-line, and is fully plastic in relation to its liquid limit. SILT M or M-SOIL is material that plots below the A-line, and has a restricted plastic range in relation to its liquid limit, and relatively low cohesion; fine soils of this type include clean silt-size material and rock-flour, micaceous and diatomaceous soils, pumice and volcanic soils, and soils containing halloysite. (Note that the alternative term M-SOIL avoids confusion with materials of predominantly silt-size, which form only part of the classification group.) The designation FINE SOIL or FINES F can be used in place of SILT M or CLAY C when it is not possible or required to distinguish between them.

As with the fine fraction of coarse soils, fine soils can be qualified according to the liquid limit value (see Fig. 4.15 and Table 4.13). Thus a typical description of a clay soil might be:

CLAY of intermediate plasticity CI

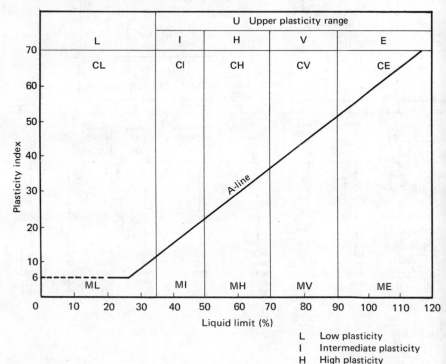

**Fig. 4.15** Plasticity chart used in the classification of fine soils and the finer part of coarse soils into CLAY C and SILT M soils. Note that O is added to the symbol of any material containing a significant proportion of organic material, e.g. MHO

**Table 4.13** Qualifying designations used with soils of various plasticities and liquid limits

| Plasticity | Liquid limit (%) | Symbol |
|---|---|---|
| Low | <35 | L |
| Intermediate | 35–50 | I |
| High | 50–70 | H |
| Very high | 70–90 | V |
| Extremely high | >90 | E |

*Organic soils* Any soil group may be qualified as organic if it contains a significant amount of organic matter. With such materials, the letter O is suffixed to the group symbol, e.g. Organic CLAY of high plasticity CHO, or Organic Sandy CLAY of high plasticity CHSO. The most important group of organic soils usually plot below the A-line on the plasticity chart. These soils, which are designated Organic SILT MO, include most M-SOILS of high liquid limit and above.

Organic soils are normally unsuitable as highway construction or foundation materials because of their compressibility characteristics.

## AASHTO system

In 1929, the US Bureau of Public Roads—then known as the Public Roads Administration—presented a system of soil classification which divided soils into eight groups designated from A-1 to A-8 inclusive. Soils were placed into particular groups according to a number of their highway-related physical characteristics. Thus a well-graded soil composed primarily of gravel and sand, but with some clay binder material present, was designated an A-1 soil, whilst other soils of lesser stability as highway foundations were placed by means of their physical characteristics into higher numbered classification groups.

As the usefulness of this simple system became apparent, various engineering organizations modified it to meet their own particular needs and soon a number of subdivisions of the various groups came into rather widespread use. In 1945, the Public Roads system was extensively revised[29] and the resultant system is given in Table 4.14. This system—which is now variously described as the Transportation Research Board (TRB), Highway Research Board (HRB), Modified Bureau of Public Roads (Modified BPR), and American Association of State Highway and Transportation Officials (AASHTO) system—is the most widely known, and used, system for classifying soils for highway purposes in the USA.

The AASHTO system is similar to the old Public Roads system in that the lower the classification number of a soil, the better it is from a highway stability point of view. The new system differs, however, in that the number of classification groups was reduced from eight to seven, twelve subgroups were officially introduced, and the number of physical properties required to place a soil was reduced to three, i.e. mechanical analysis, liquid limit, and plasticity index. In addition, the concept of a 'group index' was developed in order to subdivide the fine-grained soils (pp. 298–299).

**Table 4.14** AASHTO soil classification system

| Property | Granular materials (35% or less passing 75 μm sieve) | | | | | | | Silt–clay materials (more than 35% passing 75 μm sieve) | | | |
| | Group classification | | | | | | | Group classification | | | |
| | A-1 | | A-3 | A-2 | | | | A-4 | A-5 | A-6 | A-7* |
| | A-1-a | A-1-b | | A-2-4 | A-2-5 | A-2-6 | A-2-7 | | | | |
|---|---|---|---|---|---|---|---|---|---|---|---|
| Sieve analysis, % passing: | | | | | | | | | | | |
| ASTM sieve (Equivalent BS sieve) | | | | | | | | | | | |
| No. 10 (2.0 mm) | 50 (max.) | — | — | — | — | — | — | — | — | — | — |
| No. 40 (425 μm) | 30 (max.) | 50 (max.) | 51 (max.) | — | — | — | — | — | — | — | — |
| No. 200 (75 μm) | 15 (max.) | 25 (max.) | 10 (max.) | 35 (max.) | 35 (max.) | 35 (max.) | 35 (max.) | 36 (min.) | 36 (min.) | 36 (min.) | 36 (min.) |
| Characteristics of fraction passing ASTM No. 40 (BS 425 μm): | | | | | | | | | | | |
| Liquid limit (%) | — | — | — | 40 (max.) | 41 (min.) | 40 (max.) | 41 (min.) | 40 (max.) | 41 (min.) | 40 (max.) | 41 (min.) |
| Plasticity index | 6 (max.) | 6 (max.) | Non-plastic | 10 (max.) | 10 (max.) | 11 (min.) | 11 (min.) | 10 (max.) | 10 (max.) | 11 (min.) | 11 (min.) |
| Group index | 0 | 0 | 0 | 0 | 0 | 4 (max.) | 4 (max.) | 8 (max.) | 12 (max.) | 16 (max.) | 20 (max.) |
| Usual significant materials | Stone fragments, gravel and sand | | Fine sand | Silty or clayey gravel and sand | | | | Silty soils | Silty soils | Clayey soils | Clayey soils |
| General rating as subgrade | Excellent to good | | | | | | | Fair to poor | | | |

* The A-7 group is subdivided according to a plasticity index criterion as follows. When $PI \leqslant LL - 30$, the soil is placed in the A-7-5 subgroup. When $PI > LL - 30$, the soil falls into the A-7-6 subgroup

**Description of soil groups**
The soil materials included in the various groups of the modified system are divided into two major classes: the granular materials containing 35 per cent or less material passing the ASTM No. 200 (75 $\mu$m BS) sieve, and the silt–clay materials containing more than 35 per cent passing the No. 200 (75 $\mu$m) sieve. The granular materials are composed of the A-1, A-2 and A-3 soils, while the silt–clay soils fall into the A-4, A-5, A-6 and A-7 groups.

*Group A-1* The typical material of this group is a well-graded mixture of stone fragments or gravel, coarse sand, fine sand and a non-plastic or feebly plastic soil binder. However, it also includes stone fragments, gravel, coarse sand, volcanic cinders, etc., without soil binder. Subgroup A-1-a includes those soils which consist predominantly of stone fragments or gravel either with or without a well-graded binder of fine material. The A-1-b subgroup includes those which consist predominantly of coarse sand with or without a well-graded soil binder.

*Group A-2* This group includes a wide variety of granular materials which are borderline between the materials falling in groups A-1 and A-3, and the silt–clay materials of groups A-4, A-5, A-6 and A-7. It includes all materials containing 35 per cent or less passing the 75 $\mu$m sieve which cannot be classified as A-1 or A-3, due to having a fines content or plasticity or both in excess of the limitations for these groups.
   The subgroups A-2-4 and A-2-5 include various granular materials containing 35 per cent or less passing the 75 $\mu$m sieve and with the minus 425 $\mu$m portion having the characteristics of the A-4 and A-5 groups. These groups include such materials as gravel and coarse sand with silt contents or plasticity indices in excess of the limitations of group A-1, and fine sand with a non-plastic silt content in excess of the limitations of group A-3. The subgroups A-2-6 and A-2-7 include materials similar to those described under subgroups A-2-4 and A-2-5, except that the fine portion contains plastic clay having the characteristics of the A-6 or A-7 group. The approximate combined effect of plasticity indices in excess of 10 and percentages passing the 75 $\mu$m sieve in excess of 15 is reflected by group index values of 0 to 4.

*Group A-3* The typical material of this group is fine beach sand or fine desert blow-sand without silty or clay fines or with a very small amount of non-plastic silt. The group includes stream-deposited mixtures of poorly-graded fine sand and limited amounts of coarse sand and clay.

*Group A-4* The typical material of this group is a non-plastic or moderately plastic silty soil usually having 75 per cent or more passing the 75 $\mu$m sieve. The group includes mixtures of fine silty soil and up to 64 per cent of sand and gravel retained on the 75 $\mu$m sieve. The group index values range from 1 to 8, with increasing percentages of coarse material being reflected by decreasing group index values.

*Group A-5*　The typical material of this group is similar to that described under group A-4, except that it is usually of micaceous character and may be highly elastic as indicated by a high liquid limit. The group index values range from 1 to 12, with increasing values indicating the combined effect of increasing liquid limits and decreasing percentages of coarse material.

*Group A-6*　The typical material of this group is a plastic clay soil usually having 75 per cent or more passing the 75 $\mu$m sieve. The group includes mixtures of fine clayey soils and up to 64 per cent of sand and gravel retained on the 75 $\mu$m sieve. Materials of this group usually have high volume changes between the wet and dry states. The group index values range from 1 to 16, with increasing values indicating the combined effect of increasing plasticity indices and decreasing percentages of coarse material.

*Group A-7*　The typical material of this group is similar to that described under group A-6, except that it has the high liquid limit characteristic of the A-5 group and may be elastic as well as subject to high volume change. The range of group index values is 1 to 20, with increasing values indicating the combined effect of increasing liquid limits and plasticity indices and decreasing percentages of coarse material.

The subgroup A-7-5 includes those materials with moderate plasticity indices in relation to liquid limit, which may be highly elastic as well as subject to considerable volume change. The subgroup A-7-6 includes those materials with high plasticity indices in relation to liquid limit, which are subject to extremely high volume changes.

## Group index

A new feature of the modified system was the introduction of a subsidiary rating system as a means of placing a soil containing appreciable amounts of fine-grained material within its group or subgroup; it also gives a general guide to the load-bearing ability of the soil. The group index is simply a number between 0 and 20 which is dependent upon the percentage of material passing the 75 $\mu$m sieve, the liquid limit, and the plasticity index. A low group index is reflective of high subgrade stability, while high group indices reflect the poor stability conditions associated with high liquid limits, high plasticity indices, and low granular material contents.

The following empirical formula is used to obtain the group index of a soil:

$$GI = 0.2a + 0.005ac + 0.01bd$$

where $a$ = that portion of the percentage passing the 75 $\mu$m sieve greater than 35 and not exceeding 75, expressed as a positive whole number from 1 to 40, $b$ = that portion of the percentage passing the 75 $\mu$m sieve greater than 15 and not exceeding 55, expressed as a positive whole number from 1 to 40, $c$ = that portion of the numerical liquid limit greater than 40 and not exceeding 60, expressed as a positive whole number from 1 to 20, and $d$ = that portion of the numerical plasticity index greater than 10 and not exceeding 30, expressed as a positive whole number between 1 and 20.

The above formula is weighted so that the maximum influence of each of the three variables is in the ratio of 8 for the percentage passing the 75 $\mu$m sieve, 4 for the liquid limit, and 8 for the plasticity index. This weighting and the adopted critical ranges are based on an analysis of the average relative evaluations placed on subgrade materials by various highway organizations in the USA which use the tests involved in the classification system.

The group index of a soil is expressed to the nearest whole number and is written in parentheses after the group or subgroup designation, e.g. A-2-6(3). Even if the determined value is zero, it is still given, as this also indicates that the modified rather than the original Public Roads system was used to classify the soil.

## Textural classification system

The term 'texture' is a very difficult one to define. Perhaps it might be said that a soil is composed of particles of various sizes and shapes which give to it a distinctive appearance and 'feel', and the term which describes these features is the texture of the soil. Thus, for instance, if a soil is described as texturally harsh, then the impression is that the soil is composed primarily of particles which are sharp and angular as against one made up of flat or round particles.

It is very difficult, however, to have a common understanding of what is meant by such terms as harsh or light, and so most textural classification systems utilize descriptions of particle-size distributions as indirect means of reflecting soil texture. Textural charts such as the one illustrated in Fig. 4.16 are then used to determine the proper term for the soil in question.

The terms used to indicate the texture of a soil are purely arbitrary in nature and their meanings vary from organization to organization and from country to country. It is most important therefore that, when using a

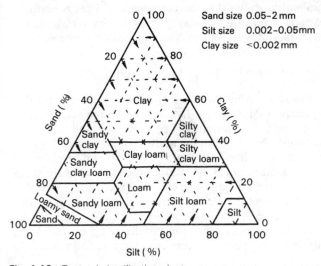

**Fig. 4.16** Textural classification chart

particular system, special care should be taken to specify the particle-size scale on which it is based. The triangular chart shown in Fig. 4.16 is that used by the Soil Survey of Great Britain and by the US Department of Agriculture Soil Conservation Service; it is based on the particle-size classification used by those organizations.

**Illustrative classification example**
The manner in which the different systems are used when classifying a soil is best illustrated by taking a typical problem. Let it be assumed that it is intended to classify a soil about which the following gradation data are available.

| BS sieve size (mm) | % passing |
|---|---|
| 6.3 | 100 |
| 2.0 | 85 |
| 0.425 | 54 |
| 0.150 | 39 |
| 0.063 | 26 |
| 0.002 | 8 |

In addition, the liquid limit of the soil is 34 per cent and its plasticity index is 13.

*BSCS* Following the procedure outlined in Fig. 4.14 it can be seen that the soil falls into the coarse-grained category, i.e. the percentage of fines is less than 35. Since the gravel component (15 per cent) is less than the sand content (61 per cent), the soil falls into the sand group and is given the suffix S; however, the gravel content is between 5 and 20 per cent so the classification can be qualified by describing the material as a gravelly SAND. Further examination shows that the percentage of fines is between 15 and 35 which indicates a very silty or clayey, gravelly SAND SF; as the liquid and plastic limit data plot above the A-line in Fig. 4.15, the soil can be finally classified as:

very clayey, gravelly SAND (clay of low plasticity) SCL

*AASHTO system* The soil can be classified with this system using Table 4.14. Plotting the gradation data shows that the percentage smaller than 75 $\mu$m is about 30; as this is less than 35 per cent the soil falls into the coarse-grained category. Next, beginning at the left-hand column of the chart and moving to the right, it is seen that the soil cannot be placed in the A-1 group as the maximum gradation and plasticity specifications are exceeded. For the same reasons, it cannot be classified according to the A-3 group. The gradation does meet the requirements of the A-2 group, so this can be further examined. Since the soil has a liquid limit of 34 per cent and a plasticity index of 13, it can only meet the requirements of the A-2-6 subgroup. The group index of the soil is next calculated as follows:

$$GI = 0.2a + 0.005ac + 0.01bd = 0.2(0) + 0.005(0 \times 0) + 0.01(15 \times 3)$$
$$= 0.45$$

As the soil has some plasticity as reflected in the group index, an appropriate AASHTO classification for the soil is therefore

A-2-6(1)

Note that the significant materials usually present in a soil group such as this are silty or clayey gravel and sand.

*Textural system* Textural systems using triangular charts can only classify on the basis of the amount of sand, silt and clay present in the soil. Thus when a soil contains a substantial amount of coarse material (usually taken as more than 10 per cent) so that it merits the description of a stony or gravelly soil, its textural class has to be determined on the basis of the percentages of sand, silt and clay adjusted to allow for the gravel or stone that must be 'excluded' in order to use the chart.

In this particular example, the soil contains 15 per cent gravel; hence it will be classified as a gravelly soil of some kind. In order to use Fig. 4.16, it is necessary to multiply the percentages of the sizes smaller than gravel by the ratio 100/85 so as to express these percentages in terms of the mass of the material exclusive of the gravel. Plotting the gradation data indicates that the percentage of sand (US Department of Agriculture definition) is $85 - 30 = 55$, that of silt is $30 - 8 = 22$, and that of clay $= 8$. These are adjusted as follows:

sand (0.05–2 mm)    $55 \times 100/85 = 65\%$

silt (0.002–0.05 mm)    $22 \times 100/85 = 26\%$

clay ( < 0.002 mm)    $8 \times 100/85 = 9\%$

With these adjusted values it is now possible to enter Fig. 4.16, and it is seen that the textural class of the adjusted soil is that of a sandy loam. The complete designation of the textural classification of this soil is therefore

Gravelly, sandy loam

## Field identification and description

Soils in the field are normally identified and described on the basis of information determined from *undisturbed* materials as seen in excavations and exposures. Additional information can be obtained from disturbed samples as recovered from excavations and tested in the laboratory. Two main approaches have been developed to describe soils as they appear in the field; these may be loosely described as the engineering approach and the pedological approach.

### Engineering approach

As would be expected, the engineering approach is aimed at allowing the most effective solution to an engineering problem to be determined, e.g. locating a highway alignment or correlating materials which occur on different parts of a site or on other sites. Few, if any, soils will have identical engineering descriptions.

In an engineering description, the main characteristics of a soil are preferably given in approximately the following order [2]:

(1)   mass characteristics: field strength or compactness, and indication of moisture condition; bedding; discontinuities; state of weathering;
(2)   material characteristics: colour, particle shape and composition; soil name, grading and plasticity;
(3)   geological formation, age and type of deposit;
(4)   classification (optional).

Thus, for example, a fairly uniform fine-grained material might be described in the field as a firm, closely-fissured, yellowish-brown CLAY of high plasticity, a London clay, whilst materials in interstratified beds might be described as dense, yellow fine SAND with thin lenses of soft, grey silty CLAY, a recent Alluvium.

## Mass characteristics

This heading refers to those soil characteristics that depend upon structure, and thus can be observed only in the field or, to a limited extent, in undisturbed samples.

Table 4.15 indicates how the *strength* or *compactness* of a fine- or coarse-grained soil, respectively, can be determined by field inspection, and the terms used to describe the result. Typically, a very soft soil would have an undrained shear strength of less than 20 kN/m$^2$, whilst a very stiff or hard soil's strength would be greater than 150 kN/m$^2$.

The term *bedding* is used to refer to the spacing between bedding discontinuities, the spacing between other discontinuities, and the openness and surface texture along mechanical discontinuities. Soil beds showing no variation in material are described as homogeneous.

*Discontinuities* in soils (and rocks) include bedding planes, joints, fissures, faults and shear planes. Their openness and surface texture, e.g. rough, smooth, polished or slickensided, are normally described as are their orientation, apparent angle of dip, and their spacing (using the spacing scale shown in Table 4.15).

Terms used to describe the *state of weathering* of a soil fabric include fresh, discoloured, decomposed, and disintegrated.

## Material characteristics

These are the characteristics that are described from a visual examination of either disturbed or undisturbed samples.

Details of the *colours* used to describe soils are given in the extreme right-hand column of Table 4.15 (see p. 305).

Soil particles visible to the naked eye or with a hand lens may be described by their *shape and composition*. Recommended terms are angularity (e.g. angular, subangular, subrounded or rounded), form (e.g. equi-dimensional, flat, elongated, flat and elongated, or irregular), and surface texture (e.g. rough, smooth, or polished).

The *soil name* is based on particle-size distribution and plastic properties, because these characteristics can be measured readily with reasonable

**Table 4.15** Field identification and description of soils[2]

| | Basic soil type | Particle size (mm) | Visual identification |
|---|---|---|---|
| Very coarse soils | BOULDERS | ——— 200 | Only seen complete in pits or exposures |
| | COBBLES | | Often difficult to recover from boreholes |
| | | ——— 60 | |
| Coarse soils (over 65% sand and gravel sizes) | GRAVELS | Coarse<br>——— 20<br>Medium<br>——— 6<br>Fine<br>——— 2 | Easily visible to naked eye; particle shape can be described; grading can be described.<br>  Well graded: wide range of grain-sizes, well distributed. Poorly graded: not well graded. (May be uniform: size of most particles lies between narrow limits; or gap graded: an intermediate size of particle is markedly under-represented.) |
| | SANDS | Coarse<br>——— 0.6<br>Medium<br>——— 0.2<br>Fine<br>——— 0.06 | Visible to naked eye; very little or no cohesion when dry; grading can be described.<br>  Well graded: wide range of grain-sizes, well distributed. Poorly graded: not well graded. (May be uniform: size of most particles lies between narrow limits; or gap graded: an intermediate size of particle is markedly under-represented.) |
| Fine soils (over 35% silt and clay sizes) | SILTS | Coarse<br>——— 0.02<br>Medium<br>——— 0.006<br>Fine<br>——— 0.002 | Only coarse silt barely visible to naked eye; exhibits little plasticity and marked dilatancy; slightly granular or silky to the touch. Disintegrates in water; lumps dry quickly; possess cohesion but can be powdered easily between fingers |
| | CLAYS | | Dry lumps can be broken but not powdered between the fingers; they also disintegrate under water but more slowly than silt; smooth to the touch; exhibits plasticity but no dilatancy; sticks to the fingers and dries slowly; shrinks appreciably on drying usually showing cracks. Intermediate and high plasticity clays show these properties to a moderate and high degree, respectively |
| Organic soils | ORGANIC CLAY, SILT or SAND | Varies | Contains substantial amounts of organic vegetable matter |
| | PEATS | Varies | Predominantly plant remains usually dark brown or black in colour, often with distinctive smell; low bulk density |

**Table 4.15** *(cont.)*

| Basic soil types | Particle nature and plasticity | Composite soil types (mixture of basic soil types) | | Compactness/strength | |
|---|---|---|---|---|---|
| | | | | Term | Field test |
| BOULDERS | *Particle shape* | Scale of secondary constituents with coarse soils | | Loose | By inspection of voids and particle packing |
| COBBLES | Angular Subangular | Term | % clay or silt | Dense | |
| | Subrounded Rounded Flat Elongated | Slightly clayey ⎫ GRAVEL<br>  or<br>Slightly silty ⎭ SAND | <5 | | |
| GRAVELS | | Clayey ⎫ GRAVEL<br>  or<br>Silty ⎭ SAND | 5–15 | Loose | Can be excavated with a spade; 50 mm wooden peg can be easily driven |
| | | Very clayey ⎫ GRAVEL<br>  or<br>Very silty ⎭ SAND | 15–35 | Dense | Requires pick for excavation; 50 mm wooden peg hard to drive |
| | *Texture* Rough Smooth Polished | Sandy GRAVEL ⎫ Sand or gravel an<br>  ⎬ important second<br>Gravelly SAND ⎭ constituent of the coarse fraction | | Slightly cemented | Visual examination; pick removes soil in lumps which can be abraded |
| SANDS | | *For composite types described as:* clayey—fines are plastic, cohesive silty—fines are non-plastic or of low plasticity | | | |
| SILTS | Non-plastic or low plasticity | Scale of secondary constituents with fine soils | | Soft or loose | Easily moulded or crushed in the fingers |
| | | Term | % sand or gravel | Firm or dense | Can be moulded or crushed by strong pressure in the fingers |
| | | Sandy ⎫ CLAY<br>  or<br>Gravelly ⎭ SILT | 35–65 | Very soft | Exudes between fingers when squeezed in hand |
| | Intermediate plasticity (Lean clay) | CLAY:SILT | <35 | Soft | Moulded by light finger pressure |
| CLAYS | | Examples of composite types | | Firm | Can be moulded by strong finger pressure |
| | High plasticity (Fat clay) | (Indicating preferred order for description)<br><br>Loose, brown, subangular very sandy, fine to coarse GRAVEL with small pockets of soft grey clay | | Stiff | Cannot be moulded by fingers. Can be indented by thumb |
| | | | | Very stiff | Can be indented by thumb nail |
| ORGANIC CLAY, SILT or SAND | | Medium dense, light brown, clayey, fine and medium SAND<br><br>Stiff, orange brown, fissured sandy CLAY | | Firm | Fibres already compressed |
| PEATS | | Firm, brown, thinly laminated SILT and CLAY | | Spongy | Very compressible and open structure |
| | | Plastic, brown, amorphous PEAT | | Plastic | Can be moulded in hand, and smears fingers |

**Table 4.15** (*cont.*)

| Basic soil types | Structure | | | | Colour |
|---|---|---|---|---|---|
| | Term | Field identification | Interval scales | | |
| BOULDERS | Homogeneous | Deposit consists essentially of one type | Scale of bedding spacing | | Red Pink Yellow |
| COBBLES | Interstratified | Alternating layers of varying types or with bands or lenses of other materials. Interval scale for bedding spacing may be used | Term | Mean spacing (mm) | Brown Olive Green |
| | | | Very thickly bedded | > 2000 | Blue White Grey |
| | Heterogeneous | A mixture of types | Thickly bedded | 2000–600 | Black etc. |
| GRAVELS | | | Medium bedded | 600–200 | *Supplemented as necessary with:* |
| | Weathered | Particles may be weakened and may show concentric layering | Thinly bedded | 200–60 | Light |
| | | | Very thinly bedded | 60–20 | Dark Mottled etc. |
| | | | Thickly laminated | 20–6 | *and* Pinkish |
| | | | Thinly laminated | < 6 | Reddish Yellowish |
| SANDS | | | | | Brownish etc. |
| SILTS | Fissured | Break into polyhedral fragments along fissures. Interval scale for spacing of discontinuities may be used | | | |
| | Intact | No fissures | | | |
| | Homogeneous | Deposit consists essentially of one type | Scale of spacing of other discontinuities | | |
| | Interstratified | Alternating layers of varying types. Interval scale for thickness of layers may be used | Term | Mean spacing (mm) | |
| CLAYS | Weathered | Usually has crumb or columnar structure | Very widely spaced | > 2000 | |
| | | | Widely spaced | 2000–600 | |
| ORGANIC CLAY, SILT or SAND | | | Medium spaced | 600–200 | |
| | | | Closely spaced | 200–60 | |
| | Fibrous | Plant remains recognizable and retain some strength | Very closely spaced | 60–20 | |
| PEATS | | | Extremely closely spaced | < 20 | |
| | Amorphous | Recognizable plant remains absent | | | |

precision, and estimated with sufficient accuracy for descriptive purposes. Table 4.15 is the key to the identification of soils by hand and eye. Note that the predominant soil name is always given in capital letters.

Clay and silt soils, both alone and in mixtures with coarser materials, have plasticity descriptions as given in Table 4.13 for fine soils.

### Geological formation, age and type of deposit

The name of the *geological formation* is most often given on the maps of the British Geological Survey, and it should be written with capital initial letters, e.g. London Clay, Bagshot Beds, Lower Lias. Terms such as Made ground, Peat, Head, Alluvium, River terrace, Brickearth, Blown (aeolian) sand, and Till may also be given in the map legend to indicate geological origin or type of deposit. These suggest to the engineer some of the general characteristics that the soil deposit can be expected to show.

## Pedological approach

Pedology is the science that treats soils in relation to their use and management. The development of this soil science gains its impetus from its relationship with agriculture, where its influence on the advancement of scientific agricultural practices has been of great significance. It is only relatively recently, however, that highway engineers have begun to see the value of the great wealth of data and knowledge accumulated over the years by pedologists. Of particular value in helping to solve highway engineering location and construction problems are the agricultural soil maps which use the pedological soil description/taxonomy system in their preparation.

With the pedological approach, a soil at a given location is described in relation to its profile (see Fig. 4.17) using, in addition to measurable properties, in situ morphological features to define soil class limits. The updated pedological system is multi-categorical and has various levels, ranging from 10 soil orders at the most general level to more than 10 000 profile units at the more precise soil series level. In the system, which is primarily a field description system, identification/classification is based on six categories: order, suborder, great group, subgroup, family, and series.

The *soil orders* reflect the kind and relative strength of the main natural soil forming processes. *Soil suborders* reflect either the presence/lack of waterlogging, or soil differences produced through the effect of climate or vegetation. *Great soil groups* are based on the kinds and sequences of major soil horizons and other compositional or morphological features. *Soil subgroups* represent the central or typic segment of the great group, or have properties of the great group and one or more properties of another group. *Soil families* are based on properties important to the growth of plants or to the behaviour of soils used for engineering. The *soil series* is the lowest category and includes soils that have profiles almost alike and a limited range in soil properties, so that the expected behaviour is the same. Most soil maps are made at the series level.

As is illustrated in Fig. 4.17, a soil profile is composed of a natural succession of soil horizons which represent alterations to the original soil

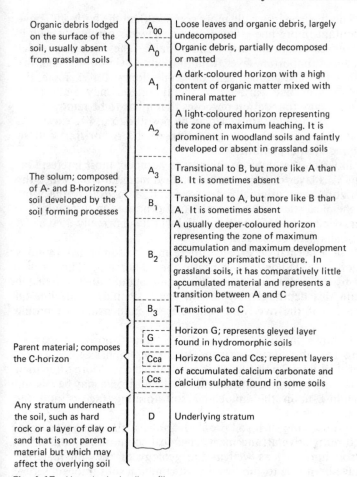

| | | |
|---|---|---|
| Organic debris lodged on the surface of the soil, usually absent from grassland soils | A$_{00}$ | Loose leaves and organic debris, largely undecomposed |
| | A$_0$ | Organic debris, partially decomposed or matted |
| The solum; composed of A- and B-horizons; soil developed by the soil forming processes | A$_1$ | A dark-coloured horizon with a high content of organic matter mixed with mineral matter |
| | A$_2$ | A light-coloured horizon representing the zone of maximum leaching. It is prominent in woodland soils and faintly developed or absent in grassland soils |
| | A$_3$ | Transitional to B, but more like A than B. It is sometimes absent |
| | B$_1$ | Transitional to A, but more like B than A. It is sometimes absent |
| | B$_2$ | A usually deeper-coloured horizon representing the zone of maximum accumulation and maximum development of blocky or prismatic structure. In grassland soils, it has comparatively little accumulated material and represents a transition between A and C |
| | B$_3$ | Transitional to C |
| Parent material; composes the C-horizon | G | Horizon G; represents gleyed layer found in hydromorphic soils |
| | Cca | Horizons Cca and Ccs; represent layers of accumulated calcium carbonate and calcium sulphate found in some soils |
| | Ccs | |
| Any stratum underneath the soil, such as hard rock or a layer of clay or sand that is not parent material but which may affect the overlying soil | D | Underlying stratum |

**Fig. 4.17**  Hypothetical soil profile

material brought about by the weathering process. In easily-drained soils with well-developed profiles, there are normally three distinct layers, known as the A-, B- and C-horizons.

The uppermost layer, the A-horizon, is often called the *zone of eluviation* because much of the original ultrafine colloidal material and the soluble mineral salts have been leached out from it by downward percolating water. The agriculturist is most concerned with this layer because it is normally rich in the humus and organic plant residues so vital to good crop growth; however, it is these characteristics which can render this horizon a highly undesirable road construction layer, i.e. the vegetative matter will eventually rot and leave voids whilst the layer as a whole often exhibits high compressibility and elasticity, high resistance to compaction, and variable plasticity.

The second layer, the B-horizon, is also known as the *zone of illuviation* since it is in this layer that the material washed down from the A-horizon accumulates. This horizon is usually more compact than the horizons above or below it, contains more fine-grained particles, is less permeable, and is usually more surface chemically active and unstable. These features render the B-horizon a most important layer from the point of view of the highway engineer. With active fine-grained soils on gentle slopes, for example, the extra accumulation of fine particles in the B-horizon may make it so unsuitable for highway foundation purposes that it has to be removed and wasted. Whereas, with sandy soils, it may be possible to utilize excavated B-horizon material to improve the gradation of the A-horizon, and so improve its foundation capabilities.

The layer in which the highway engineer is normally most interested is the C-horizon. This layer contains the unchanged material from which the A- and B-horizons were originally developed. It is in exactly the same physical and chemical state as when it was first deposited in the geological cycle by water, wind or ice. It is this material which is normally used as fill material in embankment construction.

Although not a normal occurrence, there may be sometimes found a further horizon—the D-horizon—beneath the C-horizon. This is not usually noted by the pedologist unless it is within about 1.0–1.5 m of the surface. Within this depth, the D-horizon has a significant effect upon the characteristics of the overlying soil, thereby influencing the profile development.

As is also shown in Fig. 4.17, the A-, B- and C-horizons may be subdivided into a number of sub-horizons. It must be emphasized, however, that the soil profile shown in this figure is an idealized one. More often than not, many of the sub-horizons, and sometimes the horizons, may be missing in situ, depending upon the influential soil forming factors and the erosional features present.

By carefully observing such soil profile features as the number, colour, texture, structure, relative arrangement, chemical composition, and thickness of the soil horizons, as well as the geology of the soil material, pedologists have been able to subdivide most common soils into soil series. Each soil series has the same number and arrangements of horizons, is developed from the same kind of parent material under the same climatic and vegetative conditions for the same period of time, and has the same soil forming slope on the same type of topography. In other words, soils that are described as belonging to a particular series are essentially homogeneous, only minor differences (primarily in the texture of the A-horizon material) being tolerated between the various profiles of a series.

A soil series is given a name that is usually the proper name of some place, lake, stream, or other geographical entity close to the spot where the prototype soil profile was first identified and scientifically described. Thus after a soil series is first found and named, that same name (e.g. Seacroft soil series—see Table 1.2) is used to describe all other soils which fit the same profile definition, no matter where they are found.

Soil series maps are of particular value when carrying out field sampling during highway location and construction materials' surveys, as they enable the amount of soil sampling to be reduced significantly. For example, the number of borings can be often reduced to checking profiles with each series' boundaries, with detailed profiling being only necessary at the interface transition from one soil series to another. Indeed, it has been estimated [30] that if a test pit is dug anywhere in the area delineated as that of a particular soil series, there is an 85 to 95 per cent chance of revealing a soil that has the engineering properties as given for that soil series elsewhere.

Reference 31 provides an excellent description of soil taxonomy in relation to soil survey activities.

## Selected bibliography

(1) Holtz WG, *Soil as an Engineering Material*, Water Resources Technical Publication No. 17, Washington DC, US Government Printing Office, 1969.
(2) BS 5930: *Site Investigations*, London, The British Standards Institution, 1981.
(3) Dumbleton MJ, *The British Soil Classification System for Engineering Purposes: Its Development and Relation to Other Comparable Systems*, TRRL Report LR1030, Crowthorne, Berks., The Transport and Road Research Laboratory, 1981.
(4) BS 6031: *Earthworks*, London, The British Standards Institution, 1981.
(5) Leonards GA, Engineering properties of soils, Chapter 3, in: Leonards GA (Ed), *Foundation Engineering*, London, McGraw-Hill, 1962.
(6) Millar CE, Turk LM and Foth HD, *Fundamentals of Soil Science*, New York, John Wiley, 1962.
(7) *Manual of Applied Geology for Engineers*, London, The Institution of Civil Engineers, 1976.
(8) Croney D, *The Design and Performance of Road Pavements*, London, HMSO, 1977.
(9) BS 1377: *Methods of Test for Soils for Civil Engineering Purposes*, London, The British Standards Institution, 1975.
(10) BS 1924: *Methods of Test for Stabilized Soils*, London, The British Standards Institution, 1975.
(11) Barden L, The relation of soil structure to the engineering geology of clay soil, *Quarterly Jl of Engineering Geology*, 1972, **5**, Nos 1 and 2, pp. 85–102.
(12) Jumikis AR, Soil moisture transfer in the vapor phase upon freezing, *Highway Research Board Bulletin 168*, 1957, pp. 95–114.
(13) Penner E, The mechanism of frost heaving in soils, *Highway Research Board Bulletin 225*, 1959, pp. 1–13.
(14) Jones RH and Berry AN, Influence of subgrade properties on frost heave, *Highways and Public Works*, 1979, **47**, No. 1832, pp. 17–22.
(15) Aldrich HP (Jr), Frost penetration below highway and airfield pavements, *Highway Research Board Bulletin 135*, 1956, pp. 124–149.
(16) Croney D and Jacobs JC, *The Frost Susceptibility of Soils and Road Materials*, RRL Report LR90, Crowthorne, Berks., The Road Research Laboratory, 1967.
(17) Casagrande A, Discussion on frost heaving, *Proc. Highway Research Board*, 1932, **11**, Part 1, pp. 167–172.
(18) Linell KA and Kaplar CW, The factor of soil and material type in frost action, *Highway Research Board Bulletin 225*, 1959, pp. 81–126.
(19) Head KH, *Manual of Soil Laboratory Testing*, London, Pentech Press, 1979.

(20) Road Research Laboratory, *Soil Mechanics for Road Engineers*, London, HMSO, 1952.

(21) West G and Dumbleton MJ, *Flow Charts for the British Standard Particle-Size Distribution Tests for Soils*, TRRL Report LR468, Crowthorne, Berks., The Transport and Road Research Laboratory, 1972.

(22) Committee on Significance of Tests for Highway Purposes, Significance of tests for highway materials—basic tests, *Proc. Amer. Soc. Civ. Engrs, Journal of the Highway Division*, September 1957, **83**, No. HW4.

(23) BS 5835: Part 1: *Testing of Aggregates: Compactibility Test for Graded Aggregates*, London, The British Standards Institution, 1980.

(24) Pike DC, *Shear-box Tests on Graded Aggregates*, TRRL Report LR584, Crowthorne, Berks., The Transport and Road Research Laboratory, 1973.

(25) Roe PG and Webster DC, *Specification for the TRRL Frost-heave Test*, TRRL Report SR829, Crowthorne, Berks., The Transport and Road Research Laboratory, 1984.

(26) Department of Transport, *Specification for Highway Works*, London, HMSO, 1986 (6th edition).

(27) Technical Committee Report on Testing of Road Materials, *Proceedings of the XVII World Road Congress of the Permanent International Association of Road Congresses*, pp. 76–78, October 1983.

(28) Casagrande A, Classification and identification of soils, *Proc. Amer. Soc. Civ. Engrs*, Part 1, 1947, **73**, No. 6, pp. 783–810.

(29) Allen H, Report of committee on classification of materials for sub-grades and granular-type roads, *Proc. Highway Research Board*, 1945, **25**, pp. 375–392.

(30) Bartelli LJ and McCormack DE, Morphology and pedologic classification of swelling soils, *Transportation Research Record 568*, 1976, pp. 1–8.

(31) *Soil Taxonomy: A Basic System of Soil Classification for Making and Interpreting Soil Surveys*, Agriculture Handbook 436, Washington DC, US Superintendent of Documents, 1975.

# 5
# Soil stabilization

To the highway engineer, the definition of soil stabilization which is perhaps of most interest is that ascribed to the chairman of the (now) American Transportation Research Board in 1938, as follows.

'A stabilized fill, subgrade, road surface or roadbase is one that will stay put, and stabilizing is the process by which it has been made that way.'

This definition has the beauty of emphasizing that highway soil stabilization is concerned with any process by which a soil may be improved and made more stable. Normally, the construction of roadbases and surface courses with already-stable materials, e.g. crushed rock or concrete, is not considered as falling within this definition; however, any treatment used to improve the strength of a soil (or waste material) by reducing its susceptibility to the influence of water and/or traffic—irrespective of whether the process is performed in situ or applied to the material before or after it is placed in the roadway or embankment—can be regarded as soil stabilization.

The need to pay more attention to the use of soil stabilization techniques is now becoming more appreciated by society. The continued, indeed insatiable, demand for aggregates in highly-developed countries has resulted in acute shortages in localities which previously had adequate supplies, such as many large metropolitan urban areas, locales where the aggregate supplies have historically been in low supply or difficult to access due to existing land use patterns, and areas that are now subject to environmental or zoning regulations that prohibit the quarrying and production of aggregates. In many of the developing countries, the availability of good, cheap aggregate has always been limited and unable to keep up with the needs of their burgeoning economies. These factors, with other considerations, have combined in many instances to produce an escalation in aggregate costs, with consequent increases in highway construction and maintenance costs.

It is most likely therefore that greater attention will be focused in the future on the use of substitute materials such as stabilized soils (and waste materials—see Chapter 3) to meet construction, particularly highway construction, needs. It is also likely that this focus will be on improving and automating the presently-known methods of stabilization, rather than on seeking to develop new 'magical' chemical stabilizers.

In practice, the methods by which soils are stabilized for highway purposes can be divided into the following main groups.

(1) *Mechanical stabilization*   This, by far the most widely used method of stabilization, relies for stability upon the inherent properties of the soil material. If a soil cannot be made stable simply by compaction or consolidation, then additional soil or other aggregate materials may be admixed to produce a mixture having the required stability characteristics.

Although not mechanical stabilization in the true sense of the word, the use of additives such as chlorides, lignin, and molasses is usually associated with this process. This is because only soils which already have some mechanical stability can be satisfactorily improved by these chemical additives. Other methods sometimes included in the mechanical stabilization category are the thermal procedures involving freezing and heating of the soil.

(2) *Cement stabilization*   This is a process in which cement is mixed with the soil to cause it to harden into a compact mass.

(3) *Lime and lime-pozzolan stabilization*   In this method of stabilization, the functions of the additives are twofold. They may be used to modify the soil properties—principally by chemically changing the soil gradation—and they may also cause the soil to harden into a compact mass having properties and uses similar to those of a cement-stabilized soil.

(4) *Bituminous stabilization*   In this process, bituminous materials—most usually bitumen emulsions or cutback bitumens—are mixed with soil so as to waterproof the particles and/or provide the additional cohesion necessary for stabilization.

(5) *Other experimental stabilization methods*   Whilst the mechanical, cement and bituminous stabilization processes are now well understood and accepted by highway engineers, the following statement[1] should be borne in mind.

'The alchemist of ancient times sought the philosopher's stone, which was believed to have the power to transmute the baser metals into gold. The philosopher's stone that intrigues the imagination of the highway engineer is the thing or method that will have the power to transmute cheaply any kind of soil into a material that will resist abrasion and displacement under traffic in all kinds of weather, and will retain these properties indefinitely.'

Due to the paucity of good road-making materials in many parts of the world, considerable research has been carried out since the 1940s in an effort to find a cheap 'magical' chemical which, when added in small quantities to a soil, will result in the rapid formation of a highly-stable pavement mixture. This group includes (amongst many others) the cementing inorganic stabilizer sodium silicate, the organic cationic chemicals which act primarily as waterproofers of the soil, and the natural and synthetic resinous materials which cement and/or waterproof the soil particles.

## Mechanical stabilization by treatments and with additives

When a granular structure such as a pavement has the property of resistance to lateral or vertical displacement under load, it is said to be mechanically stable. In mechanically-stable soils, this resistance is provided by the natural forces of cohesion and internal friction in the soil. Cohesion is mainly associated with the silt and clay content of the material, while internal friction is a characteristic of the coarser particles.

## Usage

Mechanical stabilization is the stabilization method most widely used in road construction throughout the world. Its popularity is based on the fact that it makes possible the maximum usage of locally available materials in highway embankments, subbases, roadbases and surface courses. Mechanically-stabilized roads may range from simple earth tracks which have been cleared of vegetation and compacted to meet the stability criteria demanded by their traffic, to highways which utilize highly sophisticated blends of different materials in one or more of their component layers.

In countries with well-developed economies, pavements formed from mechanically-stabilized, locally available materials are primarily used in rural areas, where the critical need is to provide access to lands and farms but the traffic demands are not sufficient to necessitate the construction of more expensive, higher-quality pavements. In a given situation, it may be that the estimated future traffic demand justifies a high-quality pavement but sufficient funds for construction are not available; in this case, a mechanically-stabilized pavement may lend itself to stage construction. By stage construction is meant the step-by-step improvement of the road as the expenditure is justified by the demands of increased traffic; its object is to provide, in an efficient and economic manner, adequate service to the traffic throughout the development of the highway. Thus at an early stage the pavement may be formed entirely of the mechanically-stabilized material, but at the final stage this same material might only form part or all of the roadbase and/or subbase of a bituminous-surfaced or concrete road designed to carry heavy traffic.

At this time, mechanically-stabilized soils are not used to any large extent in Britain as pavement construction materials. Their most extensive utilization is in the USA, Canada, Australia and the developing countries. A general rule-of-thumb regarding usage in the USA is that[2] properly constructed and designed mechanically-stabilized pavements are entirely satisfactory when the annual average daily traffic is less than about 50 veh/day; below this volume the loss of surface material due to abrasion is not very great and the dust problem is not serious. When the traffic exceeds about 100 veh/day, maintenance costs can be considerably reduced by the application to the surface of some type of dust palliative such as a liquid bituminous material or calcium chloride. Once, however, the traffic reaches between 200 and 300 veh/day, the mechanically-stabilized surface can no longer be maintained economically, and so a higher-quality surface will need to be constructed.

## Types of mechanical stabilization

Again there are differences amongst authorities as to what exactly is meant by the mechanical stabilization of a soil. Some go so far as to regard the drying out of a soil after a rainstorm as a form of mechanical stabilization, while others confine it to a process whereby stabilization is brought about by altering the particle-size distribution of a soil. Since it is this author's view that mechanical stabilization does not merely entail alteration of a single criterion such as gradation, but requires a consideration of many of the fundamental phenomena of soil (and earthworks) engineering, the discussion in this text will take the following broad form:

(1) *mechanical stabilization by treatments*: compaction, consolidation, and electrical and thermal methods,
(2) *mechanical stabilization with the aid of additives*: soil and aggregate, chlorides, lignin, and molasses.

## Stabilization by compaction

The need for an adequate state of compaction in highway pavements, subgrades and embankments is a fundamental consideration which is accepted by all highway engineers. There are many instances of road settlement and unstable embankment slopes which can be traced to poor compaction. Increasing the state of compaction of a soil stabilizes it by increasing its strength, controlling volume-change tendencies and reducing the possibility of settlement and, usually, minimizing changes in moisture content. Thus, if economical designs of pavements, embankments and subgrades are to be obtained, and subsequent maintenance costs reduced, it is essential that the soil used in these road components be brought to a satisfactorily stable state of compaction during the construction work.

The term 'compaction' is often, and wrongly, used interchangeably with the terms 'compression' and 'consolidation', and it is important that the distinctions between them are recognized and appreciated. By compaction is meant the artificial increase in density which is brought about by mechanical means, e.g. rolling; it is normally accomplished by expelling air from the soil mass, thereby decreasing the voids ratio. In contrast, compressibility and consolidation are associated with the increase in density due to the gradual expulsion of water from the soil pores. Whereas compaction is an 'instantaneous' process, consolidation usually results from the application of a sustained load and occurs over much longer periods of time; very often many years will pass before consolidation is complete and the final settlement is known.

In natural soils, consolidation is greatly influenced by the soil structure and the past stress history of the material. For instance, in situ soils which are the result of a sedimentation process are more compressible than their residual or aeolian counterparts. Thus, even though a soil may be compacted, consolidation may still take place if the equilibrium conditions are upset. For example, the lowering of the water-table beneath an embankment or subgrade which is 'adequately' compacted may result in an effective increase in soil stress such that a volume change will take place within compressible layers below the original water-table; this can lead to settlement of compacted material at the surface.

**Controlling compaction in the field**
In general, the in situ strength of a mechanically-stabilized soil layer is a function of its moisture content and density. Consequently, the strength criterion selected for design purposes should be based on a moisture content equal to the wettest condition likely to occur normally within the layer after the road is open to traffic. For example, in the case of a subgrade soil this moisture content is known as the equilibrium moisture content; its value is a function of the soil type, the local climatic conditions, and the depth to the groundwater table (see Chapters 4 and 6).

The adequacy of the compacted (stabilized) soil is usually ensured in the field by controlling its dry density. This is exercised either by specifying the dry density to be achieved (via a performance specification) or by specifying the compaction methods to be used (using a method specification).

*Performance specifications* In countries where the performance approach is applied, it is usual for the end-product to be prescribed as a percentage of a reference density for the material under test; normally, this density is the maximum standard or modified Proctor dry density (see Chapter 4). Typically, the relative compaction specified is related to the height location in the road structure where the layer being compacted is positioned, i.e. it depends upon whether or not the layer is likely to be highly stressed under traffic. Thus for mass earthworks compaction in an embankment a requirement of 90–95 per cent of the maximum *standard* dry density may be adequate, whereas 100–105 per cent of the maximum *modified* dry density may have to be achieved before a soil–aggregate roadbase is considered to be satisfactorily compacted.

Prior to 1969 control of most earthworks and subgrade compaction carried out in Britain was based on a percentage air voids performance specification. For most embankment compaction the maximum air content permitted was 10 per cent, whilst an upper limit of 5 per cent was specified for the highway subgrade (i.e. the top 0.6 m of the embankment). Associated with this control mechanism was the requirement that the compaction moisture contents of cohesive soils should not exceed their plastic limits plus 2 per cent, whilst soil materials imported from nearby borrow pits or cuttings had to be compacted at a moisture content within minus 2 and plus 1 per cent of the natural moisture content at the time of excavation. This control mechanism was dropped for a number of reasons, not least of which were: (a) the difficulties encountered in achieving the 5 per cent air voids criterion with many good soils, e.g. granular materials, and (b) the difficulties experienced on large projects in maintaining a rate of check-testing which was compatible with the output of modern compaction equipment.

Whatever the method of compaction used, it is quite common to find that the compacted density as measured in the field varies with roadway depth and/or width. For example, the variability of compaction density in even a uniform soil is reported [3] to be between 40 and 80 kg/m$^3$; the testing method used to check the density can account for at least 50 per cent of this variability.

Most methods of measuring field density require the determination of the mass and volume of material extracted from a compacted layer. The volume is determined either directly from the extracted material if it is cut out intact, or by measuring the resultant cavity if the soil is broken up during extraction. Most field density errors are associated with the volume determination[4].

In Britain, what are probably the most commonly used methods[5] of determining the dry density of a compacted soil in the field are the *sand replacement method*, which is applied to fine-, medium- and coarse-grained soils, and the *core-cutter method*, which is applied to fine-grained soils and chalk soils free from stones. Overseas, compact and self-contained nuclear meters[6] employing gamma rays and neutrons are used to measure the density and moisture contents of compacted soils, particularly in hot and dusty locations and in remote areas. Before use, the meters must be calibrated on standard blocks; typically, the density standard blocks are cut from rocks selected for their uniformity, whilst the moisture standard blocks are made from sand–polystyrene blends.

*Method specifications*    Since 1969 the method or 'recipe' type of specification has become widely used in Britain for soil compaction purposes. With this approach the moisture content used for compaction purposes is close to that naturally obtained in the field, whilst the required compactive effort is specified for each soil. Table 5.1 summarizes British recommendations in this respect; detailed advice regarding compaction methods and layer thicknesses for various materials are readily available in the literature[8].

Soils unsuitable for stabilization by compaction include material from swamps, marshes and bogs, and clays with liquid limits >90 and/or plasticity indices >65. With some 'suitable' soils, e.g. silts and silty clays, the compaction specified can result in over-stress—particularly if the moisture content at the time of compaction is above the specified limits—which is manifested by sponginess or heaving due to high pore-water pressures produced by roller or construction traffic. Whilst these conditions will dissipate themselves with time, e.g. through a reduction in moisture content by drying, with the more cohesive soils it may be necessary to consider other measures, such as: (a) reducing the number of passes, (b) using lighter compaction equipment, (c) temporarily ceasing compaction, (d) changing the method of excavating and hauling the material, and the size of plant used, and (e) treating the material as being unsuitable.

**Compaction equipment**
Selecting the proper compaction equipment and method is vital to the production of the long-term economy expected and desired from a highway. Essentially, there are four ways in which soil may be compacted by mechanical means. These methods, and some examples of equipment used for each, are as follows.

**Table 5.1** Typical compaction characteristics for natural soils, rocks and artificial materials used in earthworks construction[7]

| Material | Major divisions | Subgroups | Suitable type of compaction plant | Minimum number of passes for satisfactory compaction | Maximum thickness of compacted layer (mm) | Remarks |
|---|---|---|---|---|---|---|
| Rock-like materials | Natural rocks | All rock fill (except chalk) | Heavy vibratory roller not less than 180 kg per 100 mm of roll Grid roller not less than 800 kg per 100 mm of roll Self-propelled tamping rollers | 4–12 | 500–1500* | If well graded or easily broken down, then this can be classified as a coarse-grained soil for the purpose of compaction. The maximum diameter of the rock fragments should not exceed two-thirds of the layer thickness |
| | | Chalk | See remarks | 3 | 500 | This material can be very sensitive to weight and operation of compacting and spreading plant. Less compactive effort is needed than with other rocks |
| Artificial | Waste material | Burnt and unburnt colliery shale | Vibratory roller Smooth-wheeled roller Self-propelled tamping roller | 4–12* | 300 | — |
| | | Pulverized fuel ash | Vibratory roller Self-propelled tamping roller Smooth-wheeled roller Pneumatic-tyred roller | | | Includes lagoon and furnace bottom ash |
| | | Broken concrete, bricks, steelworks slag, etc. | Heavy vibratory roller Self-propelled tamping roller Smooth-wheeled roller | | | Non-processed sulphide brick slag should be used with caution |

**Table 5.1** (cont.)

| Material | Major divisions | Subgroups | Suitable type of compaction plant | Minimum number of passes for satisfactory compaction | Maximum thickness of compacted layer (mm) | Remarks |
|---|---|---|---|---|---|---|
| Coarse soils | Gravels and gravelly soils | Well-graded gravel and gravel–sand mixtures; little or no fines | Grid roller over 540 kg per 100 mm of roll | 3–12[*] | 75–275[*] | — |
| | | Well-graded gravel–sand mixtures with excellent clay binder | Pneumatic-tyred roller over 2000 kg per wheel | | | |
| | | Uniform gravel; little or no fines | Vibratory plate compactor over 1100 kg/m² of baseplate | | | |
| | | Poorly-graded gravel and gravel–sand mixtures; little or no fines | Smooth-wheeled roller | | | |
| | | Gravel with excess fines, silty gravel, clayey gravel, poorly-graded gravel–sand–clay mixtures | Vibratory roller Vibro-rammer Self-propelled tamping roller | | | |
| | Sands and sandy soils | Well-graded sands and gravelly sands; little or no fines | As above | As above | As above | — |
| | | Well-graded sands with excellent clay binder | | | | |
| | Uniform sands and gravels | Uniform gravels; little or no fines | Smooth-wheeled roller below 500 kg per 100 mm of roll | 3–16[*] | 75–300 | — |
| | | Uniform sands; little or no fines | Grid roller below 540 kg per 100 mm of roll | | | |
| | | Poorly-graded sands; little or no fines | Pneumatic-tyred roller below 1500 kg per wheel | | | |
| | | Sands with fines, silty sands, clayey sands, poorly-graded sand–clay mixtures | Vibratory roller Vibrating plate compactor Vibro-tamper | | | |

**Table 5.1** (cont.)

| Material | Major divisions | Subgroups | Suitable type of compaction plant | Minimum number of passes for satisfactory compaction | Maximum thickness of compacted layer (mm) | Remarks |
|---|---|---|---|---|---|---|
| Fine soils | Soils having low plasticity | Silts (inorganic) and very fine sands, rock flow silty or clayey fine sands with slight plasticity<br>Clayey silts (inorganic)<br>Organic silts of low plasticity | Tamping (sheepsfoot) roller<br>Smooth-wheeled roller<br>Pneumatic-tyred roller<br>Vibratory roller over 70 kg per 100 mm of roll<br>Vibratory plate compactor over 1400 kg/m² of baseplate<br>Vibro-tamper<br>Power rammer | 4–8* | 100–450* | If moisture content is low it may be preferable to use a vibratory roller.<br>Tamping (sheepsfoot) rollers are best suited to soils at a moisture content below their plastic limit |
| | Soils having medium plasticity | Silty and sandy clays (inorganic) of medium plasticity<br>Clays (inorganic) of medium plasticity<br>Organic clays of medium plasticity | As above | As above | As above | — |
| | Soils having high plasticity | Micaceous or diatomaceous fine sandy and silty soils, plastic silts<br>Clay (inorganic) of high plasticity, 'fat' clays<br>Organic clays of high plasticity | As above | As above | As above | Organic clays are generally unsuitable for earthworks<br>Should only be used when circumstances are favourable<br>Should not be used for earthworks |

*Notes:* The information in this table should be taken only as a general guide; when the material performance cannot be predicted, it may be established by earthworks trials. This table is applicable only to fill placed and compacted in layers; it is not applicable to deep compaction of materials in situ. Compaction of mixed soils should be based on that subgroup requiring most compactive effort

* Depending upon type of plant

(1)   Use heavy weights to press the particles together. Smooth-wheeled rollers are examples of compaction equipment which operate on this principle.

(2)   Knead the soil while at the same time applying pressure. This type of compaction is applied by the tamping or sheepsfoot roller. The pneumatic-tyred roller has a compaction action which is a cross between that obtained with a smooth-wheeled roller and a sheepsfoot roller.

(3)   Vibrate the soil so that the particles are shaken together into a compact mass. The vibratory compactors utilize this procedure.

(4)   Pound the soil so that the particles are forced to move closer together. This is perhaps the oldest type of compaction; hand-tamping as a means of obtaining high dry densities is literally ages old. Mechanical tampers have now been devised which make this method of compaction a most practical one in particular instances.

*Smooth-wheeled rollers*   Smooth steel-wheeled rollers have long played an important part in road construction and are acknowledged to be the oldest form of mechanical compaction. The early steam roller consisted of three steel wheels on a body which was self-propelled by a steam engine; the wheels were arranged so that the central track of the front wheel was not overlapped by the two rear wheels. By contrast, modern smooth-wheeled rollers either are self-propelled by petrol or diesel engines and have two or three rolls in line behind each other (so that each roll follows in the track of the front one), or operate as a single towed roller.

Smooth-wheeled rollers range in size from 1.7 to 17.0 t deadweight. Their mass can be increased by adding damp sand or water ballast to the hollow steel drum rolls, or by placing ballast weights on the frame of the roller. The optimum operating speeds of these rollers are generally in the range 2.5–5.0 km/h.

While satisfactory results can be obtained with smooth-wheeled rollers on most soils, experience has shown that they are most suitable for compacting gravels, sand and other materials where a crushing action is needed. When used on moist, plastic soils, smooth-wheeled rollers can have difficulty in maintaining traction, and they frequently create a crust on the surface which can prevent the proper compaction of the soil material beneath; this 'bridging' effect is most noticeable with heavy, plastic soils.

The principal characteristics of a smooth-wheeled roller which affect its compacting performance are the mass per unit width under the compaction rolls, and the width and diameter of the rolls themselves. The mass per unit width and the roll diameter control the pressure near the surface of the soil, while the gross mass of the rolls affects the rate with which this pressure decreases with depth. Thus, for the relatively shallow compaction layers used in much highway construction, it is most important that the mass per unit width of roll be specified.

*Grid rollers*   This type of compaction equipment, which is generally towed at speeds in the range 5 to 24 km/h, typically consists of a box-girder framework within which two grid rolls are mounted end-to-end. The surface of each roll is composed of a heavy, square-patterned, steel mesh.

The core of each roll is a conical container with its minimum diameter to the outside of the roller; these cores can hold sand or water ballast, and they also cause material which passes through the grid to be ejected outside the path of the roller. The chassis of the grid roller is constructed so that specially-designed concrete ballast weights can be carried on it; typical plant varies from 5.5 t net to 15.0 t when ballasted.

When used on fine-grained soils, the grid roller action is partly that of compaction through direct contact pressure, and partly that of compaction by a kneading action. When used on coarser materials, e.g. marls or soft sandstones, the roller has a crushing action which can reduce relatively large boulders (often obtained during ripping) to macadam-size fragments. These rollers are particularly useful when it is desired to break and force the larger stones below the subgrade surface, leaving the top few centimetres of the layer to be graded and compacted (by other equipment) to a uniform and smooth surface[9].

*Tamping* (*sheepsfoot*) *rollers*   The main virtue of this type of equipment is that a high contact pressure per unit area can be applied to the soil without having to use an excessive mass of roller, e.g. as with a smooth-wheeled roller, to obtain the same contact pressure. A roll on this type of roller consists of a cylindrical steel drum with steel projections or 'feet' extending in a radial direction outward from the surface of the cylinder; the drums are manufactured in diameters ranging from 1.0–1.8 m and of mass, when loaded, ranging from 2.7–27.0 t. The tamping area of each projecting 'foot' is at least 0.01 m², and it can be circular, square or rectangular in shape; the feet can also be of different lengths and tapers. The rollers can be self-propelled, but more commonly they are towed by track or pneumatic-tyred tractors—with up to three rollers being towed in tandem—at speeds of 4–10 km/h.

It is said that the concept for this type of roller came to a contractor as he saw the compaction caused by a flock of sheep crossing an earth road in California—which is why the most common example of this compaction equipment is known as the sheepsfoot roller.

As opposed to other rollers, the tamping roller compacts from the bottom of the lift up. It operates in the following manner. During the first pass over a lift of loose soil, the feet penetrate to near the base of the layer so that the bottom material is well compacted. As additional passes are made, the feet penetrate to lesser depths as the density, and thus the bearing capacity, of the soil is increased. Eventually, the soil becomes so well compacted that the feet of the roller will only penetrate into the ground to a depth of a few centimetres, in which case the roller is said to have 'walked-out' of the layer.

The tamping roller is designed to break up the surface 'crust' on a soil by compacting small areas at high load concentrations. The principal characteristics affecting its performance are the contact pressure and the coverage of ground obtained per pass. The contact pressure applied by each foot is given by the roller weight divided by the total area of one row of tamping feet. This pressure should be as large as possible, but should not exceed the bearing capacity of the soil being compacted. If this occurs, the roller will sink into the ground until enough adjacent feet, or the drum itself, come into contact with the ground and the contact pressure is that which the soil's bearing capacity can sustain.

Since compaction is obtained by the feet penetrating and applying a high vertical pressure while at the same time providing lateral pressure, the tamping roller is most efficient in compacting fine-grained soils. Unfortunately, however, it produces a larger amount of air voids in a soil than do smooth-wheeled or pneumatic-tyred rollers; this can be very detrimental in the case of subgrades in which a large air content increases their liability to absorb moisture. A further factor which limits the usage of this type of roller in Britain is the fact that, when high dry densities are required, the optimum moisture contents required by these rollers are often less than those naturally found in fine-grained soils in the field.

*Pneumatic-tyred rollers*   For many years, it was common practice for earthworks to be compacted by directing the regular construction haul units to travel over freshly placed material until it was quite dense. This led eventually to the development of special rubber-tyred rollers to compact most types of soil.

Pneumatic rollers can be divided into three types or classes: medium, heavy and super-heavy weight. The medium class includes both tow-type and self-propelled units up to about 12 t rolling capacity. The heavy class covers the range beyond this up to 50 t rollers, while the super-weights—which are mostly used for compacting airport runways and taxiways, and for proof-rolling of highway subgrades—include rollers up to 200 t capacity. With all types of pneumatic roller, ballast boxes are carried over or between the axles; these are filled with suitable materials to provide the necessary compaction load. Optimum compaction speeds range from 1.6 to 24.0 km/h.

The pneumatic wheels are set on one or two axles, depending upon the type being used. On two-axle rollers, one axle generally has one less wheel than the other, and the wide-faced tyres are arranged so that full ground coverage is achieved by always having an overlap between the front and the rear wheels. Individual or pairs of wheels are capable of a certain amount of vertical movement, so that the roller can negotiate uneven ground whilst maintaining a steady pressure on the soil. Many pneumatic rollers are fitted with wobbly wheels which provide an additional type of kneading action to the soil.

The characteristics of a pneumatic-tyred roller which most affect its performance are the tyre-inflation pressures and the load carried by each wheel. Controlled compaction studies have shown that there appears to be little point in employing tyre-inflation pressures much in excess of $275-345$ kN/m$^2$ with wheel loads of about 5 t when compacting clayey soils[10]. For the compaction of granular soils, there appears to be some advantage in employing the highest tyre-inflation pressure and the heaviest wheel load practicable, consistent of course with avoiding over-stressing of the soils.

*Vibratory compactors*   These consist of a vibrating unit of either the out-of-balance mass type or a pulsating hydraulic type mounted on a screed, plate or roller in such a way that the net effect is an up-and-down vibratory movement of the compactor at a frequency in the range of the natural frequency of the material being compacted.

All types of vibratory compactors achieve densification by producing vibrations in the material being compacted; these vibrations momentarily reduce the internal friction between particles, following which the impact of the compaction machine—which is all the greater because of the high accelerations of the vibrator unit—forces the particles closer together.

First developed in Britain in 1946, there are now many designs of *vibrating roller* on the market. Whilst these employ various types of vibration units, they can be divided into two main groups[11]:

(1) those which provide unrestrained particle movement in all directions, and which usually employ a rotating out-of-balance mass to create vibration,
(2) those in which all horizontal components of vibration are cancelled out—often through the use of counter-rotating masses which are phased to give the desired effect—so that particle motion occurs only in a vertical direction.

With the type (1) rollers, the particles can more easily reorient themselves, the air voids are more easily reduced, and a homogeneous mass which can extend to a considerable depth is obtained. One important advantage of this roller is its ability to cause material to compact thoroughly about pipes, thus avoiding the danger of fracture at a later date.

With the type (2) rollers, the particles most affected are always under the roll. As a result, the compacted surface tends to be at a higher state of densification than is achieved with the first system; however, this is at the expense of depth, i.e. the density—depth curve tends to fall away more quickly.

Vibrating rollers range in size from 0.5 to 17.0 t, and can be towed, self-propelled or pedestrian-guided. Repeated passes at high speed are generally not as effective as fewer passes at lower speed for a given depth of lift, and so the towed and self-propelled machines are generally operated at speeds of 4–5 km/h. As would be expected, these rollers are most effectively used with granular soils. However, they can also be effective with fine-grained soils. Thus Fig. 5.1 illustrates the results of some pressure measurements taken beneath a 2.5 t vibrating roller, with the front roll not vibrating, as well as vibrating, while a silty, clayey soil was being compacted. With the front roll not vibrating the results were those expected from a basic smooth-wheeled roller, whereas when the front roll was vibrating the maximum pressure produced under the roll was doubled.

*Vibrating plate compactors* vary in mass from 100 kg to 2 t. They are essentially machines with a baseplate (of area 0.16–1.60 m$^2$) to which is attached a source of vibration consisting of one or two eccentrically-loaded shafts. Mainly manually operated, they are particularly suitable for compacting small and awkwardly-shaped areas whilst travelling at speeds of less than 1 km/h.

*Vibro-tampers* are machines in which an engine-driven reciprocating

## 324 *Soil stabilization*

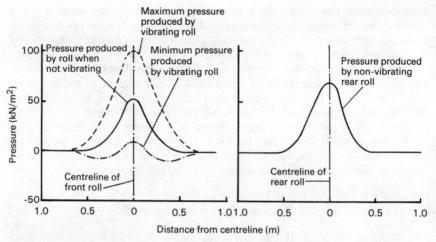

**Fig. 5.1** Pressures produced at a depth of 200 mm in a silty clayey soil by a 2.5-tonne vibrating roller

mechanism acts on a spring system through which oscillations are set up in a compacting baseplate. Also manually guided, these compactors are most appropriately used in confined spaces.

*Impact compaction* Obviously, the methods of compaction which have been presented so far all involve fairly substantial pieces of equipment which require large manoeuvring space for satisfactory results to be obtained. When trenches have to be back-filled or soil compacted near abutments, walls or columns, it will very often not be possible to use large compactors, and so recourse is made to smaller, portable impact compactors such as the internal-combustion-type *power rammer*. Generally of about 100 kg mass, the power rammer is actuated by an explosion in an internal-combustion engine—each explosion being manually controlled by the operator—which causes the machine to be driven upward in the first instance. The subsequent downward impact of the baseplate constitutes one 'pass' of the compactor. Also known as 'frog' rammers, these compactors are quite effective in compacting relatively small areas.

Another type of impact compactor is the *dropping-weight compactor*. As its name implies, this consists of a weight that is set between guides and dropped from a given height.

An *impact roller* (otherwise known as the 'square wheel') has been developed, and is reported[12, 13] to be particularly effective in compacting fine sands at their natural low moisture contents. The roll of this towed roller—it consists of a steel casing filled with concrete and has a mass of 10 000 kg—is a square 1.5 m × 1.5 m. The compactive effort of the roller is derived from the energy of the mass falling from the corners to the faces, as it is towed at 8–14 km/h by a wheeled tractor; this produces compaction forces many times greater than those obtained from its static mass. The impact roller is not intended for use as a surfacing compactor because it does not densify the upper 100 mm or so due to the shearing of surface layers which causes lateral movement of the soil. However, the impact roller is very suited to the densification of deep layers, e.g. 300–500 mm layers for cohesive/granular material and up to 3 m for certain fine sands.

## Stabilization by consolidation

As discussed previously (see Chapter 1), highway engineers normally seek to locate new roadways on well-drained, stable ground. However, due to circumstances beyond their control—particularly in highly-developed countries—many constraints can now restrict the freedom of location, so that highway engineers are often faced with the need to construct significant lengths of road embankment on compressible ground. Such difficult subsoil conditions are frequently encountered near major rivers or estuaries, where deposits of soft fine-grained or organic soils exist to considerable depths.

An engineering process commonly used to stabilize these soft foundations, prior to constructing the formal pavement, is to consolidate them by *preloading*. Properly carried out, this process will result in a large increase in the bearing capacity of the underlying soil, and very significant decreases in the amount of subsequent settlement that might otherwise be expected under the completed pavement. Methods of preloading used in practice involve embankment construction: (a) by full or stage construction and (b) by accelerated construction.

Other such stabilization methods involve consolidation by lowering the water-table (see p. 314), and consolidation by atmospheric pressure.

**Preloading by full or stage construction**
Preloading by direct construction is by far the most common way of prestressing a soft soil. It is also a very effective way of improving the load-carrying properties of land areas covered by substantial depths of uncompacted fill materials, e.g. domestic, industrial and mining wastes, and opencast mining backfill[14].

The purpose behind preloading is not to displace the underlying soft material but rather to consolidate it. For example, peat may have an in-place dry density between 80 and 160 kg/m³ and a moisture content of over 1000 per cent by mass of dry peat; its shear strength is normally less than 27.5 kN/m². However, if an embankment is properly constructed on top of the peat, it will compress considerably, its moisture content will be decreased, and its dry density and shear strength increased—and the whole construction will be quite stable.

The consolidation of a soft foundation soil beneath an embankment has four components.

(1) *Settlement arising from the elastic compression of the subsoil* By elasticity is meant the property of a material which allows it to be compressed under a load, and then to rebound to its original shape when the load has been removed. No soil can be said to be truly elastic, although some possess elasticity to the extent that they can cause substantial fatigue damage to an overlying pavement. These soils are primarily silts and clays

having sizeable quantities of flat, flakey particles such as mica, certain diatomaceous earths, and those containing large quantities of organic colloids. Peat can be included in this last category, the degree of elasticity being particularly associated with the more fibrous and less hummified varieties of peat.

(2) *Settlement arising from the primary consolidation of the subsoil*   In this instance, the application of the embankment load results in a reduction in the volume of the soil voids as the soil attempts to consolidate. When the soil is saturated, the particles pressing about the saturated pores cause the load to be transferred to the incompressible water for a length of time which will depend upon the type and compaction state of the subsoil. For example, if the subsoil is a granular one having a high coefficient of permeability, the pore water will be expelled very quickly and settlement will take place rapidly; for this reason, the consolidation of sands is rarely a problem as whatever deformation is going to take place occurs as the load is being applied. Conversely, if the subsoil is a saturated fine-grained material, the water will not be able to escape quickly due to this soil's relative impermeability; however, the increased pore-water pressure resulting from the sustained loading will ensure that the water will continue to seek to escape until the excess pressure is dissipated and the soil's structure gradually takes up the load.

In the case of a clay subsoil, settlement may take place over a long period of time, with the rate being relatively rapid at the beginning of primary consolidation but decreasing with time. In the case of peat, the time required for primary consolidation can be even longer; i.e. whereas with a clayey soil the settlement time can be regarded as varying with the square of the length of the drainage path, with the coefficient of permeability being kept constant, this is not so with peat. Since there is a much greater change in the voids content of peat, its permeability decreases significantly with time, and this, coupled with the continuing decrease in pore-water pressure, means that the consolidation of peat can take place over a period of years—depending, of course, upon the depth and type of peat being stressed.

(3) *Settlement arising from secondary consolidation*   Studies of long-term settlement behaviour have shown that, *after* the excess pore-water pressures were largely dissipated, settlement still continued, but at a rate which produced a linear relation between settlement and the logarithm of time. In practice, secondary consolidation is assumed to commence when 90 per cent of primary consolidation (as predicted by Terzaghi's theory of consolidation) is complete.

(4) *Settlement arising from plastic deformation*   Regions in the subsoil approaching a state of failure cause some further consolidation of a soft foundation soil.

An obvious problem associated with consolidating a soft soil is the possibility of an *instability* developing if the subsoil has insufficient shear strength to carry the stresses set up during construction of the embankment. Whilst the layers in the subsoil will gain strength with the progress of consolidation, a serious stability failure will occur if the rate of increase in strength is less than the shearing stresses generated by the loading. Such instability is usually manifested by a lateral displacement of the subsoil, a bulging upward of the adjacent soil, and excessive settlement of the embankment.

*Construction methods* One simple way of reducing the possibility of subsoil failure during construction of an embankment is to use *lightweight fill material*. Pulverized fuel ash has been used very effectively for this purpose in Britain; however, whilst this can reduce the stresses by over 50 per cent as compared with normal embankment material, it can be quite expensive, especially if the fly ash has to be hauled a long way to the construction site. Sawdust has also been used as a lightweight embankment material.

With or without special lightweight fill, *flatter side slopes* and the use of *berms* will help to prevent displacement of the subsoil. However, these solutions may not always be possible and are likely to involve extra land acquisition and more expenditure on the project.

Perhaps the most widely used approach to avoiding subsoil instability is to utilize *stage construction* of the embankment. This is a long-term process whereby the embankment is first built to a height which is limited by the shearing strength of the foundation material; further construction is then delayed until measurements of pore-water pressure have shown that the excess stress induced in the subsoil has dissipated. When the stress has been reduced to a safe value, an additional height of fill is placed and the process repeated until the embankment is finally completed.

A procedure has been developed by the Transport and Road Research Laboratory[15, 16] which is most helpful in monitoring the safe stage construction of an embankment. It involves the use of control charts that are prepared in advance for the embankment on the basis of laboratory and field tests. These charts enable the factor of safety to be read off at any given time in the first, relatively uncontrolled, stage of construction, so that if it appears that the factor of safety is falling to an unacceptable value, construction is immediately stopped. Measurements of pore-water pressure in the subsoil, as determined during construction and the first-stage pause, are then used to prepare revised control charts; these revised charts are, in turn, used to control the rate of construction of subsequent stages.

Note that at the embankment site shown in Fig. 5.2 construction was halted at a height of 8.4 m as the factor of safety obtained from the control charts was 1.25. Corresponding to this stage, a significant increase in the rate of lateral movement of the subsoil occurred, and this behaviour substantiated the stability analysis which indicated that the foundation was approaching a state of limited equilibrium.

Figure 5.2 also shows a comparison of the recorded settlement with predicted settlement using consolidation parameters determined from small-scale laboratory tests and from field tests. These relationships illustrate the very powerful advantage of using field data to predict the settlement behaviour of embankments.

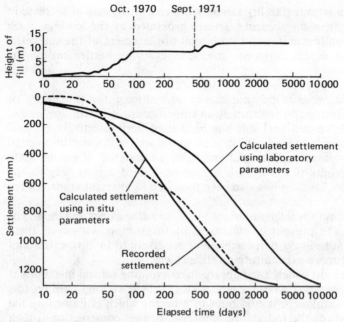

**Fig. 5.2**    Settlement history of the Over Causeway Bypass embankment[17]

### Preloading by accelerated construction

In many instances, the settlement analysis will suggest that the time required for consolidation to be completed is longer than the construction period, so that movements of the completed road structure could well occur. If it is anticipated that these movements will occur in a relatively uniform way over the length of the highway, its riding quality will be unaffected and preventative measures will not be necessary. However, if significant differential settlements (e.g. > 25 mm over a 10 m length) are anticipated after construction of the highway pavement, it may be considered necessary to accelerate the settlement by means of: (a) surcharge, (b) vertical drains, (c) horizontal drains, or (d) dynamic methods of consolidation.

*Surcharge method*    Probably the most common (and cheapest) way of accelerating the rate of settlement of an embankment is to add a sufficient quantity of extra fill to attain (during the construction period) the ultimate settlement predicted for the required final height of embankment and highway pavement. Settlement will occur more rapidly under the combined design and surcharge load than under the design load only; then, after the desired settlement has been achieved, the surcharge material is removed, and the pavement constructed in the normal way.

A major danger associated with the use of a surcharged embankment is that of subsoil instability. Care also needs to be taken with certain subsoils to ensure that they are not over-consolidated by the surcharge load, as there is a danger that swelling could subsequently occur which could affect the long-term riding quality of the pavement surface.

*Vertical-drain method* Considerable success is often claimed for the technique whereby the consolidation process is accelerated by means of vertical sand or wick drains installed through the soft subsoil. The theory is that by providing shorter drainage paths, the time taken for the pore water to escape is speeded up, and the settlement time is considerably reduced.

The classic *sand-drain method* is similar to the surcharge method, except that vertical sand drains are used to hasten the consolidation of the soft subsoil beneath the embankment. These drains are constructed by boring vertical holes through the first embankment layer and down through the subsoil until firm soil is reached below.these holes, which are typically 500–750 mm in diameter and 9–18 m deep, are filled with a clean, uniform, coarse sand; the tops of the vertical drains and the initial construction layer are then covered with a sand blanket of the same coarse-grained material to a depth of 1.0–1.5 m. The normal embankment is constructed on top of this horizontal sand blanket, and a surcharge added as necessary.The sand drains are normally spaced alternately about 3–6 m apart.

A range of techniques is available for forming the boreholes for sand drains. These include shell and auger drilling, powered auger drilling, water-jetting using a mandrel, flight-augering, washboring and driven mandrels. The mandrel is simply a hollow tube with a closed flap on the bottom; this is most usually forced into the soil to the required depth by means of a pile-driver. The tube is then filled with the coarse sand and, as it is withdrawn, the bottom flap opens and the sand flows out and fills the hole. Less disturbance to the drainage properties of the subsoil is caused by the jetted-mandrel method. This is similar to the driven-mandrel method, except that jets of water under high pressure are used to prepare the way for the tube as it is inserted into the soil. The sand is then allowed to flow through the tube and into the hole as the mandrel is withdrawn.

Notwithstanding the apparent effectiveness of the sand-drain method, it is now used relatively infrequently in highway construction—mainly because it is fairly expensive. A measure of the effect of sand drains upon the rate of consolidation of an alluvium soil can be gained from Fig. 5.3.

Sand drains have occasionally been used in attempts to improve the rate of consolidation of peat, but not with very much success, i.e. primary consolidation of peat occurs fairly quickly because of its relatively high permeability, whilst secondary consolidation—which is most usually associated with reorientation of the soil particles—is helped but little by the additional drainage.

The *cardboard wick drain* has a cross-section of 100 mm by 3 mm with ten drainage channels preformed internally. For design purposes, the drain is considered equivalent to a sand column of 50 mm diameter. During installation, the drain is enclosed within a mandrel which is driven into the subsoil; on extraction of the mandrel, the wick remains. Advantages of this drain over conventional sand drains include[19] low cost, better maintenance of the vertical continuity of the drains, and a greater degree of acceleration of consolidation due to the very close spacing of the drains. The limitations of the installation equipment are such that the maximum depth to which these drains can be installed is about 20 m.

The *sand-wick drain* is composed of a preformed sand-filled plastic

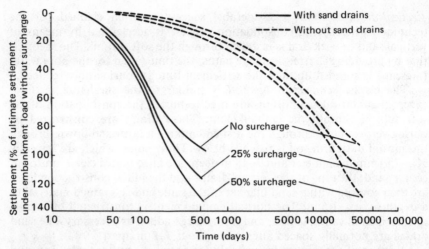

**Fig. 5.3** Comparison of effects of various accelerated consolidation measures upon the settlement of an embankment over a hypothetical alluvium soil[18]

*Notes*
(1)  Depth of compressible soil = 10 m with one-way drainage.
(2)  Coefficient of vertical consolidation = 1 $m^2$ per year.
(3)  Coefficient of horizontal consolidation = 1 $m^2$ per year.
(4)  Spacing of the water-jetted sand drains (of diameter 225 mm) without surcharge = 1.48 m to a square pattern grid.
(5)  Embankment height = 5 m, with 2 : 1 side slopes.
(6)  Loading applied at a uniform rate over a period of 60 days without surcharge.
(7)  Surcharge = 25 or 50 per cent of the embankment height.

sleeve, about 65 mm in diameter, that is made of water-permeable material. The advantages claimed for this system are that only relatively small diameter boreholes are required and, since the sand is contained within a sleeve, the continuity of the drain is maintained, even though large lateral displacements may occur within the soft subsoil.

*Horizontal drains*  Deep land drains have also been used to accelerate the consolidation process. The technique involves the use of a machine that was originally developed for use in groundwater lowering operations. This machine is able to excavate a 250 mm wide trench to a depth of 6 m, and back-fill it with drainage material in a continuous operation (see also Chapter 2).

*Dynamic methods of consolidation*  The relatively new process of dynamic consolidation—which was developed in France in the late 1960s—is considered to be at its most useful in accelerating the consolidation of fairly large areas where the ground consists of granular materials, partially-saturated clay fills, or older deposits of refuse and other debris. The process consists essentially of the controlled tamping of the area to be treated on a predetermined pattern[19] with a large mass (8–40 t) dropping in free fall from heights of 6–30 m, thereby subjecting the soil to impacts in the range 48–1200 t-m. In soft soil conditions, however, the ground surface must first be covered with a 0.5–1.0 m layer of hardcore or granular material before the dynamic loading is initiated (using large cranes to lift the loads); this improves the accessibility to the impact points, and helps the subsequent surface drainage process—as well as stopping clay lumps from being ejected in all directions during the tamping process. Cycles of the tamping process are carried out over the area of poor soil in a systematic fashion, and with delays to allow for dissipation of the pore-water pressures. This is continued until a stage is reached where in situ tests indicate that the consolidated ground is able to support the weight of the structure to be placed upon it, without danger of instability or excessive differential settlement.

This method of accelerated consolidation is reported to be applicable to soft soil thicknesses of up to 30 m or so. It can be applied to a poor subsoil or to an embankment placed on top of the soft ground. It is claimed that the large, local deformations induced in the underlying soil by the dropping mass result in locked-in stresses equivalent to a surcharge effect. Furthermore, as a result of the shock waves and large dynamic stresses produced, partial liquifaction of the soil occurs; preferential drainage paths are then created because of cracks forming in the soil as a consequence of the over-stressed conditions produced.

**Atmospheric consolidation**
A most interesting method of stabilizing a soil by consolidation has been developed by the Royal Swedish Geotechnical Institute; it uses atmospheric pressure as a temporary surcharge and vertical sand drains to accelerate consolidation[20]. In the field the soil area which is being stabilized is covered with a sand filter 400–500 mm thick, and on top of this a tight, impermeable membrane, i.e. sheet plastic or a layer of clay or a bituminous covering, is placed. Outside the width of the filter the covering membrane is connected tightly to the underlying soft clay, which is free from cracks and root channels and is beneath the normally dry soil at the surface of the ground. A suction pipe is then carried through the membrane and into the filter, and a pump starts sucking air out of the filter and, gradually, out of the clay. In any horizontal plane the total normal pressure, i.e. atmospheric pressure plus the weight of the overlying soil, remains constant and therefore the grain pressure increases as the pore pressure decreases. Thus the pump sucks the water out of the clay, which is forced to consolidate accordingly.

## Stabilization by electrical and thermal methods

Frozen soils, irrespective of whether they are granular or cohesive, cannot be compacted satisfactorily. For example, Fig. 5.4 shows that the maximum dry densities produced by both the standard and modified Proctor tests are reduced significantly if compacted at temperatures below freezing; also, the optimum moisture content decreases, and may disappear, at below-freezing temperatures. The source of this behaviour is believed to be the viscosity of

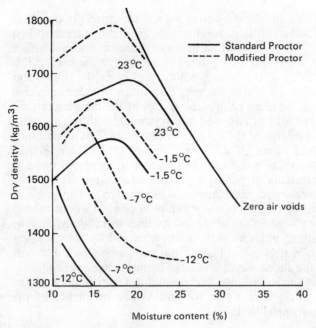

**Fig. 5.4**  Effects of temperature upon Proctor moisture–density relationships for a fine sand with some silt

the water, which determines the ease or difficulty with which the soil particles and aggregates can reorient during the compaction process. Furthermore, water cannot be added to borrow materials in freezing temperatures—which is why highway pavement and embankment construction generally ceases during winter in cold regions.

Nonetheless, a method of soil stabilization that has been used to a limited extent is that of *solidification by freezing*. This process relies upon the fact that freezing of the water in the pore spaces of a soil gives a very high strength to the material. Soil-freezing has been used very successfully for the temporary stabilization of the foundations of buildings, sinking of shafts, enlarging of a railway tunnel, etc., but other than on these isolated projects little work has been done in this area.

What would appear to be much more promising (but expensive) is *soil stabilization by heating*. Again this is a method which has been pioneered in non-highway-engineering schemes; however, research has shown it to be practical in those areas where there is an extreme shortage of natural aggregates[21]. The method relies upon the fact that when a clay soil is heated its mass is reduced, this mass loss being due to the removal of adsorbed and interlayer moisture held by the clay minerals and, above certain temperatures, to changes in the actual structure of the clay minerals. This phenomenon, which has been observed by dehydration curves, differential thermal analysis, and X-ray diffraction studies, has been used to obtain road aggregates in Guyana, the Sudan and Australia, and as a means of stabilizing foundation soils in Rumania and the USSR.

These changes in structure brought about by heating clay soils result in hard, durable road materials which, although of relatively low quality when compared with the normal types of stone used in road construction, can be used to advantage where high-quality materials are not available. Heating causes the plasticity index to decrease, while the attraction for water is considerably reduced. Permeability generally increases due to shrinkage of the clays by desiccation and the formation of cracks and fissures. Compressibility, both soaked and unsoaked, is reduced due to the decrease in water sensitivity.

## Soil–aggregate stabilization

Stabilization by altering the gradation of a soil constitutes soil–aggregate stabilization. A soil–aggregate stabilized mass is analogous to Portland cement concrete in that the coarse aggregate content plays a role similar to that of the aggregate in concrete while the fines act as a mortar; the general aim therefore in changing the gradation is to obtain the proper proportions of particle-size fractions that will give a dense, homogeneous mass. The main use of this form of stabilization is for subbase construction for high-quality roads and in roadbases and surface courses for lower-quality roads.

### General requirements of surfaces and roadbases

It is necessary for the engineer to have a clear understanding of the functions of the various layers in a stabilized soil roadway in order to be able to decide which soil–aggregate materials may or may not be included in each layer. Apart from the common requirement of sufficient stability to meet the loads placed upon them, each layer has different material needs. These can be illustrated by discussing the requirements of the two most important elements, the roadbase and surface course, of a road pavement in which stabilized soil materials are to be used.

Granular stabilized soil surface courses should only be used in rural areas where traffic is quite light. The material requirements for these layers, enunciated some fifty years ago [22], are still valid:

(1) stability to support the weight of traffic,
(2) resistance to abrasive action of traffic,
(3) ability to shed a large proportion of the rain which falls on the surface, since a large amount of water penetrating the surface might cause loss of stability in the surface course or softening of the subgrade,
(4) capillary properties to replace the moisture lost by surface evaporation and thus maintain the desirable damp conditions in which the soil–aggregate particles are firmly bound together.

From the point of view of stability and resistance to abrasion, the materials used in a surface course must consist of hard, tough, durable fragments of stone or gravel, and a filler of sand or other finely-divided mineral matter, together with sufficient binding material to permit the consolidation and formation of a tightly bonded layer. Experience has shown that it is undesirable to use aggregate larger than 25 mm size in a surface course as it is liable to be torn from the surface by a motor grader carrying out maintenance. Best aggregate interlock is obtained by using angular particles; for this reason, glacial or crushed gravels and sands are preferred to river materials. A certain amount of clay binder must also be present to help in preventing the smaller particles from being whipped away under the action of traffic, especially in dry weather.

From the point of view of stability, it is desirable that as little water as possible should penetrate the surface course. Rainwater must be shed from the surface very quickly; for this reason, A-type crowns are better with granular stabilized surfaces than are the more conventional parabolic ones. The clay content can also play an important role in preventing moisture infiltration, as during wet weather the clay particles will swell and plug the soil pores. In this case, however, care must be taken to ensure that the clay content is only just sufficient to perform this function, and that it will not swell and cause dislocation in the granular materials. In hot climates, the clay fraction will help to retain against evaporation the moisture content necessary for stability and, if there happens to be an underlying source of available moisture, it may be able to replenish evaporated moisture by capillary attraction.

The requirements of a roadbase are very different from those of a surface course; this is often the reason why roadbases containing 'unscientifically-converted' surface courses have failed. The primary requirement of a soil–aggregate roadbase is that it should be able to withstand the stresses imposed upon it. This it is able to do if it is composed of a dense mixture of coarse and fine soil materials which has high shear strength. Dense mixtures may be obtained when their particle-size distributions tend towards the theoretical distribution given by *Fuller's power-grading law*:

$$p = 100(d/D)^n$$

where $p$ = percentage by mass of the total mixture passing any given sieve size, $d$ = aperture size of that sieve (mm), $D$ = size of the largest particle in the mixture (mm), and $n$ = an exponent whose value is between 0.3 and 0.5.

The particle-size distribution limits adopted by most highway authorities in standard soil–aggregate specifications generally approximate the above distribution; a maximum particle size of 19 mm is also frequently used. A mixture having a continuous distribution of particle sizes starting at the 19 mm size, and represented by a gradation curve corresponding to an $n$-value of 0.45, will usually provide a high-quality roadbase. If $n$ is less than 0.3, the fines content will be excessive and the mixture may lack stability; if $n$ is greater than 0.5, the mixture will tend to be stony and porous, and will usually require additional fines to obtain good stability.

The clay content of a soil–aggregate stabilized roadbase must be very carefully controlled. Whereas, in a surface course, a non-porous layer is required in order to prevent water infiltration, the opposite is normally true in any roadbase, particularly one which is to be covered by, for example, an impermeable bituminous surfacing. The presence of a significant quantity of clay in the roadbase will attract water which, since it cannot escape by evaporation, will accumulate within the layer; this, in turn, will cause a softening of the roadbase and may eventually lead to the complete destruction of the pavement.

## Usage

Scientific investigation into the composition of good soil–aggregate roads was initiated in the USA as early as 1906 by C M Strachan of South Carolina who endeavoured to correlate the performances of sand–clay roads with their mechanical analyses. Interest in this work developed rapidly and since then a considerable amount of theoretical and practical research has been carried out into the factors influencing the desirable service qualities of soil–aggregate roads. Nevertheless, it must be said that at this time there is no theoretical basis underlying the prescription for the exact amount and nature of fine material used in soil–aggregate pavements; rather, most criteria are based on experience, and different materials may be considered satisfactory in different areas. As a general guide, however, it can be said that soil–aggregates to be used in *unsealed* pavements should have liquid limits no greater than about 35 and should have plasticity indices in the range 4–9; however, if the pavement is to have a *bituminous surfacing*, the liquid limit should not exceed 25 and the plasticity index should be not greater than 6.

Examples of gradations that have been found suitable overseas are available in the many publications of, for example, the American Association of State Highway and Transportation Officials (AASHTO) and the National Association of Australian State Road Authorities (NAASRA). (Reference 23 is a particularly useful guide to the factors underlying the design of soil–aggregate roads.) As a basic premise, however, advice regarding soil–aggregate gradations to be used in particular geographical locations should be sought in those locales in the first instance.

Soil–aggregate pavements are relatively rarely constructed in Britain, particularly those in which part of the stabilized material forms the surface course. However, experience in Britain has resulted in the acceptance of a gradation specification for the use of sands and gravels in the subbase construction of new major roads. This specification also requires that the material passing the 425 $\mu$m BS sieve should have a plasticity index of less than 6, and that it should be laid and compacted at a moisture content within the range 2 per cent below to 1 per cent above the optimum percentage determined in accordance with the vibrating hammer method of test [24].

## Blending soils and aggregates

The design of a mechanically-stable soil–aggregate mixture involves testing the individual materials, proportioning them to meet the selected criteria, and making up trial batches to ensure that the preferred proportions satisfy the selected specification and have the required stability qualities. In some localities, deposits of naturally occurring soils will be found which meet the soil–aggregate specifications. More often than not, however, two or more soils will have to be blended in proper proportions to produce mixtures meeting these requirements. Generally, this involves either adding coarse aggregate to the in situ soil, or adding fine material to in situ granular material that is not sufficiently cohesive, or proportioning mixtures of fine soil and aggregate for plant mixing, or adding non-cohesive material of the proper composition to a surface course which is to be rebuilt for use as a roadbase. As noted above, methods for determining the proportions to blend are still essentially by trial and error. They involve either estimating trial gradations or estimating the proportions which will give the desired plasticity index; in either case, this will be followed by preparing test mixtures and testing for gradation and plasticity. Some of the more commonly used guide-procedures for blending soils are as follows.

(1)   *Blending two materials by gradation*   The graphical procedure outlined in Chapter 3 is normally quite adequate for this purpose.
(2)   *Blending two materials by plasticity index*   The proportions to be blended to give the required plasticity index can be estimated from the following equations:

$$a = \frac{100S_B(P - P_B)}{S_B(P - P_B) - S_A(P - P_A)}$$

and   $b = 100 - a$

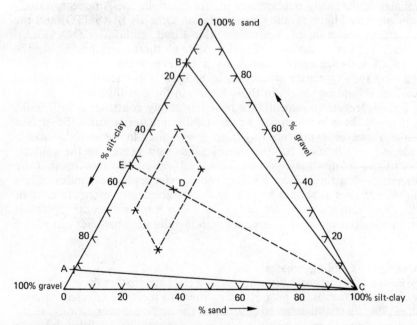

**Fig. 5.5**  Chart for combining three soil materials to meet a specified gradation

where $a$ = percentage of material A in final mixture, $b$ = percentage of material B in final mixture, $P$ = required plasticity index of final mixture, $P_A$ = plasticity index of material A, $P_B$ = plasticity index of material B, $S_A$ = percentage passing the 425 $\mu$m sieve in material A, and $S_B$ = percentage passing the 425 $\mu$m sieve in material B.

(3) *Blending three materials by gradation* This method will be described by an example. Figure 5.5 illustrates a triangular chart procedure which is perhaps the most commonly used method of blending three different soil materials. Let it be assumed that three materials which are to be blended are designated A, B and C, and that their gradings are as shown in Table 5.2(a); their component proportions of gravel, sand and silt-clay are shown in Table 5.2(b). The blending procedure is then as follows.

**Table 5.2** Example blending problem: (a) soil gradations, (b) component proportions of each soil, and (c) derived gradation of combined soil

| Sieve size (mm) | Percentage passing | | | |
|---|---|---|---|---|
| | Soil A | Soil B | Soil C | Specification |
| 28 | 95 | 100 | 100 | 100 |
| 20 | 70 | 100 | 100 | 85–100 |
| 10 | 21 | 100 | 100 | 65–100 |
| 5 | 11 | 100 | 100 | 55–85 |
| 2 | 7 | 85 | 100 | 40–70 |
| 0.425 | 2 | 55 | 100 | 25–45 |
| 0.063 | 0 | 0 | 100 | 10–25 |

(a)

| Soil | Size fraction (%) | | |
|---|---|---|---|
| | Gravel | Sand | Silt-clay |
| A | 93 | 7 | 0 |
| B | 15 | 85 | 0 |
| C | 0 | 0 | 100 |

(b)

| Sieve size (mm) | A (= 0.405) | B (= 0.405) | C (= 0.19) | Percentage passing | |
|---|---|---|---|---|---|
| | | | | Combination | Specification |
| 28 | 38.4 | 40.5 | 19 | 98 | 100 |
| 20 | 28.4 | 40.5 | 19 | 88 | 85–100 |
| 10 | 8.5 | 40.5 | 19 | 68 | 65–100 |
| 5 | 4.5 | 40.5 | 19 | 64 | 55–85 |
| 2 | 2.8 | 34.4 | 19 | 56 | 40–70 |
| 0.425 | 0.8 | 22.2 | 19 | 42 | 25–45 |
| 0.063 | – | – | 19 | 18 | 10–25 |

(c)

*Step 1* On the triangular chart plot the points A, B and C to represent the component fractions of each material. Join A to B to C. Note that the triangle ABC includes all possible soil combinations from the three different sources.

*Step 2* Plot the specification limits on the chart. The parallelogram obtained includes the combinations of the three materials which will meet the specifications. Select point D at about the centre of this area and join C to D and continue it onwards until it intersects at point E.

*Step 3* Using any convenient scale, determine the measured lengths of various lines as follows. The length of the line AB, $L_{AB} = 63.6$ mm, $L_{AE} = 31.8$ mm, $L_{EB} = 31.8$ mm, $L_{EC} = 70.3$ mm, $L_{ED} = 13.1$ mm, and $L_{DC} = 57.2$ mm.

*Step 4* Determine the following ratios:

$$\frac{L_{AE}}{L_{AB}} = 0.5 \qquad \frac{L_{EB}}{L_{AB}} = 0.5 \qquad \frac{L_{ED}}{L_{EC}} = 0.186$$

Note that in this example point E represents a possible combination of materials A and B in the ratio of 50 per cent to 50 per cent, while point D represents a possible combination of material C with the already combined materials A and B in the ratio of about 19 per cent C to about 81 per cent A and B.

*Step 5* Determine the proportions in the final mixture as follows:

material A $= 0.50 \times 81 = 40.5\%$

material B $= 0.50 \times 81 = 40.5\%$

material C $\qquad\qquad = 19\%$

*Step 6* Check that the gradation of the mixture meets the specification. Table 5.2(c) is thus derived.

*Step 7* Prepare a trial mix at this combination and determine its gradation. It may then be found necessary to adjust the proportions slightly.

## Chloride stabilization

The first modern usage of chloride for stabilizing roads precedes the year 1910 and probably occurred when seawater was used as a dust palliative on macadam roadways near the ocean. It was noticed that, by adding seawater, dust prevention was provided for much longer periods of time than when freshwater was used for this purpose, and this led to investigations which eventually resulted in the use of chlorides as additives to freshwater in inland areas.

### Types of chloride

The chlorides used to stabilize soils are calcium chloride and sodium chloride. Sodium chloride occurs naturally in the ocean (as rock-salt), in salt lakes, and in brines present in cavities in rock formations; of these, the most important source by far is rock-salt which may be 99 per cent pure

NaCl. Calcium chloride is obtained from these same natural sources, but, in addition, great quantities are obtained by refining the $CaCl_2$-rich waste liquors from the soda-ash industry. (Soda-ash, which utilizes salt, lime and ammonia as raw materials in its preparation, is a necessary ingredient in the manufacture of many chemicals, such as caustic soda and sodium carbonate.)

**Mechanism of stabilization**
Chlorides stabilize roads by a number of mechanisms, and under certain conditions one or more of these play more important parts than others. These may be outlined as follows.

(1)   Chlorides have excellent hygroscopic and deliquescent properties. The hygroscopicity of a material is a measure of its ability to absorb moisture from the air, while a deliquescent material is a hygroscopic one which will dissolve in moisture. Their relative deliquescence properties are indicated by the fact that calcium chloride will dissolve in moisture absorbed from the air at 25 °C when the relative humidity is only 29 per cent, whereas sodium chloride dissolves in absorbed moisture at the same temperature when the relative humidity is 76 per cent. Calcium chloride is much more hygroscopic than sodium chloride; at 25 °C and a relative humidity of 36 per cent, 1 kg of $CaCl_2$ will take up 1 kg of water, while at a relative humidity of 95 per cent, 1 kg is capable of absorbing 3.75 kg of water.

These two properties of the chlorides are perhaps their most important ones. They mean that in dry climates moisture which is evaporated from the roadway during the day can be replaced by moisture from the atmosphere during the night. Provided that the atmospheric humidity is sufficient, chloride-treated soil–aggregate roads will remain dust-free until the chlorides are leached out. Furthermore, the mechanical stability given to the soil or soil–aggregate material by cohesive water bonds can be maintained, while other advantageous features resulting from having chloride brine distributed throughout the mixture can also be preserved.
(2)   Chlorides have the ability to lower the vapour pressure of the water in which they are dissolved. Since the rate of evaporation of a liquid is dependent upon its vapour pressure, this means that moisture evaporation from chloride-treated soils takes place at a slower rate than if pure water were mixed with the soil.
(3)   Chlorides present in water–soil mixtures cause an increase in the surface tension of the water. This has two important effects. First of all, by increasing the surface tension of the pore water, the rate of evaporation is reduced. Some evaporation will take place, however, so the pore moisture content is reduced. This, in turn, causes the second effect, which is that the surface tension is further increased, and the water films may then cause the compacted soil particles to 'tighten' together, thereby increasing the density and stability of the material. Allied with this latter property is the possibility of the appearance of fine cracks in the roadway, but their effects are apparently negligible in comparison with the benefits gained.
(4)   The addition of either of the chlorides to a soil usually results in an

increase in the dry density obtainable with a given compactive effort. Chloride solutions are good soil lubricants, with the result that a given soil dry density can be obtained with less compactive effort than if water only is used. Calcium chloride is a better lubricant than sodium chloride.

(5)   Compaction in dry weather can be carried on for a longer period of time at a given moisture content, since evaporation takes place more slowly when chlorides are present.

(6)   In dry weather also, sodium chloride will crystallize in the surface of the roadway into a dense, hard crust which is capable of withstanding considerable abrasion from traffic.

(7)   Perhaps the most widely known property of the chlorides is their ability to lower the freezing temperature of water. The extent to which they protect a soil against being frozen is dependent upon the type of chloride used and the concentration present in solution in the pores. For instance, if the pore solution contains a 10 per cent $CaCl_2$ concentration, then freezing of the water may begin at a temperature of about $-4.5\,^{\circ}C$. As soon as the water freezes, however, the chloride content of the remainder increases, with the result that the temperature has to be lowered before more water will freeze. Complete freezing will not occur until the $CaCl_2$ concentration of the unfrozen solution reaches 30 per cent—this is called the *eutectic* point of the solution—and the temperature has been lowered to $-51\,^{\circ}C$. In the case of sodium chloride solutions, the eutectic solution is 25 per cent and complete freezing occurs at $-19.5\,^{\circ}C$.

(8)   The admixing of chlorides to a soil may change its plasticity characteristics. When calcium chloride is added, the exchange reaction which takes place may result in a reduction of the plasticity index, due to the calcium cations being preferentially adsorbed onto the surfaces of the soil particles. If sodium chloride is the admixing material, the result may be an increase in the plasticity index, due to the ability of the $Na^+$ ions to become highly hydrated during moist weather. In temperate climates this can mean that it may not be possible to use sodium chloride to stabilize certain soil–aggregate roadbases.

(9)   Although not too much is known about the extent to which this actually occurs, the presence of sodium chloride is believed to increase the solubility of limestone particles in water. Eventually, the calcium ions precipitate out of solution as minute amounts of calcium carbonate. The calcium carbonate then acts as a very weak cement which, in a well-graded soil–aggregate mixture, may help to bind the particles together.

**Usage**

A successful chloride-stabilized pavement is of necessity a mechanically-stable one; chlorides are not cementing agents and therefore the material being stabilized must already have high stability. The best results are obtained when well-graded materials are compacted to dense, impervious masses, as these reduce considerably the ease with which the chlorides may be leached downwards from the upper portions of the pavement. Open-graded materials, although they may be mechanically stable, are not suitable for chloride stabilization as they are much more permeable.

The development of ravelling and corrugation conditions on soil–aggregate surface courses in warm climates is considerably retarded by the addition of chlorides. Chlorides aid by providing firm, hard-packed wearing surfaces which have a smoothness and riding quality approaching those of more permanent, higher-cost pavements. Ravelling is reduced since it is harder for aggregates to be plucked from these surfacings. Corrugations are formed as a consequence of the oscillatory pounding actions of moving vehicles that are produced when these vehicles encounter irregularities on the road surface[25]; thus the smoother the surfacing, the less easily that corrugations are formed. In general, calcium chloride is more successful than sodium chloride in serving this purpose—albeit, of course, that its capital cost is greater than that of sodium chloride. Most economical usage is obtained by periodic surface grading, and reapplication of chlorides to prevent deterioration of the pavement surface.

Use of calcium chloride in soil–aggregate roadbases is also advantageous. If the surface course is permeable and contains $CaCl_2$, and the climate is a temperate one, the calcium chloride leached from the roadbase will be replenished to a certain extent by the downward movement of moisture through the surface course. Furthermore, the calcium chloride in the roadbase will reduce the deleterious effects resulting from frost action in the pavement.

Details regarding chloride stabilization are available in the literature[26,27].

## Lignin stabilization

Lignin is a natural, cementitious material that binds the cellulose fibres together in wood, and lignin derivations are a major byproduct of the paper-making industry. In general, it can be assumed that for each tonne of pulp that a mill produces, about 0.5 t of lignin results as a byproduct[28]. As such, lignin is one of the 'road materials' that is expected to be available in continued large supply in countries where timber is a major resource.

Basically, two types of wood lignins are commercially available: *lignin sulphonate* and *kraft lignin*.

For more than one-hundred years, 'pulp' for the manufacture of paper and other products in the form of cellulose fibres has been produced from woody tissue by the sulphite process; this process requires aqueous solutions of bisulphite and sulphurous acid to be used at high temperatures to dissolve lignin and some carbohydrates, and leave behind the cellulose sulphite pulp fibres. After the pulp fibres have been separated by filtration, the liquid remaining is called spent sulphite liquor; it contains lignin sulphonates, certain sugars from the wood, and also the process chemicals. The sulphonates, which are produced as calcium, magnesium, sodium or ammonium salts, are commonly sold in the form of spray-dried powders or as 40–60 per cent solutions in water (usually containing the sugars formed in the pulping process).

Kraft lignin, also known as *thiolignin*, is the major constituent of kraft black liquor solids. It is a polymeric material consisting of about 65 per cent carbon, 5 per cent hydrogen, and 30 per cent oxygen, which is recovered in a reasonably high yield by acidifying and filtering the precipitated lignin. Whilst sulphonated kraft lignins are more expensive to produce than lignin sulphonates, they have the significant advantages of being free of carbohydrate constituents and insoluble in water. Kraft lignin is recovered as its sodium salt or as free lignin containing very little ash; both forms when dry are free-flowing brown powders.

**Mechanism of stabilization**
Whilst both types of lignin are used to stabilize pavements in and adjacent to forested areas in Sweden, Canada and parts of the USA, not too much is known of the exact mechanism by which they stabilize soils. Work that has been done, however, indicates that the addition of either type of lignin to soils results in higher dry densities and decreased permeabilities. As regards the latter, sulphonates are excellent clay-dispersing agents and thus, when it rains on a lignin-stabilized surface course, the dispersed clay particles swell and plug the pores, thereby reducing water penetration. After lignin has cured, it becomes cementitious and binds the soil particles together; unfortunately, the cement formed with lignin sulphonate is water soluble and, if not protected, may disappear with the onset of wet weather. However, kraft lignins, and lignin sulphonates in the absence of rain, will maintain soil–aggregate pavement surfaces smooth and dust-free for a long period of time. Lignin sulphonate applications of 2.5 l/m$^2$ (liquid) or 0.5–1.0 kg/m$^2$ (powder) have been recommended[29] as being appropriate for this purpose.

Frost heave and subsequent break-up in warmer temperatures are also reduced by having lignin present in a soil–aggregate pavement; this reduction is due both to a slight lowering of the freezing point of the soil moisture and to the increased impermeability of the lignin-stabilized roadbase. Lignins also have hygroscopic properties due to the sugars which are present. However, the moisture-retention properties are limited as bacteria will attack these sugars.

**Usage**
As with chlorides, the most advantageous usage of lignin is with soil–aggregate pavements which are already stable. Best results are obtained when these pavements are very dense, since this prevents rapid leaching of the lignin and promotes good cementation. Although lignin will also increase the stability of poorly-graded soils, it is apt to be leached out very rapidly; in areas where lignin is readily available, however, this may make little difference. At the present time it appears that effective use of lignin is confined to hot climates and on roadways adjacent to sources of the material.

## Molasses stabilization

Molasses used for highway soil stabilization purposes is a waste residue known as 'black strap molasses' which is obtained as a byproduct of the manufacture of sugar from sugar cane. It is a very thick, syrupy liquid which contains resinous and some inorganic constituents which render it unfit for human consumption.

### Mechanism of stabilization

Black strap molasses is a hygroscopic material and this enables it to take up moisture from the air and to control the evaporation of water from the soil–aggregate pavement as it is being compacted. It is also a cementing agent; unfortunately, however, the cement formed is water soluble, but if water can be kept away the binding action is very strong indeed.

### Usage

At this time the use of molasses as a stabilizing agent is confined to tropical localities where cane sugar is produced. In these areas it is primarily used as a dust palliative and surface binder, usually in the form of surface treatments to roads which initially are mechanically stable. The outstanding limitation to its use is that it is readily soluble in water and will easily leach out of the pavement. However, if an impermeable material is used in the surface course, there would appear to be no reason why molasses could not be used to improve the stabilities of soil–aggregate roadbases.

# Cement stabilization

Of all the methods of soil stabilization now in use, that which utilizes cement as the stabilizing agent is second only to mechanical stabilization in importance and usage. Modern usage of cement for stabilization purposes can perhaps be said to date back to 1917 when J H Amies took out a patent in the USA on soil and cement mixtures labelled 'Soilamines'. While usage in Britain can be said to have begun in 1920 with experiments involving the addition of cement to chalk soil in earth cottage construction near Amesbury, systematic use was not initiated until about 1939 when the (now) Transport and Road Research Laboratory followed up a study of American experience with a programme of laboratory tests and field trials on cement-treated soil mixtures.

Factors which have helped to make the use of Portland cement so popular as a soil stabilizer in nearly every other country in the world are as follows.

(1)   Cement is readily available in most countries as a home product.
(2)   Cement is manufactured on such a large scale for concrete construction that its price is comparatively low.
(3)   Use of cement generally involves less care and control than many other methods of stabilization.
(4)   More information is generally available on cement-treated soil mixtures than on other types of soil stabilization.

(5) Almost any soil can be stabilized with Portland cement if enough cement is used in combination with the right amount of water and proper compaction and curing.

## Types of cement-treated soil mixtures

Cement-treated soil is a simple, intimate mixture of pulverized soil, Portland cement and water. All cement-treated soil mixtures are very often, and erroneously so, called soil-cement mixtures. In fact, there are three different types of cement-treated soil mixtures, of which soil-cement is just one. The other two are termed cement-modified soil and plastic soil-cement. It is important that the engineer should distinguish between the three so as to know how and when each may be used most advantageously.

### Soil-cement

This is a hardened material formed by curing a mechanically-compacted, intimate mixture of pulverized soil, Portland cement and water. In other words, sufficient cement is added to the soil to harden it, and the moisture content of the mixture is adequate for compaction purposes and for hydrating the cement. Inherent in the definition is the assumption that a soil-cement mixture is capable of meeting particular criteria relating to stability and/or durability.

Soil-cement has a number of uses of which by far the most important is as a roadbase and/or subbase material in roadways and parking areas, airport runways, taxiways and aprons. Another important use has been as a foundation material for large structures. It has also been used in the construction of low-cost buildings, particularly in arid climates. Soil-cement is not used in road surfacings as it has poor resistance to abrasion. Hence another superimposed material, e.g. a concrete pavement or bituminous surfacing, must be used to protect it from the wheels of traffic.

### Cement-modified soil

Some soils cannot be *economically* stabilized with cement. For instance, the amount of cement required to stabilize a particular clay soil so that it can be used as a roadbase for a major highway could be as much as 20–30 per cent. As a consequence of the high cost this would involve, it will probably be more economical to use an imported aggregate in the roadbase whilst adding sufficient cement to the in situ soil to *modify* its properties to make it acceptable as a subbase material. Alternatively, a normally substandard granular material having a relatively high plasticity and low bearing value may be made acceptable for pavement construction purposes by the addition of sufficient cement to modify its properties.

In both of the above examples, the amount of cement added is, by definition, insufficient to harden the soil enough to meet soil-cement stability and durability criteria; the resultant material is *intended* to fragment under the action of traffic. In other words, the addition of the cement is for the purpose of improving the physical characteristics of the soil. Usually, the soils chosen for modification purposes have high water-holding capacities and volume-change characteristics; hence they have low supporting values, as their moisture contents vary with the weather.

**Plastic soil-cement**
This is a hardened material formed by curing an intimate mixture of pulverized soil, cement and enough water to produce a mortar-like consistency at the time of mixing and placing. By comparison, soil-cement is mixed and placed with only enough moisture to permit adequate compaction and cement hydration. However, soil-cement and plastic soil-cement are similar in that they are both capable of meeting specified durability and/or stability criteria.

Plastic soil-cement is used primarily as an erosion-control material for paving steep, irregular or confined areas, and as lining on the sides of ditches and canals. It has application also for levee and earth-dam facings where the use of soil-cement might present construction problems. Plastic soil-cement has also been used to cast construction blocks for building purposes in under-developed areas.

In general, plastic soil-cement mixtures require about four per cent more cement than soil-cement mixtures in order to meet the same criteria[30].

## Mechanism of cement stabilization

When water is added to neat cement, the major hydration products are basic calcium silicate hydrates, calcium aluminate hydrates, and hydrated lime. The first two of these products constitute the major cementitious components, while the lime is deposited as a separate crystalline solid phase. When cement is present in a granular soil, the cementation is probably very similar to that in concrete, except that the cement paste does not fill the voids between the soil particles. In other words, cementation is primarily by means of adhesion bonding of the calcium silicate and aluminate hydrates to the rough mineral surfaces. When cement is used to stabilize a fine-grained soil, the adhesion bonding again takes place but, in addition, the clay phase also contributes to the stabilization process through solution in the high pH environment and reaction with the free lime from the cement.

As the silt-clay content of a soil is increased, its particle surface area is also much increased, and so the opportunity is much greater for additional chemical reactions to take place between the hydrated cement and the particle surfaces. The free lime given off during hydration is believed to play a prominent part in these reactions. First of all, it is probable that there is an exchange reaction with cations already absorbed onto the particles. In addition, the lime reacts with the soil silica (and alumina) to form secondary hydrous calcium silicates (and aluminates) on the silica particle surfaces. (These reactions are explained in more detail in the discussion on lime and lime-pozzolan stabilization.) The effect of the cation-exchange reaction is to change the plasticity properties of the soil, whilst the secondary silicates are cementitious and further contribute to interparticle bonding. The greater the fines content of the soil and the more reactive the clay minerals, the more important are both of these secondary reactions.

The manner in which cement stabilizes fine-grained soils can perhaps be demonstrated by visualizing the grains of cement as a nucleus to which the fine soil particles adhere. As the cement content of the soil is increased, the quantity of free silt-clay is progressively reduced and a coarser-grained material of lower water-holding capacity and increased volume stability and supporting value is obtained; this is a cement-modified soil. As more and more cement is added, the quantity of the coarser-grained material is increased until the point is reached where all the soil grains remain in a solid mass as befits a structural material; this is soil-cement.

## Factors affecting cement–soil properties

It is literally impossible to list and discuss all the factors which affect the physical properties of cement-treated soil mixtures, for there are an infinite number of soils and an infinite number of combinations. While the literature on this subject is tremendous, there are two references[31, 32] which are outstanding in summarizing research and practical data in this area on the international scene; in addition, there are some useful publications which summarize work in Britain[33-35] and Europe[36].

The following discussion is concerned with those factors which primarily affect cement–soil mixture characteristics; these are

(1)  nature and type of soil,
(2)  amount and type of cement,
(3)  moisture content,
(4)  mixing and compaction,
(5)  curing conditions and length,
(6)  use of chemical additives.

### Soil

The nature and type of soil is perhaps the single most important factor affecting the stability of a cement-treated soil. Any soil can be stabilized if sufficient cement is added, but the cement content required to achieve a given stability must normally be increased as the silt-clay content is increased, other factors remaining constant. Thus it may not be economically possible to stabilize with cement certain soils such as heavy clays; this will depend upon an economic analysis of this and other, alternative, methods of construction. Excessive amounts of clay-size particles may cause considerable problems when pulverizing, mixing and compacting cement–soil mixtures.

The American Portland Cement Association's experience is that the soils most suitable for cement stabilization are well-graded materials that possess sufficient fines to produce a floating matrix. The Association recommends[37] that gradings which meet this floating aggregate matrix concept should generally fall within the following band:

| | |
|---|---|
| <4.75 mm | 55% (minimum) |
| <2 mm | 35% (minimum) |
| 0.075–2 mm | 25% (minimum) |

An extensive analysis of the literature by the USA Air Force resulted in the recommendations shown in Fig. 5.6 in relation to soil materials most suitable for stabilization by various means (including cement); these place limits upon the plasticity index ($PI$) of the soil. The $PI$ should be $< 30$ for sandy soils, whilst the $PI$ and $LL$ (liquid limit) should be $< 20$ and $< 40$ per cent, respectively, for fine-grained soils if they are to be considered suitable for stabilization with cement. This limitation is considered necessary to ensure proper mixing of the stabilizer with the soil. For gravel-type materials, a minimum of 45 per cent passing the 4.75 mm sieve is desirable. In addition, the $PI$ of the soil to be stabilized with cement should not exceed the number indicated by the following empirical equation:

$$PI \leqslant 20 + \frac{50 - \text{fines content}}{4}$$

The US Bureau of Public Roads recommends that cement should be used as a stabilizer when a soil has $< 35$ per cent passing the 0.075 mm sieve and a $PI < 20$. This implies that soils classified as A-2 and A-3 under the AASHTO system (see Chapter 4) can be best stabilized with cement.

Experience in Britain is that soils with $LL > 45$ per cent and $PI > 20$ cannot normally be economically utilized in soil-cement construction. The upper grading limit for material considered suitable for cement stabilization is shown in Table 5.3; materials coarser than this are considered unsuitable because of possible damage to mixers during the mixing process, and because of construction difficulties related to their liability to segregate, and the difficulty of controlling levels.

Also shown in Table 5.3 are the gradation limits prescribed for 'as dug' cement-bound granular materials and for lean concrete, both of which belong to the soil-cement family. Both soil-cement (rarely) and cement-bound granular material (more often) are used in subbase construction in Britain. Lean concrete is also often used as a roadbase in pavements covering the full spectrum from housing estates to motorways, with CBM4 being used in the more-heavily-trafficked roads.

In respect of Table 5.3, it should be noted that the term soil-cement (CBM1) is used to describe not only natural soils stabilized with cement, but also such diverse materials as pulverized fuel ash, washed or processed granular material, and crushed rock or slag, with processing being carried out by mix-in-place methods or by plant mixing. When a 'soil' is poorly graded, it may require an uneconomically high cement content for satisfactory stabilization; to overcome this possibility, it is usual practice in Britain to specify that such materials should have a uniformity coefficient of not less than 5, i.e. the ratio of the 60 per cent particle size to the 10 per cent size should be not less than 5.

When the material to be stabilized is well graded and restricted to a naturally occurring gravel–sand, a washed or processed granular material, crushed rock, or slag, it is normally described as a cement-bound granular material (CBM2), and only plant mixing is allowed. Lean concrete mixes (CBM3 and 4) involve the use of washed and graded aggregates suitable for

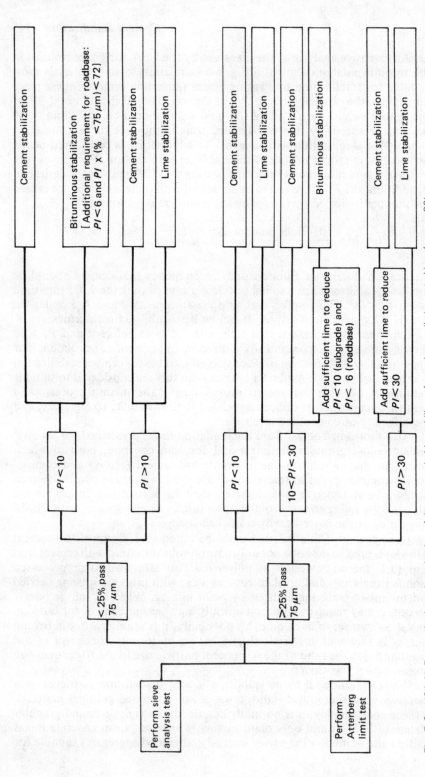

**Fig. 5.6** USA Air Force criteria re the selection of the most suitable stabilizers for various soils (reported in reference 32)

**Table 5.3** British grading requirements for cement-stabilized material—cumulative percentage passing by mass[8]

| Sieve size (mm) | Soil-cement (CBM1) | Cement-bound granular material (CBM2) | Lean concrete: nominal maximum size (mm) | |
|---|---|---|---|---|
| | | | 40 (CBM3) | 20 (CBM4) |
| 50 | 100 | 100 | 100 | – |
| 37.5 | 95 | 95–100 | 95–100 | 100 |
| 20 | 45 | 45–100 | 45–80 | 95–100 |
| 10 | 35 | 35–100 | – | – |
| 5 | 25 | 25–100 | 25–50 | 35–55 |
| 2.36 | – | 15–90 | – | – |
| 0.600 | 8 | 8–65 | 8–30 | 10–35 |
| 0.300 | 5 | 5–40 | – | – |
| 0.150 | – | – | 0–8 | 0–8 |
| 0.075 | 0 | 0–10 | – | – |

*Note*: Reference 8 identifies all of these as cement-bound granular materials, coded CBM1, 2, 3 and 4

pavement-quality concrete; any type of mixer suitable for mixing ordinary concrete is used in the preparation of this material.

The type of clay mineral is also of considerable importance in soil stabilization in that the expansive types of clay are more difficult to stabilize. This particular aspect is discussed in greater detail in relation to lime stabilization.

Organic matter is almost invariably present in the surface layers of soil and may extend to a depth of 1.5 m in well-drained sandy soils. Its presence very often renders a soil unsuitable for stabilization with cement—which is one reason why it is necessary to strip *at least* the topsoil before attempting this form of stabilization. Soils with B- and C-horizons which can fall into this category tend to have acidic, podzolic profiles and were formed under wooded vegetative conditions. They can be easily detected by making up a cement–soil paste using 10 per cent Portland cement and determining the pH value of the paste one hour after the addition of water. If the pH is less than 12.1, the soil should be rejected, as this indicates the presence of organic matter capable of hindering the hardening of the cement.

The presence of calcium sulphate in the soil water also influences its suitability for cement stabilization[38]. Research has shown that a soil cannot be economically stabilized with cement if it contains a sulphate content in excess of about 0.25 per cent. In Britain, sulphates are rarely found in freely-draining soils since any that did exist would be removed by leaching; they can be frequently encountered in clay soils at depths (due to leaching) in excess of 0.75–1.00 m. In practice, the hazard arises from the possibility that the sulphates may be transported by the seasonal movement of the groundwater from an area below the water-table into the stabilized soil above it. Unsuitability for stabilization is due to the ability of the sulphate to combine with the tricalcium aluminate in the hydrated cement and produce calcium sulpho-aluminate. This new mineral expands to occupy a greater volume than the reactants from which it is formed, thereby breaking the cementitious bonds in the soil-cement.

## Cement

Any type of cement may be used to stabilize soils, but normally ordinary Portland cement is used. A high early strength cement may be used if high strengths are required quickly, or if the soil is contaminated by organic matter. Sulphate-resistant cement can be of limited value in the stabilization of materials containing sulphates since, if clay is present, reaction can still occur between the sulphates, clay minerals and lime.

British practice now is to specify the desired stabilities of most soil-cement mixtures in terms of minimum unconfined strengths and not, as formerly, in terms of minimum cement contents. In other words, it is up to the contractor to add as much cement to the soil as is necessary to achieve the specified strength at some minimum state of compaction. The current specifications[8] for soil-cement (CBM1) require an average minimum seven-day value of 4.5 $N/mm^2$ for cubical specimens. Cubical specimens formed from cement-bound granular material (CBM2) are expected to achieve an average strength of 7.0 $N/mm^2$ after seven days, whilst lean concrete cube strengths are expected to achieve average seven-day cube strengths of 10 and 15 $N/mm^2$ for CBM3 and 4 mixtures, respectively.

Lean concrete (which uses washed and processed aggregate) has a high modulus of elasticity—it is close to that for conventional concrete—and is very effective in reducing the vertical stresses transmitted to a subgrade; however, it will develop high tensile stresses due to wheel loadings or to restrained dimensional changes. It is therefore a rigid material with an inherent cracking problem[35]. At the other extreme, soil-cements involving fine-grained soils will tend towards having a low modulus of elasticity, whilst cement-bound granular materials—as befits an intermediate material —will have intermediate values.

In the USA, because of its continental climate, the cement content is primarily selected to meet frost action durability requirements, i.e. the implied assumption is that strength needs will automatically be met. The cement contents indicated in Table 5.4 are typical of those required to meet the American durability needs; however, for many applications, e.g. treated subgrades and milder climatic conditions, satisfactory treatment can be achieved using lower cement contents.

## Moisture

It is essential for water to be present in a cement–soil mixture in order to hydrate the cement, to improve workability, and to facilitate compaction. This water should be relatively clean and free from harmful amounts of alkalis, acids or organic matter.

The amount of moisture present in the mixture has a considerable effect upon the strengths and densities obtained with a cement–soil mixture. For example, fully-hydrated cement takes up about 20 per cent of its own mass

**Table 5.4** American recommendations with respect to the amount of cement required to stabilize B- and C-horizon soils[37]

| AASHTO soil group | Usual range in cement requirement | |
|---|---|---|
| | Percentage by volume | Percentage by mass |
| A-1-a | 5–7 | 3–5 |
| A-1-b | 7–9 | 5–8 |
| A-2 | 7–10 | 5–9 |
| A-3 | 8–12 | 7–11 |
| A-4 | 8–12 | 7–12 |
| A-5 | 8–12 | 8–13 |
| A-6 | 10–14 | 9–15 |
| A-7 | 10–14 | 10–16 |

of water. At high soil moisture contents, the cement has no difficulty in obtaining this water, but if the water content is decreased, the cement has to compete with the soil for moisture; if the material has a high suction potential, it may have a greater affinity for the moisture, the cement will not fully hydrate, and the strength will be reduced from what it should be.

As with natural soils, cement-treated soils exhibit the same type of moisture–density relationships, i.e. for a given compactive effort there is one moisture content which will give a maximum dry density. It is important to realize that the optimum moisture content for maximum dry density is not necessarily the same as that for strength. This is illustrated in Fig. 5.7, which further shows that the optimum value for strength may vary, depending upon the manner and duration of curing prior to testing for strength. In general, the optimum moisture content for maximum strength tends to be on the dry side of the optimum for maximum dry density for sandy soils, and on the wet side for clayey soils. For the clayey soils, the location of the optimum value for strength is dependent not only upon the amount of clay present in the soil, but also upon the type of clay mineral.

**Mixing and compacting**
In general, the more uniformly that cement, water and soil are mixed, the greater are both the stability and durability of the cement–soil product. Alternatively, high mixing efficiencies will result in lower cement contents in order to achieve a given cement–soil field strength.

The chemical reaction between cement and water begins at the time of mixing, and strength-giving products of hydration begin to form after about one hour. In the case of a fixed compactive effort, increasing the moist mixing time and/or delaying compaction after ending the moist mixing generally results in an increase in the optimum moisture content for maximum dry density of the cement–soil mixture, while its dry density, durability and unconfined compressive strength are decreased. The extent to which each occurs in any particular instance is dependent upon the type of soil, the period of mixing and/or delay, the amount of cement present, and

## 352 Soil stabilization

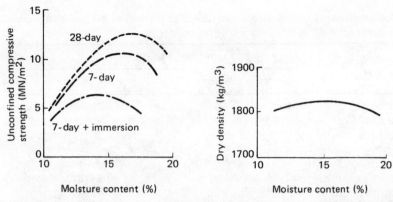

Molsture content (%)  Moisture content (%)

**Fig. 5.7** Influence of moisture content upon the dry density and strengths of soil-cement mixtures composed of 20 per cent cement and a 50:50 mixture of dune clay and montmorillonite clay

the amount of compaction applied. The reduction in dry density can be attributed to the extent to which bonding of particles occurs as the cement hydrates during the delay period so that the particles are prevented from easily sliding over each other during compaction.

If the compactive effort is increased to ensure that the original dry density is achieved—and provided that no significant amount of cement hydration has occurred during the delay period—no adverse effects upon strength or durability will be noted. In general, however, time delays of more than one to three hours may increase the required compactive effort for stabilized soils to a level which may well be beyond the capabilities of ordinary compaction equipment. As a result, many specifications now place an upper limit on the length of time between moisture being added to the mixture and compaction being completed. For instance, in Britain the current specifications for cement-bound materials require that compaction be completed within two hours of mixing being initiated.

For a given cohesionless soil, water and cement mixture it can generally be said that the greater the dry density, the more stable and durable the hardened structural material will be. In general also, the highest strengths are associated with mixtures prepared with cohesionless soils, and the less plastic the soil, the smaller the deformation required to cause failure.

### Curing conditions
The environmental conditions under which curing takes place have a considerable effect also upon the extent to which a soil may be stabilized with cement. As illustrated in Fig. 5.7, the strength of soil-cement increases with age; this strength gain is similar to that which is achieved with concrete and continues for many years. As in the case of concrete, soil-cement must be moist cured during the initial stages of its life so that moisture sufficient to meet the hydration needs of the cement can be maintained in the mixture.

Cement-treated soils exhibit shrinkage cracking on curing and drying. Field observations of soil-cement pavements indicate the cracks to be typically from 3 to 6 mm wide at spacings of 3 to 6 m, with the small crack spacings being more usually associated with the higher clay content soils[32]. Some factors influencing the degree of shrinkage cracking include: (a) moisture loss or the internal redistribution of moisture as the cement hydrates, (b) material contraction as the ambient temperature falls, (c) the extent of the restraint imposed upon a roadbase by the subbase or subgrade, and (d) the tensile properties of the hardening soil-cement in terms of its strength, strain capacity, modulus of elasticity, and the ability to relieve critical conditions through creep[39]. Shrinkage cracking is more likely to occur in poorly-compacted layers, at early ages, at low cement contents and, in the case of lean concrete, at higher moisture contents[40].

The ideal curing condition which minimizes shrinkage cracking due to differential drying is to enclose the soil-cement completely in an impermeable membrane so that no moisture can escape; the shrinkage that occurs under these conditions has been called *autogenous shrinkage*. At the other extreme, *drying shrinkage* occurs, and the likelihood of cracking is increased, when moisture is allowed to dry freely from soil-cement.

High strength results are obtained with soil-cement following curing at higher temperatures. This factor—which is due to a pozzolanic reaction between the clay and the lime released by the cement during hydration—can be of economic importance in countries with warm climates when the design criterion is based simply on compressive strength. For instance, in a hot country where the compacted soil-cement is able to cure at an average temperature of, say, $38\,^\circ$C, lower cement contents will be required to achieve a given strength over a period of time than in Britain, say, where the average summer temperature is about $15\,^\circ$C.

## Additives

Work on the evaluation of chemical admixtures to soil-cement mixtures has been carried out for many years and, depending upon the reasons for which they are used, several very successful additives have been discovered. For instance, the detrimental effects associated with organic soils can very often be negated by the pre-admixing of up to 2 per cent hydrated lime or 0.5 per cent calcium chloride. With highly-plastic soils it is common practice to premix a small quantity of lime to initiate cation-exchange and flocculation/agglomeration reactions which immediately reduce the soil's plasticity and improve its workability; the subsequent addition of the cement then ensures rapid strength development.

Trace chemicals have been found which, when added to soil-cement mixtures, can dramatically increase the early strengths obtainable; these are especially advantageous when rapid strength gain is required under cooler weather conditions. Where high early strength is not the principal objective, a reduction in cement content may be obtained without loss of long-term strength by the addition of a reactive fly ash to the cement–soil mixture.

## Lime and lime-pozzolan stabilization

### Limes and lime-pozzolans

Lime has been used successfully as a soil stabilizing agent in highway construction since the early 1940s. The limes most commonly used for this purpose are hydrated high calcium lime ($Ca(OH)_2$), monohydrated dolomitic lime ($Ca(OH)_2.MgO$), calcitic quicklime ($CaO$), and dolomitic quicklime ($CaO.MgO$). The use of quicklime for soil stabilization increased very significantly during the 1970s; in the USA it accounts for more than 10 per cent of the total amount of stabilization with lime, whilst in continental Europe quicklime is the major type used[41].

Details of the limes used in highway construction are given in Chapter 3, and will not be repeated here.

Lime is used as a soil treatment for a variety of reasons, e.g. to expedite construction on weak subgrade soils, to improve the engineering properties of 'dirty' granular materials, and to improve the strength and durability of fine-grained soils. Lime-treated soils are used in highway pavements as improved subgrades, subbases and roadbases; they are never used in road surfacings due to their inability to resist abrasion under traffic.

#### Pozzolans

A *pozzolana* or pozzolanic material is a siliceous or siliceous and aluminous material which in itself possesses little or no cementitious value, but will—when in a finely-divided form and in the presence of moisture—chemically react with lime at ordinary temperatures to form compounds possessing cementitious properties. The term pozzolana is derived from Pozzuoli, the name for a port near Naples in Italy. It was there that the early Romans found a local volcanic ash which formed a stabilized product when mixed with sand and lime.

Pozzolanic materials can be roughly divided into natural and artificial pozzolanas. The most active natural pozzolanas are clayey or siliceous materials of volcanic origin such as tuff and trass, which are characteristically glassy or non-crystalline in structure. Fine-grained soils, particularly montmorillonitic clays, are also capable of reacting with lime in the presence of moisture, and so these too can be classed as natural pozzolanas. Whilst ground bricks, pulverized blastfurnace slag and burnt shale all fall into the category of artificial pozzolanas, the artificial pozzolanic material with the greatest potential as a soil stabilization construction material is pulverized fuel ash (see Chapter 3).

### Mechanism of lime stabilization

When lime (or a mixture of lime and pulverized fuel ash) is added to a fine-grained soil, a number of complex reactions take place. These reactions are not fully understood at this time (see, for example, reference 42) and so the following discussion is confined to providing a simplified overview of the reactions most generally accepted. These reactions are: (a) cation exchange and flocculation/agglomeration, (b) pozzolanic reaction, and (c) carbonation.

### Cation exchange and flocculation/agglomeration
When lime and a moist, clayey soil are intimately mixed, an immediate flocculation effect can be observed. This alteration of soil character is most probably due to two main reactions.

Firstly, a cation-exchange reaction takes place which causes a change in the relationship between clay particles, from a state of mutual repulsion to one of mutual attraction; this results from excess $Ca^{2+}$ replacing dissimilar cations from the exchange complex of the soil. In the case of soils that are $Ca^{2+}$ saturated before the addition of lime, cation exchange and flocculation will be minimized.

In relation to cation exchange, it should be noted that, as a general rule, the order of replaceability of the common cations associated with soils follows the lyotropic series

$$Na^+ < K^+ < Ca^{2+} < Mg^{2+}$$

with cations on the right tending to replace cations to the left in the series and monovalent cations being usually replaceable by multivalent cations.

Secondly, flocculation and agglomeration produce an apparent change in texture with the clay particles 'clumping' together into larger-sized aggregates or lumps, possibly due to the increased electrolyte content of the pore water and as a result of ion exchange by the clay to the calcium form. It may also be that the diffusion of lime through these lumps leads to the rapid formation of cementitious calcium aluminate hydrate products that are deposited at or near the clay mineral crystal edges, and which also sustain the agglomeration process.

These reactions suggest that the modification of a clay soil by the addition of lime is clearly dependent upon the nature of the dominant cation originally adsorbed, and also upon the type of clay. For example, a sodium-dominated montmorillonite (which has a high cation-exchange capacity) will require a relatively large addition of lime to achieve calcium saturation and the full potential flocculation effect. In contrast, a kaolinitic clay will require a considerably smaller amount of lime to achieve the full potential flocculation effect for that soil.

### Pozzolanic reaction
When lime is added to a moist, cohesive soil, the slow, long-term cementing together of the soil particles at their points of interaction commences. This reaction, which is still not fully understood, possibly starts simultaneously with the flocculation process. It is believed to be a pozzolanic reaction which involves the lime and the alumina and silica present in the soil in the formation of hydrous calcium aluminates and silicates which are similar to the reaction products of hydrated cement. Possible sources of silica and alumina in typical soils include clay minerals, quartz, feldspars, micas and other silicate or alumino-silicate minerals, either crystalline or amorphous in nature.

When a substantial amount of lime is added to a soil, the pH of the soil–lime mixture is significantly raised—typically to about 12.4 which is the pH of saturated lime water. The solubilities of silica and alumina are greatly increased at high pH values, which, in turn, promotes the soil–lime reaction. It may be that the high pH causes silica to be dissolved out of the structure of the clay minerals, thereby becoming available to combine with the $Ca^{2+}$ to form calcium silicates, and that this reaction continues as long as the $Ca(OH)_2$ exists in the soil and there is available silica. It has further been postulated that the reaction processes in the highly alkaline soil–lime system involve a dissolution at the edges of the silicate particles followed by the precipitation of the reaction products. It is also possible that the lime reacts directly at the surface of clay mineral particles, and that new phases nucleate directly upon the surfaces of the clay particle.

Whatever is the nature of the exact mechanism, the following gives an over-simplified, qualitative view of some typical soil–lime reactions[41]:

$$Ca(OH)_2 \rightarrow Ca^{2+} + 2(OH)^-$$

$$Ca^{2+} + 2(OH)^- + SiO_2 \rightarrow CaO.SiO_2.H_2O = CSH$$
$$\text{(clay silica)}$$

$$Ca^{2+} + 2(OH)^- + Al_2O_3 \rightarrow CaO.Al_2O_3.H_2O = CAH$$
$$\text{(clay alumina)}$$

where C is shorthand for $CaO$, S for $SiO_2$, A for $Al_2O_3$, and H for $H_2O$.

The extent to which the soil–lime pozzolanic reaction proceeds is influenced by the quantity and type of lime, the mixture curing time and temperature and, most importantly, those inherent properties and characteristics of the soil which influence its lime-reactivity, i.e. soil pH, organic carbon content, natural drainage, presence of excessive quantities of exchangeable sodium, clay mineralogy, degree of weathering, presence of carbonates, extractable iron, silica–sesquioxide ratio, and silica–alumina ratio.

If a soil is non-reactive, significant pozzolanic strength development will not be achieved, irrespective of lime type or content, or curing conditions of time and temperature. As a general guide, soils that react with lime to produce strength increases less than about 345 $kN/m^2$ after twenty-eight days curing at 22.8 °C are usually considered as being unreactive, whilst those which produce greater strength increases are called reactive.

Highly reactive soils, e.g. montmorillonitic soils, which contain large amounts of reactive silica, may require several years before the pozzolanic reaction is completed and equilibrium is reached; in contrast, soils such as coarse silts and sands, which contain small amounts of reactive silica and alumina, react very little with lime. In the latter, the cementitious strength gains are usually very low and inadequate for highway purposes, and hence lime is rarely used to stabilize granular soils in which the clay content ($< 2 \mu m$) is less than about 10 per cent.

The pozzolanic reaction is considerably influenced by the amount and type of lime used (see also Fig. 5.6 for plasticity guidelines). If the lime content is low, there may be only sufficient $Ca^{2+}$ present in the soil–lime system to enable the cation-exchange and flocculation/agglomeration reactions to take place; the soil–lime product then obtained is called a *lime-modified soil*. If sufficient lime is present to enable excess $Ca^{2+}$ to become involved in pozzolanic reactions, so that strength increases to meet specified strength and/or durability criteria (e.g. as for soil-cement) can be achieved, then the product obtained is termed a *lime-stabilized soil*.

In general, strength increases as the lime content is increased, but for a given curing period there may be an optimum lime content; furthermore, the exact optimum content in any given instance is influenced by the amount and type of clay present. Several studies have suggested that, under ambient conditions, dolomitic monohydrate limes are more effective than calcitic hydrated limes in producing strength (possibly due to the ability of the unhydrated MgO to act as an accelerator of the pozzolanic reaction); however, some doubt still exists as to the general effectiveness of dolomitic lime with all types of clayey soils [43].

Quicklimes are more effective than hydrated limes in producing strength increases; this results from the greater amount of $Ca^{2+}$ available from a given mass of quicklime as compared with the same mass of hydrated lime. Hydraulic limes generally tend to give higher strengths than non-hydraulic limes. Again, while this reaction mechanism is not completely understood, it is probably a combination of two reactions: firstly, the gel-formation reaction which occurs when a cement is hydrated and, secondly, the pozzolanic reaction between the hydrated lime present and the clay particles.

The strength of a soil–lime mixture will normally increase with age until all the free lime is used up. Soil–lime pozzolanic reactions—and thus strength gains—are curtailed at temperatures below about $10\,^{\circ}C$; however, soil–lime mixtures will still undergo strength increases when curing conditions become more favourable for the pozzolanic reactions. High temperatures are very beneficial to the rate of strength increase; this is one of the major reasons why lime stabilization is used frequently in hot climates.

*Reaction with pulverized fuel ash*   As has been noted above, the amount of cementation developed in a soil–lime mixture is related to the reactivity and amount of pozzolanic material which occurs naturally in the soil. If the reactive pozzolanic content is low, as with sandy and gravelly soils, both the rate of strength gain and the strength ultimately attained will be low. In such soils, strength development can be improved by adding to the soil–lime mixture a highly pozzolanic material such as fly ash which will react preferentially with the free lime. Stability is also improved in such mixtures as a result of the fly ash particles acting as fillers which reduce the air voids in the soil, thereby increasing the dry density and producing a more compact stabilization product.

In the case of fine-grained soils, the pulverized fuel ash (pfa) particle sizes are generally larger than the air voids, and so the only role for the fly ash is that of a pozzolana. Since many clays (but not all) are natural pozzolanas, they may benefit relatively little from the addition of pfa. Thus silts are the only fine-grained soils that will certainly benefit in most instances from admixtures of lime and fly ash.

Pozzolanic materials are generally considered to have no cementitious properties of their own. In the case of fly ash, however, this assumption is not always entirely true (see Chapter 3). Exploratory studies have shown that, in fact, some fly ashes produce cementation when mixed with soil without the addition of lime. Further studies have indicated that this is due to some fly ashes containing significant quantities of water-soluble lime (CaO and MgO) and calcium sulphate which become involved in pozzolanic reactions.

The choice of which fly ash to use with a particular granular or silty soil, in combination with lime, is a most difficult one to make because the cementation effects are difficult to predict from the physical and chemical characteristics of the ashes. A quick test has, however, been suggested for the rapid evaluation of a fly ash[44] to consider its suitability as a soil stabilizing agent.

**Carbonation**
Carbon dioxide from the air and rainwater can convert free calcium and magnesium oxides and hydroxides to their respective carbonates. Carbonation is particularly noticeable in industrial areas where the carbon dioxide content of the air is considerably higher than in rural areas. Here it is found that soil–lime and soil–lime–fly-ash mixtures are likely to develop lower strengths than might be predicted by the laboratory tests on mixture specimens cured under rigidly controlled and protected conditions. This is mainly because some of the lime, which would normally take part in the pozzolanic reactions, is now unavailable for this purpose due to carbonation having taken place.

In practice, the carbonation problem means that lime should be specially protected while in storage and in shipment prior to being used in the field. During construction, it is advisable to protect the mixture from prolonged exposure to the atmosphere, and so long, intensive mixing and processing should be avoided, and compaction should take place as soon as possible.

## Some properties of lime-treated soils

In general, the addition of lime to clayey soil results in immediate and substantial reductions in the *plasticity index*, and in many instances the soil may be made non-plastic; this is due to the liquid limit decreasing and the plastic limit increasing. The higher the initial plastic limit, the greater will be the lime content required to make the soil non-plastic, if this is at all achievable; however, the first increments of lime addition (up to say 1.5 per cent by mass) are generally most effective for this purpose, with further additions being less beneficial.

The reduced plasticity of the lime-treated soil, and its consequent agglomerated and friable texture, means that its *workability* is considerably improved. This expedites the subsequent manipulation and placement of the treated soil at all stages of construction, including in wet weather conditions.

The *compaction characteristics* of a lime-treated soil, i.e. its moisture–density relationships, are important for two reasons: (a) an adequate level of compaction is necessary in order to ensure satisfactory results, and (b) dry density is used as a construction control.

For a given compactive effort, lime-treated soils have lower maximum dry densities (typically by 50–80 kg/m$^3$) and higher optimum moisture contents (typically by 2–4 per cent) than the original, untreated soils. Furthermore, the maximum density normally continues to decrease as the lime content is increased. Similarly, if the soil–lime is allowed to cure so that it gains strength in a loose state prior to compaction, further reductions in maximum dry density and increases in optimum moisture content can occur. Thus it can be seen that moisture–density relationships are constantly changing, and it is therefore important that the appropriate relationship be selected for field control purposes.

As with soil-cement, the optimum moisture content for maximum strength is not necessarily the same as that for maximum dry density. With clayey soils the optimum moisture content for strength tends to be on the high side of the value for dry density, whilst with silty soils the opposite may be true. Furthermore, the strength optima may vary for different curing periods.

Calcium-saturated clays have a reduced affinity for water. This, combined with the formation of a cementitious matrix, means that the *swelling potential and swelling pressures* are normally very significantly reduced when, for example, an expansive clay soil is treated with lime.

*Shrinkage* due to moisture loss from soil is important in relation to shrinkage cracking. Lime treatment increases the shrinkage limit of the soil. Furthermore, field measurements suggest that the moisture content changes in stabilized soil–lime are not large and that the in situ water content stabilizes at approximately optimum, so that subsequent shrinkage is not extensive.

The addition of lime to clayey soils normally produces immediate and substantial improvements in *stability*. These changes are reflected in terms of improved shear strength, California Bearing Ratio, cone index, static-compressive modulus of elasticity, and resilient modulus of the 'uncured' soil–lime mixtures. As curing progresses, and the soil–lime pozzolanic reaction occurs, the treated soil develops much higher levels of strength and stiffness characteristics which may well meet roadbase and/or subbase requirements.

Field data indicate that some soil–lime mixtures continue to gain strength for up to ten years. As the magnitudes of the stress repetitions, i.e. traffic wheel loads, applied to a pavement are relatively constant throughout its design life, this means that the stress level applied to such mixtures (as a percentage of ultimate flexural strength) will decrease as time progresses, and their fatigue life will increase.

Lime treatment affects the compressive-stress–strain characteristics of a soil, i.e. the failure stress is increased and the ultimate strain is decreased for soil–lime mixtures relative to the raw soil. Figure 5.8 demonstrates the marked effect of four per cent lime upon the compressive-stress–strain properties of a fine-grained soil. Soil–lime mixtures tested in triaxial

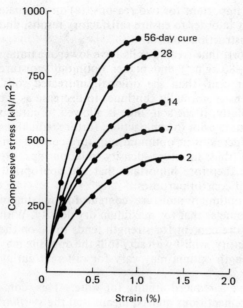

**Fig. 5.8** Compressive-stress–strain relationships for cured clay soil and 4 per cent lime mixtures (reported in reference 32)

compression are strain sensitive and the ultimate strain (for maximum compressive stress) is approximately one per cent, regardless of the soil type or curing period.

# Bituminous stabilization

Bituminous materials are believed to have been first used for modern stabilization purposes as dust palliatives on natural soil roads in Southern California in 1898. Interest in their usage as stabilizing agents grew particularly in the 1920s and 1930s, so that by the end of World War II a voluminous amount of literature was already available relative to bituminous soil stabilization knowledge and practice[45]. In spite of this wealth of early knowledge and some intensive research which has been carried out since then, the use of bituminous-stabilized soil is still generally limited at the present time to the construction of lightly-trafficked roadways in dry areas where coarse mineral aggregates are very scarce, although bituminous-stabilized soil has been used successfully in forest roads[46] which have to carry high percentages of log-hauling vehicles.

## Mechanism of stabilization

The mechanisms involved in the stabilization of a soil with a bituminous material are very different from those involved with cement and lime.

When the bituminous material is dispersed through a soil, there are two main beneficial effects. First and most important, with respect to fine-grained soils, it acts as a waterproofing agent (sealant), thereby maintaining the existing soil strength. Secondly, with coarse-grained soils, it also acts as a cementing agent (lubricant/adhesive) and binds soil particles together. Obviously, in many soils a combination of these mechanisms occurs.

**Waterproofing action**
How a bituminous material waterproofs a soil may be explained by two theories. The *membrane theory* visualizes thin bituminous films as coating soil particles or soil agglomerates, resulting in a membrane that prevents or impedes the penetration of water which, under normal conditions, would cause a decrease in shear strength, compressive strength, tensile strength, flexural strength, and elastic modulus. According to the *plug theory*, bituminous globules serve the same function by literally acting as plugs or stoppers in the soil voids, thereby removing the flow channels along which surface water might enter (and mix water might leave) the soil. In practice, of course, what happens is a combination of both of these concepts.

The fundamental feature to be emphasized is that the function of the bituminous material is to protect strength inherent in the soil, from the destructive effects of moisture changes. This means that, from a purely waterproofing aspect, the greater the amount of bituminous material present and the more thorough the mixing procedure, the more water-proofed is the soil—thick bituminous films and plugs are obviously more impermeable than thin ones. However, perfect waterproofing cannot be obtained without introducing so much additive that the soil will become too lubricated, so that compaction cannot be carried out in a satisfactory manner and hence stability will drop. Thus it must be remembered that the stability of a waterproofed product does not necessarily improve with the amount of bituminous material added, but declines in quality once an optimum amount is reached.

**Cementation action**
According to the *intimate mix theory*, the effectiveness of the cementing action of a bituminous material can be mainly explained on the basis of the adhesion which takes place between the binder and the soil particle. This adhesion is the combined effect of the action of surface tension, adsorption, and other properties of the solid and liquid surfaces. Since water has a much lower viscosity than any bituminous binder, it has a greater wetting power, so true adhesion (or cementation) will only be achieved when the binder displaces any water on the surface. If, for instance, due to the lower surface tension of the binder, it does not displace the water, then coverage of the particle *and* water will occur, but adhesion will not take place between the particle proper and the binder, and cementation will be reduced accordingly. However, adhesion is promoted if the soil particle and the binder are of different polarity.

Once adhesion has been established between the added bituminous material and the soil particles, the binder acts as a 'bridge' holding the particles together. It is important to understand its exact role in this process.

In the case of, for example, a cohesionless soil the addition of a bituminous binder helps considerably by providing cohesive strength. Thus the emphasis is upon thorough mixing of the binder so that each and every particle is coated. However, if too much binder is added and the film coatings about the particles become too thick, then contact between the particles will be prevented and strength will be lowered, since the bituminous cohesion will be essentially the only component contributing to the final stability of the mixture. Thus, as a general rule, it can be said that the thinner the bituminous film, the greater will be the increases in tensile strength, compressive strength, flexural strength, and elastic modulus.

## Usage

The term 'bituminous stabilization' has been loosely referred to a variety of treatments, ranging from the application of unknown quantities of bituminous materials to undisturbed soil, to the construction of high-stability pavements containing controlled and intimately mixed amounts of soil and bitumen. For descriptive purposes, the processes commonly employed may be divided into the following four main types:

(1)   sand–bituminous-material mixtures,
(2)   sand–gravel–bituminous-material mixtures,
(3)   soil–bituminous-material mixtures,
(4)   oiled-earth treatments.

Table 5.5 shows gradations suitable for stabilization with bitumen for the first three of these processes.

The type of bitumen used in any given instance depends primarily upon the method of construction to be used, and also upon the equipment available. The grade selected, including its setting or curing characteristics, is influenced by the gradation and the amount of fine particles in the aggregate, the ambient climatic conditions during and after construction, the type of mixing equipment and, to a certain extent, the magnitude of the loads expected on the pavement. In general, penetration-grade bitumens are used with hot central plant types of operation, whilst emulsions are used with mix-in-place operations and some cold or warm central plant operations. The use of cutbacks is now discouraged due to problems with air quality, safety, and the belief that the cutting liquid used in their preparation could be utilized for more important purposes[32].

As a guide to the selection of a suitable stabilizer content for pre-design laboratory testing purposes, soils and granular materials normally require the addition of 2–5 per cent by mass of *residual* bitumen, irrespective of whether it is added in the form of penetration-grade bitumen, a cutback bitumen, or a bitumen emulsion.

**Sand–bituminous-material mixtures**
In these mixtures the bituminous material provides cementitious strength to such cohesionless materials as loose beach, river, dune or other types of clean sand. Proper application of the binder should provide cohesive

**Table 5.5** Engineering properties of materials suitable for bituminous stabilization (adapted from reference 32)

| Property | | Sand–bitumen | Sand–gravel–bitumen | Soil–bitumen |
|---|---|---|---|---|
| Percentage passing standard sieves: | | | | |
| AASHTO sieve | Nearest equivalent BS sieve (mm) | | | |
| 1½ inch | 37.5 | – | 100 | – |
| 1 inch | 28 | 100 | – | – |
| ¾ inch | 20 | – | 60–100 | – |
| No. 4 | 5 | 50–100 | 35–100 | 50–100 |
| No. 10 | 2 | 40–100 | – | – |
| No. 40 | 0.425 | – | 13–50 | 35–100 |
| No. 100 | 0.150 | – | 8–35 | – |
| No. 200 | 0.063 | 5–12 | – | – |
| Liquid limit (%) | | – | – | Good: 3–20<br>Fair: 0–3 and 20–30<br>Poor: > 30<br>Good: < 20<br>Fair: 20–30<br>Poor: 30–40<br>Unusable: > 40 |
| Plasticity index | | 10 | 10 | Good: < 5<br>Fair: 5–9<br>Poor: 9–15<br>Unusable: > 12–15 |

strength with little interference to the existing stability resulting from friction between the particles. Proper application implies using an optimum binder content so that the overall stability is increased.

Sand–bituminous-material mixtures may be used for a variety of purposes, the exact usage in a given situation depending primarily upon the quality of mixture-material desired, and also upon experience with and availability of the bituminous binders. These binders may be any one of the following.

(1) *Penetration-grade bitumens* American experience suggests that the most suitable bitumen grades are those with 85–100 and 120–150 penetration, but higher grades are also used. The use of these grades of material requires that the sands be preheated, and that both mixing and construction take place at high temperatures in a central mixing plant. Usually, the binder content used lies in the range 4 per cent (for soils with rounded and smooth aggregate particles) to 6 per cent (for angular and rough particles).
(2) *Cutbacks* Prior to the early 1970s—and the onset of the 'oil crisis'—American practice was for rapid-curing liquid cutback bitumens to be most commonly used to stabilize sandy soils; now, however, these cutbacks are less used, for reasons given previously (see Chapter 3).

The nearest equivalent British procedure[47], which was developed in the 1950s and is now rarely used, involved the pre-addition of a small amount of lime or cement to damp sand, together with a quantity of a special tar or cutback bitumen containing organic acid. The purpose of the acid was to promote a reaction between the binder and the hydrated lime to produce secondary products which enhanced adhesion to the sand particles. Mixing of the ingredient materials took place at ambient temperatures in paddle mixers, after which the mixture was spread by hand or machine in layers up to about 40 mm thick. Known as the 'wet-aggregate (hydrated lime) process', it was used for surface course construction; however, since the sand carpets formed in this way had relatively poor resistance to abrasion, they had to be covered with a surface dressing at the first sign of fretting.
(3) *Emulsions* Emulsions are not at all used in Britain to stabilize soils. They tend to be used mostly in warmer climates, e.g. the southern half of the USA, where the climatic conditions are more favourable. As the labile and semi-labile anionic emulsions tend to break up too quickly on application to the soil, fully-stable emulsions are mostly used for sand stabilization. Slow-acting cationic emulsions have also been successfully used for this purpose. Usually, mix-in-place types of mixers and blade-graders are used to mix the binder with the soil. After mixing, the mixture is normally allowed to aerate until the liquid content is down to the desired level for compaction, after which rolling is commenced.

### Sand–gravel–bituminous-material mixtures
These mixtures are generally used under similar conditions and circumstances as the sand–bituminous-material mixtures. Normally, a sand–gravel material falling into this category has a fairly good gradation and possesses good frictional characteristics, but has little cohesion. The

function of the added bituminous material is to act both as a binding and as a waterproofing agent. British recommendations in respect of sandy gravel to be used in the wet-aggregate (hydrated lime) process are also given in reference 47.

**Soil–bituminous-material mixtures**
This is a general term used to describe those mixtures in which a bituminous binder is used to stabilize the moisture contents of soils containing significant amounts of fine-grained material. The consensus of American experience is that a soil that can be satisfactorily stabilized with bitumen has less than 25 per cent of the material passing the 75 $\mu$m sieve size, a plasticity index less than 6, and the product of the plasticity index and the percentage less than 75 $\mu$m is less than 72 (Fig. 5.6).

Soils of greater plasticity cannot normally be used because of the difficulties experienced in dispersing the bitumen throughout the system. Soils being stabilized should contain little or no acid organic matter as this can be detrimental to the stability of a soil–bituminous-material mixture. Fine-grained soils which are very alkaline—these are usually found in arid and semi-arid regions—are also particularly difficult to stabilize with bituminous materials.

Only liquid bituminous materials are suitable for stabilizing cohesive soils; best results have been obtained with the more fluid of the medium-curing cutbacks.

The clay minerals present in the soil have a quite significant effect upon the stability of a soil–bituminous-material mixture. Kaolinitic soils are easy to stabilize, but montmorillonites can be difficult due to mixing problems. The greater the silica content of the clay mineral, the greater will be the amount of bituminous stabilizer required.

Lime has also been used jointly with a bituminous binder to stabilize soils for use in secondary roads and residential streets. Lime slurry pretreatment of the soil (at about one per cent lime content) reduces the plasticity index and promotes better mixing and coating with the bitumen. When the bitumen is added, the gain in strength and water resistance of the lime–bitumen-stabilized material can be far greater than simply the sum of the two binding actions taken separately. The addition of lime also promotes the curing of emulsified bitumen-treated mixtures.

It might be noted that an economic process (now patented) has been developed[48] which involves the introduction of hot or cold water under controlled flow and pressure into hot penetration-grade bitumen in a specially designed foaming chamber which discharges the foamed bitumen into the material to be stabilized. With this *foamed asphalt process*, clayey, sandy or granular soils can be satisfactorily stabilized in a moist condition with refinery bitumens using either stationary plants or mobile road mix plants. In many instances, the soils stabilized with this process would normally be considered unsuitable for stabilization with bitumen.

*Moisture content*    It is appropriate here to discuss the role which moisture plays as an ingredient of soil–bituminous-material mixtures. At first glance it might appear that, if it is desired to stabilize a soil by waterproofing it, the very last thing that is wanted is the addition of extra water to the mixture. In practice, however, not only are cohesive soils practically impossible to pulverize adequately without the presence of water, but water is also an essential ingredient during the actual mixing and compacting. During mixing, water facilitates the even distribution of the bituminous material throughout the soil mass. It is known, for example, that the amount of moisture required for the thorough distribution of cutback bitumen increases as the amount of fine material in the soil increases; in any given instance, the most uniform distribution is obtained at a moisture content somewhere in the neighbourhood of the liquid limit of the soil. In compaction, the amount of water is important mainly because of its effect upon dry density. Again, it is known that the moisture content for maximum dry density of the soil–bituminous-material mixture is different from that required for the soil alone.

While it is generally recognized that water is necessary in the mixture, there is not full agreement as to what exact content should be utilized in any particular situation. For instance, a value of moisture content which has gained a certain acceptance is called the *fluff point* of the soil. In itself, the term fluff point is a misnomer, since it is actually a range of moisture content points which gets narrower as the plasticity index of the soil increases. This range, which is usually between one-third and one-half of the standard Proctor optimum moisture content for the soil, brackets the water contents at which the soil will 'fluff' to its maximum extent. The logic here is that, since this is the condition where the greatest amount of voids is apparent in the soil water mixture, this should be the best condition at which to admix the bituminous material.

The effects resulting from the bituminous volatiles which are present during the compaction of soil–bituminous-material mixtures are also not clearly understood. For example, during the course of stabilization with cutback bitumens, it is usual to include a period of aeration between mixing and compaction to allow the volatiles to escape; this is because bitumen-volatile loss is associated with increases in the strength of compacted mixtures. Again, however, there are considerable differences in the recommended aeration periods. These have ranged from that required for a reduction of at least one-fifth to that for a reduction of one-half of the original combined percentage of water and bitumen volatiles. What can be said categorically at this time is that the percentages of mixing water required to produce maximum strength, maximum dry density, minimum absorption during immersion, and minimum swelling of soil–bituminous-material mixtures are different for each property mentioned [49].

**Oiled-earth treatments**
The term oiled-earth is used when a bituminous material of low viscosity is applied to the exposed surface of a moist, densely compacted soil. While in Sweden the same term is applied to surfacings composed of premixed mixtures of gravel and heated road oils [50], it is normally reserved for processes in which the bituminous material is applied cold to the surface of the

in situ soil and allowed to penetrate downwards under the force of gravity. Since its main functions are simply to protect the underlying material from the deleterious effects brought about by changes in moisture content and to minimize the dust nuisance, the process may be used with any type of soil. Normally, however, it is utilized only when use of the other, higher forms of bituminous stabilization is not feasible.

Most effective results have been obtained with the oiled-earth process when slow-curing cutbacks were applied to the clean surfaces of soils which were mechanically stable, well compacted and well drained. The use of slow-curing cutbacks is to be preferred for a number of reasons. Not only do the volatiles not escape so rapidly, thereby allowing more time for the bituminous material to seep into the soil, but it is also found that, when seepage is complete, fractionation of the cutback has occurred with the heavier bitumen remaining at the top of the stabilized layer. This has the additional advantage that the lower and more liquid constituents of the bituminous material act to replace water which might otherwise have evaporated in hot, dry weather, thereby helping to prevent the ravelling of the surface which would occur if the soil was allowed to dry out.

## Some other chemical stabilization methods

Before discussing some of these other stabilization methods, it must be emphasized that they are all still regarded as being in the experimental stage—notwithstanding that their usage has been studied over many decades.

### Sodium silicate

Sodium silicate is available in various forms, e.g. sodium ortho-silicate ($Na_2SiO_7$), sodium sesquisilicate ($Na_6Si_2O_7$), sodium metasilicate ($Na_2SiO_3$), and sodium disilicate ($Na_2Si_2O_5$). Sodium silicates have various uses to which they can be put—e.g. as adhesives, cements, detergents, deflocculents, rust inhibitors and catalyst bases—and so they are readily available and easily obtained for commercial use.

The best known sodium silicate stabilization process is that originally developed by the Dutch engineer, H Joosten, for use as a grout into deep foundations. He found that an injection of sodium silicate followed by an injection of calcium chloride resulted in the instantaneous formation of an insoluble gel of calcium silicates which filled the soil voids and provided considerable strength, while at the same time preventing the seepage of water. Another injection method of interest is that developed by C Langer of France in 1934, in which the precipitation reaction is much slower than in the Joosten two-shot method. This process enables the admixture of the second chemical to the sodium silicate solution to take place prior to injection, and the combination is then injected as a single shot.

The use of sodium silicate as a soil stabilizing agent on its own is due to its ability to react with soluble calcium salts in water to form cementing agents composed of insoluble, gelatinous calcium silicates. From the relatively limited evidence[51] that is available, it would appear that sodium silicate alone or in combination with certain chemical precipitants can stabilize sandy soils and produce a roadbase or subbase that could well retain its beneficial effects in mild climates. However, the total cost of the sodium silicate additives necessary to achieve stability is probably greater than that of stabilizers such as Portland cement with which much more experience is available.

Sodium silicates with or without precipitants are of little value in dust-proofing or waterproofing fine-grained soils. On the basis of laboratory tests, various sodium silicates used as secondary additives appear to improve the strength and durability of non-plastic soils stabilized with Portland cement, lime, or lime–fly-ash. They appear to be especially useful in increasing the resistance of cement-stabilized soils to sulphate attack.

## Organic cationic stabilizers

Organic cationic chemicals are those compounds, organic in nature, which dissociate in water to produce organic cations with exceedingly complex structures. Compared with the inorganic cations such as calcium, magnesium, hydrogen or sodium, the organic cations are very large; hence the term 'large organic cations' which is frequently used in the literature when discussing these stabilizers.

Numerous organic cationic chemicals have been tested for effectiveness as soil stabilizing agents[52] and several shown to be feasible for use in road construction. Of these, a quarternary ammonium chloride will be described here as an illustration of how an organic cationic chemical may stabilize a soil.

A quarternary ammonium chloride may be thought of as an organic counterpart of ammonium chloride ($NH_4Cl$) which has all its hydrogen atoms replaced by organic groups. One of the more effective of these salts is a dihydrogenated, tallow, dimethyl ammonium chloride, which is available in the USA under various trade names. When added to a soil, a rapid cation-exchange reaction takes place between the organic cationic compound and the inorganic cations on the clay surfaces. This has the effect of tending to flocculate the clay particles and lowering the plasticity index by reducing the surface charges of the particles, thereby lessening the ability of the clay to take up moisture. In the case of montmorillonitic soils, the organic cations are also adsorbed between layers of the expandable lattice minerals, thereby retarding changes in the thickness of the water film between these layers and reducing swelling and shrinking. In addition, the organic cations partially coat the clay surfaces with thin hydrophobic films which have little or no affinity for water; thus the soil particles are waterproofed. Hence it can be seen that the water stability of an aggregated, clayey soil can be increased by the waterproofing action of the organic cationic compound.

## Resinous stabilizers

A resin may be defined as a solid or semi-solid, complex, amorphous mixture or organic substance which has no definite melting point and shows no tendency to crystallize. It is characterized by such physical properties as a typical lustre and a conchoidal fracture rather than by a definite chemical composition. Common plastics are composed of synthetic resins and filler material. Thus it is a useful analogy to consider soil stabilized with resin as essentially a mixture in which the soil particles act as filler material in a kind of plastic.

*Vinsol resin* and *rosin* are two natural resinous agents which have been studied[53] for their waterproofing characteristics. Vinsol resin ($C_{27}H_{30}O_5$) is made from the residues obtained after the distillation of pine tree stumps in the manufacture of turpentine. Rosin is also obtained as a byproduct of turpentine extraction and its chief constituent is abietic acid ($C_{19}H_{29}COOH$). Resins are believed to waterproof a soil by forming thin coatings on the moisture at the air–water interfaces in soil pores. When an initial amount of moisture has been absorbed by the soil, the air spaces become filled and the air–water interface diminishes in area. This, in turn, causes the resin film coating to be crowded into a smaller surface area. The resistance of the film to compression reduces the surface tension of the water to zero, thereby opposing the further entry of water.

The maximum waterproofing effect of these resinous materials is developed within about three days after mixing takes place. There appears to be an optimum amount of admixture for a given soil, as when too much is added the water absorption of the mixture increases. Stability is dependent upon the original strength characteristics of the untreated soil, which the resins then simply help to preserve.

*Calcium acrylate* is a white powder which has the special advantage of being about 30 per cent soluble in water at normal temperatures; this means that it is very easily added to and dispersed throughout a soil. When a catalyst (ammonium persulphate) and an activator (sodium thiosulphate) are added to the solution, polymerization takes place and results in the formation of a water-insoluble gel which imparts unique rubbery properties to the soil within a few hours. When dried so that the polymer contains less than about 25 per cent water, cross-linkages are formed; this results in a hard, rigid, stabilized soil which in this state is an excellent pavement material. Unfortunately, this rigid state is not permanent, for when it is again subjected to excessive moisture it reverts to its former rubbery condition.

American field studies have shown that between four and six per cent of this chemical can stabilize a loess soil sufficiently in four to six hours to allow temporary lorry traffic over it. However, because of its reversible characteristics—as well as its high cost—it can only be considered as an emergency stop-gap method where the rate of hardening is critical. In this sense, it is important to note that the polymerization rate is easily controlled by adjusting the catalyst–activator concentration; a greater concentration will reduce the polymerization rate.

# Selected bibliography

(1) Meyers B, Iowa studies surfacing problems, *Better Roads*, 1947, **17**, pp. 29–31.
(2) Huang EY, *Manual of Current Practice for Design, Construction and Maintenance of Soil–aggregate Roads*, Urbana, Illinois, The University of Illinois Engineering Experiment Station, 1959.
(3) Metcalf JB, *Introductory Pavement Lectures*, ARR Report 47A, Vermont South, Victoria, The Australian Road Research Board, 1981.
(4) Searle PG, Traditional testing methods, *Proceedings of the NAASRA/ARRB Workshop on the Use of Relative Compaction in the Control of Roadworks*, pp. 107–122, Vermont South, Victoria, The Australian Road Research Board, 1982.
(5) BS 1377: *Methods of Test for Soils for Civil Engineering Purposes*, London, The British Standards Institution, 1975.
(6) Hamory GI, Calibration, stability and use of nuclear meters, *Proceedings of the NAASRA/ARRB Workshop on the use of Relative Compaction in the Control of Roadworks*, pp. 139–150, Vermont South, Victoria, The Australian Road Research Board, 1982.
(7) BS 6031: *Earthworks*, London, The British Standards Institution, 1981.
(8) Department of Transport, *Specification for Highway Works*, London, HMSO, 1986.
(9) Morris PO, *Compaction—A Review*, ARR Report 35, Vermont South, Victoria, The Australian Road Research Board, 1975.
(10) Lewis WA, *Investigation of the Performance of Pneumatic-tyred Rollers in the Compaction of Soil*, Road Research Technical Paper No. 45, London, HMSO, 1959.
(11) Jeffries TG, Fill compaction by vibrating rollers: Theory and practice, *Highways and Road Construction*, 1973, **41**, No. 1767, pp. 33–36.
(12) Clifford JM, The impact roller—problems solved, *The Civil Engineer in South Africa*, 1978, **20**, No. 12, pp. 321–324.
(13) *The Impact Roller*, Transport and Road Digest No. 6, Pretoria, SA, The National Institute for Transport and Road Research, August 1978.
(14) Charles JA, Burford D and Watts KS, Improving the load carrying characteristics of uncompacted fills by preloading, *Municipal Engineer*, 1986, **3**, No. 1, pp. 1–19.
(15) Murray RT and Symons IF, *Embankments on Soft Foundations*: *Settlement and Study at Tickton in Yorkshire*, TRRL Report LR643, Crowthorne, Berks., The Transport and Road Research Laboratory, 1974.
(16) Symons IF and Murray RT, *Embankments on Soft Foundations*: *Settlement and Stability Study of Over Causeway By-pass*, TRRL Report LR675, Crowthorne, Berks., The Transport and Road Research Laboratory, 1975.
(17) Lewis WA, Murray RT and Symons IF, Settlement and stability of embankments constructed on soft alluvial soil, Part 2, *Proc. Inst. Civ. Engrs*, 1975, **59**, pp. 571–593.
(18) Cross JE, *An Economic Assessment of Methods of Accelerating the Consolidation of Natural Soils*, TRRL Report SR203, Crowthorne, Berks., The Transport and Road Research Laboratory, 1977.
(19) Pearce RW, Contribution to the discussion: Construction, placement and methods of treatment of clay fills, *Clay Fills*, pp. 279–281, London, The Institution of Civil Engineers, 1979.
(20) Kjellman W, Consolidation of clay soil by means of atmospheric pressure, *Conference on Soil Stabilization*, pp. 258–274, Boston, Massachusetts, The Massachusetts Institute of Technology, 1952.

(21) Grainger GD, A study of burnt clay as a roadmaking aggregate, *Recherches et Essais sur les Structures en Terra Cuite, Symposium RILEM*, Milan, 1962, Rome, 1965.

(22) Willis EA, Design requirements for graded mixtures suitable for road surfaces and base courses, *Proc. Highway Research Board*, 1938, **18**, Part II, pp. 206–208.

(23) *Structural Design of Low-volume Roads*, Transportation Technology Support for Developing Countries Synthesis 4, Washington DC, The Transportation Research Board, 1982.

(24) BS 5835: Part 1: *Testing of Aggregates: Compactability Test for Graded Aggregates*, London, The British Standards Institution, 1980.

(25) Ola SM, Corrugations on gravel and lateritic roads, *Transportation Engineering Journal of ASCE*, 1978, **104**, No. TE2, pp. 227–237.

(26) Davidson DT and Handy RL, Soil stabilization with chlorides and lignin derivatives, in: Woods KB, *Highway Engineering Handbook*, Maidenhead, McGraw Hill, 1960.

(27) Thornburn TH and Mura R, Stabilization of soils with inorganic salts and bases: A review of the literature, *Highway Research Record 294*, 1969, pp. 1–22.

(28) Terrel RL et al, *Evaluation of Wood Lignin as a Substitute or Extender of Asphalt*, FHA Report No. FHWA/RD-80/125, Springfield, Virginia, The National Technical Information Service, October 1980.

(29) Road Research Laboratory, Dust-laying on unsurfaced earth and gravel roads, in: *Surface Treatment*, Transportation Technology Support for Developing Countries Compendium 12, Text 1, Washington DC, The Transportation Research Board, 1980.

(30) Catton MD, Early soil–cement research and development, *Proc. Amer. Soc. Civ. Engrs, Journal of the Highway Division*, January 1959, **85**, No. HWI, Paper No. 1899.

(31) Committee on Soil–Portland-cement Stabilization, Soil stabilization with Portland cement, *Highway Research Board Bulletin 292*, 1961.

(32) Terrel, Epps, and Associates, *Soil Stabilization in Pavement Structures: A User's Manual*, Volumes 1 and 2, Washington DC, Federal Highway Administration, October 1979.

(33) Sherwood PT, *The Properties of Cement Stabilized Materials*, RRL Report LR205, Crowthorne, Berks., The Road Research Laboratory, 1968.

(34) Lilley AA and Williams RIT, Cement-stabilized materials in Great Britain, *Highway Research Record 442*, 1973, pp. 70–82.

(35) Williams RIT, Lean concrete roadbases, *Highways and Road Construction International*, 1976, **44**, No. 1795, pp. 5–11 and p. 26, and No. 1796, pp. 4–11.

(36) Walker BJ, Dry and wet cement stabilized materials for concrete pavement and subbases, *Proceedings of the International Colloquium on Concrete Roads*, pp. 8–20, Besancon, September 1978.

(37) *Soil Cement Laboratory Handbook*, Chicago, Illinois, The Portland Cement Association, 1956.

(38) Sherwood PT, Effect of sulphates on cement and lime-stabilized soils, *Highway Research Board Bulletin 353*, 1962, pp. 98–107.

(39) Bofinger HE, Hassan HO and Williams RIT, *The Shrinkage of Fine-grained Soil-cement*, TRRL Report SR398, Crowthorne, Berks., The Transport and Road Research Laboratory, 1978.

(40) Kolias S and Williams RIT, *Cement-bound Road Materials: Strength and Elastic Properties Measured in the Laboratory*, TRRL Report SR344,

Crowthorne, Berks., The Transport and Road Research Laboratory, 1978.

(41) Committee on Lime and Lime–fly-ash Stabilization, *State of the Art: Lime Stabilization*, Transportation Research Circular 180, September 1976.

(42) Stocker PT, *Diffusion and Diffuse Cementation in Lime and Cement Stabilized Clayey Soils*, Special Report 8, Vermont South, Victoria, The Australian Road Research Board, 1972.

(43) Ormsby WC and Kinter EB, Effects of dolomitic and calcitic limes on strength development in mixtures with two clay minerals, *Public Roads*, 1973, **37**, No. 4, pp. 149–156.

(44) Mateos M and Davidson DT, Steam curing and X-ray studies of fly ashes, *Proc. ASTM*, 1962, **62**, pp. 1008–1018.

(45) *Soil Bituminous Roads*, Current Road Problems No. 12, Washington DC, The Highway Research Board, 1946.

(46) Williamson R, State of the art of emulsion pavements in Region 6 of the US Forest Service, in: *Low Volume Roads*, Special Report 160, Washington DC, The Transportation Research Board, 1975.

(47) Road Research Laboratory, *Bituminous Surfacings Made by the Wet-aggregate (hydrated lime) Process*, Road Note 16, London, HMSO, 1953.

(48) Lee DY, Treating marginal aggregates and soils with foamed asphalt, *Proceedings of the Association of Asphalt Paving Technologists*, 1981, **50**, pp. 211–245.

(49) Katti RK, Davidson DT and Sheeler JB, Water in cutback asphalt stabilization of soil, *Highway Research Board Bulletin 241*, 1960, pp. 17–49.

(50) Hallberg S, A brief account of Swedish experiments with oil treatment of gravel roads, *Roads and Road Construction*, 1958, **36**, p. 421.

(51) Hurley CH and Thornburn TH, Sodium silicate stabilization of soils: A review of the literature, *Highway Research Record 381*, 1972, pp. 46–79.

(52) Hoover JM and Davidson DT, Organic cationic chemicals as stabilizing agents for Iowa loess, *Highway Research Board Bulletin 129*, 1956, pp. 10–25.

(53) Clarke KE, The waterproofing of soil by resinous materials, *J. Soc. Chem. Ind.*, 1949, **68**, pp. 69–76.

# 6
# Flexible pavements: design and construction

## Terminology

A highway pavement is a structure consisting of superimposed layers of selected and processed materials placed on a subgrade, whose primary function is to support the applied traffic loads and distribute them to the basement soil. The ultimate aim is to ensure that the transmitted stresses are sufficiently reduced that they will not exceed the supporting capacity of the subgrade. Two types of pavement are arbitrarily recognized as serving this purpose—flexible pavements and rigid pavements.

A flexible pavement is a pavement structure that maintains intimate contact with, and distributes loads to, the subgrade; it depends upon aggregate interlock, particle friction, and cohesion for its stability. The distinguishing feature of a flexible pavement lies in its structural mechanics—the pressure is usually *assumed* to be transmitted to the subgrade through the lateral distribution of the applied load with depth, rather than by beam and slab action as with a concrete slab. Thus a flexible pavement can be most easily defined by contrasting it with a rigid Portland cement concrete pavement.

When the subgrade deflects beneath a rigid pavement, the concrete slab is able to bridge over localized failures and areas of inadequate support because of its rigidity and high modulus of elasticity. The major factor influencing the design of a rigid pavement is the structural strength of the concrete, and its thickness is relatively little affected by the quality of the subgrade as long as it meets certain minimum criteria.

In direct contrast to this, the strength of the subgrade is a major factor controlling the design of a flexible pavement. When the subgrade deflects, the overlying flexible pavement is assumed to deform to a similar shape and extent. In fact, this does not necessarily happen, e.g. pavements with bituminous-bound or chemically stabilized roadbases have beam strengths which increase with thickness and help support the imposed loads. Nonetheless, these pavements are still generally classed as flexible pavements, and the assumed basic design criterion is that a depth of pavement is required that will distribute the applied surface load through the various pavement layers to the subgrade so that the subgrade is not over-stressed.

In its simplest form, a flexible pavement is generally considered to be any pavement other than a concrete one. It is this definition that is accepted by the great majority of practising engineers and so it is the one that will be used here. It should be clearly understood, however, that the term is simply one of convenience and does not truly reflect the characteristics of the many different and composite types of construction masquerading as 'flexible' pavements.

## Elements of a flexible pavement

Before discussing in detail the various features of a flexible road, it is necessary to mention briefly some terminology. As illustrated in Fig. 6.1, the cross-section of a flexible road is composed of a *pavement* superimposed on the basement soil or subgrade. The intersection of the subgrade and the pavement is known as the *formation*.

Whether it is a pavement for an expensive motorway or a simple country road, the basic structural cross-section is essentially that illustrated in Fig. 6.1; it is composed of several distinct layers superimposed on the subgrade in the manner indicated.

The subgrade is normally considered to be the in situ soil over which the highway is being constructed. It should be quite clear, however, that the term subgrade is also applied to all native soil materials exposed by excavation and to excavated soil that may be artificially deposited to form a compacted embankment. In the latter case, the added material is not considered to be part of the road structure itself but part of the foundation of the road.

### Surface course

The uppermost layer of a flexible pavement is called the surface course. The highway materials used in a surface course can vary from loose mixtures of soil and gravel to the very-highest-quality bituminous mixtures. The choice of materials used in any particular situation depends in most countries upon the quality of service required of the highway.

If a surface course is composed of bituminous materials—as is the normal practice for flexible pavements in Britain—it may consist of a single homogeneous layer or, in the higher-quality roads, of two distinct sub-layers known as a wearing course and a basecourse. The *wearing course* provides the actual surfacing on which the vehicles run, whilst the *basecourse* acts as a regulating layer to provide the wearing course with a better

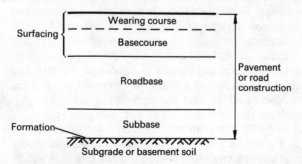

**Fig. 6.1**  Diagrammatic illustration of the structural elements of a flexible pavement

riding quality. The basecourse is normally composed of a more pervious material than the wearing course.

The primary function of the surface course, and especially of its wearing course component, is to provide a safe and comfortable riding surface for traffic. It must also withstand the most concentrated stresses due to traffic, and protect the pavement layers beneath from the effects of the natural elements.

Bituminous surfacings are generally expected: (a) to contribute to the structural strength of the pavement, (b) to provide a high resistance to plastic deformation and resistance to cracking under traffic, and (c) to maintain such desirable surface characteristics as good skid-resistance, good drainage, and low tyre noise.

### Roadbase

This layer must not be confused with the basecourse, which is an integral part of the surface course. One is a sub-layer within the bituminous surfacing, while the other is normally the thickest element of the flexible pavement on which the surfacing rests.

From a structural aspect, the roadbase is the most important layer of a flexible pavement. It is expected to bear the burden of distributing the applied surface loads so that the bearing capacity of the subgrade is not exceeded. Since it provides the pavement with added stiffness and resistance to fatigue, as well as contributing to the overall thickness, the material used in a roadbase must always be of a reasonably high quality. Roadbase materials range from unbound soils and/or aggregates, to chemically stabilized soils, to cement/bitumen-bound materials.

### Subbase

In its simplest sense, this layer can be considered merely as an extension of the roadbase; in fact, it may or may not be present in the pavement as a separate layer. Whether or not it is utilized in a pavement depends upon the purpose for which it is to be used. Its function can be examined from a number of aspects, as follows.

(1)   As a structural member of the pavement the subbase helps to distribute the applied loads to the subgrade. The subbase material must always be significantly stronger than the subgrade material and capable of resisting within itself the stresses transmitted to it via the roadbase.

(2)   A coarse-grained material may be used in the subbase to act as a drainage layer, i.e. to pass to the highway drainage system any moisture which falls during construction or which enters the pavement after construction. The quality of the material used must be such that the free-draining criterion of the subbase is always met; in certain instances, this may require a *dual-layer* subbase, i.e. an open-graded layer with a protective filter.

(3)   On fine-grained subgrade soils a granular subbase may be provided: (a) to carry constructional traffic and act as a working platform on which subsequent layers can be constructed, (b) to act as a cutoff blanket and

prevent moisture from migrating upward from the subgrade, or (c) to act as a cutoff blanket to prevent the infiltration of subgrade material into the pavement.

The type of material used in any of these designs depends upon the purpose for which it is being used and the grading of the subgrade soil.

## Basic stress considerations

As compared with many other engineering design procedures, the design of flexible pavements is at an early stage. The development of a rational design procedure is at present being investigated from two aspects. Firstly, studies are being carried out by means of theoretical and laboratory analyses of the static and dynamic stresses induced by traffic, the stress–deformation characteristics of the layers in the road under various forms of loading, and the variation of these properties with time. The second approach leans towards the construction and observation of full-scale experimental test roads, of which the most notable examples are the WASHO[1] and AASHO[2] roads in the USA and the Boroughbridge and Alconbury Hill test roads[3–5] in Britain.

Before describing some of the practical design procedures that have emerged from these studies, the following discussion on stress considerations presents some of the variables which must be evaluated in developing a rational design procedure.

### Stress distribution

The vertical pressure on any horizontal plane in or beneath a pavement, due to the wheel load applied at the surface, is distributed over an area that is considerably larger than the area of contact between the tyre and the carriageway. While the total vertical pressure on the horizontal plane is equal to the applied load at the surface, the greatest vertical stress occurs directly beneath the centre of the tyre–carriageway contact area; it reduces as the horizontal distance away from the centre increases.

Thinking in terms of a three-dimensional graph which has two horizontal axes drawn to linear scales, while the remaining (vertical) axis has force units, then simplistically the pressure distribution on any horizontal plane in the pavement or subgrade can be considered to be represented by a helmet-shaped surface. The base of this pressure-helmet tends to have an elliptical shape because of the approximately elliptical outline of the contact area between the tyre and the carriageway. The height of the helmet, which represents the maximum pressure, varies according to the depth of the horizontal plane beneath the surface; its height decreases and the helmet-shaped stress surface flattens out as the depth increases.

#### Boussinesq theory

If the material through which the applied stresses are being transmitted is considered to be an idealized, elastic, homogeneous and isotropic mass which extends infinite distances both laterally and vertically downwards from where the load is applied to a level surface, it is possible to determine the stresses at any point within the mass by means of the theoretical equations developed by the French elastician Boussinesq. These equations, which completely define the normal stresses at various coordinate distances from the point of application of a concentrated load, $P$, are given below.

$$\sigma_z = \frac{3P}{2\pi} \frac{z^3}{R^5} = \frac{3P}{2\pi} \frac{\cos^5 \theta}{z^2}$$

$$\sigma_x = \frac{P}{2\pi} \left[ \frac{3x^2 z}{R^5} - (1 - 2\mu) \left( \frac{x^2 - y^2}{Rr^2(R + z)} + \frac{y^2 z}{R^3 r^2} \right) \right]$$

$$\sigma_y = \frac{P}{2\pi} \left[ \frac{3y^2 z}{R^5} - (1 - 2\mu) \left( \frac{y^2 - x^2}{Rr^2(R + z)} + \frac{x^2 z}{R^3 r^2} \right) \right]$$

where $\mu$ is Poisson's ratio and the other symbols are as given in Fig. 6.2.

Here the normal and shear stresses which keep a minute cube of material in equilibrium are denoted by $\sigma$ and $\tau$. Their subscripts denote the orientation of the lines of action; thus $\sigma_z$ is a normal stress acting on the plane normal to the $z$-axis and $\tau_{xz}$ indicates the shearing stress acting in a plane normal to the $x$-axis and on a line of action parallel to the $z$-axis.

These equations have been integrated to determine the stresses beneath a uniformly loaded circular area. The vertical and horizontal normal stresses at any point directly below the centre of the loaded area are given by

$$\sigma_z = p \left[ 1 - \frac{z^3}{(a^2 + z^2)^{3/2}} \right]$$

and $\quad \sigma_x = \sigma_y = \frac{p}{2} \left[ 1 + 2\mu - \frac{2z(1 + \mu)}{(a^2 + z^2)^{1/2}} + \frac{z^3}{(a^2 + z^2)^{3/2}} \right]$

In the latter equations, $p$ is the uniform load applied over a circular area of radius $a$, and the other symbols are as given above.

It should be noted here that these equations are independent of the soil modulus of elasticity. In addition, the vertical stress equation is independent of Poisson's ratio as well.

*Poisson's ratio*  Poisson's ratio ($\mu$) is defined as the ratio of the strain normal to the applied stress to the strain parallel to the applied stress. It is an inherent property of an elastic material and ranges between zero and 0.5. A material such as cork has a $\mu$-value approximately equal to zero. An incompressible material will have a maximum $\mu$-value of 0.5; this occurs when the decrease in volume of a vertical cylinder under vertical compression is approximately equal to the increase in volume due to lateral expansion. Values obtained for some typical pavement materials are given in Table 6.1.

*Deflection equations*  Accepting the Boussinesq vertical and horizontal stress equations, it can be shown that the total elastic deformation at the

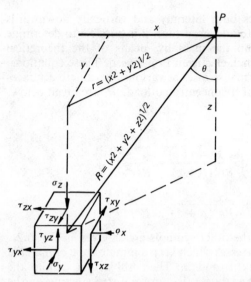

**Fig. 6.2**   Stresses acting on an element due to a point load according to Boussinesq

surface at the centre of the applied uniform load is given by

$$\Delta = \frac{2pa}{E}(1 - \mu^2)$$

where $\Delta$ = total deflection, $p$ = applied uniform load, $a$ = radius of circular contact area, $E$ = modulus of elasticity of material, and $\mu$ = Poisson's ratio.

If a pavement of depth $z$ is interposed between the subgrade and the applied load at the surface, then the total elastic deformation in the subgrade, i.e. from depth $z$ to infinity, is given by

$$\Delta = \frac{p}{E}\left[(2 - 2\mu^2)(a^2 + z^2)^{1/2} - \frac{z^2(1 + \mu)}{(a^2 + z^2)^{1/2}} + z(\mu + 2\mu^2 - 1)\right]$$

When Poisson's ratio is taken as equal to 0.5, the two above deflection equations become

$$\Delta = \frac{1.5pa^2}{E}$$

and   $$\Delta = \frac{1.5pa^2}{E(a^2 + z^2)^{1/2}}$$

respectively.

It should be noted that the deflections obtained from these two equations become the same when $z$ approaches zero, and it is clear that the deflections in the pavement itself are not taken into account by the equations.

*Validity of Boussinesq equations*   The values obtained by the Boussinesq equations can be considered to be quite valid for a very uniform (non-

**Table 6.1** Stiffness characteristics of some pavement materials[6]

| Material | Stiffness modulus | Poisson's ratio ($\mu$) |
|---|---|---|
| Asphaltic concrete | $30 \times 10^3$ MPa at short times of loading and cold temperatures ($<4.5\,^\circ$C) to 140 MPa at long times of loading and high temperatures ($<49\,^\circ$C) | 0.3 for high stiffness to 0.5 for low stiffness |
| Cement-treated | | |
| granular materials | $7 \times 10^3$ to $35 \times 10^3$ MPa | 0.1 to 0.2 |
| fine-grained soils | $0.7 \times 10^3$ to $7 \times 10^3$ MPa | 0.15 to 0.35 |
| Untreated granular materials | Triaxial compression repeated load test: modulus $= kA^n$ where $A = \sigma_1 + 2\sigma_3$, $n = 0.4$ to $0.6$, and $k = 7 \times 10^3$ to $70 \times 10^3$ when $A$ is in kPa | 0.30 to 0.35 |
| Subgrade soils | General range: 6.9 to 350.0 MPa (fine-grained soils) Triaxial compression repeated load test: modulus $= k\sigma_d^n$ where $\sigma_d = \sigma_1 - \sigma_3$ and $n$ is a negative coefficient | 0.3 to 0.5, depending upon the degree of saturation |

layered) soil in which the boundary conditions are compatible with the theoretical assumptions and the modulus of elasticity of the soil is constant.

Usually, however, the environmental conditions are different from the theoretical assumptions and, as a result, the theoretical Boussinesq values are considerably different from the actual ones. In particular, for a flexible pavement superimposed upon a subgrade soil the equations clearly do not hold true. For instance, the deflection equation takes no account of the stress distribution properties of the stronger materials in the pavement and assumes that the deflection in the subgrade is simply a function of the radial distance, $a$, the applied surface load, $p$, and the modulus of elasticity of the subgrade soil, $E$. As a result, the theoretical deflections in the subgrade are usually greater than the actual values beneath a road pavement.

The reliance placed upon the modulus of elasticity is also subject to discussion, as soils and pavement materials are not truly elastic and do not exhibit constant stress–strain relationships. Instead of being a straight line, the stress–strain relationship under any one cycle of load is more likely to take the form of a convex curve such that the ratio decreases as the strain increases. Thus, to determine the modulus, it is necessary to choose a point arbitrarily on the curve and to draw a line from this point through the origin; the slope of this line is then taken as the secant modulus of elasticity.

As a consequence of the non-truly-elastic nature of pavement materials and soils, the worldwide tendency in recent years has been to use the overall term resilient modulus instead of the term modulus of elasticity. In this context, the resilient modulus is defined as the quotient of repeated axial stress in triaxial compression by the recoverable axial strain.

Strain depends upon the temperature and the time for which the stress is applied in the case of viscoelastic tar- or bitumen-bound materials. For this reason, the term *stiffness* or *stiffness modulus* (see Table 6.1) is usually substituted for modulus of elasticity as the ratio of stress to strain for

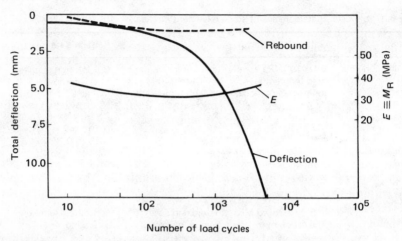

**Fig. 6.3**    Rebound–deflection history of a crushed stone material

bituminous materials. Under moving traffic conditions, the more specific term *dynamic stiffness* is used, i.e. dynamic stiffness is thus seen as depending upon temperature and vehicle speed (which defines the loading time).

Whatever the nomenclature used, it should be appreciated that the modulus can also vary according to the number of load cycles applied before the modulus is determined. Figure 6.3 shows a plot of deflection, rebound and modulus of elasticity versus number of loading cycles (measured under triaxial conditions[7]) for a crushed stone material used in the AASHO Road Test. From this figure it can be seen that: (a) the total deflection increased as the number of load cycles increased, and (b) the modulus first decreased as loads were applied and then increased (after about 500 load cycles).

In the case of bituminous materials, increases in temperature result in decreases in stiffness—which in practice means that the ambient temperature influences the magnitude of the maximum stresses transmitted to subsequent pavement layers and the subgrade.

While the Boussinesq equations are not directly applicable to roadway design conditions, they have been presented here because of the basic concepts that they illustrate, and because of the considerable importance that is currently attached to elastic theory as a means of estimating the stresses and deflections in and beneath the pavement. A measure of the importance of elastic theory can be gained by considering Table 6.2 which lists various flexible pavement design concepts presented at a major international conference in 1982, which utilized theory in their development.

Examination of the literature shows that there is disagreement among investigators regarding the properties to be assigned to the layers above the subgrade. The uppermost layer is regarded by some as an elastic plate, by others as an elastic layer. The difference between the two approaches is that an elastic plate is considered to undergo bending deformation but no vertical deformation under direct stress, whereas in an elastic layer all the stresses are considered and no restrictions are placed upon the deflections. The elastic layer concept is thus a more general treatment of the problem. Actual measurements show that transient compression of the upper layer does occur, indicating that it behaves as an elastic layer and not as a plate. Some data illustrating the validity of this statement are presented in Fig. 6.4.

There are also some differences of opinion regarding continuity conditions between the different layers. Some theories assume the interfaces between the layers to be perfectly smooth and without friction, while others assume them to be rough so that the strains are completely transmitted across them. The interfaces occurring in practice are unlikely to be ideally rough, but they are certainly far from being smooth. The theories can only deal with the two extreme conditions, so it seems preferable to consider the interfaces as rough, since it is closer to the condition which actually exists in the field.

It is generally accepted that Burmister[10] was the first to develop theories which were reasonably close to actual conditions in a flexible road pavement. In the practical design procedures, based on a semi-theoretical/ theoretical approach, which are proposed for use today, stresses and strains induced in the subgrade and the layers making up the highway pavement are generally determined by generalization of Burmister's theoretical approach.

Stress and deformation values obtained by Burmister's theories are dependent upon the moduli of the different layers. Since typical flexible roads are normally composed of layers whose moduli decrease with depth, the net effect is that the Burmister equations predict stresses and deflections in the subgrade that are considerably less than those obtained from the Boussinesq equations. This is illustrated for the two-layer system in Fig. 6.5, which compares results obtained by the Boussinesq theory and Burmister's two-layer theory.

On the left-hand side of Fig. 6.5, the applied wheel load can be considered as resting directly on a subgrade with a modulus $E_2$. On the right-hand side of the figure, a pavement of thickness $h_1$ and modulus $E_1$ is inserted and the stresses calculated taking this into account. The data are plotted in the form of bulbs of pressure for the two systems. A bulb of pressure is a surface obtained by connecting points of equal stress on the

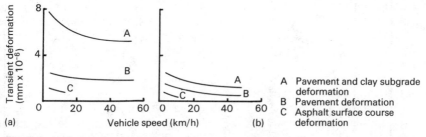

**Fig. 6.4** Variation of transient deformation with vehicle speed[9]: (a) 31.15 kN dual wheel and (b) 11.1 kN single wheel

**Table 6.2** Some semi-theoretical pavement design procedures[8]

| | Author/organization | Pavement representation | Distress modes | Environmental effects | Pavement materials | Design format |
|---|---|---|---|---|---|---|
| 1 | Brown, Brunton and Pell, University of Nottingham, UK | Multilayer elastic solid | Fatigue in treated layers<br>Rutting | Temperature | Hot rolled asphalt<br>Dense bituminous macadam<br>Untreated aggregate | Computer program<br>Design charts |
| 2 | Shook, Finn, Witczak and Monismith, The Asphalt Institute, USA | Multilayer elastic solid | Fatigue in treated layers<br>Rutting | Temperature<br>Freezing and thawing | Asphaltic concrete<br>Asphalt-emulsion-treated bases<br>Untreated aggregate | Computer program<br>DAMA<br>Design charts |
| 3 | Verstraeten, Veverka and Francken, Centre de Recherches Routieres, Belgium | Multilayer elastic solid | Fatigue in treated layers<br>Rutting | Temperature | Asphaltic concrete<br>Asphalt-stabilized bases<br>Untreated aggregate | Computer program<br>Design charts |
| 4 | Battiato and Verga, ASSORENI, Italy | Viscoelastic layered solid | Fatigue in treated layers<br>Rutting | Temperature | Asphaltic concrete<br>Gussasphalt<br>Untreated aggregate | — |
| 5 | Hsia, Richter and Padgett, US Forest Service, Pleasant Hill Engineering Center, CA, USA | Multilayer elastic solid | Fatigue in treated layers<br>Rutting | Temperature<br>Road aspect | Asphaltic concrete<br>Untreated aggregate | Computer program |
| 6 | Lister, Powell and Goddard, TRRL, UK | Multilayer elastic solid | Fatigue in treated layers | Temperature | Hot rolled asphalt<br>Dense bituminous macadam<br>Untreated aggregate | — |
| 7 | Roberts, von Quintus and Hudson, ARE for US FHWA | Multilayer elastic solid (VESYS III) | Fatigue in treated layers<br>Rutting<br>Ride quality (roughness)<br>Thermal cracking | Temperature<br>Frost effects | Asphaltic concrete<br>Asphalt-treated bases<br>Open-graded asphalt concrete drainage layer<br>Untreated aggregate | Computer program<br>Design charts |

| | Author/organization | Pavement representation | Distress modes | Environmental effects | Pavement materials | Design format |
|---|---|---|---|---|---|---|
| 8 | Gschwendt and Poliacek, Road Research Laboratory, Bratislava, Czechoslovakia | Multilayer elastic solid | Fatigue in treated layers | Temperature Frost effects | Asphaltic concrete; dense bituminous base mix Cement-stabilized bases Untreated aggregate | Computer program Catalogue of design |
| 9 | Lytton, Michalak and Scullion, Texas A&M University, USA | Elastic plate(s) on elastic solid | Serviceability index | — | — | — |
| 10 | Bissada, Hamdani and Guirguis, Ministry of Public Works, Kuwait | Multilayer elastic solid | Rutting | Temperature | Asphaltic concrete Sand asphalt | Computer program |
| 11 | Freeme, Maree and Viljoen, NITRR, South Africa | Multilayer elastic solid | Fatigue in treated layers Rutting (shear failure) | Temperature | Gap-graded asphalt mix Asphaltic concrete (continuously graded) Cement-stabilized materials Untreated aggregate | Computer program |
| 12 | Autret, De Boissoudy and Marchand, LCPC, France | Multilayer elastic solid | Fatigue in treated layers | Temperature | Asphaltic concrete Asphalt-treated bases Cement-stabilized materials Untreated aggregate | Computer program Catalogue of design |
| 13 | Kenis, Sherwood and McMahon, FHWA, USA | Multilayer elastic or viscoelastic solid | Fatigue in treated layers Rutting Roughness | Temperature | Asphaltic concrete Cement-stabilized materials Sulphur-treated materials Untreated aggregate | Computer program(s) |
| 14 | Bolk, Rijkswaterstaat, The Netherlands | Multilayer elastic solid | Rutting | Temperature | Asphaltic concrete | — |

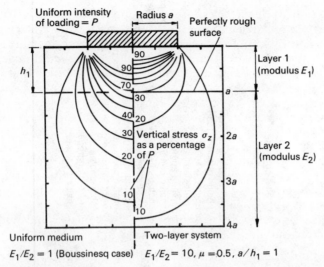

**Fig. 6.5**  Theoretical comparison of the vertical stress distributions in a uniform material and a two-layer system[11]

various horizontal planes at various depths. The pressure at any one point on the surface of a bulb is the same as that at any other point. Pressures at points inside any given bulb are greater than those on the bulb, while pressures outside the bulb are less.

Figure 6.5 illustrates admirably the main function of a pavement, which is to reduce to an acceptable level the pressures applied to the subgrade. As can be seen, the stresses in the subgrade at a depth $h_1$ are considerably influenced by the insertion of the stronger pavement material. With the pavement inserted, the vertical stress at the interface and directly below the centre of the applied load, $P$, is estimated to be approximately 30 per cent of $P$; whereas, without the pavement, the stress at a depth $h_1$ is approximately 70 per cent of $P$.

## Effects of various factors

### Tyre pressure

*Solid tyres*  Solid tyres are not entirely obsolete at this time—even in the more-highly-developed countries such as Britain they are still used for special purposes. Designed to carry abnormal and heavy loads at low speeds, they can be encountered on certain routes, although, it must be pointed out, not in any significant numbers. In developing countries, solid tyres are still often fitted on bullock carts and similar types of rolling vehicle.

There are few data published on the actual stresses transmitted to a pavement surface by solid tyres, although it is well known that these pressures are significantly greater than those transmitted by pneumatic tyres under similar wheel loads. Nonetheless, it is not normally necessary to pay special attention to the requirements of solid-tyred vehicles when designing highway pavements in Britain. The design procedure in use at this time is based on results obtained from examining pavement performances under existing traffic loads, and hence the occasional solid-tyred vehicle is automatically taken into account. However, for pavements on which excessive numbers of solid-tyred vehicles can be expected, care should be taken when using the routine design procedures, since they may not adequately meet the more stringent requirements of the solid-tyred vehicles.

*Pneumatic tyres* Highway engineers are interested in the tyre-*contact* pressure at the pavement surface. In practice, tyre-*inflation* pressure, being easy to measure, is often used as a proxy for contact pressure when applying elastic theory to pavement design.

Tyre manufacturers generally strive towards using higher inflation pressures. Typical reasons given for this are as follows.

(1) Higher inflation pressures are associated with higher safe tyre loadings.
(2) Low tyre pressures are associated with higher tyre deflections which lead to heat build-up and the premature failure of tyres.
(3) Low tyre pressures may increase the danger of aquaplaning and may influence skid-resistance.
(4) Rolling resistance increases with decreasing inflation pressure at constant load.

Most tyres on private cars have recommended inflation pressures of less than 205 kPa. Tyre-inflation pressures of 450–585 kPa are common on medium-sized lorries of the 5 t class. The normal type of heavier commercial vehicle may use tyres inflated to well over 700 kPa, while special vehicles often have inflation pressures of up to 1000 kPa. Given that recommended inflation pressures for aircraft tyres are as high as 3000 kPa, it is possible that tyres with pressures much higher than 800–1000 kPa will be commonplace on heavy commercial vehicles in future years.

It might also be noted that tyre-inflation pressure is a variable quantity during a given journey. Due to the flexing of the tyre walls, energy is converted into heat which causes a temperature build-up of the tyre and inflation gas; this, in turn, results in an inflation pressure increase. Simultaneously, for a given wheel load, the contact area—which is approximately elliptical in shape—decreases as the inflation pressure increases.

A measure of the *average contact pressure* exerted on a highway surface by a commercial vehicle's pneumatic tyre at a given inflation pressure can be obtained from the following equations [12, 13]:

(1) *for recommended combinations of wheel load and inflation pressure*

$$p_c = 0.610p_i + 145$$

(2) *for constant values of wheel load*

$$p_c = 0.349p_i + 315 \quad \text{(for a wheel load of 18.0 kN)}$$

and

$$p_c = 0.279 p_i + 258 \qquad \text{(for a wheel load of 12.6 kN)}$$

where $p_c$ and $p_i$ are the average contact and inflation pressures (kPa), respectively.

These equations indicate that under normal combinations of wheel load and inflation pressure:

(1)  the average contact pressure between the tyre and the pavement surface is less than the inflation pressure,
(2)  at constant inflation pressure, the contact pressure varies with load, e.g. a 100 per cent increase in load normally is associated with a 30–40 per cent increase in contact pressure,
(3)  at constant load, a 100 per cent increase in inflation pressure is associated with an average increase of 30 per cent in contact pressure,
(4)  if both the wheel load and the tyre-inflation pressure are changed in accordance with the tyre manufacturer's recommendations, the change in inflation pressure will be associated with a 60 per cent change in the contact pressure.

In practice, contact pressures of 500 kPa [14] or 600 kPa [6] are generally used for flexible pavement design purposes.

There is ample evidence available (see, for example, reference 9) to indicate that the effects of high contact pressures are most pronounced in the upper layers of a pavement and have relatively small differential effects at greater depths. In other words, for a given wheel load the tyre-inflation pressure has little effect upon the depth of pavement required above the subgrade, but it is this pressure which controls the quality of the materials used in the upper layers.

**Wheel and axle loads**
Whilst the tyre-inflation pressure influences the quality of the materials used in the upper layers of a pavement, it is the total applied wheel load which determines the depth of pavement required to ensure that the subgrade is not over-stressed. The extent of this influence is illustrated in Fig. 6.6, which shows how the stresses at the top and bottom of a pavement were

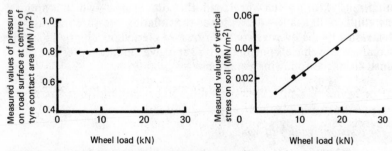

**Fig. 6.6**  Effect of changing the applied wheel load [9]

changed when the tyre-contact pressure was kept constant while the load applied to the smooth-treaded tyre of the test vehicle was progressively increased from 4.45 to 22.24 kN.

In this illustration it can be seen that as the wheel load was increased, the vertical stress at the pavement–subgrade interface was increased in direct proportion to the extra load. Thus it is clear in this case that as the wheel load is increased, the depth of pavement of a given composition must also be made greater if the stress transmitted to the subgrade is not to be increased.

*Wheel configuration* Many commercial vehicles have axles with twin-tyred wheel assemblies and, theoretically, these can influence the stress distribution and deflections within and below the highway pavement. The most definitive investigations into the effect of various wheel arrangements have been carried out on airport pavements, where they are of considerable importance because of the greater wheel loads.

Theoretically, it can be shown that the single-wheel load required to reproduce the same maximum stresses in a homogeneous material as are produced by a twin-tyred assembly is given by

$$P_E = P + \frac{Pz}{(z^2 + S^2)^{5/2}}$$

where $P_E$ = equivalent single-wheel load, $P$ = load on each twin-tyre, $z$ = depth to the plane being stressed, and $S$ = distance between the centres of the individual tyres.

This relationship clearly illustrates the two most important features of a twin-tyred assembly. Firstly, the calculated stresses at the pavement surface (where $z = 0$) are due only to the individual wheels of the assembly and there are no interacting effects. Secondly, the distance between the tyre centres plays an important part in the stress distribution beneath the surface. At greater depths, however, where the $S$-value is small in comparison with the depth, the stresses due to the twin-tyres become near-additive.

Studies carried out by the US Corps of Engineers in the course of airport pavement investigations indicate that the maximum significant depth at which each tyre of a twin-tyred assembly acts as an independent unit happens to be about half the distance $d$ between the inner faces of the two tyres. At depths greater than $d/2$ the pressure-helmets on a given plane begin to overlap; at a depth of $2S$, which is twice the distance between the centrelines of the tyres, the twin-tyred assembly acts essentially as a single unit carrying a load equal to $2P$. These factors are illustrated schematically in Fig. 6.7.

These airport studies also showed that at shallow depths the maximum deflections take place beneath the centres of the individual tyres, whereas at a depth of $2S$ the maximum deflection shifts to beneath the centreline of the assembly. At intermediate depths the maximum deflections occur at lateral points between the centreline of the assembly and the centreline of each tyre of the assembly.

It was also shown that a twin-tyred assembly which caused the same

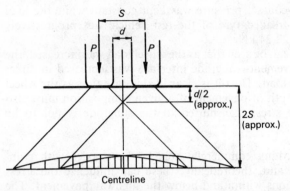

**Fig. 6.7**   Schematic diagram of vertical stresses under a twin-tyred wheel assembly

maximum deflections in a material as a single-wheel load actually produced less strain in the material. This is best explained by referring to Fig. 6.8, in which the broken line indicates the deflection under an equivalent twin-tyred assembly. In each the depth of the maximum deformation is the same, but the shapes of the deformed areas are different. This is most significant, since it is not so much the amount of the deflection which causes a flexible pavement to crack, but rather the degree of curvature of the deformed surface. Thus it can be seen that the pavement will be much more severely stressed at points A, B and C under the single-wheel load than under the twin-tyred assembly. (Note that a typical commercial vehicle's twin-tyred assembly has *d*- and *s*-values of 105 and 210 mm, respectively.)

*The fourth-power law*   The physical characteristics of a commercial goods vehicle, i.e. the unladen mass of each of its axles, its dimensions, the spacing of its axles, its trailer/platform length, and the position of its king-pin (if articulated), affect the proportion of the gross mass which is carried by each of its axles and hence its wheel assemblies.

In Britain the *Motor Vehicle (Construction and Use) Regulations* lay down the legal limits for commercial vehicles, and each such vehicle is required to carry a plate on which is stamped its maximum allowable gross mass and the maximum load permitted for each axle. Figure 6.9 shows the distribution of commercial vehicles by maximum permitted gross vehicle weight (*PGW*) in 1973 and 1981, excluding those less than 3.5 t *PGW*. Note that between 1973 and 1981 the population of goods vehicles became increasingly concentrated in five *PGW*-bands corresponding to the maximum permitted gross vehicle weights for two-axle (16.26 t), three-axle

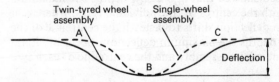

**Fig. 6.8**   Schematic diagram of deflections under single- and twin-tyred wheel assemblies

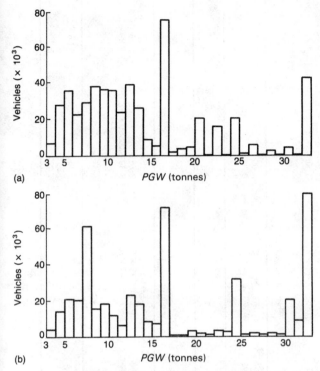

(a)

(b)

**Fig. 6.9** Commercial vehicle population greater than 3.5 t plated gross weight[15]: (a) in 1973 and (b) in 1981

(24.39 t), four-axle rigid (30.49 t), and four-axle articulated (32.52 t) vehicles, plus (after April 1976) the maximum weight of vehicle (7.5 t) that can be driven by a driver without a heavy goods vehicle driver's licence. (Note also that in May 1983 the maximum permitted gross weight for articulated vehicles was raised from 32.52 to 38 t, and that all vehicles over 32.52 t must now have at least five axles.)

The load on each axle of a vehicle of any configuration can be calculated in terms of the payload mass with the aid of simple linear equations derived from the unladen axle masses of the vehicle and its dimensions. Thus Table 6.3 shows these equations for typical examples of the two most common types of commercial vehicle. The 'central' column on the right-hand side of this table gives the axle load equations under the assumption that the vehicle was designed for its payload to be uniformly distributed over the carrying space of the vehicle, e.g. if a load of 10.4 t is centrally positioned on the two-axle vehicle, then 2.24 t are carried by axle (1) and 8.16 t by axle (2), whilst the total axle loads are $3.94 + 2.24 = 6.18$ t and $1.86 + 8.16 = 10.02$ t, respectively.

If the payload's centre of mass is displaced from the position for which the vehicle was designed, then the axle masses can easily exceed their 'plated' levels even if the gross mass of the vehicle is below the plated limit.

**Table 6.3** Axle load calculations: (a) for a two-axle rigid vehicle and (b) for a four-axle articulated vehicle[16]

Diagrams of typical vehicles and axle loads (all dimensions in metres and masses in tonnes)

(a)

| | Payload | | Plated |
|---|---|---|---|
| | 0.0 | 10.4† | masses |
| Axle 1 | 3.94 | 6.18 | 6.50 |
| Axle 2 | 1.86 | 10.02 | 10.16 |
| Total | 5.80 | 16.20 | 16.26 |

Position of load's centre of mass (CM) with respect to the centre of the loading area

| | Central | 1 m forward | 1 m back |
|---|---|---|---|
| | Axle load equation | | |
| Axle 1 | $3.94 + 0.215 \times PL$* | $3.94 + 0.406 \times PL$ | $3.94 + 0.024 \times PL$ |
| Axle 2 | $1.86 + 0.785 \times PL$ | $1.86 + 0.594 \times PL$ | $1.86 + 0.976 \times PL$ |
| | Vehicle damage factor | | |
| PL | | | |
| 0.0 | 0.057 | 0.057 | 0.057 |
| 2.2 | 0.123 | 0.145 | 0.115 |
| 10.4 | 2.599 | 1.938 | 4.751 |

(b)

| | Payload | | Plated |
|---|---|---|---|
| | 0.0 | 22.0† | masses |
| Axle 1 | 3.85 | 5.06 | 6.10 |
| Axle 2 | 2.76 | 9.78 | 10.16 |
| Bogie | 3.89 | 17.68 | 18.30 |
| Total | 10.50 | 32.51 | 32.51 |

| | Central | 1 m forward | 1 m back |
|---|---|---|---|
| | Axle load equation | | |
| Axle 1 | $3.85 + 0.055 \times PL$ | $3.85 + 0.073 \times PL$ | $3.85 + 0.036 \times PL$ |
| Axle 2 | $2.76 + 0.319 \times PL$ | $2.76 + 0.427 \times PL$ | $2.76 + 0.211 \times PL$ |
| Bogie | $3.89 + 0.627 \times PL$ | $3.89 + 0.500 \times PL$ | $3.89 + 0.753 \times PL$ |
| | Vehicle damage factor | | |
| PL | | | |
| 0.0 | 0.069 | 0.069 | 0.069 |
| 10.5 | 0.738 | 0.918 | 0.754 |
| 22.0 | 4.955 | 6.492 | 5.705 |

* PL is the symbol for the mass of the payload (in tonnes)
†Maximum

Examples of equations which relate payload mass to axle load when the payload is displaced are also given on the right-hand side of Table 6.3.

As noted previously, an extensive series of pavement tests was carried out in 1959–60 in the USA. One outcome of this major study[2] was the development of an equation of the form

$$\text{pavement damage} \propto (\text{axle load})^n$$

which related wheel load (i.e. half the axle load) to riding quality, rut depth, and the percentage of the area of the pavement that was cracked under traffic.

The relationship was derived by comparing the number of repetitions of a standard 80 kN axle load required to cause the same amount of structural damage to a flexible pavement as was caused by various other axle loads. Whilst there is wide agreement about the validity of the form of this equation, there is some debate about the value of the exponent $n$, e.g. one British partial re-analysis[17] of the AASHO data concluded that for heavy wheel loads on pavements of medium or high strength, the values of $n$ lay in the range 3.2–5.6. In practice, however, a value of $n = 4$ is very often used.

The consequences of the fourth-power law can be rather surprising. For example, it indicates that a 6 t axle—although it applies three-quarters of a standard axle load to a pavement—only causes damage equivalent to less than 0.3 standard axle, whereas a 10 t axle is equivalent in damaging power to 2.3 standard axles. For the 5.8 t two-axle rigid vehicle Table 6.3 shows that the effect of increasing the payload from zero to 2.2 t (the average for this vehicle operating in 1977) to 10.4 t (its full rated value) is to increase the damage factor from 0.057 to 0.123 to 2.599, respectively. This table also shows that if the maximum payload is displaced in position on the vehicle, the effect can be to increase the damage factor very significantly. From these data (and those in Table 6.9, p. 413), it is clear that the heaviest axles in a stream of commercial vehicles cause a disproportionately large amount of structural damage to a flexible pavement, especially if they are badly loaded.

**Vehicle speed**
The resilient modulus of some pavement materials and subgrades depends upon the rate at which they are loaded, with the modulus increasing with increased rates of loading. In the highway this is reflected in a decrease in pavement deflection with increasing vehicle speed. Typical results for the particular case of a loaded twin-tyred assembly moving at creep speed indicate a 5 per cent change in deflection for each 1 km/h change in speed[18].

The effects of transient loads upon deflections and stresses are indicated in Figs 6.4 and 6.10. For the data in both of these figures, the stresses and deflections decrease as vehicle speed increases from creep speed to about 24 km/h; above 24 km/h the values tend to be constant. In the study from which these data were abstracted it was found that the speed effect was more significant when the roadbase consisted of bituminous-bound materials as compared with cement-bound ones.

The analytical approach to the design of highway pavements requires

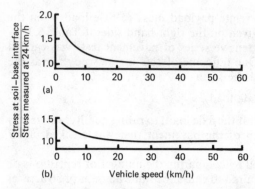

**Fig. 6.10**   Variation of vertical stress at the subgrade–pavement interface with vehicle speed[9]: (a) 200 mm asphalt base and (b) 200 mm soil-cement base

the determination of the dynamic stiffness values for various layers of the pavement. In the case of bituminous-bound layers, the stiffness values are particularly influenced by both vehicle speed, i.e. the effective loading frequency, and temperature. As is discussed elsewhere, temperature is by far the more important of the two, e.g. increasing the vehicle speed—and hence the effective load frequency—by factors of two and twenty produces the same changes in effective modulus as reductions in temperature of 2.5 and 10.0 °C, respectively. Consequently, provided that the loading frequency is realistic, the speed value selected for design purposes is not very critical. Typical speed values chosen for commercial vehicles are in the range 60–80 km/h.

In concept, the speed effect also suggests that for a given volume of traffic, greater thicknesses and/or higher qualities of paving materials may be required for pavements in urban areas than for those in rural areas because of the lower average speeds in urban areas. Similarly, pavement requirements for uphill gradients may be more demanding than for downhill gradients; there is little doubt that the increased distress shown by uphill traffic lanes can at least be partly attributed to the vehicle speed effect.

**Pavement thickness and material**
As already stated, the basic concept underlying flexible pavement design is that if the subgrade is over-stressed and deflects, then the pavement will deflect. Thus most design procedures attempt to evaluate the stability of the subgrade in some fashion, so that the thickness of the overlying material needed to distribute safely the applied wheel load to it can be estimated. In so doing, some thickness design procedures pay relatively little attention to the quality of the pavement materials and merely specify that they should meet certain minimum criteria.

It is here that the great weakness of empirical methods is reflected, since it is not only the pavement thickness but also the qualities of the pavement

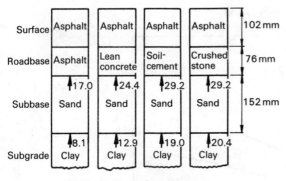

Vertical compressive stress
(kN/m2 per tonne of wheel load)

**Fig. 6.11** Effect of type of roadbase upon subgrade stress[5]

materials which determine stress distribution and resultant deformation. Figure 6.11 presents the results of some dynamic stress measurements taken at a heavily-trafficked road on a uniform clay subgrade; the stresses shown were measured before the road was opened to general traffic. The stresses under the rolled asphalt roadbase were lower than those under the other sections, lean concrete was next, while the soil-cement and crushed stone wet-mix were least successful in spreading wheel loads. Measurements were also made at intervals for several years after the highway was open to traffic. It was found that the stress under the rolled asphalt roadbase did not increase with time, whereas the stress under the lean concrete doubled during the first year of traffic and increased still further during the second year. The deterioration of the load-spreading properties of the lean concrete was considered to be due to excess cracking arising from the tensile stresses generated within it.

The data in Fig. 6.12 show clearly that the deformation history of a pavement of a fixed material composition is greatly influenced by the thickness of each layer as well as by the total thickness above the subgrade. Note that all pavement sections exhibit an initial phase of relatively rapid deformation, followed by a second phase during which the rate of deformation is lower and relatively constant. The total deformation accumulated after the passage of a given number of standard axles is greatly dependent upon the behaviour during the first phase.

In general, both Figs 6.11 and 6.12 suggest that there are significant reductions in subgrade stresses and deflections when stiffer materials are employed in the upper layers of a flexible pavement. For any given subgrade soil, therefore, the better load-spreading capabilities of those stiff layers allow each to be thinner than the equivalent layer of unbound granular material required to meet permitted subgrade distress or limiting deformation criteria. However, it should also be appreciated that whilst the use of stiff layers reduces the potential for subgrade distress, there is an allied increase in tensile stress at the bottom of each layer as well as a significant increase in horizontal shearing stress.

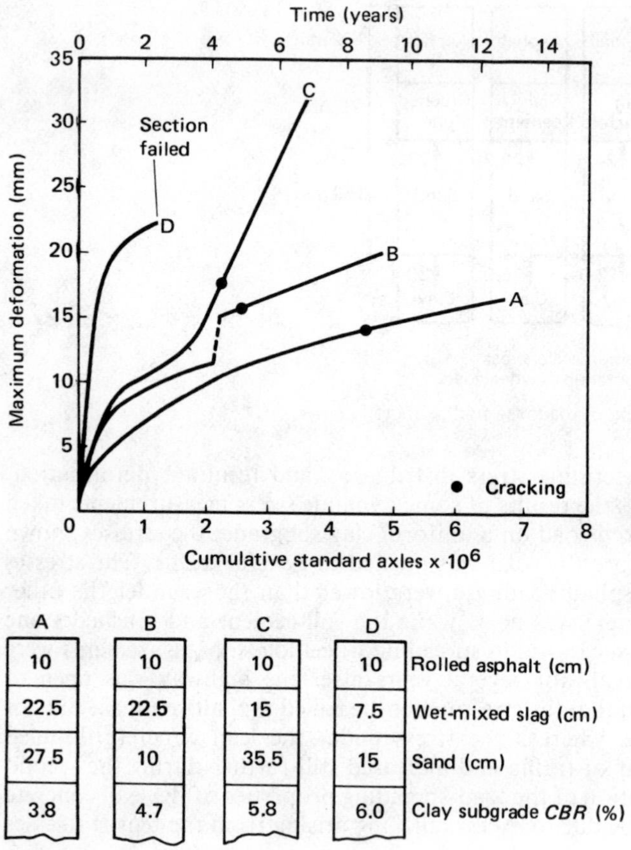
Time (years)
0 2 4 6 8 10 12 14
35
30
25
20
15
10
5
0
Maximum deformation (mm)
Section failed
D
C
B
A
Cracking
0 1 2 3 4 5 6 7 8
Cumulative standard axles x 10^6
A B C D
10 10 10 10 Rolled asphalt (cm)
22.5 22.5 15 7.5 Wet-mixed slag (cm)
27.5 10 35.5 15 Sand (cm)
3.8 4.7 5.8 6.0 Clay subgrade *CBR* (%)

**Fig. 6.12** Deformation history of a flexible pavement constructed with bases of varying thicknesses at Alconbury Hill[19]

**Failure mechanisms**

The two flexible pavement failure mechanisms that are of particular interest to highway engineers in Britain are excessive permanent deformation of the whole structure and cracking of the bituminous layer.

When a wheel load passes over a point in a flexible pavement, each of its constituent layers responds in the general way shown in Fig. 6.13. The applied stress pulse is caused by the wheel mass, and the resulting strain pulse consists of a resilient and permanent component. The resilient strain component is of importance for elastic-layer analysis of pavement response to individual wheel loads, as it allows the critical strains to be calculated for design. The permanent strain component, although relatively small for a single-load application, is cumulative and hence can become substantial over the large number of load applications normally considered for design. It is the excessive accumulation of these permanent strains from all layers that leads to failure via *surface rutting*. In practice, the rut depth as meas-

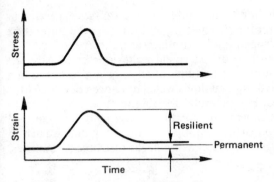

**Fig. 6.13** Conceptual response of flexible pavement materials to load

ured under a 1.8 m straightedge is used as the main measure of pavement serviceability in Britain.

The potential for cracking results from the phenomenon of *fatigue* in bituminous materials.

Fatigue has been defined as the phenomenon of fracture under repeated or fluctuating stress having a maximum value generally less than the tensile strength of the material[19]. Under traffic loading, bituminous pavement materials in particular are subjected to repeated stressing, and the possibility of damage by fatigue cracking continually exists. Binder content and type are known to be primary factors affecting fatigue performance on the basis of applied strain, with longer lives being obtained for a given strain when the relative volume of binder is increased or when a binder having a higher ring and ball softening point is used.

Fatigue cracking is assumed to originate at the bottom of bound pavement layers, and its onset to be controlled by the horizontal strains repeatedly generated at this level by traffic loading. The cracks are then assumed to propagate upwards through the bound layers to the pavement surface. As this occurs, there is a progressive weakening of these layers, which in turn increases the level of stress transmitted to the lower layers and subgrade to a level that brings about excessive deformation. As the transmitted stresses increase, the development of permanent deformation is accelerated.

The two design criteria that are widely used in elastic design to deal with the above two failure mechanisms are tensile strain at the bottom of the bituminous layer for fatigue cracking, and vertical strain at the top of the subgrade for permanent deformation[20].

**Temperature**
Studies carried out to measure the effects of road temperature upon the load-spreading properties of flexible pavement materials have shown the importance of taking temperature conditions into account when designing a flexible pavement, particularly when high wheel loads are involved[21].

In general, the performance of a bituminous pavement deteriorates with rising temperature. This is due in part to the fact that the effective resilient moduli of bituminous-bound materials (and hence the stresses generated in the pavement) are temperature dependent, and in part because their resistance to deformation drops rapidly with increasing temperature.

The effects of temperature upon pavement behaviour emphasize the need to take considerable care when deciding whether or not to utilize in a given climatic area empirical design methods which have been developed for different climatic conditions. For example, a design method which aims to withstand the pavement temperature conditions normally encountered during the busy traffic period of the months of June, July and August in Britain might not be adequate for the climatic needs of tropical countries.

**Edge loading**
One of the most striking conclusions derived from various road tests has been concerned with the effect that the lateral positioning of vehicles has upon pavement distress. Figure 6.14 shows a typical transverse road profile on one carriageway of the full-scale road experiment at Alconbury Hill. Note that the greatest deformation is along the wheel paths of the lane carrying the greatest proportion of commercial vehicles. The farside traffic lane, which primarily serves overtaking vehicles—mostly cars—is relatively little distressed.

Furthermore, deformation in the wheel tracks develops rapidly in the early life of a road. In addition to being influenced by the basic deformation behaviour of the pavement layers, the form of this initial phase is also influenced both by the compacting effect of the traffic upon the granular layers of the pavement and by the moisture changes in the subgrade after the disturbance of the construction period. On pavements that do not fail at this stage, subsequent deterioration occurs at a slower rate, but progress to final failure is normally accompanied by a rapid increase in the rate of deformation.

Deformation development near the edge of a carriageway is likely to be accelerated if the roadbase is not carried through the shoulder, and if the shoulder does not have an impervious covering. The lack of impervious

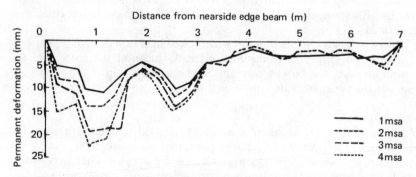

**Fig. 6.14** Typical transverse deformation profiles on the same pavement section, composed of 100 mm rolled asphalt surfacing, 250 mm wet-mix slag roadbase, and 170 mm sand subbase, at four different levels of traffic flow[22]

surfacing beyond the carriageway edges means that moisture can find easy entrance into, and exit from, the pavement and subgrade, thus rendering them more susceptible to deformation. Shear failure and lateral displacement of the pavement and/or subgrade can more easily occur because of the discontinuity of the pavement.

Accelerated failure at the pavement edge can also be explained in the context of a failure mechanism which assumes that as a result of the applied force at the surface, the particles in any layer of the pavement or subgrade are displaced along a curved path and develop an upward force against the underside of the layer above. The resistance to the subgrade displacement is provided by the interparticle friction and cohesion in the subgrade, the weight of the overlying pavement, and the flexural strengths of the overlying layers. Now, if the pavement is not continuous, as in the case where there is no hardshoulder along the edge of the carriageway, the resisting force is very severely reduced and failure may take place more quickly.

## Basic methods of design for new roads

The objective of any pavement design procedure is to provide a structure that will be suitable in a specific environment and be able to sustain the anticipated traffic loading. As has been discussed previously, pavements deteriorate with time and from traffic load repetitions. All design methods seek to control or limit this loss in serviceability.

Prior to the early 1940s, little attention was directed towards the problems of pavement design, primarily because the methods of construction then in use were considered to give satisfactory results for the traffic of those times. With the onset of World War II, however, scientific attention became focused in this direction because of the urgent need to construct great lengths of roads and airport runways for heavy traffic, as quickly and as economically as possible. Since then the subject of pavement design has continued to receive much attention and, as regards roads in particular, it has been accepted that reliable methods of design can lead to important economies by avoiding costly failures and wastage due to over-design.

It must be made clear at this stage that there is no universal agreement amongst engineers as to which design procedure is the 'best'. There are very many design procedures in use throughout the world today; some of these differ only in their method of application, while others are based on entirely different procedures (see also reference 23). Whilst some of these also differ considerably in their reliability, they all have the common feature that they still depend upon the experience and academic knowledge of the engineer utilizing them.

It is not practicable in the space available here to discuss all the design methods that have been or are now in use; nor, indeed, is it necessary, since most of these methods can be gathered into four main classification groups, viz.: (a) methods based on precedent, (b) empirical methods based on a soil classification test, (c) empirical methods based on a soil strength test, and (d) theoretical and semi-theoretical methods.

## Methods based on precedent

Design methods of this group might also be called design procedures by rule-of-thumb. Basically, they rely upon standard thicknesses of pavement for particular classifications of road. Thus in very many cases the same thickness of construction may be placed on weak clay subgrades as on strong granular ones, as long as the highway type designates it.

Many satisfactory highways have been, and are being, constructed on the basis of precedent experience and there is no reason why this method of design should not continue to be used on a purely local basis where prior experience definitely indicates that economic and reliable results can be expected. However, the highway engineer should be very wary of designing on this basis over larger areas. For instance, normal subgrade strengths in Britain vary over a range of at least twenty-five to one, and if standard pavement thicknesses were to be utilized blindly on a national scale, the inevitable result would be instances where insufficient, thin pavements would be laid on weak subgrades and unnecessarily thick pavements on strong subgrades.

## Empirical methods using a soil classification test

Pavement thicknesses as determined by procedures falling into this group rely upon previous experience of the thicknesses required for various wheel loads on different types of soil. Soil classification tests utilizing particle-size analyses, and liquid limit and plastic limit tests, may be used to describe the soils.

In Chapter 4 there is presented a soil classification system now known as the AASHTO system. Within this classification system, groups of soils are differentiated according to a particle-size analysis, liquid limit and plasticity index. Soils within each group are differentiated by means of a qualifying group index number obtained from the following formula:

$$GI = 0.2a + 0.005ac + 0.01bd$$

where $a$ = that portion of the percentage passing the No. 200 sieve, between 35 and 75 per cent, expressed as a positive whole number (1 to 40); $b$ = that portion of the percentage passing the No. 200 sieve, between 15 and 55 per cent, expressed as a positive whole number (1 to 40); $c$ = that portion of the numerical liquid limit, between 40 and 60, expressed as a positive whole number (1 to 20); $d$ = that portion of the numerical plasticity index, between 10 and 30, expressed as a positive whole number (1 to 20).

When the AASHTO classification system was first presented it was accompanied by a discussion presenting a simplified pavement thickness design method based on the group index of the subgrade soil[24]. The original design curves associated with this method are shown in Fig. 6.15. These curves have since been modified by various highway agencies for their own purposes.

As can be seen from Fig. 6.15, two of the main variables that the group index design procedure attempts to take into account are the intensity of

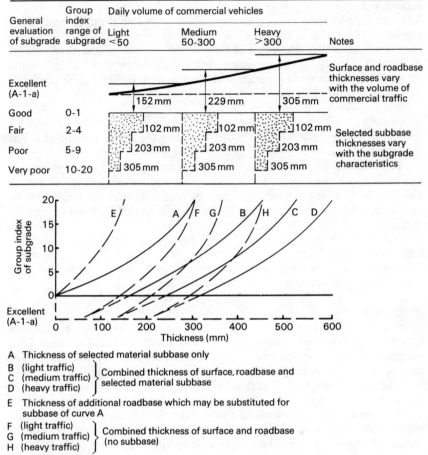

| General evaluation of subgrade | Group index range of subgrade | Daily volume of commercial vehicles | | | Notes |
|---|---|---|---|---|---|
| | | Light <50 | Medium 50-300 | Heavy >300 | |
| Excellent (A-1-a) | | | | | Surface and roadbase thicknesses vary with the volume of commercial traffic |
| | | 152 mm | 229 mm | 305 mm | |
| Good | 0-1 | | | | |
| Fair | 2-4 | 102 mm | 102 mm | 102 mm | Selected subbase thicknesses vary with the subgrade characteristics |
| Poor | 5-9 | 203 mm | 203 mm | 203 mm | |
| Very poor | 10-20 | 305 mm | 305 mm | 305 mm | |

A  Thickness of selected material subbase only
B  (light traffic)  ⎫
C  (medium traffic) ⎬ Combined thickness of surface, roadbase and selected material subbase
D  (heavy traffic)  ⎭
E  Thickness of additional roadbase which may be substituted for subbase of curve A
F  (light traffic)  ⎫
G  (medium traffic) ⎬ Combined thickness of surface and roadbase (no subbase)
H  (heavy traffic)  ⎭

**Fig. 6.15**  Original group index design curves

traffic and the characteristics of the subgrade. The number of commercial vehicles per day is taken as the traffic criterion and it is assumed that the proportion of daily wheel loads greater than 40 kN does not exceed 15 per cent.

The manner in which the charts in Fig. 6.15 can be used for design purposes is illustrated by the following examples.

**Example 1**
The subgrade soil is A-1-a and the number of commercial vehicles is 40 per day.

In this case, the subgrade soil is composed of an excellent roadbase material in its own right, and so the addition of another roadbase is not necessary. For the traffic conditions expected, it will be quite sufficient to cover the subgrade with a 50 mm surface course; this is usually a bituminous surfacing.

**Example 2**
The subgrade soil has a group index equal to unity and the daily number of commercial vehicles is 40.

From curve B a combined roadbase and surface course thickness of 152 mm is obtained. The pavement will then be composed of at least a 50 mm bituminous surface course and a granular or crushed stone roadbase of a thickness of 102 mm.

**Example 3**
The subgrade soil has a group index of 9 and the number of commercial vehicles is 40.

From curve B it is seen that approximately 355 mm of pavement is required above the subgrade, while curve A indicates that only 203 mm of this can be of subbase material. Thus the constructional thickness may be made up of 50 mm of bituminous surfacing, 102 mm of granular or crushed stone roadbase, and 203 mm of subbase material.

An alternative solution would be to omit the subbase material entirely and, using curve F, have a total pavement thickness of 250 mm. In this case, the thickness may be composed of 50 mm of bituminous surfacing on top of 203 mm of granular or crushed stone roadbase material.

**Discussion**
The curves presented in Fig. 6.15 were expected to provide adequate pavement thicknesses for most climatic conditions. In areas of severe frost penetration, however, it was recommended that the values given by the curves should be qualified by local knowledge based on experience.

The thicknesses recommended by this method of design were based on the assumptions that the top 152 mm of the subgrade were compacted to at least 95 per cent of the standard Proctor dry density and that the subbase and roadbase materials were compacted to not less than 100 per cent of the standard Proctor values. They also assume that the water-table is maintained at least 1.00–1.25 m below the carriageway.

The group index method of pavement design has the particular advantage that it is a most simple design procedure. The data utilized directly are those normally collected as part of the standard soil classification procedure and thus no extra tests are required. It is scientific in that it attempts to allow for both the traffic conditions and the characteristics of the subgrade soil. Rather than trying to evaluate the subgrade material by means of some empirical test, it attempts to take into account the effects of the various constituents which make up the soil. Thus a clayey soil, which would normally have a high group index, requires a substantial thickness of pavement above it, while a granular soil requires a relatively thin coverage.

In general, however, the pavement thicknesses recommended by the group index design procedure tend to err on the safe side; while this has certain advantages, it has the disadvantage that uneconomical pavement thicknesses may often be constructed. The most obvious reason for this lies in the fact that no attempt is made to take into account the different load-spreading abilities of pavement materials. A further important disadvantage of the procedure is that its usage is entirely dependent upon particular conditions of subgrade moisture and compaction: if these conditions are not met in the field, the design curves are not applicable.

## Empirical methods using a soil strength test

These procedures normally utilize particular forms of penetration or bearing tests that are only applicable to their associated design methods. Each procedure then recommends the necessary pavement thickness on the basis of past experience or, as in Britain, on test road results.

The best known of these methods is the California Bearing Ratio (*CBR*) procedure, which is based on a standard penetration test. This will be discussed here in some detail, since not only is it the procedure that is most widely used throughout the world today but it also forms the first step in the empirical design method in use in Britain at this time.

### *CBR* test

The California Bearing Ratio design procedure was, as its name suggests, originally devised by engineers of the California Division of Highways following an intensive investigation into flexible pavement failures in California in the nine years prior to 1938[25]. It was taken up by the US Corps of Engineers during World War II and adapted for use in the design of airport pavements. As a result of the extensive investigations undertaken by the Corps, other organizations began to take an active interest in the design method and its acceptance became widespread after the war[26].

To use the method in designing a pavement, it is necessary to carry out a standard penetration-type load–deformation test and then, using values obtained from the test, an empirical design chart is entered and the pavement and/or layer thickness required is read off the proper curve. The original test procedure and design curves developed by the Californian investigators have since been modified by various agencies for their own purposes. While some of these modifications are minor in form and others represent fairly extensive changes, they all have the same basic outline in common, so that the engineer who has carried out the complete procedure according to one set of specifications can quite readily carry it out according to a different agency's requirements.

For this reason, no attempt will be made here to discuss in detail the original *CBR* procedure or to describe the various modifications to it. Instead, emphasis will be placed upon the method as used in Britain[27]; the development and particular features associated with this procedure will be discussed in detail.

*Laboratory test*   The *CBR* penetration test is carried out in the laboratory in the following manner.

A sample of soil is placed in a steel mould with attached collar that is 152 mm in diameter by a total of 178 mm high. This soil is then compacted until a specimen 152 mm in diameter by 127 mm high is obtained that is at the moisture and density conditions which the site investigation and consideration of available constructional methods and equipment indicate to be appropriate.

Following compaction, the sample, still in the mould, is subjected to a surcharge weight equivalent to the estimated weight of flexible pavement expected above the layer from which the test soil is selected. Annular weights, each equivalent to 63.5 mm of flexible pavement, are used for this purpose. Small errors in estimating the surcharge load are of minor importance, except in tests on cohesionless soils.

The specimen is next placed in a testing machine and a cylindrical plunger having an end diameter of exactly 49.6 mm is caused to penetrate the specimen at a rate of 1 mm per minute. The penetration of the plunger is measured by a dial gauge, and readings of the applied force taken at intervals of penetration of 0.25 mm to a total penetration not exceeding 7.50 mm.

After the test, a smooth load versus penetration curve is drawn for the data obtained and, as is illustrated by curve A in Fig. 6.16, this is normally convex upwards.

In practice, an initial seating load is applied to the plunger before the loading and penetration gauges are set to zero and this seating load is then neglected in subsequent calculations. It sometimes happens, however, that the plunger is still not perfectly bedded in the soil and, as a result of this and other factors, a load–penetration curve with a shape similar to that of curve B in Fig. 6.16 may be obtained instead of the more normally shaped curve

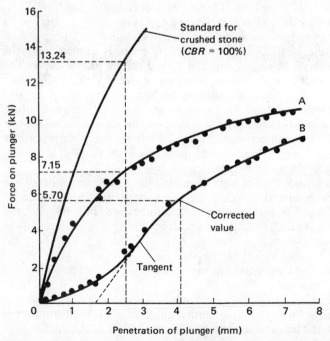

**Fig. 6.16** Example of California Bearing Ratio load–penetration curves

illustrated by curve A. When this happens, the curve must be corrected by drawing a tangent at the point of greatest slope and then projecting it to cut the penetration axis as shown for curve B. The curve is then shifted to the left so that the point of intersection of the tangent with the penetration axis coincides with the origin; this gives the corrected curve from which the *CBR*-value is determined.

The *CBR*-value of a soil is then obtained by reading off from the curve the force which causes a penetration of 2.50 mm and expressing this as a percentage of the load (13.24 kN) which produces the same penetration in a standard crushed stone mixture. The standard penetration curve corresponding to a *CBR*-value of 100 per cent is also shown in Fig. 6.16; the forces corresponding to this curve are 11.5 kN at 2 mm penetration, 17.6 kN at 4 mm, 22.2 kN at 6 mm, 26.3 kN at 8 mm, 30.3 kN at 10 mm, and 33.5 kN at 12 mm. The *CBR*-values obtained for curves A and B in Fig. 6.16 are 54 and 43 per cent, respectively.

Typical *CBR*-values derived from tests on common British soils are given in Table 6.4.

**Factors affecting *CBR* test results**
The *CBR* test is entirely empirical and cannot be considered as even attempting to measure any basic property of the soil. Hence the *CBR*-value of a soil can only be considered as an undefinable index of its strength which, for any particular soil, is dependent upon the condition of the material at the time of testing. This means that the soil must be tested in a condition that is critical to the design. To ensure that proper values are obtained, it is necessary for the designer to have a clear understanding of the effects of the method of compaction, the dry density, and the moisture content on the *CBR*-value of a soil sample.

**Table 6.4** Typical laboratory *CBR*-values for British soils compacted at their natural moisture contents

| Type of soil | Plasticity index | CBR-value (%) | |
|---|---|---|---|
| | | Well drained[*] | Poorly drained |
| Heavy clay | 70 | 2.0 | 1.0 |
| | 60 | 2.0 | 1.5 |
| | 50 | 2.5 | 2.0 |
| | 40 | 3.0 | 2.0 |
| Silty clay | 30 | 5.0 | 3.0 |
| Sandy clay | 20 | 6.0 | 4.0 |
| | 10 | 7.0 | 5.0 |
| Silt | — | 2.0 | 1.0 |
| Sand | | | |
| poorly graded | Non-plastic | 20.0 | 10.0 |
| well graded | Non-plastic | 40.0 | 15.0 |
| Well-graded sandy gravel | Non-plastic | 60.0 | 20.0 |

[*]Water-table at least 0.6 m below formation level

*Method of compaction*   The highway designer is concerned with the strength of a soil when it is at a particular condition of moisture content and dry density. The *CBR* specimen is most usually brought to this condition by either of two methods of compaction.

With the *static* compaction method, which is that favoured in Britain, the mass of wet soil required for one specimen to be compacted to the appropriate dry density is first calculated from the equation:

$$m_1 = 23.05(100 + w)\psi_d$$

where $m_1$ = mass of wet soil (g), $w$ = design moisture content (%), and $\psi_d$ = design dry density (Mg/m$^3$).

The calculated amount of wet soil is then poured slowly into the assembled steel *CBR* mould and its attached collar, whilst being tamped continuously with a steel rod. When 'rodding' is completed, the top of the soil should be about 5 to 10 mm above the top of the mould. A 50 mm thick plug is then placed in the collar and the specimen is compressed in the compression testing machine until the top of the plug is flush with the top of the collar. The soil specimen will then be exactly 127 mm high, and ready for testing.

The main advantage of this method lies in the fact that the desired dry density is obtained directly without the need for any preliminary testing. In addition, it requires less physical effort than other methods. Its principal disadvantage is that a vertical compaction gradient may be obtained within the specimen. Thus if dry density measurements are made of the top, middle and bottom thirds of the specimen, significantly different values may be obtained.

With the second method of compaction, the specimen is prepared *dynamically*. The predetermined amount of wet soil is placed in the mould in five equal layers, each layer being compacted by applying a required number of blows with the standard or modified Proctor compaction hammer. The number of blows needed to compact each layer to ensure that it occupies one-fifth of the height of the mould is determined on the basis of preliminary testing. When compaction is completed, the final level of the soil should be just above the top of the mould; the collar is then removed and the soil trimmed flush using a steel straightedge.

This latter method has the advantage that a more uniformly compacted mixture is obtained in the specimen. In addition, it produces a soil structure that is believed by many authorities to be closer to that which is actually obtained under roller compaction in the field. Its main disadvantage is that some preliminary experimentation is necessary to find the thickness of each layer and the number of blows per layer that will produce the desired dry density.

*Dry density*   At any given moisture content, the strength of a soil will be increased if its dry density is increased, i.e. if the air content of the soil is decreased. Figure 6.17 indicates the manner in which the *CBR*-value of a heavy clay[28] decreases as the dry density is decreased, the moisture content of the soil being kept constant. For this reason, great emphasis must be

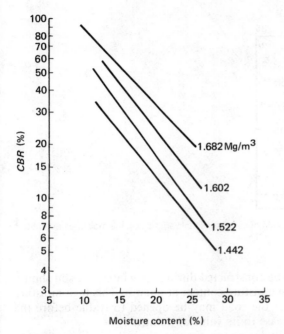

**Fig. 6.17** Effect of moisture content and dry density upon the *CBR*-value of a heavy clay (London clay: *LL* = 75 per cent, *PL* = 27 per cent, and *PI* = 48)

placed upon the concept of selecting a design dry density which corresponds to the minimum state of compaction which it is anticipated will be achieved in the field at the time of construction.

*Moisture content*    Figure 6.17 also shows that the strength of a soil varies with its moisture content. Hence it is most important that the design *CBR*-value should be assessed at the highest moisture content that the soil is liable to have subsequent to the completion of roadworks. The selection of this moisture content requires an understanding of the way in which moisture moves within a soil.

Before a soil is covered by a road pavement, its moisture content will fluctuate seasonally. At any given time the uncovered soil may be drier or wetter than the ultimate condition that will be reached when an impervious road structure is constructed over it. For instance, a gradient of moisture within the soil profile that is determined during the summer might look like curve A in Fig. 6.18, while another taken in the winter might look like curve B. Sometime after the construction of the pavement, the soil moisture conditions will become stabilized and subject only to changes due to fluctuations in the level of the water-table. When this has happened, the moisture gradient might look like curve C.

Examination of Fig. 6.18 leads to the following conclusions regarding the moisture content at which the *CBR* specimen should be tested if it is to be used to determine design values.

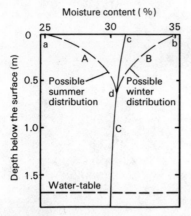

**Fig. 6.18**  Diagrammatic illustration of some seasonal variations in the moisture content of a heavy subgrade soil

(1)   If the pavement is to be constructed during the winter, the soil should be tested at whatever is the moisture content at point b. This high moisture content must be used since the road may be opened to traffic before the moisture content can decrease to its value at point c.

(2)   If the road is to be built during the summer, the soil should be tested at the moisture content at point c, since this will ultimately be its stable moisture content.

Methods have been developed by which the ultimate moisture content at point c can be estimated for a given soil when the water-table is at a given depth[28,29]. These require laboratory suction tests on samples taken from the proposed formation level using a suction corresponding to the most adverse anticipated water-table conditions.

If facilities for conducting suction tests are not available, an estimate of the ultimate moisture content can be obtained from measurements taken at a point below the zone of seasonal fluctuation but at least 0.3 m above the water-table. This is at or below point d in Fig. 6.18. In cohesive soils in Britain, particularly those supporting dense vegetation, the moisture content at a depth of 1.00–1.25 m will normally provide a good estimate of the ultimate moisture content. Sandy soils, however, do not normally support a dense cover of deep-rooted grasses and therefore seasonal fluctuations of moisture content are confined close to the surface. Thus the moisture content at a depth of 0.3–0.6 m will usually be adequate for estimating the *CBR* test moisture content for this type of soil.

If a cohesive soil is to be used as an embankment material and then compacted, the disturbance to the soil structure is likely to cause the ultimate moisture content to be increased above the normal ultimate value for the undisturbed soil. To take this into account, the moisture content measured at a depth of 1.00–1.25 m should be increased by about 2 per cent if a heavy clay is to be used as embankment material. For lighter silty and sandy clays used in embankments, a corresponding addition of 1 per cent should be made.

In all cases, of course, the soil at the depth at which the moisture content is estimated must be the same as the soil which is to be compacted.

## British design procedure

What has happened in Britain relative to the application of the *CBR* test as a basis for pavement design is in itself a useful illustration of the fact that the highway engineer must continually keep abreast of research developments.

The original Californian investigators concluded that subgrade soils having the same *CBR*-value required the same thickness of overlying flexible construction in order to prevent plastic deformation of the subgrade. Two design curves were originally prepared relating pavement thickness to the *CBR*-value of the underlying materials, one for heavy traffic and the other for light traffic. An implied assumption underlying each of these curves was that all kinds of flexible construction of the macadam type spread the applied wheel load to the same extent.

The use of a range of wheel loads to identify the different design curves was never accepted in Britain, as it was considered to lead frequently to over-design through catering so fully for the heaviest vehicles likely to use the road. Instead, curves were developed (see Fig. 6.19) which took direct account of the total number of commercial vehicles having unladen masses in excess of 1.53 t that were carried in the course of a busy 24-hour day. Commercial vehicles were chosen because they cause the main damage to roads. The number of vehicles was determined from traffic counts in both directions for a single carriageway road, or on both carriageways for a dual carriageway road.

Note that each design curve shown in Fig. 6.19 assumed a relation between the *CBR*-value of a soil material and the thickness of flexible

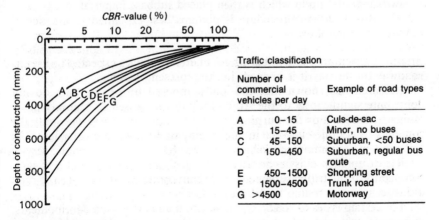

Total thickness curves

**Fig. 6.19** The first stage in the development of the current British pavement design curves

construction to be placed above the layer from which the soil material was taken, so that it would not be over-stressed when loaded. If the material under evaluation was the subgrade soil, then the design curve gave the total thickness of pavement required. If the test was carried out on subbase material, then the curves were used to estimate what combined thickness of roadbase and surfacing was required, *irrespective of what materials were used in these layers*.

The design curves shown in Fig. 6.19 were superseded in 1960 by a new series of design charts. The overall thickness requirements recommended by these charts were based on failure investigations of roads which had generally been in service for at least twenty years after construction or major maintenance and, hence, these new designs were based on the traffic intensity expected after twenty years and not on the initial traffic. Unless other data were available, a growth rate of 4 per cent per year was assumed in calculating this future traffic.

By 1965, sufficient information had been gathered from the British test roads to differentiate between the performance characteristics of different roadbase materials, and so the curves were again amended to take this into account. As a consequence, a new governmental design guide[30] was issued in 1970 to take increasing axle loads and vehicle numbers into account.

The new thickness design relationships as originally devised, and then amended, which are used in association with the *CBR*-test results, are given in Fig. 6.20 and in Tables 6.5 and 6.6. Note that only the subbase design now makes direct use of the *CBR*-value of the subgrade in its thickness determination. The remaining design data are arranged so that the surfacing and roadbase thicknesses of various materials, to be used under varying volumes of commercial vehicle flow in a given direction, are specified independently.

In relation to Tables 6.5 and 6.6, it should be noted that when the subgrade *CBR*-value is less than 5 per cent, current British practice is to place a capping layer of selected fill (see Table 6.7) on the weak soil to form a new 'subgrade' upon which is then placed subbase material.

The British design procedure is perhaps best explained as a series of design steps, as follows.

*Step 1*   Determine the number of commercial vehicles expected to use the roadway on the day it is opened, i.e. the 'present' traffic.

Research has shown that the loads imposed by private cars do not contribute significantly to the structural damage caused to highway pavements by traffic. For the purpose of structural design, therefore, only the numbers of commercial vehicles and their axle loadings are considered. In this context, a commercial vehicle is defined as a goods or public service vehicle of unladen mass exceeding 1500 kg.

Details of the traffic survey methods employed for various types of road are discussed in Volume 1 of *Highways*.

For certain types of roads, e.g. residential and associated developments, it is quite common for accurate current data not to be available, and a detailed traffic survey may not be justified. In such instances, the Transport and Road Research Laboratory recommends that the initial values given in Table 6.8 be assumed.

*Step 2* Determine the cumulative number of commercial vehicles (one direction of traffic) expected to use the design lane over its design lifetime.

The design lane is the more-heavily-travelled lane of a two- or three-lane single carriageway road, or the 'slow' or nearside lane on each carriageway

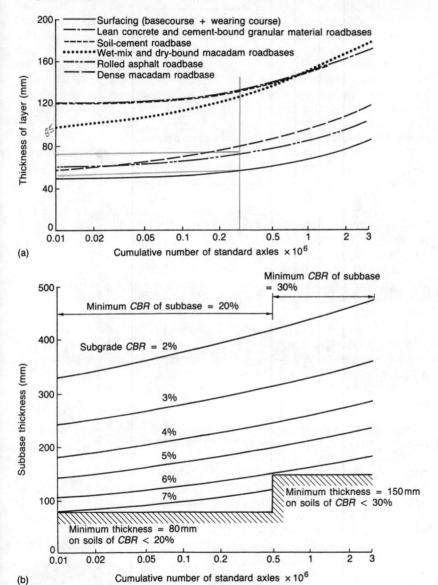

(a)

(b)

**Fig. 6.20** Flexible pavement design curves based on Road Note 29[30]: (a) surfacings and roadbases, and (b) subbases

**Table 6.5** Thickness design table for flexible pavements with bituminous-bound roadbases[31]

| Traffic category[1] (msa) | Surfacings (mm) Wearing course | Surfacings (mm) Basecourse | Roadbases (mm) Hot rolled asphalt | Roadbases (mm) Dense tarmacadam or dense bitumen macadam |
|---|---|---|---|---|
| >60-80 | 40 | 60 | 205 | 250 |
| >40-60 | | | 185 | 230 |
| >25-40 | | | 160 | 205 |
| >20-25 | | | 160 | 180 |
| >17-20 | | | 135 | 180 |
| >11-17 | | | 135 | 155 |
| >7-11 | | 50 | 115 | 135 |
| >6-7 | | | | → 120 |
| >5-6 | | 40 | 100 | 120 |
| >3-5 | | | 100 | 120 |
| 2.5-3.0 | | | | |

Subbases[2] (mm)

| Traffic category[1] (msa) | Subgrade CBR (%) 5 | 6 | 7 | 8-29 | ≥30 |
|---|---|---|---|---|---|
| ≥25 | 300 | 240 | 200 | 150 | 0 |
| >6-25 | 270 | 210 | 170 | 150 | 0 |
| >2-6 | 240 | 180 | 150 | 150 | 0 |

*Notes:*
(1) Below 2.5 msa, the thickness for construction should be taken from Fig. 6.20.
(2) If the subgrade is frost susceptible, the subbase thickness should be increased so that the pavement thickness is 450 mm.

**Table 6.6** Thickness design table for flexible pavements with non-bituminous-bound roadbases[31]

| Traffic category[1] (msa) | Surfacings (mm) Wearing course | Base-course | Roadbase group D, excluding lean concrete[2] | Roadbases (mm) Cement-bound granular | Lean concrete | Wet-mix[4] | Dry-bound macadam | Subbases[5] (mm) Subgrade CBR (%) 5 | 6 | 7 | 8–29 | ≥30 | Traffic category[1] (msa) |
|---|---|---|---|---|---|---|---|---|---|---|---|---|---|
| >60–80 | 40 | 60 | 100 | n.a.[3] | 210 | 260 | n.a.[3] | 300 | 240 | 200 | 150 | 0 | ≥25 |
| >40–60 | → | 60 | 80 | → | → | → | → | → | → | → | → | → | → |
| >30–40 | → | 60 | 60 | → | → | 245 | → | → | → | → | → | → | → |
| >25–30 | → | 60 | 60 | → | → | → | → | 270 | 210 | 170 | → | → | >6–25 |
| >17–25 | → | 105 | n.a.[3] | → | → | → | → | → | → | → | → | → | → |
| >15–17 | → | 90 | → | → | → | 230 | → | → | → | → | → | → | → |
| >11–15 | → | 90 | → | → | 190 | 230 | → | → | → | → | → | → | → |
| >9–11 | → | 75 | → | → | → | 210 | 220 | → | → | → | → | → | → |
| >7–9 | → | 75 | → | → | → | → | 210 | → | → | → | → | → | → |
| >6–7 | → | 60 | → | → | → | → | → | → | → | → | → | → | → |
| >5–6 | → | → 50 | → | → | → | → | → | 240 | 180 | 150 | → | → | >2–6 |
| >4–5 | → | 50 | → | 180 | 180 | 190 | 190 | → | → | → | → | → | → |
| >3–4 | → | 50 | → | 180 | 180 | 190 | 190 | → | → | → | → | → | → |
| 2.5–3.0 | → | 50 | → | 170 | 170 | 170 | 170 | → | → | → | → | → | → |

*Notes:*

(1) Below 2.5 msa, the thickness for construction should be taken from Fig. 6.20.

(2) For roads with more than 25 msa, the extra surfacing is normally required in bituminous roadbase material (see reference 31 for a description of group D).

(3) n.a. = not applicable.

(4) Wet-mix macadam should not be used for motorways and dual two- or three-lane trunk roads.

(5) If the subgrade is frost susceptible, the subbase thickness should be increased so that the pavement thickness is 450 mm.

**Table 6.7** Thickness of selected fill to be used as capping layers in new flexible pavements on weak subgrades[32]

| | | Capping layer thickness (mm) | | | |
|---|---|---|---|---|---|
| Traffic category (msa) | CBR-value of capping layer (%) | CBR-value below capping layer (%) | | | |
| | | <2 | 2 | 3 | 4 |
| >25 | ≥30 | 600 | 450 | 300 | 210 |
| >6–25 | ≥30 | 540 | 390 | 260 | 170 |
| 2–6 | ≥30 | 500 | 350 | 220 | 140 |
| >25 | 15–29 | 700 | 550 | 400 | 260 |
| >6–25 | 15–29 | 640 | 480 | 340 | 220 |
| 2–6 | 15–29 | 570 | 410 | 270 | 160 |
| >25 | 10–14 | 800 | 650 | 470 | 330 |
| >6–25 | 10–14 | 750 | 560 | 400 | 240 |
| 2–6 | 10–14 | 600 | 440 | 290 | 190 |
| 2–6 | 7–9 | 750 | 550 | 400 | 300 |

*Note:* Subbase thickness = 150 mm

of dual carriageway roads. Curves were provided[32] which enabled the vehicles travelling in the slow lanes to be estimated for various growth rates; these curves also took into account the fact that the percentage of commercial vehicles using the slow lane of a multilane dual carriageway carrying 3000 commercial vehicles per day typically declines to about 70 per cent for 13 000 commercial vehicles per day, whilst the commercial vehicle usage of the adjacent lanes generally rises in a corresponding fashion.

For most flexible roads, a design life of twenty years was normally chosen. This was seen as catering for a terminal pavement condition at which partial reconstruction or a major overlay would be necessary to revive the pavement and extend its life.

*Step 3* Determine the equivalent 'life' number of standard axles to be used for design purposes for the commercial vehicle mix on the new highway.

Having calculated the number of commercial vehicles expected for the

**Table 6.8** Estimated commercial vehicle flows on roads for which survey data are not available

| Type of road | Estimated traffic flow in each direction (commercial vehicles per day) |
|---|---|
| 1 Culs-de-sac and minor residential roads | 10 |
| 2 Through roads and roads carrying regular bus routes involving up to 25 psv/day in each direction | 75 |
| 3 Major through roads carrying regular bus routes involving 25–50 psv/day in each direction | 175 |
| 4 Main shopping centre of a large development carrying goods deliveries and main through roads carrying more than 50 psv/day in each direction | 350 |

selected design year, the next step was to convert this number into an equivalent axle value that could be used for design purposes. Empirical road tests have indicated that different combinations of axle load and configuration will cause different amounts of damage to a pavement; however, for design purposes these can be related to a standard axle load of (in Britain) 80 kN in terms of their damage effects, through the use of equivalence damage factors (see Table 6.9). To allow for the traffic mix, the damage factors or numbers of standard axles per commercial vehicle recommended for use on different types of road were 1.08 for motorways and trunk roads designed to carry over 1000 commercial vehicles per day in each direction at the time of construction, 0.72 for roads carrying between 250 and 1000 commercial vehicles per day in each direction, and 0.45 for all other public roads. (These standard axle relationships have since been varied[33-35]; see also Table 6.10, p. 421.)

These factors are then multiplied by the cumulative number of commercial vehicles expected to use the design lane throughout the design life of the pavement, in order to obtain the standard axle total to be used for design purposes.

*Step 4*   Determine the subbase thickness.

This was done by entering Fig. 6.20(a) or, subsequently, Tables 6.5, 6.6 or 6.7 with the appropriate cumulative number of standard axles and the subgrade *CBR*-value.

*Step 5*   Determine the roadbase and surfacing thicknesses.

These thicknesses were obtained from Fig. 6.20(b) or, subsequently, from Tables 6.5 or 6.6.

**Table 6.9**   Relative damaging powers of different axle loads, originally determined for Road Note 29

| Axle load (kN) | Damage factor |
| --- | --- |
| 8.92 | 0.0002 |
| 17.76 | 0.0025 |
| 26.68 | 0.01 |
| 35.61 | 0.03 |
| 44.54 | 0.09 |
| 53.37 | 0.19 |
| 62.29 | 0.35 |
| 71.22 | 0.61 |
| 80.05 | 1.00 |
| 88.98 | 1.50 |
| 97.90 | 2.30 |
| 106.83 | 3.20 |
| 115.66 | 4.40 |
| 124.59 | 5.80 |
| 133.51 | 7.60 |
| 142.44 | 9.70 |
| 151.27 | 12.10 |
| 160.10 | 15.00 |
| 169.03 | 18.60 |
| 177.95 | 22.80 |

*Comment* Note that the design procedure described above started out by using the *CBR*-value to determine the total thickness of pavement, and the thickness of each layer within each pavement. As time progressed, and more data became available from the road experiments carried out by the Transport and Road Research Laboratory (and from pavement experiments overseas), the use of the *CBR* test to determine thicknesses other than that of the subbase has declined.

## Methods based on theory

These methods can be divided into two groups, viz. semi-theoretical methods and theoretical methods.

*Semi-theoretical methods* can be defined [36] as those which are based on the observance of the performance of actual highway pavements, together with extrapolation of this experience to other pavement structures. This extrapolation is most often based on elastic multilayered theory and on the determination of the mechanical characteristics of the pavement layers, typically their moduli, resistance to fatigue cracking, and resistance to permanent deformation.

By contrast, *theoretical methods* are those which are based on mechanical models and which primarily still require practical verification.

One framework within which these design procedures can be viewed is illustrated in Fig. 6.21. Essentially, the thickness selection (design) process consists of determining an appropriate combination of materials and layer thickness which mitigate various forms of distress induced in a specific pavement from traffic and environmentally related factors. The semi-theoretical/theoretical design procedures used for this purpose normally utilize complex computer programs to calculate the governing stresses, strains and deformations within the pavement layers.

### Shell method

The Shell method of pavement design [37], for example, is possibly the most widely known semi-theoretical procedure. With this design process, which was originally published in 1963, the pavement is regarded as a three-layer system in which the lowest of the layers (assumed infinite in the vertical direction) represents the subgrade; the middle layer represents the combined unbound roadbase and subbase, whilst the uppermost layer includes all bituminous-bound materials above the roadbase. A 'full-depth' bituminous-bound pavement resting directly on the subgrade is dealt with by assuming zero thickness for the unbound layers.

The Shell design approach involves estimating the bituminous-bound and unbound layer thickness required to satisfy governing strain criteria. These criteria are:

(1) the compressive strain in the surface of the subgrade, i.e. if this is excessive, permanent deformation will occur at the top of the subgrade and this will cause deformation at the pavement surface,

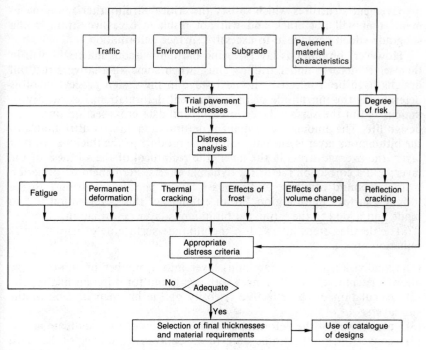

**Fig. 6.21** A framework for pavement design using methods based on theory

(2)   the horizontal tensile strain in the bituminous-bound layer, generally at its bottom, i.e. if this is excessive, cracking of the layer will occur.

The permissible value for compressive subgrade strain was derived from analysis of data from AASHO Road Test pavements [2] which conformed to *CBR* design. The permissible strain in the bituminous layer was determined from extensive laboratory measurements for various bituminous-mix types at different stiffness moduli.

Other criteria taken into account include the permissible tensile stress or strain in any cementitious base in the middle layer and the integrated permanent deformation at the pavement surface due to deformations in the individual layers.

A complex computer program *BISAR* has been developed by Shell which enables all stresses, strains and displacements at any point in the pavement system to be determined under any number of vertical and/or horizontal surface loads. However, as the highway engineer may still have difficulty in obtaining access to the sophisticated computer hardware required to run the program, a series of 296 design charts has been prepared for the *Shell Manual*; these charts obviate the need to carry out complex calculations. Instead, the engineer is able to enter these charts with input data reflecting the subgrade modulus, bituminous-mix design, traffic volume, and mean annual air temperature, and derive various combinations of pavement structures which satisfy the critical strain criteria, i.e. pavements that will not crack and will not result in excessive strain in the subgrade which could lead to excessive surface deformation.

However, bituminous layers, being partially viscous materials, will in themselves deform under traffic. Thus, when some alternative structural designs have been selected, the next stage in the design process involves determining the magnitude of the permanent deformation, i.e. rut depth, anticipated in the surface layer in each candidate cross-section during its design life. The amount of permanent deformation directly attributable to the bituminous layer is estimated from the product of the thickness of that layer, the average stress in the layer, the reciprocol of the stiffness of the layer, and a correction factor for dynamic effects. Permanent deformation in the unbound roadbase and subbase layers can also contribute to the ultimate surface deformation, so an estimate of this deformation is also made and added to the estimated bituminous-layer deformation.

The detailed steps involved in the ultimate surface deformation determination are:

(1)　subdivision of the bituminous layer into a number of sub-layers to allow for temperature differences with depth and for different mix types,
(2)　calculation of the effective viscosity of the bitumen in each of the sub-layers,
(3)　assessment of the deformation characteristics of the candidate mixes,
(4)　conversion of the traffic data to an equivalent number of standard single design wheels, each with a contact stress of $6 \times 10^5 \ \text{N/m}^2$,
(5)　determination of the mix stiffness of each of the bituminous sub-layers,
(6)　determination of the average stress in each sub-layer,
(7)　determination of the estimated permanent deformation in each bituminous sub-layer (as described above),
(8)　estimation of the roadbase and subbase deformation,
(9)　estimation of the total surface deformation.

The estimated total surface deformation in each candidate pavement design is next compared with the allowable depth of rut, and either judged acceptable or not acceptable. The final choice of pavement design is then made from the acceptable candidates, normally on the basis of economics.

## Nottingham method

As is suggested in Table 6.2, British researchers at the University of Nottingham and the Transport and Road Research Laboratory have (separately and cooperatively) taken a leading role in developing design procedures which are based on theory. The methods developed by both of these bodies will be discussed here as they complement each other.

The basic philosophy underlying the approach to pavement design developed at the University of Nottingham is that the design of a highway pavement structure should be treated in the same way as the design of other civil engineering structures, as follows.

(1)  Specify the loading.
(2)  Estimate the proportions.
(3)  Consider the materials available.
(4)  Carry out a structural analysis using theoretical principles.
(5)  Compare critical stresses, strains or deflections with allowable values.
(6)  Make adjustments to materials or geometry until a satisfactory design is achieved.
(7)  Consider the economic feasibility of the result.

Figures 6.22(a) and (b) illustrate diagrammatically the two modes of failure considered using the Nottingham design method, which the designer

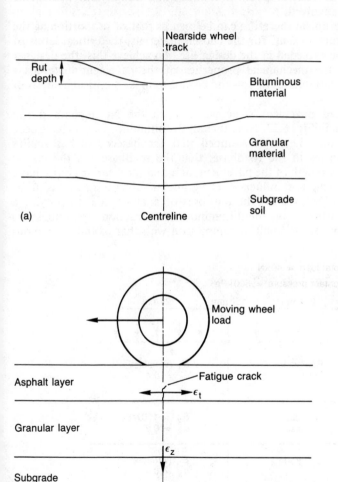

**Fig. 6.22**  Failure modes and critical strains in bituminous pavements, considered in the Nottingham design method[38]: (a) permanent deformation and (b) fatigue cracking and critical strains

seeks to avoid within the pavement design life. The deterioration of a pavement is considered to be essentially a fatigue phenomenon in that it is the result of stresses and strains in the pavement caused by the magnitude and number of load applications. *Cracking* of the bituminous layer is considered to arise from repeated tensile strain, the maximum value of which occurs at the bottom of the layer (Fig. 6.22(b)). The crack, once initiated, propagates upwards and causes a gradual weakening of the pavement. *Rutting* arises from the accumulation of permanent strain throughout the pavement structure. If the vertical strain in the subgrade, $\varepsilon_z$ (Fig. 6.22(b)), is kept below a certain level, excessive rutting will not occur—unless, of course, poor bituminous-mix design and inadequate compaction are involved.

The design problem therefore can be seen as that of proportioning the pavement structure so that, for the chosen materials, the critical levels of strain will not be exceeded in the design life. To achieve this, the designer needs to know the mechanical properties of the pavement materials— especially of the bituminous ones—and be able to make a critical analysis of the structure.

The simplified pavement structure used in the Nottingham design method is shown in Fig. 6.23. Note that all the bituminous layers have been combined into one, i.e. it is assumed that the basecourse has similar structural properties to the roadbase, that the roadbase has the largest influence on the strength of the pavement, and that the wearing course has a relatively small structural influence. The granular subbase is assumed to be a standard 200 mm layer for the purposes of analysis, and to provide a construction platform for the bituminous construction operations; its structural significance is small in comparison with that of the bituminous layer.

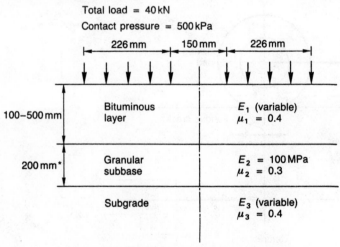

Total load = 40 kN

Contact pressure = 500 kPa

* Adjustments may be made to solutions for other subbase thicknesses

**Fig. 6.23**   The pavement structure considered in the Nottingham design method

To carry out the structural analysis, a value of elastic modulus, $E$, and Poisson's ratio, $\mu$, have to be specified for each layer. Since some of the materials involved are not perfectly linear elastic, the parameter 'elastic stiffness' is used in place of Young's modulus. Figure 6.23 indicates that the variables in the design problem are therefore reduced to three, viz. the elastic stiffness of the bituminous layer, the thickness of the bituminous layer, and the elastic stiffness of the subgrade.

The actual design process is summarized in the flow diagram in Fig. 6.24. Its application is most easily described in a series of steps which are based on an excellent publication available in the literature[38]. The reader is also referred to a series of papers[39] published by the Nottingham researchers which provide the background to this design procedure.

*Step 1*  Determine the average annual air temperature, $T$, to be used for design purposes.

This is easily determined from records at the closest appropriate Meteorological Office.

*Step 2*  Determine the average speed of commercial vehicles, $V$.

This speed is best determined from a knowledge of the road situation. If uncertainties exist, the speed estimated should err on the slow side, as this will result in a lower stiffness for the bituminous layer.

*Step 3*  Calculate the cumulative number of standard axles, $N$, expected during the design life.

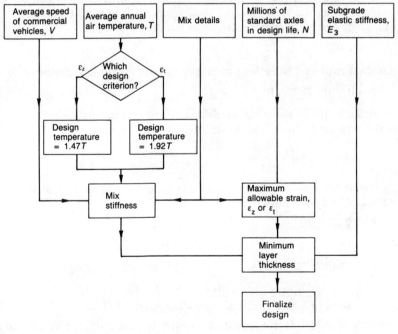

**Fig. 6.24**  Flow diagram for the Nottingham design procedure[38]

The number of standard axles to be used for design purposes is determined as follows[40].

(1)   Establish the 24 h annual average daily one-way flow, $F_o$, of all commercial vehicles in the initial year. When carrying out this determination, the directional split in the flow of commercial vehicles should be calculated, where possible, from census data; a 50:50 percentage split, for example, should only be assumed for a trunk road in the absence of more specific data.

(2)   Establish the expected commercial vehicle growth rate, $r$, that will apply during the design life. This rate, which should be expressed as a fraction rather than as a percentage, can be different from that applying to all traffic. Where specific knowledge of local circumstances is available, e.g. in relation to the development of an industrial estate or the opening of a feeder route, it should be used; in the case of trunk roads and motorways, a growth rate of 0.02 per annum can generally be used without serious loss of accuracy. If sufficient information is available to enable the design life to be broken into consecutive periods so that a separate assessment of cumulative standard axles can be made for each, then this should be done.

(3)   Calculate the 24 h annual average daily one-way flow of commercial vehicles at the mid-term of the design life, $F_m$, from the equation

$$F_m = F_o(1 + r)^{0.5n}$$

where $n$ = design life (years).

(4)   For the mid-term year also, determine the proportion, $P$, of commercial vehicles using the slow (design) lane, from the following formulae.

For single carriageway general-purpose roads,

$$P = 1.00$$

For dual two- and three-lane carriageway roads including motorways,

$$P = 0.970 - 0.385(10^{-4}) \times F_m$$

(5)   Calculate the total (cumulative) number of commercial vehicles, $T_n$, using the slow lane during the design life from the equation

$$T_n = 365 P F_o \left( \frac{(1 + r)^n - 1}{r} \right)$$

(6)   Convert the number of commercial vehicles, $T_n$, to equivalent standard axles, $N$ msa, as follows:

$$N = T_n D \times 10^{-6}$$

where

$D$ = vehicle damage factor at the mid-term of the design life

$$= \frac{0.35}{0.93^{t_d} + 0.082} - \left( \frac{0.26}{0.92^{t_d} + 0.082} \right) \left( \frac{1.0}{3.9^{F_m/1550}} \right)$$

The vehicle damage factor equation, which is based on the results of dynamic weighbridge measurements carried out over a number of years, is

**Table 6.10** Examples of current vehicle damage factors

| Year | Annual average daily flow of commercial vehicles | | | |
|------|------|------|------|------|
| | 250 | 1000 | 2000 | 4000 |
| 1985 | 0.78 | 1.64 | 2.17 | 2.49 |
| 1990 | 0.93 | 1.89 | 2.49 | 2.84 |
| 1995 | 1.18 | 2.12 | 2.76 | 3.14 |
| 2000 | 1.22 | 2.31 | 3.00 | 3.40 |
| 2005 | 1.34 | 2.47 | 3.18 | 3.60 |
| 2010 | 1.43 | 2.60 | 3.33 | 3.76 |

able to relate the vehicle damage factor for any given year, $D$, to the 24 h annual average daily flow of commercial vehicles for that year, $F$, and the number of years difference between the given year and the year 1945, $t_d$. Thus, for example, in the above equation $t_d$ equals the initial calendar year (i.e. the road opening year) plus half the design life minus 1945.

As can be seen from Table 6.10, this equation generates vehicle damage factors that vary with time and the annual average daily flow of commercial vehicles.

*Step 4* Determine the subgrade stiffness, $E_3$.

Also known as the elastic stiffness or resilient modulus, $E_3$ is most usually estimated from the laboratory California Bearing Ratio of the subgrade soil. Thus

$$E_3 = 10(CBR)$$

where $E_3$ is in MPa. In the case of cohesive soils, however, the laboratory *CBR* test is considered to be not particularly reliable so that, for average British conditions, $E_3$ is better estimated from the plasticity index, as follows.

$$E_3 = 70 - PI$$

*Step 5* Determine the bituminous design temperature for the strain criterion being considered.

Whilst pavement temperatures vary continually, one of the simplifications of the Nottingham design method is to use an average annual value for design purposes. However, the actual value used is different for each of the two governing criteria.

For permanent deformation, i.e. subgrade strain, the design temperature is taken as 1.47 times the average annual air temperature. This factor takes into consideration the effects of diurnal variations in both temperatures and traffic loading.

For fatigue cracking computations, i.e. bituminous strain, the design temperature is taken as 1.92 times the average annual air temperature. In this instance, the factor also takes into consideration cumulative damage effects.

*Step 6* Determine the stiffness of the bituminous layer, $E_1$.

The stiffness of a bituminous mix is best determined by means of a suitable laboratory test[41]. Alternatively, the elastic mix stiffness can be calculated from that of the binder, $S_b$, and the voids in mixed aggregate, $VMA$, as follows.

$$E_1 = S_b \left[ 1 + \frac{257.5 - 2.5 VMA}{n(VMA - 3)} \right]^n$$

where $n = 0.83 \log(4 \times 10^4 / S_b)$.

This relationship is considered valid for $VMA$-values between 12 and 30 per cent, and for voids contents greater than 3 per cent.

The following equation[42] can be used to calculate the binder stiffness, $S_b$, over a limited but practical range of conditions.

$$S_b = 1.157 \times 10^{-7} t^{-0.368} 2.718^{-PI_r} (SP_r - T)^5$$

where $S_b$ = binder stiffness (MPa), $t$ = loading time (s), valid within the range 0.01 to 0.10 s, $PI_r$ = recovered penetration index of the bitumen binder, valid within the range $-1$ to $+1$, $SP_r$ = recovered softening point of the bitumen, and $T$ = design temperature, where $(SP_r - T)$ is valid within the range 20 to 60 °C.

A reasonable estimate of the loading time, $t$, for bituminous layers between 100 and 350 mm thick can be obtained from the following empirical relationship.

$$t = 1/V$$

where $V$ = average commercial vehicle speed (km/h).

Alternatively, a more precise estimate can be obtained from the equation

$$\log t = 5 \times 10^{-4} h - (0.2 + 0.94 \log V)$$

where $h$ = estimated thickness of the bituminous layer (mm).

In analytical flexible pavement design, the binder characteristics which are of most interest are those which refer to its state in the roadway following the hardening that takes place during mixing and laying—hence the need to determine the *recovered* properties of the binder after it has been reclaimed from the pavement. The recovered penetration index of the binder, $PI_r$, can be determined from the following equation.

$$PI_r = \frac{1951.4 - 500 \log P_r - 20 SP_r}{50 \log P_r - SP_r - 120.14}$$

where $P_r$ = recovered bitumen penetration and $SP_r$ = recovered softening point of bitumen (°C).

If the recovered binder properties are not known, they may be estimated from the initial penetration of the bitumen, $P_i$, as follows.

$$P_r = 0.65 P_i$$

and    $SP_r = 98.4 - 26.35 \log P_r$

These two equations are based on the results of numerous tests on recovered binders[38].

*Step 7* Determine the maximum allowable strain for the criterion being considered.

As noted previously, the design criterion to prevent failure by fatigue cracking is tensile strain, and the maximum value is normally assumed to occur at the bottom of the bituminous layer midway between the dual wheels in a horizontal, tangential direction (see Fig. 6.22(b)) in the direction of movement of traffic. To prevent fatigue failure, i.e. failure which occurs from repeated applications of strain below that which would cause rupture in a single application, the fatigue strength of the proposed mix needs to be known or, alternatively, the mix must be designed to provide the desired fatigue characteristics. This characteristic can be expressed as a relationship between the tensile strain, $\varepsilon_t$, and the number of cycles to failure, $N_f$, as follows.

$$N_f = C(1/\varepsilon_t)^m$$

where $C$ and $m$ are constants which depend upon two simple mix parameters, the volumetric proportion of the binder, $V_B$, and its initial softening point, $SP_i$. (Note that when calculating stiffness the recovered softening point was used. The use of $SP_i$ in this instance stems simply from the way in which various estimation procedures were developed quite independently.)

Research at Nottingham[43] has determined that the maximum allowable tensile strain (in microstrain), for a given 'life' in terms of numbers of load applications (in msa), can be estimated from the following equation.

$$\log \varepsilon_t = \frac{14.39 \log V_B + 24.2 \log SP_i - 46.06 - \log N}{5.13 \log V_B + 8.63 \log SP_i - 15.8}$$

where $V_B$ = percentage of binder in the mix by volume, $N$ = cumulative number of standard load applications, $SP_i$ = initial softening point of the bitumen in the mix, and $\varepsilon_t$ = maximum permissible tensile strain in the bituminous layer. The above equation can be rearranged to calculate the maximum permissible number of load applications, $N$, in terms of the other parameters, as follows.

$$\log N = 15.8 \log \varepsilon_t - 46.06 - (5.13 \log \varepsilon_t - 14.39)\log V_B - (8.63 \log \varepsilon_t - 24.2)\log SP_i$$

Prevention of *excessive rutting* is dealt with by limiting the maximum vertical strain in the subgrade, $\varepsilon_z$. The equation developed for prediction purposes in this instance is as follows.

$$\varepsilon_z = 451.3/(N/f_r)^{0.28}$$

where $N$ = cumulative number of standard load applications, $f_r$ = a rut factor (to allow for the use of different bituminous mixtures), and $\varepsilon_z$ = maximum permissible compressive strain in the subgrade.

If the life of the pavement is to be calculated from the strain, then

$$N = f_r(3 \times 10^9/\varepsilon_z^{3.57})$$

The rut factors derived for use with the above two equations are given in

Table 6.11. The properties of the four mixes to which these factors apply are listed in Tables 6.12–6.14. For design purposes, the particular bituminous mix being used must be identified as a type which is similar to one of the four typical ones, when dealing with permanent deformation, in order to determine an appropriate rut factor. When there is doubt about the identification of the proposed mix, it should be assumed to resemble the standard hot rolled asphalt.

Note that the dense bitumen macadam, modified rolled asphalt, and modified dense bitumen macadam all offer greater resistance to permanent deformation than the standard hot rolled asphalt. As a consequence, they can be expected to achieve longer lives for equivalent design situations.

*Step 8*    Determine the minimum layer thicknesses for the strain criterion.

Design charts relating the elastic stiffness of the bituminous layer, the thickness of the bituminous layer, the elastic stiffness of the subgrade, and the critical strains have been devised by the Nottingham researchers. Each

**Table 6.11**   Rut factors used in the compressive strain equations to allow for different bituminous mixes

| Mix type | Rut factor, $f_r$ |
|---|---|
| Hot rolled asphalt | 1 |
| Dense bitumen macadam | 1.56 |
| Modified hot rolled asphalt | 1.37 |
| Modified dense bitumen macadam | 1.52 |

**Table 6.12**   Properties of the typical roadbase materials upon which the Nottingham research was carried out

| Mix type | Binder content (%) | Voids content (%) | $VMA$ (%) | $V_B$ (%) |
|---|---|---|---|---|
| Hot rolled asphalt | 5.7 | 5.0 | 18.1 | 13.1 |
| Dense bitumen macadam | 3.5 | 10.0 | 17.9 | 7.9 |
| Modified hot rolled asphalt | 5.0 | 4.0 | 15.7 | 11.7 |
| Modified dense bitumen macadam | 4.5 | 6.0 | 16.4 | 10.4 |

*Notes*:
Relative density of aggregate = 2.70
Relative density of bitumen = 1.02

**Table 6.13**   Properties of the binders assumed for the mixes in Table 6.12

| Initial properties | | Recovered properties | | |
|---|---|---|---|---|
| Penetration | Softening point (°C) | Penetration | Softening point (°C) | Penetration index |
| 50 | 53.6 | 32.5 | 58.6 | −0.2 |
| 100 | 45.7 | 65.0 | 50.6 | −0.4 |

**Table 6.14** Properties of the typical surfacing layers upon which the Nottingham research was carried out

| Mix type | Initial penetration of bitumen | Binder content (%) | Voids content (%) |
|---|---|---|---|
| Hot rolled asphalt wearing course | 50 | 7.9 | 4.0 |
| Dense bitumen macadam wearing course | 100 | 5.0 | 5.0 |
| Friction course | 100 | 5.0 | 14.0 |

chart is for a different subgrade stiffness and values of 20, 30, 50 and 70 MPa, approximately corresponding to *CBR*s of 2 to 7 per cent, so as to cover most practical subgrade situations in Britain. Figure 6.25 is one of these design charts. Note that the subgrade strain is determined from the upper part of the chart and the bituminous tensile strain from the lower part. The required thickness for a given critical strain, subgrade stiffness, and the bituminous stiffness may be determined from this figure also.

*Step 9* For granular subbase thicknesses greater than 200 mm, reduce the required thickness of the bituminous layer.

The Nottingham researchers have extended their work to allow for the situation where the subbase is thicker than 200 mm. Thus, if the granular layer exceeds 200 mm by $\Delta h_2$, then the corresponding change in the bituminous layer thickness $\Delta h_1$, for a given strain, is calculated as follows.

For the subgrade strain criterion,

$$\Delta h_1 = \frac{\Delta h_2\,(53 - 2.8E_1 + 0.5E_3)}{300}$$

For the bituminous strain criterion,

$$\Delta h_1 = \frac{\Delta h_2\,(26.5 - 0.5E_1 - 0.23E_3)}{300}$$

where $E_1$ = bituminous mix stiffness (GPa) and $E_3$ = subgrade stiffness (MPa).

*Step 10* Repeat Steps 5–9 for the other design criterion.

The design bituminous layer thickness is the larger of the two determined for each criterion.

*Step 11* If the type and thickness of the surfacing layer are known, calculate the equivalent roadbase thickness and subtract this from the thickness determined at Step 10 to determine the final thickness of the roadbase layer.

The Nottingham method can also be applied to a four-layered pavement. Thus, if a surfacing layer and a roadbase layer are to be treated separately, then $h_s$ mm of the surfacing layer can be considered as equivalent to $h_b$ mm of the bituminous roadbase, where

$$h_b = h_s E_s / E_1$$

and $E_s$ and $E_1$ are the elastic stiffnesses of the surfacing and roadbase layers, respectively. Thus, for example, if a pavement has a 40 mm hot rolled asphalt wearing course with an elastic stiffness of 4000 MPa and a 180 mm hot rolled asphalt roadbase layer ($E_1 = 8000$ MPa), then the surfacing layer is equivalent to

$$h_b = 40 \times 4000/8000 = 20 \text{ mm}$$

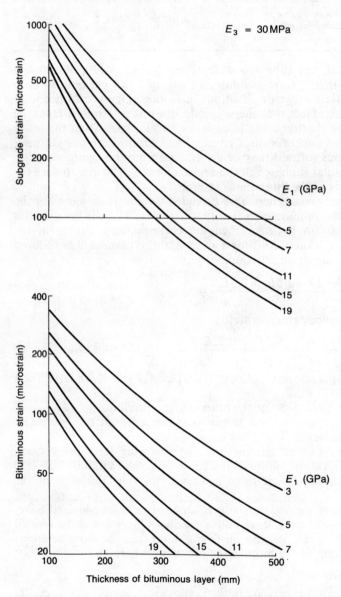

**Fig. 6.25**  Critical strains as functions of stiffness and thickness of the bituminous layer[38]. (Note: Subgrade elastic stiffness = 30 MPa and subbase thickness = 200 mm.)

**Example of the Nottingham method of flexible pavement design[38]**
A single carriageway highway was designed to open in 1984 in a locality with an average annual air temperature of $9\,^\circ$C. Detailed traffic analysis showed that the initial traffic volume was 1500 commercial vehicles per day and the growth rate was 3 per cent. The average speed of commercial vehicles was 60 km/h, and the design life was 20 years. The subgrade soil had a plasticity index of 38. Carry out detailed design calculations using the four typical roadbase mixes described in Table 6.12, for a three-layered pavement structure having a 200 mm thick subbase.

*Solution*

design temperature for deformation (*Step 5*) $= 1.47 \times 9 = 13.2\,^\circ$C

design temperature for fatigue (*Step 5*) $= 1.92 \times 9 = 17.3\,^\circ$C

cumulative number of commercial vehicles (*Step 3*) $= 14.7$ msa

damage factor (*Step 3*) $= 2.72$

Therefore

$$
\text{cumulative number of standard axles } (Step\ 3) = 2.72 \times 14.7
$$
$$
= 40 \text{ msa}
$$

$$
\text{elastic stiffness of the subgrade } (Step\ 4) = 70 - 38
$$
$$
= 32 \text{ MPa (say 30 MPa)}
$$

The bituminous-mix stiffness calculated (*Step 6*) is as given in Table 6.15. The maximum allowable bituminous strain and subgrade strain calculated (*Step 7*), in microstrain, for each layer are given in Table 6.16.

**Table 6.15** Elastic stiffnesses determined for the mixes in the example

| | For deformation | | For fatigue | |
|---|---|---|---|---|
| Bituminous material | $S_b$ (MPa) | $E_1$ (MPa) | $S_b$ (MPa) | $E_1$ (MPa) |
| Hot rolled asphalt | 126 | 8900 | 79 | 6740 |
| Dense bitumen macadam | 57 | 5760 | 32 | 4030 |
| Modified hot rolled asphalt | 126 | 12790 | 79 | 9940 |
| Modified dense bitumen macadam | 126 | 11440 | 79 | 8820 |

**Table 6.16** Maximum allowable strains determined for mixes in the example

| | Maximum allowable strain (in microstrain) | |
|---|---|---|
| Layer | Bituminous strain | Subgrade strain |
| Hot rolled asphalt | 130 | 161 |
| Dense bitumen macadam | 54 | 182 |
| Modified hot rolled asphalt | 120 | 175 |
| Modified dense bitumen macadam | 108 | 181 |

**Table 6.17**    Final layer thicknesses determined for the example

|  | Layer thickness (mm) | | |
| --- | --- | --- | --- |
| Bituminous material | For deformation | For fatigue | For design |
| Hot rolled asphalt | 290 | 170 | 290 |
| Dense bitumen macadam | 320 | 410 | 410 |
| Modified hot rolled asphalt | 240 | 150 | 240 |
| Modified dense bitumen macadam | 250 | 170 | 250 |

Determine the minimum bituminous layer thickness for each strain criterion from Fig. 6.25 (*Step 8*), and select a design thickness (*Step 10*). These data are shown in Table 6.17.

**TRRL method**

The semi-theoretical procedure developed by the Transport and Road Research Laboratory is now in practical use.

The empirical design method[30] described previously, which was based on observation of the performance of a number of experimental roads and which used subgrade tests to determine the subbase thickness for the pavement, was the only official method of pavement design used in Britain in the 1970s and early 1980s. Whilst the method is generally considered to have been effective, it can be said to have a number of significant deficiencies, as follows.

(1)    It is unresponsive to changes in construction processes or improvements in materials.

(2)    Its validity only applies to designs for up to about 40 msa, whereas many major roads now carry well over 50 msa, and some up to 150 msa on particular stretches of motorway, during a twenty-year life.

(3)    The end of the twenty-year design life was associated with a surface rut of 20 mm or more or severe cracking and crazing, when the pavement was considered to be in a failed state and in need of a major strengthening or partial reconstruction; however, it has subsequently been shown that strengthening a pavement in this damaged condition does not necessarily result in satisfactory subsequent performance.

*Design criteria*    The new TRRL method of pavement design[35,44,45] requires the pavement to satisfy the following structural criteria (see Fig. 6.26).

(1)    The subgrade must be able to sustain traffic loading without excessive deformation; this is controlled by the vertical compressive stress or strain at formation level.

(2)    Bituminous materials and cement-bound materials used in roadbase designs for long life must not crack under the influence of traffic; this is controlled by the horizontal tensile stress or strain at the bottom of the roadbase.

(3)    In pavements containing a considerable thickness of bituminous

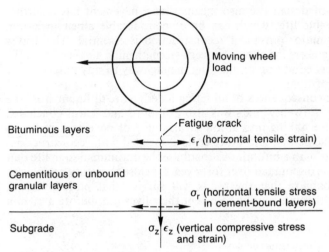

**Fig. 6.26** Critical stresses and strains in a bituminous pavement considered by the TRRL researchers[35]

materials, the internal deformation of these materials must be limited; their deformation is a function of their creep characteristics.

(4)  The load-spreading ability of granular subbases and capping layers must be adequate to provide a satisfactory construction platform.

Basic inputs into the design method are the design life to be specified, the traffic load to be carried, and the strength of the subgrade upon which the pavement is to be built.

*Design life concept*  Throughout the 1970s and early 1980s there were considerable increases in the damaging power of commercial vehicles using the major road network, and it became clear that most heavily-trafficked roads needed to be designed for cumulative traffic up to ten times that envisaged when the first motorways were opened. This led to an increase in the need for major reconstruction work, and to recognition that such reconstruction would in most instances be facilitated if the life of a pavement was defined in terms of the *onset* of critical structural conditions rather than in terms of when the failure actually occurred. On this basis, the decision was taken that in future the design life of a pavement would be defined as a rutting in the wheel paths of 10 mm or the beginning of cracking in the wheel paths; these surface indicators are normally the precursor of significant structural deterioration and mark the latest time when the application of an overlay can be expected to make best use of the original structural quality of the pavement in order to extend its life.

It is now accepted that pre-emptive overlaying at the onset of critical conditions is preferable to allowing the road to deteriorate until extensive pavement reconstruction is necessary. Since this approach makes best use of the strength of the existing pavement, it also results in a pavement of more uniform strength. As deterioration can be more readily anticipated by in situ deflection measurements, reconstruction can be more readily planned.

This concept of design life also means that a pavement has a further period of serviceable life, which can be of considerable albeit uncertain duration, before major pavement reconstruction is essential. This leaves open to future engineers the choice between strengthening a pavement at the onset of the critical condition or allowing the highway to stay in service for a further period of time.

The economic consequences of adopting a design life different from the conventional one of twenty years was also examined and it was concluded (see Fig. 6.27), after taking into account variability of pavement performance, cost of traffic delays, and other costs associated with reconstruction, that for pavements with a bituminous roadbase the optimum design life that minimizes the costs discounted over forty years is close to twenty years, with 85 per cent probability that the roads will survive that period without requiring a strengthening overlay to extent their lives (i.e. before a 10 mm rut is achieved).

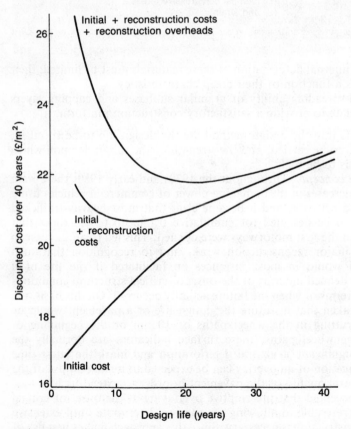

**Fig. 6.27**   Costs of construction and reconstruction discounted over forty years for road pavements with bituminous roadbases[35]. *Notes*: subgrade *CBR* = 5%, discount rate = 7%, growth rate = 2%, cumulative traffic = 40 msa in twenty years, and probability of survival to design life = 85%.

*Traffic loading*   The design traffic loading is the cumulative number of equivalent standard 80 kN axles that is forecast to be carried in the nearside traffic lane during the design life of the road.

As discussed in relation to the Nottingham method, the total number of commercial vehicles, $T_n$, using the slow lane over the design life, $n$ years, can be expressed in terms of the initial daily flow, $F_o$, the commercial vehicle growth rate, $r$ (normally taken as 2 per cent, unless more definitive data are available), and the proportion of commercial vehicles using the slow lane, $P$, as follows:

$$T_n = \frac{365 PF_o[(1 + r)^n - 1]}{r}$$

In order to convert this cumulative number of commercial vehicles to equivalent standard axles, $T_n$ must be multiplied by the number of equivalent standard axles per commercial vehicle (i.e. the vehicle damage factor) at the mid-term of the design life. The formula which gives an estimate of the vehicle damage factor, $D$, for any mid-term year $t_d$, based on the 24 h annual average daily flow of commercial vehicles for the year, $F$, has already been described in relation to the Nottingham method, and will not be repeated here. Note that in this formula the base year is 1945, so that the year 1985 corresponds to $t_d = 40$.

*Subgrade*   In the TRRL design methodology the strength and stiffness of the subgrade are required for the following two reasons:

(1)   to characterize the subgrade as the foundation for a haul road to carry construction traffic—for this purpose, the strength of the subgrade just before placing the capping layer or subbase is needed,
(2)   to establish the likely in-service long-term strength and stiffness of the subgrade after the disturbance of the construction phase is over, and when moisture equilibrium has been established within it.

The *CBR* test value is used as the measure of subgrade strength as, in spite of its limited accuracy, it is widely understood and accepted, and it can be related within reasonable limits to subgrade stiffness.

If it is not possible to carry out a *CBR* test on the subgrade soil, the *CBR* to be used for the design of capping layers and subbases is estimated for cohesive soils from Fig. 6.28.

Table 6.18 indicates reasonable estimates of equilibrium values of *CBR* for combinations of poor, average and good construction conditions, high and low water-tables, and thick and thin pavements. Good conditions imply that the subgrades never get wetter than their equilibrium moisture contents beneath the finished pavement. A high water-table is one 300 mm beneath formation level and is consistent with effective subsoil drainage; a low water-table is 1 m down. A thick pavement is of 1200 mm depth (including a 650 mm capping layer) and is typical of a motorway construction; a thin pavement is 300 mm deep. For pavements of intermediate thickness founded on plastic soils, an equilibrium value of *CBR* can be interpolated.

Measurements of the stiffness modulus, $E$, of the subgrade soil are required for use in calculating the stresses and strains in the pavement and

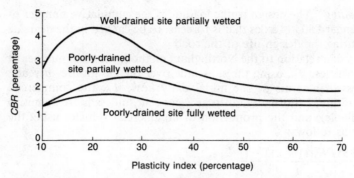

**Fig. 6.28**   Estimating the subgrade *CBR* for pavement construction from the plasticity index[35]

in the subgrade soil. This is estimated from the following equation

$$E = 17.6(CBR)^{0.64} \text{ MPa}$$

where the *CBR*-value is a percentage value. This relationship provides a reasonable lower bound estimate of stiffness over the *CBR*-range from 2 to 12 per cent.

*Subbase and capping layers*   The *subbase* is a structurally significant layer whose initial construction function is to provide a working platform on which roadbase materials can be transported, laid and compacted. It also acts as a level regulating layer and insulates the subgrade against the action of weather. Normally, the subbase is a well-graded granular material; however, open-graded cement and bitumen-bound materials are also used.

The strength of the subbase material depends upon the anticipated traffic loading. For flexible pavements that are expected to carry a design traffic load of more than 2 msa, the subbase strength should be at least equivalent to a *CBR* of 30 per cent; for traffic ranges below 2 msa, the strength may be reduced to a *CBR* of 20 per cent.

The thickness of the subbase can be estimated from Fig. 6.29, based on the likely *CBR*-value of the subgrade *at the time of construction*. In this figure the Corps of Engineers' curve is based on the thickness required to limit rut depth to 40 mm during construction, i.e. the minimum deformation that can be tolerated if the subbase surface is to be reshaped and recompacted efficiently and serious rutting is to be avoided in the subgrade. The elastic analysis curve is based on the thickness of subbase required to reduce the dynamic vertical strain in the subgrade at the formation to a level that will not bring about major deformation within it.

Given the imprecise nature of both analyses, there is good agreement between the two methods in predicting the subbase thicknesses required for haul roads to carry traffic of between 100 and 1000 standard axles, a range which caters for the majority of both minor and major highway works.

Figure 6.29 also provides a guide to the length of highway that can be constructed on a given thickness of subbase. Note, for example, that a

**Table 6.18** Equilibrium suction index $CBR$-values for subgrades subject to different water-table and construction conditions, under thin and thick pavements[35]

| Soil type | Plasticity index | High water-table | | | | | | Low water-table | | | | | |
|---|---|---|---|---|---|---|---|---|---|---|---|---|---|
| | | Poor | | Average | | Good | | Poor | | Average | | Good | |
| | | Thin | Thick | Thin | Thick | Thin | Thick | Thin | Thick | Thin | Thick | Thin | Thick |
| Heavy clay | 70 | 1.5 | 2.0 | 2.0 | 2.0 | 2.0 | 2.0 | 1.5 | 2.0 | 2.0 | 2.0 | 2.0 | 2.5 |
| | 60 | 1.5 | 2.0 | 2.0 | 2.0 | 2.0 | 2.5 | 1.5 | 2.0 | 2.0 | 2.0 | 2.0 | 2.5 |
| | 50 | 1.5 | 2.0 | 2.0 | 2.5 | 2.0 | 2.5 | 2.0 | 2.0 | 2.0 | 2.5 | 2.0 | 2.5 |
| | 40 | 2.0 | 2.5 | 2.5 | 3.0 | 2.5 | 3.0 | 2.5 | 2.5 | 3.0 | 3.0 | 3.0 | 3.5 |
| Silty clay | 30 | 2.5 | 3.5 | 3.0 | 4.0 | 3.5 | 5.0 | 3.0 | 3.5 | 4.0 | 4.0 | 4.0 | 6.0 |
| Sandy clay | 20 | 2.5 | 4.0 | 4.0 | 5.0 | 4.5 | 7.0 | 3.0 | 4.0 | 5.0 | 6.0 | 6.0 | 8.0 |
| | 10 | 1.5 | 3.5 | 3.0 | 6.0 | 3.5 | 7.0 | 2.5 | 4.0 | 4.5 | 7.0 | 6.0 | >8.0 |
| Silt* | — | 1.0 | 1.0 | 1.0 | 1.0 | 2.0 | 2.0 | 1.0 | 1.0 | 2.0 | 2.0 | 2.0 | 2.0 |
| Sand (poorly-graded) | — | ←———— 20 ————→ | | | | | | | | | | | |
| Sand (well-graded) | — | ←———— 40 ————→ | | | | | | | | | | | |
| Sandy gravel (well-graded) | — | ←———— 60 ————→ | | | | | | | | | | | |

*Estimated—assuming some probability of material saturating

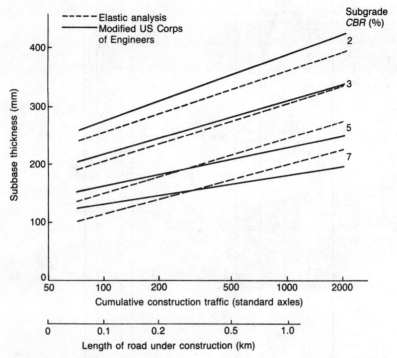

**Fig. 6.29**　Thickness of subbase required to carry construction traffic[35]

single subbase layer of 225 mm will generally be satisfactory providing the length of roadbase and surfacing under construction is less than about 1 km and the subgrade *CBR* is not less than 5 per cent.

When a capping layer is not employed on weak subgrades of less than 5 per cent, the thickness of subbase will exceed the maximum permitted for a single layer, 225 mm, and must be laid in two layers. In this case, the lower layer should be as thick as possible, preferably 225 mm, in order to avoid the danger of damaging the subbase or subgrade during compaction.

On subgrades weaker than a *CBR* of 5 per cent, it is common practice to use a *capping layer* of low-cost granular material to a lower specification than the subbase. The functions of the capping layer are: (a) to protect the subgrade from the adverse effects of wet weather, (b) to provide a working platform on which subbase construction can proceed with minimum interruption from wet weather, and (c) to allow the full load-spreading capability of the subbase to be realized, which would not be possible were it to be laid directly on top of a weak subgrade.

This capping layer is normally composed of material with a minimum *CBR* of 15 per cent. Analysis shows that if 150 mm of subbase is laid on 350 mm of capping layer with a *CBR* of more than 15 per cent, the load-spreading ability of the combined layers will meet the requirements for a satisfactory construction platform over subgrades with *CBR*-values of 2, 3 and 4 per cent. An additional thickness of capping layer of 250 mm is normally required if the subgrade *CBR* is less than 2 per cent. The design of roadbase and surfacing is then the same as that for pavements constructed on a subgrade *CBR* of 5 per cent or more and a subbase of 225 mm, i.e. the basic design criterion.

*Roadbase and surfacing*  Figures 6.30(a) and 6.31(a) and (b) show the design thicknesses derived analytically for bituminous, wet-mix and lean

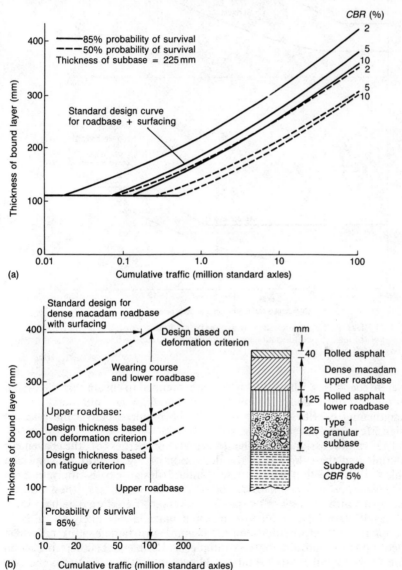

(a)

(b)

**Fig. 6.30**  Design curves for roads with bituminous roadbases[35]: (a) standard designs at different levels of subgrade *CBR* and probability of survival, and (b) designs for traffic in excess of 80 msa

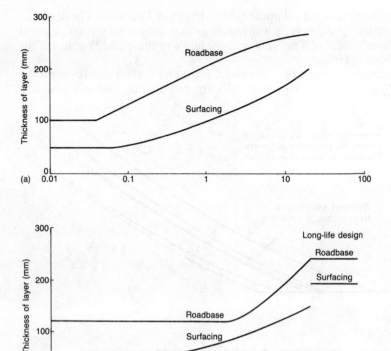

**Fig. 6.31**   Design curves for roads with non-bituminous roadbases[35]: (a) wet-mix road-bases and (b) lean concrete roadbases. *Notes*: subgrade $CBR = 5\%$, thickness of granular subbase = 225 mm, and probability of survival = 85%.

concrete roadbases. These thicknesses are intended to ensure that the design criteria described above in relation to Fig. 6.26 are met, and that a strengthening overlay will not normally be required before the planned design life of the pavement is exceeded.

The values assigned to the structural properties of the pavement materials and the subgrade in the derivation of Fig. 6.30(a) are shown in Table 6.19. Note that whilst these standard design curves apply to both *dense bitumen macadam* and *rolled asphalt* roadbases, they do not necessarily mean that both types of pavement deteriorate in the same manner. Deterioration of dense bitumen macadam is likely to be by a combination of deformation and the beginning of fatigue cracking, whilst rolled asphalt is considerably less fatigue susceptible and is therefore much more likely to fail by deformation. However, as the stiffness of the two materials is broadly similar and their design thickness is the same, the critical strains at the bottom of the roadbase and in the subgrade will also be the same.

**Table 6.19** Input data used in the development of the standard design curves for bituminous pavements as shown in Fig. 6.30(a)

| Material | Property | Value |
|---|---|---|
| Bituminous material | Loading frequency | 5 Hz |
| | Equivalent temperature | 20 °C |
| | Modulus | |
| | of dense bitumen macadam (100 pen) | 3.1 GPa |
| | of hot rolled asphalt (50 pen) | 3.5 GPa |
| | Poisson's ratio | 0.35 |
| | Fatigue criterion | |
| | for dense bitumen macadam (100 pen) | $\log N_f = -9.38 - 4.16 \log \varepsilon_r$ |
| | for hot rolled asphalt (50 pen) | $\log N_f = -9.78 - 4.32 \log \varepsilon_r$ |
| | | where $N_f$ is the road life in standard axles and $\varepsilon_r$ is the horizontal tensile strain at the underside of the bound layer under a standard wheel load |
| | Deformation criterion | $\log N_d = -7.21 - 3.95 \log \varepsilon_z$ |
| | | where $N_d$ is the road life in standard axles and $\varepsilon_z$ is the vertical compressive strain at the top of the subgrade under a standard wheel load |
| Subbase (type 1) | Modulus | The modulus of each layer that has been compacted separately is given by: |
| | | $E_n = 3E_{n+1}$ for $E_{n+1} \leqslant 50$ MPa |
| | | $E_n = 0.15$ GPa for $E_{n+1} > 50$ MPa |
| | | where $E_{n+1}$ is the modulus of the underlying layer and the upper limit for the thickness of a compacted layer is 225 mm |
| | Poisson's ratio | 0.45 |
| Capping layer | Modulus | Range between 50 and 100 MPa |
| | Poisson's ratio | 0.45 |
| Subgrade (cohesive soil) | Modulus | $E = 17.6(CBR)^{0.64}$ MPa |
| | Poisson's ratio | 0.45 |
| Standard wheel load | Load | 40 kN |
| | Contact radius | 0.151 m |

Figure 6.30(a) also shows the effect of the equilibrium *CBR* of the subgrade upon the design thickness. Furthermore, it includes curves showing the thickness associated with 85 per cent and 50 per cent probabilities of achieving the design life before a strengthening overlay is required. The lower probability design thickness is only used when designing less important roads where a greater risk of failure can be tolerated, or where it is anticipated that openings for public utilities and/or the effect of road widening or realignment are likely to limit the effective life.

Note that for lightly-trafficked bituminous roads a minimum thickness of bituminous layers of 110 mm is recommended. This thickness is close to the minimum that can be laid and is sufficient to avoid excessive subgrade stress under the occasional very heavy wheel load that might subsequently be experienced on hot days.

The standard designs shown in Fig. 6.30(a) were derived from theoretical work and observed performance of experimental roads in which the roadbase binder was 100 pen bitumen. If the bitumen penetration is changed, say from 100 to 50 pen, it has no significant effect upon the laboratory fatigue or deformation characteristics of the bituminous material, but the stiffness modulus at 20 °C is approximately doubled. For a given level of traffic, the appropriate thickness of the new material can be calculated for each of these criteria using elastic theory and the permissible subgrade strains and tensile strains at the bottom of the bituminous material as determined from the fatigue and deformation equations in Table 6.19.

The greater of these thicknesses should be selected for design purposes. For example, at 10 msa, the permissible strain in the subgrade at formation level is $2.5 \times 10^{-4}$, whereas the corresponding horizontal tensile strain at the bottom of the bituminous roadbase is $1.1 \times 10^{-4}$. For a standard wheel load of 40 kN, an effective temperature of 20 °C, and a foundation consisting of a subgrade with a *CBR* of 5 per cent and a 225 mm granular subbase, the TRRL researchers used elastic theory to predict that the thickness of bituminous material corresponding to these strain levels are 235 and 210 mm, respectively, assuming that the stiffness modulus of the bituminous roadbase and basecourse with 50 pen bitumen is double that of dense bitumen macadam containing 100 pen bitumen. The effect of this change in stiffness modulus upon the thickness of the bound layer over the full range of design traffic is shown in Fig. 6.32.

Note that the subgrade strain criterion demands the greater thickness over the full range of traffic and is therefore appropriate for design purposes. For a given design life in msa, it can be seen that the use of 50 pen bitumen in place of 100 pen bitumen has the benefit of allowing a reduced design thickness of bound material of typically 15–20 per cent, due to the marked increase in stiffness modulus of the material. Alternatively, the design engineer has the choice of using the same thickness of pavement and extending the design life of the pavement. (Note also that Fig. 6.32 shows the corresponding design curve for when the roadbase and basecourse macadam contain 200 pen bitumen, assuming that the stiffness modulus of this material at 20 °C is half that of 100 pen bitumen.)

Traffic delays are particularly undesirable on very-heavily-trafficked

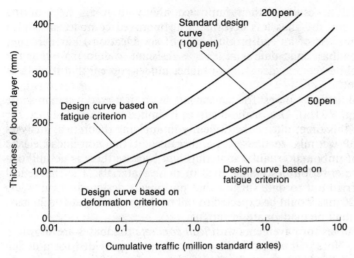

**Fig. 6.32** Effect of change in penetration of binder upon the design thickness of a pavement containing a dense bitumen macadam roadbase and basecourse[35]

roads. For these roads therefore, it is especially desirable to avoid cracking in the roadbase as this will require major reconstruction to replace both the roadbase and the surfacing. The design curve and pavement cross-section recommended for traffic loads in excess of 80 msa are shown in Fig. 6.30(b).

With this heavy-duty design, the main structural layer of dense macadam is placed between a rolled asphalt wearing course and a rolled asphalt lower roadbase. The thickness of the wearing course (40 mm) and lower roadbase (125 mm) is constant in all designs, whilst the thickness of the upper roadbase is determined from the appropriate curve in Fig. 6.30(b). The well-compacted dense macadam upper roadbase, which has proven high resistance to internal deformation, is the stratum whose thickness governs the design life[46]. Selection of the curve for design purposes which gives the thicker upper roadbase is intended to ensure that the structure deteriorates primarily through deformation, with little risk of fatigue cracking in the roadbase.

Overall, this pavement structure offers the following advantages[47].

(1) The highly fatigue-resistant hot rolled asphalt is placed in the zone where the pavement is at greatest risk with respect to fatigue, i.e. at the bottom of the roadbase where the highest horizontal tensile strains generally occur and fatigue failure can be expected to originate.
(2) Hot rolled asphalt is easier to compact than dense bitumen macadam, and is therefore preferred as a first layer on top of the relatively less stiff subbase; it also provides a good working platform for construction traffic.
(3) The surfacing and upper roadbase are the layers that are subject to the highest (climatic) temperatures, and hence are more vulnerable to permanent deformation. However, the thicker upper roadbase layers which are permitted by the omission of a separate basecourse, can be better

compacted as a result of their improved ability to retain heat during compaction and are thus less deformable. (Improved compaction is also assured by the use of an end-product type of specification.) Furthermore, the dense roadbase macadam is at least as resistant to deformation as the conventional basecourse macadam of higher binder content that it replaces in the design.

Standard design curves for pavements with *wet-mix* roadbases are shown in Fig. 6.31(a). Use of these curves is limited to roads designed for <20 msa at this time, due to the difficulty in applying theoretical analyses to design of wet-mix roadbases, i.e. because of the non-linear elastic behaviour of unbound granular materials and because there is no authoritative failure criterion describing yield in these materials. The theoretical analyses carried out to date suggest that pavements designed to carry less than about 20 msa would be expected to fail by deformation; above 20 msa, the designs may be inadequate in fatigue.

Design curves for pavements with *lean concrete* roadbases are shown in Fig. 6.31(b). Note that with this diagram curves are provided for a design with a limited life (up to, say, 20 msa) and for a long life.

Whilst lean concrete roadbases are in wide usage, analysis of their structural behaviour under the stresses generated by traffic and vertical temperature gradients is far from straightforward. Transverse shrinkage cracks occur very early in the life of all lean concrete pavements, typically at about 4 m intervals, and the design for a heavily-trafficked road must therefore seek to ensure that the roadbase is not further cracked by the combined vehicular and temperature effects. If excessive further cracking is permitted, expensive reconstruction will usually be required. In the case of less-heavily-travelled roads, however, where the effects of traffic delays associated with major reconstruction may be less serious, it may be more economic to allow a thinner roadbase to crack gradually and break up under traffic. This is the rationale underlying the use of two design curves in Fig. 6.31(b), one for a limited life and the other for a long but indeterminate life during which no significant deterioration of the lean concrete roadbase is expected.

The standard designs in Fig. 6.31(a) and (b) are based on a subgrade with a *CBR* of 5 per cent and a subbase thickness of 225 mm. For a design *CBR* of less than 5 per cent, a capping layer will normally be required beneath the subbase. If a capping layer is not used, then the subbase will need to be made thicker to carry the construction traffic, and the design thickness of roadbase modified as appropriate to take this into account.

## Design in frost areas

The pavement design procedures that have so far been described are applicable only to what might be termed 'normal' soil conditions. When constructing a roadway in an area where resistance to frost action is a controlling design criterion, then the normal procedures may not be adequate. The following discussion refers to the design and construction of flexible pavements under these extreme conditions.

## Detrimental effects of frost action

Highway engineers have recognized since Taber's experiments in 1929[48] that serious damage to pavements can result from frost action. There are two main detrimental effects associated with frost action in soil. The first of these is frost heaving resulting primarily from the accumulation of moisture in the form of ice lenses at the freezing plane in the soil. (The mechanism by which this occurs has already been described in Chapter 4.) Secondly, there is a decrease in supporting strength when thawing takes place. Other detrimental effects which may occur in conjunction with these are loss of compaction, development of permanent roughness, restriction of drainage by the frozen layers, and the cracking and deterioration of the pavement surface.

### Heave damage

Frost heaving itself would cause little damage if it occurred in a uniform manner. However, due to variations in soil composition, moisture content and other factors, severe heaving is seldom uniform in nature. In Britain, such heaving is most usually associated with very severe winters, i.e. those having forty or more days of continuous frost[49].

Differential heaving is indicated by the presence of pavement surface irregularities, bumps and general surface roughness in winter at sites where non-uniform conditions of soil and water availability exist. Distinctive transverse cracking of the wearing surface can be caused by severe differential heave at locations where subgrades change from clean non-frost-susceptible sands to silty frost-susceptible materials, at abrupt transitions from cut to fill where the groundwater is close to the surface, or where excavation exposes water-bearing strata. Drains, culverts or public utility ducts placed in frost-susceptible subgrades can result in abrupt differential heaving due to different backfill material or compaction, or to the changed thermal regime resulting from a buried pipe being left open to the atmosphere.

Longitudinal heaving may be attributed to two factors. The first is the incomplete removal of snow, so that the snow along the edges of the pavement acts as an insulator and retards the frost penetration beneath it, while the cleared areas permit deeper frost penetration and hence greater uplift of the pavement along the centreline. More important from the British viewpoint is the second factor, i.e. the differential uplift caused by the difference in subgrade moisture between the edges and mid-portion of the pavement.

### Thaw damage

Most serious to both flexible and rigid pavements is the effect of the softening of the roadbed due to the thawing of the frozen soil beneath and the resulting reduction in the load-carrying capacity of the pavement. As thawing begins, the ice melts primarily from the top down. If thawing occurs at a faster rate than the melt water can escape into underdrains or into the more pervious layers of the pavement system, or be reabsorbed into adjacent drier areas, then the onset of heavy traffic loads results in the generation of excess pore-water pressures which cause a decrease in the load-carrying capacity of the pavement and shorten its service life.

If thawing does not proceed at the same rate over all parts of the pavement, non-uniform subsidence of the previously heaved surface will result, causing transient pavement roughness and non-uniform subgrade support for the pavement. Differential thaw can be due to several factors, such as: (a) differing thermal properties of adjacent pavement sections, caused by non-uniformity of subsoil strata and soil conditions, (b) non-uniform exposure to the sun's rays and differing angles of incidence, (c) shaded portions of the pavement due to deep cuts, trees, overpasses, or buildings, (d) proximity to surface and subsurface drainage, and (e) differing colours of pavement.

Another undesirable consequence of the thawing of a frost-susceptible subgrade is the subsidence of coarse, open-graded subbase materials into thaw-weakened silt and clay subgrade soils as the latter flow into the large pore spaces in the coarse material[50]. There have been numerous instances where a non-frost-susceptible pavement has become frost-susceptible as a result of the impregnation of a silt subgrade upwards into the subbase. Furthermore, a subbase contaminated with a fine subgrade soil occupies less volume than the two materials separately, thereby resulting in irregular subsidence of the pavement surface.

If the melt water content is sufficiently high and the traffic conditions are sufficiently heavy to cause considerable reworking of the soil, a free-flowing mud may be formed which is forced out at the pavement edges or at breaks in the pavement. This type of action, termed 'frost boil', is common to both flexible and rigid pavements, but especially to rigid ones.

The more usual damage to flexible pavements in the thaw season is initially reflected in the form of a close network of cracks accompanied by distortion of the carriageway.

## Frost-action design

The design of pavements from a frost-action point of view is usually based on one or a combination of the two following criteria:

(1)   removal of frost-susceptible soils to below the level of frost penetration and replacement with non-frost-susceptible material,
(2)   accommodation of the frost action (heave and thaw weakening) during the structural design process by strengthening the pavement design and removing discontinuities leading to differential heave.

In Britain, these criteria are simply interpreted[51] as meaning that no frost-susceptible material should be permitted within 450 mm of the newly-designed road surface.

Analysis of temperature records[52] now suggests, however, that the above design practice is too stringent and too expensive and could be relaxed, as it is based on the untenable assumption that all road pavements in Britain should be treated as being at equal risk. There are certain areas, notably in the south-west and western areas of the country, where there is little risk of frost penetration into the unbound layers of the pavement. In such areas, it would be appropriate to reduce the thickness of non-frost-susceptible material that is required to about 200 mm; conversely, there are other areas, e.g. the Scottish Highlands, where penetrations of about 450 mm are commonplace and no relaxation of the 450 mm requirement should be contemplated. For most of inland lowland Britain, frost penetration into the unbound layers of the road is likely to occur at least once in the design life of the road, albeit it is not clear that the penetration will reach 450 mm.

Numerous laboratory tests have been devised to determine the frost-susceptibility of soils and granular highway materials. These have been grouped into five major categories[53], viz. tests based on: (a) particle-size characteristics, (b) pore-size characteristics, (c) soil–water interaction, (d) soil–water–ice interaction, and (e) frost heave. In British practice, the TRRL frost heave test[54] is used to define a frost-susceptible material.

Soils generally regarded as being frost-susceptible are described in Chapter 4, and will not be discussed here again.

If a subgrade material is identified as frost-susceptible, then either it is removed (in the case of soil 'pockets') or the pavement is raised by adding a suitable depth of subbase. Granular materials most usually employed in subbases are described in Table 6.20. Type 1 materials can be either crushed rock or slag, crushed concrete, or well-burnt, non-plastic shale, whilst the fraction passing the 425 $\mu$m sieve must be non-plastic. Type 2 granular material can be natural sands or gravels, crushed rock or slag, crushed concrete, or well-burnt non-plastic shale, and the fraction passing the 425 $\mu$m sieve must have a *PI* < 6. Both types of subbase material should have a 10 per cent fines value of 50 kN.

## Drainage
Adequate surface and subsurface drainage is essential in areas of seasonal frost because water is responsible for the majority of the ill-effects of low temperatures (see Chapter 3). Underdrains or interceptor drains are widely used to lower the water-table; if this is not feasible, then the gradeline of the carriageway should be raised to provide greater separation between the water-table and the subgrade.

**Table 6.20** Granular materials commonly used in subbases of new roads[51]

| BS sieve size (mm) | Percentage passing by mass | |
| | Type 1 | Type 2 |
| --- | --- | --- |
| 75 | 100 | 100 |
| 37.5 | 85–100 | 85–100 |
| 10 | 40–70 | 45–100 |
| 5 | 25–45 | 25–85 |
| 0.600 | 8–22 | 8–45 |
| 0.075 | 0–10 | 0–10 |

**Special considerations**
When constructing the pavement, the subgrade should be properly graded and compacted prior to the placement of the subbase. The subbase should always be able to carry the construction traffic that can be expected to use it as a working platform, and this traffic should be so routed that the risk of rutting is minimized. If this is not done, and the thickness of the subbase (and the capping layer, in the case of a weak subgrade) is inadequate, then upward mixing of the frost-susceptible soil with the pavement materials may take place. Achievement of the design density of subgrade and bases is at all times most important in relation to good pavement performance.

One of the first requirements during construction should be a thorough inspection of the subgrade to verify the validity of design assumptions, and to locate silt pockets, frost-susceptible materials, seepage, groundwater or capillary water, logs, tree stumps, boulders and other non-uniform subgrade conditions.

A potentially dangerous instance of frost action under pavements arises from what is known as 'chimney action' in culverts. This is especially noticeable in cross-road pipes of large diameter. Cold air circulating through the pipe will result in differential vertical and horizontal heaving if the surrounding soil is frost-susceptible and sufficient moisture is available. The best remedy for chimney action is to place non-frost-heaving material round the pipe for a thickness equal to the frost penetration around the pipe.

Transition points between cut and fill and over culverts may require special treatment if differential heaving is to be avoided. The exact treatment will vary from location to location, but basically it amounts to interposing a transition wedge which will mitigate the effects of any abrupt change in material.

Cut sections are often sources of trouble because they alter the natural drainage and provide ample supplies of water from adjoining high ground. In some cases, the problem can be eased by subsurface drainage or, again, by undercutting and removing unstable materials.

**Soil stabilization**
Stabilization is widely used as a method of processing subgrade and base materials to improve their performance under traffic and climatic conditions.

Extensive laboratory and limited field experience over the years has shown that various additives can be effective in reducing the frost-susceptibility of subgrade soils such as dirty gravels, sandy clays, and silty sands. Uniform silts and plastic clays are the least responsive to additives, with severe mixing problems being encountered with wet clays. Some of the approaches adopted are as follows.

(1)   *Plug soil voids*   This approach is based on the concept that if the voids can be effectively plugged or sealed so that water is unable to migrate, then ice lenses cannot grow.

Bituminous materials have been mainly used for this purpose. As well as plugging soil voids, they also waterproof the subgrade soil (see Chapter 5). Their main drawback is that the percentage of additive required can be so high that the procedure is economically impracticable.

Various resins ( > 1 per cent by mass) have also been tried, with promising results. In situ polymerization has been attempted with calcium acrylate ( > 5 per cent by mass); however, the results obtained were poor due to the difficulty of controlling the polymerization in the field. The addition of natural fines ( > 6 per cent by mass) to the in situ soil has also been attempted; whilst interesting in concept, this approach also provided unusual mixing and processing problems.

(2) *Cement the soil particles* This approach is generally related to the plugging of soil voids, and good results have been obtained. Cement, of course, is a very effective soil-binding agent; however, the major problem associated with this method is that the cement content required for many soils can be quite large with the result that the method can be very expensive.

(3) *Alter characteristics of the pore fluids* Salts may be added to lower the freezing point of the pore fluid in the soil. This reduces the depth of frost penetration under a given set of temperature conditions but does not affect the heave characteristics of the soil. The main disadvantage of this method is its non-permanency.

(4) *Alter soil properties by aggregation* The soil fines are primarily responsible for the frost-susceptibility of soils. 'Dirty' gravels, for instance, can be rendered non-frost-susceptible by washing out the fines. When this is not feasible, the effective quantity of fines can be reduced by admixing additives, such as lime, that cause small particles to aggregate into larger units, thus effecting a 'cleaner', coarser soil which is less vulnerable to moisture migration and the formation of ice lenses. Most promising results have been obtained with this method (see Chapter 5 for further details on the effects of adding small quantities of lime to soils).

(5) *Alter soil properties by dispersion of fines* This approach is reported[55] to be most promising as a means of improving frost-susceptible soils containing clay fines. The concept involves increasing the interparticle repulsion within the soil fines so that aggregates do not stick together but are dispersed. The dispersed particles can then be manipulated into a more orderly structure.

Dispersants such as tetrasodium pyrophosphate are most effective in dirty sands and gravels. The reason why is not exactly known but it is suggested that disaggregating the fines permits them to pack into smaller spaces, thereby enlarging the voids among the gravel particles; the dispersed fines are then eventually leached out of the soil, thus cleaning it.

(6) *Alter characteristics of the surfaces of soil particles* Use of the proper additives enables mineral surfaces to be made hydrophobic (water-hating). A soil so waterproofed cannot be wetted and should have little or no absorbed moisture. Conversely, coating a fine-grained soil with additives that have high polar groups exposed to the soil moisture can increase the amount of absorbed moisture; these decrease the air voids content, thereby

reducing the permeability of the soil sufficiently to make it non-frost-susceptible.

## Pavements on soft soils

Probably the most difficult problem that can confront a highway engineer is that of constructing a roadway over a compressible soil. Such soils include a variety of peats, marls, and organic and inorganic silts and clays. These deposits may be localized, as in a peat bog or stream crossing, or they may cover large areas, such as tidal marshes or glacial lake beds. The compressible material may occur at the surface, or it may exist in abandoned stream channels, lake beds, or peat bogs that are covered by a desiccated crust or by a more recent soil deposit.

Soft soils are associated with a number of types of highway pavement and embankment problems. For example, the foundation material may displace laterally under the mass of the fill, causing major movements and disruptions of the embankment. If the construction is such that lateral displacement is prevented, the soft basement soil will compress and cause settlement.

Some settlement can be anticipated in almost all embankments on soft soils; however, it is detrimental only if it results in pavement fracture or excessive roughness. The amount of settlement that can be tolerated after construction of the pavement is not well defined, although American experience[56] would suggest that 0.15–0.30 m of settlement can be tolerated on long embankments, if any variations in the settlement are uniformly distributed along the length of the embankment.

In this situation there is no absolute method of 'design' that the engineer can turn to for guidance; rather, the problem is one of deciding the most economical way of 'constructing' the pavement foundation so that it will not deform unduly, or in an unanticipated way, over a given period of time. In the following discussion, therefore, an outline is given of the various methods used to construct pavements and/or embankments over compressible soils[57–63].

## Methods of construction

When constructing a highway over soft soils, the traffic demand and the level of service required of the roadway largely determine the exact design and methods to be used. Existing methods of construction vary from direct construction of the pavement on the soft soil, to constructing an embankment (capped by a pavement) on the compressible material, to carrying the road on piles, to complete removal of the soil and replacement by embankment material. In addition, there are a number of ancillary methods of providing support for roads over compressible soils.

### Direct lightweight construction
It is always cheaper initially to construct a pavement directly on top of the compressible soil. None of the methods available, however, gives any

guarantee that large deformation of the road surface and high maintenance costs will not subsequently become a permanent feature of the highway. For this reason, considerable thought needs to be given to the cost of future maintenance before a final decision is made about constructing a pavement directly upon a soft soil.

In direct construction of this type, it is obviously desirable to keep the applied load as small as possible. For example, roads over peat which carry low volumes of traffic are sometimes composed of a foundation layer of lightweight material, acting as a raft, which is covered by a thin, flexible pavement. This can be very expensive and in practice the raft is seldom thick enough to give much buoyant support to the pavement. Nevertheless, the raft does help in keeping settlements small for a time; it is of particular value where a road has to be widened with as little disturbance as possible to the adjacent peat.

Fascines of brushwood or logs form the traditional raft construction. These, however, must be maintained below the water-table or they will rot within a few years. The reasons for installing fascine are to provide a certain amount of buoyancy for supporting the pavement, to spread the weight of the road as evenly as possible and so reduce differential settlement, and to prevent the pavement material from penetrating and sinking into the soft material. A typical fascine mattress used for these purposes might consist of two frameworks of logs set about 750 mm apart, the space between them being filled with loose brushwood laid criss-cross in three layers. The frameworks can be constructed by cording together 125 and 175 mm diameter logs or fascines in a grid-patterned network.

A considerable amount of hand-labour is involved in making and laying fascines. This makes the process a costly one and it is therefore dying out in most highly-developed countries. Other materials are continually being studied in order to produce alternative, acceptable lightweight forms of construction. One such approach that has been developed in respect of soft, clayey soils is to place a synthetic engineering fabric or geotextile as an interlayer between the pavement subbase and the top of the soft subsoil.

*Fabric-reinforced pavements*   Since the late 1960s considerable practical research (see, for example, references 60 and 61) has been carried out into the use of geotextiles in highway construction at locations where soft, low-strength soil conditions prevail. In such construction, the geotextile has been most commonly used with locally available crushed stone or gravel aggregates in planned stage construction for a high-quality road, or in low-cost access roads to construction sites and logging, mining and quarrying operations.

Relatively large numbers of synthetic fabrics are available commercially for use in road construction; these are commonly categorized according to their construction and fibre composition. Basically, the two types of construction are woven and non-woven, whilst the fibre composition may be (most commonly) polypropene or polyester. Whilst the optimum properties and characteristics of fabric for use in highways have yet to be firmly established, experimental evidence would suggest that a high-modulus woven fabric has superior performance qualities to a lower-modulus non-woven fabric.

Numerous mechanisms have been postulated as to the manner in which the fabric interlayer improves pavement stability, although the exact contribution of all of these mechanisms has not yet been established. However, there is no doubt but that an interlayer of fabric between an aggregate pavement and a soft subgrade leads to improved performance; alternatively, the fabric can allow reductions (of between 25 and 40 per cent) in the aggregate layer thickness of a non-fabric-reinforced pavement for the same level of performance.

In general, fabric interlayers are considered to improve performance by providing separation and reinforcement benefits to the pavement system.

In the *separation function*, the fabric prevents the fine-grained subgrade soil from intermixing with the coarse-grained aggregate material, and thereby reducing its shear strength and stability. In the *reinforcement function*, the fabric improves performance under traffic by:

(1)  the restraining effect of the fabric upon the aggregate and subgrade layer, which increases both the resistance to shear flow of the subsoil from beneath the wheel path and the resistance to lateral aggregate movement below the wheel path at the soil–aggregate interface,
(2)  the membrane effect, which results in a reduced stress being transmitted to the subgrade because the fabric becomes stretched under load and develops in-plane tensile stress,
(3)  the friction and boundary layer effect, which results from the friction developed along the interface between the aggregate–fabric and the friction-adhesion of the fabric–soil interface, i.e. a composite material of aggregate and soil is created immediately adjacent to the fabric which possesses more favourable properties of ductility and tensile strength,
(4)  a local reinforcement effect, whereby the fabric serves to distribute the applied wheel load, to reduce localized stresses and, in general, to provide increased resistance to vertical displacement.

It might be noted here that there is no general design procedure available at this time that can be used to design pavements incorporating all types of fabric interlayers.

**Direct embankment construction**
Where the available funds do not permit the use of another suitable method, the construction of an embankment with the objective of consolidating the soft subsoil often becomes an acceptable alternative when a heavily-trafficked highway has to be located over poor ground. Construction methods used for this purpose include stage construction with or without the use of flat side slopes and/or berms, and accelerated construction methods such as vertical sand drains, cardboard wick drains, horizontal land drains, dynamic consolidation, and surcharged embankments. These construction methods have been discussed in Chapter 5, and so will not be repeated here.

It is useful to consider Fig. 6.33 which summarizes the results of a study[62] of the comparative costs of the various methods used to accelerate consolidation of soft subsoils. The main conclusions are as follows. For nearly all areas and depths of soil, the installation of 225 mm sand drains using water-jetting techniques is almost always an equally economic option. The use of sand wick drains installed by vibratory displacement driving appears to be the most economical method when the area to be treated is greater than 2000 m², with a subsoil depth not exceeding 3 m. The installation of land drains to achieve consolidation prior to the construction of the embankment, appears to be the most economical method of treating subsoils with an area of less than 5000 m² and a depth not exceeding 6 m. Dynamic consolidation is only economic for greater depths over land areas of more than 10 000 m².

## Roads on piles
If local conditions, such as the presence of buildings founded on soft soil adjacent to the line of a road, or perhaps a multiplicity of services, such as water mains and electric cables which are buried in the soil, limit movement of the foundation material, then consideration may have to be given to constructing that section of the roadway on piles. These piles, which are normally between 1.5 and 3.0 m apart, are used to transfer the weight of the road to the firm strata beneath the soft soil.

Normally, this is considered a very expensive method of construction and hence is not generally recommended. However, instances can arise, e.g. due to a shortage of a suitable locally available fill material[63], where pile construction may be a relatively economical method of road construction.

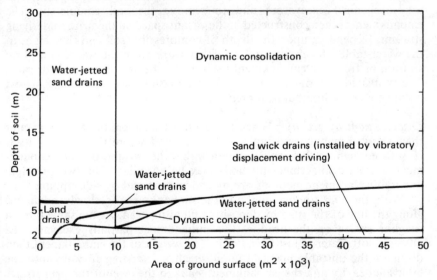

**Fig. 6.33**  Economic comparison of the methods used to accelerate subsoil consolidation[62]

**Removal and replacement**
The only completely reliable method of constructing a roadway across a soft soil is to remove the soil completely to the depth of firm strata beneath and then to construct a stable embankment in its place. While this requires a large initial outlay, it can often be justified when considering the very large maintenance costs that may be saved. Of course, the depth beyond which excavation ceases to be the most economical treatment for a given site will depend upon the soil type and groundwater conditions experienced; however, as a guide, the complete removal approach is generally most economical when the soft soil does not extend to depths beyond 5.0–6.5 m.

The principal advantage of complete removal of the soft subsoil is the certainty that potential foundation problems will be eliminated. Whilst peat bogs and marshes are most easily removed, the method can become costly and impracticable in the case of extensive deposits of compressible clays or soft deposits that are buried beneath a mantle of good material. Also, every cubic metre of excavated subsoil must be replaced by an equivalent quantity of good fill material—hence the availability of adequate quantities of suitable borrow material becomes an important criterion affecting the use of the removal and replacement method. Another influential factor is whether the subsoil material is to be excavated from below the water-table; if so, special procedures may be required to dewater the excavation or to place the fill under water.

There are three main methods of removing the soft soil and installing an embankment in its place: mechanical excavation and replacement, displacement by gravity, and displacement by blasting.

*Mechanical excavation and replacement*   When the depth of the unstable material is less than about 5 m, it is often an economical proposition to use mechanical excavators and to remove the soil completely. The embankment is then constructed in the vacant space on the firm, underlying stratum. Depending upon the depth of compressible soil and the height of the water-table, the excavators can either work from the underlying, firm stratum or from the embankment itself as it is being constructed forward. The excavated material is usually wasted alongside the embankment, unless it happens to be in a built-up area.

*Displacement by gravity*   When the depth of unstable material is greater than about 5 m but less than about 15 m, and where the material itself is soft enough to be moved laterally by the weight of the embankment, simple displacement methods may be adequate. The two principal gravity displacement methods are by end-tipping and by side-tipping.

With the *end-tipping* method, the embankment is slowly advanced along the line of the road by depositing fill at its head. At the same time, a dragline sitting on the head of the embankment partially excavates the unstable soft material just ahead of it. The weight of the embankment then displaces the unstable material upon which it is resting forward into the excavated cavity and the embankment sinks to the level of the firm strata. When the embankment has settled, new filling is begun ahead again and the same procedure carried out.

The more usual method of *side-tipping* requires a shallow ditch to be cut through the surface mat of the unstable soil to the depth of the water-table and along the proposed centreline of the road. Its purpose is to form a plane of weakness within the compressible soil. Fill material is then added symmetrically on either side of this line, until its weight displaces the underlying soil to the side.

The displacement method is straightforward but very slow. If the underlying material is too stiff to be displaced by the weight of the embankment alone, it may have to be softened by using jets to impregnate it with water. The usual method of jetting is to sink pipes of about 25 mm diameter through the embankment down to the bottom of the soft material. Water under a pressure as high as 1.7 $MN/m^2$ is then forced into the peat or soft clay as the pipes are slowly withdrawn. Alternatively, the jets are used to inundate the fill with water so that the unstable material is displaced by the increased weight of the embankment.

A further disadvantage of the displacement method is that if it is not very carefully controlled, large pockets of unstable material may be trapped beneath the embankment; this may give rise to further settlement with time. In addition, the symmetrical tipping methods may give rise to weak shoulders because of poor lateral penetration of the fill material.

In general, the gravity displacement method appears to be most useful at locations where the unstable material is very soft and where a plentiful supply of granular fill material is available from nearby borrow pits.

*Displacement by blasting*  Explosives have been used successfully, mainly in the USA, Germany and Ireland, to blast away peat either in front of or from beneath embankments. The principal methods of blasting are known as trench-shooting, toe-shooting, and underfill blasting.

In the *trench-shooting* method, the explosive charges are placed near the bottom of the peat, usually by jetting, in longitudinal rows in front of the embankment being constructed. This is illustrated in Fig. 6.34(a). The charges are placed apart at distances equal to one-half to two-thirds the thickness of the peat. When they are fired, an open trench is formed into which further fill material is then placed. This method of bog blasting is used for depths of peat up to 6 m thick. It is especially suitable for the excavation of fairly stiff peat that is not liable to slip back into the trench.

In the *toe-shooting* method, the end of the embankment is advanced and its head height raised until the peat is partially displaced from below and heaved up ahead of it. As illustrated in Fig. 6.34(b), charges are then placed at the bottom of the peat just immediately ahead of the embankment. When the charges are fired simultaneously, the peat is displaced and the embankment drops into the void left by the explosion.

As in the case of trench-shooting, the toe-shooting method is used for moderately shallow depths of up to about 6 m. It is particularly suitable for fairly soft peats which can nearly flow by gravity displacement alone. For deeper deposits up to about 15 m thick, the peat can be displaced in the same way if *torpedo-blasting* is used. This is the same as toe-shooting except that, instead of all the charges being set off at the bottom of the peat, they are attached at regular intervals to long posts which are placed

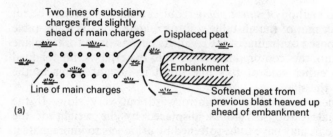

(a)

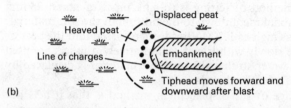

(b)

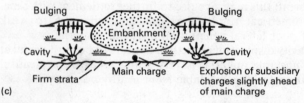

(c)

**Fig. 6.34** Methods of bog blasting: (a) trench-shooting method (plan view), (b) toe-shooting method (plan view), and (c) underfill method (section view)

vertically in the peat. The charges are then exploded simultaneously and the peat is displaced to the required depth.

The *underfill* method of bog blasting is illustrated in Fig. 6.34(c). In this method, the full desired width and height of the embankment is placed over the peat and charges are placed beneath it and near the bottom of the peat. The charges are usually in three rows: one row of main charges is placed under the centre of the embankment and a row of subsidiary charges is placed beneath each edge. The subsidiary charges are detonated just before the main charges so that the peat is blasted outwards in the most effective way. The embankment material then drops neatly into the continuous cavities left by the explosions.

The underfill method of bog blasting can be used for any depth of peat, although for the greater depths several series of blasts may be required. It is particularly useful when a sound material layer overlies the unstable soil. When the peat is over 9 m deep, wide embankments will usually have to be built by constructing a narrow embankment first; this embankment is then widened either on one or both sides by further underfill blasting.

Considerable preliminary site investigation, as well as experience with explosives, is required if underfill blasting is to be carried out successfully. Nevertheless, it can be a most efficient and economical method of carrying out excavation to relatively great depths.

**Ancillary methods**
The following methods are normally used in conjunction with other more general methods of construction over soft soils, especially peat. They are designed to provide additional support for the road, either by some form of stiffening or stabilizing of the soft material itself, or by introducing external support.

*Lateral support* Lateral support can be given to a road by installing sheet piling in the soft soil or by constructing a berm of fill material along the side of the road. For instance, sheet piling is usually used to protect nearby buildings from any lateral disturbance that may occur when a road is built over a soft soil. At the same time, additional support is provided to the roadway by the sheet piling. In a similar manner, sand is often dumped alongside the road to form low, wide berms which will increase the resistance to sliding and/or bulging of underlying soft layers.

*Drainage measures* It is common practice to lay fairly deep open ditches along the sides of minor roads constructed over peat bogs, the intention being to drain the upper layers of peat and make them more firm. Although the shear strength of the peat is thus increased, the process is a slow one and there is a considerable volume of shrinkage of the soft material which inevitably results in deformation of the pavement. Furthermore, the construction of ditches removes a certain amount of lateral support for the road and the underlying material may be pushed into them. Other disadvantages are that the deep ditches require frequent maintenance and regrading. In addition, they may have to be extended considerable distances in order to obtain a suitable outfall, since peat bogs often occur in low hollows.

Only very shallow drainage should ever be carried out close to a road on an embankment that has been constructed on a peat soil. General drainage, other than for the removal of surface water, should not normally be undertaken *after* the pavement is constructed; almost without exception it is more economical and more practical to correct adverse subsurface drainage conditions *before* construction rather than to attempt to handle these as a maintenance problem.

# Preparation of the subgrade

## Clearing the site

The first step in preparing the subgrade for *either* a flexible *or* a rigid pavement is to clear the site of all extraneous material. In rural areas this is usually a straightforward problem involving primarily the removal of what might be termed the natural waste materials, i.e. clearing and grubbing. In urban and suburban locations, however, the problem is complicated by the need to remove footpaths, derelict buildings and other such man-made obstructions. In addition, the preparation of the subgrade in built-up areas is hampered by the necessity of locating and relocating extensive (and expensive) public utility mains and facilities.

## Clearing and grubbing

The initial approach to clearing a site is to remove from the right-of-way all trees, tree stumps, underbrush, vegetation and rubbish. Generally, heavy chains drawn between two crawler tractors can be used to remove most of the vegetative matter. Blasting may be required in some instances to remove tree roots that cannot be dug out by backacters. All tree stumps and matted roots should be removed to a depth of at least 500 mm below the stripped ground level on which the pavement is to be constructed. This is necessary also to avoid possible later settlement within the subgrade and, more important, to prevent interference with the compaction of the subgrade. All holes left by the removal of the stumps should be filled and thoroughly compacted prior to compacting the subgrade as a whole.

If trees or shrubbery are not contained within the width of the roadway proper, it is usually sufficient to cut the stumps level with the ground surface. Indeed, where possible, every effort should be made to preserve such vegetation unless it interferes with the road construction or the movement of traffic on the completed facility. In such cases, it may be necessary to construct temporary fences about the protected trees and shrubs to ward off construction traffic.

Within the roadway width, the topsoil should be removed to at least the depth controlled by the penetration of the plant roots and stockpiled for later reuse; towed or motor scapers are usually used for this purpose. If possible, in clayey soils the complete plastic B-horizon should also be removed until the C-horizon is exposed, so it can be used as the foundation soil. However, this is often not economically feasible, and stripping is confined to a depth that will ensure the complete removal of vegetative matter, i.e. if this matter is allowed to stay, it will eventually decay and leave voids in the subgrade that may lead to settlement and failure of the pavement.

If the site contains man-made material, it will need to be demolished and removed. Dozers, with or without rippers or scarifiers, can be used to break up masonry and concrete and push it into stockpiles. Backacters fitted with attachments such as grabs and impact hammers can be used to demolish normal structures, superficial obstructions, and flexible pavements and to load lorries, etc. However, special equipment and techniques may be required to demolish concrete pavements and significant structures and obstructions.

## Utilities

In clearing a site in an urban area, it is usually necessary to tear up footpaths and old pavements and to knock down derelict buildings in order to prepare the subgrade. While these present certain initial problems, they are usually straightforward compared with those associated with the maintenance, relocation and installation of underground public utilities such as sewers, drains, water and gas mains, and telephone and electricity mains. In addition, the problem of relocation may be complicated by the fact that these utilities are often the heritage of bygone days and the plans indicating their exact locations are no longer in existence.

This could become more of a problem in the future, both because of the increasing demand for these services and because of the increasing trend towards placing more and more of them below ground. Ideally, as many of these utilities as possible should be placed under footways and verges instead of under carriageways. In practice, surface water and foul sewers, the lowest of all the utilities (in case of leakage), are usually laid under the carriageway; there is little risk of interference to traffic as sewers rarely need to be uncovered for repairs. Figure 6.35 shows desirable locations of the remaining utilities under a wide footway. Note that the water mains should always be beneath the depth of frost penetration; however, the actual depth of these and the other mains will vary, depending upon the topography. All electric power lines should be above all water mains; they should also be horizontally away from them in order to avoid corrosion resulting from the water mains being within the electric field of the power lines. Communication mains should also be away from the electric power mains, and they should be above the water mains. The communication mains may contain ducts for telephone, telegraph, fire alarm and police lines, plus extra ducts to allow for future expansion.

## Compaction

The subgrade must be sufficiently dense and stable to withstand the stresses transmitted to it by the pavement. This means that all cavities determined during the clearing of the site should be cleaned out and back-filled with suitable material. In other words, the state of compaction attained in the subgrade must be essentially that anticipated in the design procedure.

There is no general agreement as to the depth at which the subgrade

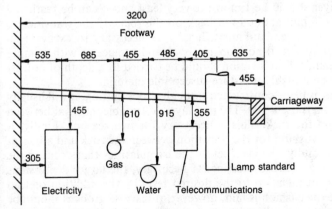

**Fig. 6.35** Diagram of the relative locations of public utilities (all dimensions are in millimetres)

should be compacted to this design state. It is certain, however, that if the basement soil is part of a high embankment, the top 300 mm at least, and preferably the top 750 mm, should be thoroughly compacted to this state. In cut sections, the problem can be more complicated. If the basement soil is a heavy clay, it may be found that a light roller can be used only to smooth the surface of the soil; undisturbed heavy clays cannot usually be further compacted beyond their natural state, and rolling with a heavy roller will only result in exudation of moisture with resultant remoulding and weakening of the soil. However, if the basement soil in the cutting is relatively coarse and loose, it may be quite easy to compact it to a substantial depth.

The principles and problems associated with soil compaction have been discussed in some detail in Chapters 4 and 5, so they will not be discussed here. A point to be mentioned, however, concerns the compaction of the subgrade soil in highway cuttings. In many instances, in order to obtain the necessary depth of compacted material, it may be necessary first to remove a layer of soil, compact the exposed surface, and then to replace and recompact the removed soil. The need for this method of compaction depends upon the type of soil and the available compaction equipment at a particular site; in fact, it can really only be determined by field trials at the site at the time of construction.

Detailed recommendations regarding the use of compaction equipment with soils and climatic conditions experienced in Britain are available in the literature[51] (see also Table 5.1).

**Transitions**
When the subgrade passes from cut to fill, care should be taken that there is no abrupt change in the degree and uniformity of compaction. This is of particular importance when the change is from rock to soil.

In all such cases, a soil transition layer should be installed to allow any differential effects to occur gradually. At the 'point' of change, the depth of the transition layer should be 1 m at the very least and it can be feathered down to about 150 mm about 14 m back on the rock. If the transition is from cut in soil to an embankment, it may be necessary to excavate an exposed band of plastic B-horizon material and replace it with a more suitable soil. Again, this excavation should be carried to a depth of at least 1 m, as this can be a highly-moisture-susceptible material.

If the highway is being constructed through a rock cutting, it will usually be necessary to interpose a 100–150 mm layer of suitable material between the pavement and the rock. This is necessary for two reasons. Firstly, it helps to provide a cushion for the transition between the rock and adjacent subgrade soil. Secondly, the layer levels the irregularities that occur in the rock surface during the rock-blasting. If necessary, the larger depressions can be filled and brought up to the desired level by the addition of lean concrete. Before the cushion is laid, however, transverse grooves should be cut in the rock surface to allow lateral drainage of any moisture accumulations that may occur then or in the future.

## Shaping

After the subgrade soil has been compacted, the surface will still be fairly rough. The next stage is to shape the rough surface to the final shape of carriageway. This ensures both that the pavement will be constructed to its proper shape and that any moisture intruding into the subgrade will drain away rapidly.

This final shaping can be easily carried out with a blade-grader. When it is completed, the loose material is removed from the surface and any irregularities that may still be apparent are removed by light rolling with smooth-wheeled or pneumatic-tyred rollers.

Once the final shape of the formation has been attained, only the most essential traffic should be allowed onto it prior to the construction of the pavement being initiated. This is particularly important when the subgrade soil is finely grained and subject to deformation.

# Subgrade stabilization with cement, lime and bitumen

When constructing a pavement with stabilized soil involving cement, lime or a bituminous material, the objective is to obtain an intimate mix of the pulverized soil or soil–aggregate material with the specified amount of stabilizer, and to add enough fluids to permit the desired compaction and strength gain to be achieved. Successful stabilization depends largely upon the care taken in achieving this objective.

Specifically, equipment must be selected, operated and sequenced to provide the proper water content (uniformly mixed), the proper stabilizer content (uniformly mixed), and the attainment of some minimum specified density. The work should be carried out when the temperature and moisture conditions are favourable for strength development during the curing period. Also, when the initial construction is complete, there should be adequate protection of the stabilized surface from traffic to prevent abrasion and to ensure adequate time for strength development.

The main types of equipment used in stabilized soil pavement construction are travelling mixing machines and (stationary) central mixing plants. The choice of equipment depends very much upon economic considerations. If the in situ soil can be economically stabilized, the travelling mix-in-place method normally should be used; if the soil material has to be obtained from a borrow pit and the project is of sufficient size, central plant mixing techniques (discussed later) may be preferred. In practice, mix-in-place construction is rarely employed in Britain but is widely used in warmer climates overseas.

## Mix-in-place construction

Mix-in-place operations involve either mixing the stabilizer with the in situ subgrade soil, or mixing with a borrow material either at the construction site or (sometimes) at an off-pavement site and transporting it to the pavement. The first method is most commonly used in direct subgrade stabilization, and the second in subbase and roadbase construction on a prepared subgrade. In either case—and irrespective of whether cement, lime or a bituminous material is the stabilizing agent—the following construction steps are typically employed:

(1)  soil preparation,
(2)  stabilizer application,
(3)  pulverization and mixing,
(4)  compaction,
(5)  curing.

The following brief discussion regarding these steps is mainly based on an excellent report in the literature[64].

*Step 1*    After the ground has been brought to the proper line, grade and crown as shown on the construction drawings, an initial scarification and partial pulverization is performed to the specified depth and width of stabilization. Grader-scarifiers and/or disc harrows are commonly used for initial scarification, and disc harrows and rotary mixers for pulverization.

*Step 2*    Cement or lime is applied either by mechanical spreaders or by hand. The machines are able to spread the bulk stabilizer uniformly over the pulverized soil at the required rate; the manual method requires labourers to 'spot' bags of lime or cement at calculated intervals, and then the contents are spread manually to the desired uniform coverage. Bagged lime or cement is most practical for small projects, e.g. streets, secondary roads, and maintenance patching, whereas bulk distribution is used for large rural stabilization projects where dusting is not a problem.

In most lime–pulverized-fuel-ash construction, the lime and the fly ash are spread separately. The 'conditioned' fly ash containing a residual moisture content of 15–25 per cent (to reduce blowing) is normally delivered in open dump trucks, dumped, and spread to the desired coverage with the available spreading equipment.

If the soil is very dry, it may be possible to add the lime as a slurry application, using conventional water distributors. This reduces construction costs by combining the lime spreading and watering operations into one.

Bituminous materials are spread by conventional distributors or, preferably, during the mixing process through mixing equipment with built-in spraying systems. The application rate is matched to the width and forward speed of the mixer, and to the density of the in-place soil. It is important for the soil to be at the desired moisture content prior to the admixture of the bituminous material if uniform mixing is to be achieved.

*Step 3*    Single- and multiple-shaft rotary (flat-type) mixers are typically used to pulverize and mix cement, lime, lime–fly-ash, and bituminous materials with subgrade soils. Mixing difficulty increases with increasing fineness and plasticity of the soils being treated. In-place mixing efficiency—as measured by the strength of the treated soil—is typically only 60–80 per cent of that obtained in the laboratory. (This reduction is sometimes accounted for by increasing the stabilizer content from that determined in the laboratory testing programme by 1–2 per cent).

For cement stabilization, pulverization is normally continued until 100 and 80 per cent of the mixture pass the 28 and 5 mm sieves, respectively, exclusive of any gravel or stone. (In situ mixing of cement and dry uniform fine sand is impractical because of the difficulties which vehicles have in traversing this type of soil.) For lime and lime–fly-ash stabilization, the process is normally continued until the percentages passing the 28 and 5 mm sieves are 100 and 60, respectively.

Water contents consistent with good compaction are normally obtained during the pulverization and mixing step, for both lime and cement.

Mixing of bituminous materials with soil and water is normally continued until a uniform mixture is obtained. This may require several repetitions of bitumen distribution and mixing.

*Step 4*  Compaction is normally initiated as soon as possible after uniform mixing of water and lime, lime–fly-ash, or cement. Most specifications require that compaction be initiated within 4 h of mixing, and be completed on the same day.

For maximum strength, lime-stabilized soil should also be compacted soon after uniform mixing has been achieved. However, since the soil–lime pozzolanic reaction takes longer than the reaction with cement, additional pre-compaction time is available—which is particularly useful with highly-plastic soils which may have to receive a double treatment of lime and extra pulverization.

Experience suggests that the compaction of emulsified bitumen mixes should begin as the emulsion starts to break. At about this time, the moisture content of the mixture is sufficient to act as a lubricant between the soil–aggregate particles, but is reduced to the point where it does not fill the void spaces, thus allowing air voids reduction under compaction. With cutback bitumens, the current view is that the correct aeration is achieved when the volatile content is reduced to about 50 per cent of that in the original bituminous material, and the moisture content does not exceed 2 per cent by mass of the total mixture.

*Step 5*  The curing of cement-, lime- and lime–fly-ash-stabilized soils is important because strength gain is dependent upon time, temperature, and the presence of water. Proper curing requires ensuring that the moisture is retained in the stabilized layer. One successful procedure involves sprinkling water to keep the surface damp, together with light rolling with pneumatic rollers to keep the surface knitted together. However, the preferred method is membrane curing, whereby the stabilized soil is sealed with one shot of cutback bitumen within one day of final rolling, or primed with increments of bitumen emulsion applied on several occasions during the curing period.

## Subbases and roadbases: material usage

As soon as the subgrade has been prepared, the structural layers are normally constructed as quickly as possible. The materials used in subbases and roadbases include stabilized soil, crushed stone, gravel or slag, cement- or bituminous-bound aggregate or slag, and (in particular circumstances) various waste materials.

Most of these materials have been described elsewhere in this text, so this discussion will concentrate on the *manner* in which they are utilized in a pavement.

One point which must be mentioned is that, with some obvious exceptions, no attempt will be made in the following discussion to prove that any particular form of construction material is 'best'. Indeed, it would be extremely foolish to do so since the choice in any particular situation is really a function of the amount of money available for the project, the volume and composition of the traffic, the availability and cost of particular forms of construction, the conditions of the subgrade, the prevalent weather conditions, and the economic life anticipated from the pavement. All of these factors must be taken into account before the decision can be taken as to which type of construction should be utilized in any particular situation.

One further point which may be emphasized is that, irrespective of the type of material used, the structural performance and riding quality of a road are strongly influenced by the accurate and uniform laying of the pavement materials to the appropriate design thickness[65]. Whilst this is most noticeable in respect of the surface profile of the wearing course vis-à-vis that of the basecourse, unevenness in the lower base layers can also result in unevenness in the finished road surface. Permitted tolerances in the surface levels of the various pavement courses are listed in Table 6.21.

## Bases of waste material

Clinker, quarry waste, burnt colliery shale, spent oil shale, hardcore, and other similar waste materials have been used successfully in the past as pavement ingredients. In industrial areas, in particular, accumulations of waste materials are usually available in large quantities at low cost and there is often pressure for them to be utilized in highway construction.

It used to be emphasized that the use of waste materials in highway construction was something that should not be taken too seriously—and if consideration had to be given to it, then its role should be only that of a bulk-fill in embankment construction. In recent years, however, it has been recognized as being in the national interest to make use of lower-grade and waste materials as alternatives to naturally occurring aggregates in pavement construction, as this conserves the dwindling supplies of good-quality aggregates and assists in problems arising from the disposal of unwanted materials.

**Table 6.21**  Permitted tolerances in surface levels of pavement courses[51]

| Pavement course | Tolerance (mm) |
| --- | --- |
| Road surfaces | 3 |
| Basecourse | 6 |
| Upper roadbase in pavements without basecourse | 6 |
| Subbase under concrete pavement surface slabs laid full thickness in one operation by machines with surface compaction | 10 |

The current notes on the standard specifications for highway works[66] permit the use of waste materials under cement-bound roadbases provided that: (a) the soluble sulphate content does not exceed 2.2 g/litre in a 2 : 1 water to material extract, (b) structures are isolated by 500 mm of sulphate-free material, and (c) good drainage of the subbase and subgrade is certain.

## Colliery shale

Shale used in highway pavements is usually specified as hard, well-burnt material free from ashy refuse and rubbish which may soften under the action of moisture. Normally, material of less than 76 mm maximum size is preferred for ease of laying and compaction.

The way in which colliery shale is produced and dumped in waste heaps means that it is quite varied in terms of both quality and gradation. Thus it is left to the highway engineer (supplemented by appropriate testing) to determine whether or not the material is suitable for inclusion in pavements; colour is not a reliable guide to its quality.

As has been discussed in Chapter 3, colliery shale is essentially a clayey material, and is vulnerable to break down under conditions of moisture and frost. Hence it cannot normally be assumed that colliery shale, particularly the unburnt variety, can be used in the pavement structure within the zone of freezing, i.e. in Britain this is currently regarded as being within about 450 mm of the pavement surface.

Many well-burnt, non-plastic colliery shales comply with the strength and gradation specifications for granular subbases. Some of these also meet the requirements with regard to frost-susceptibility, and therefore can be used directly in subbases; the majority do not, however, and their frost-resistant properties have to be improved by the addition of cement (normally not more than about 5 per cent) before such usage.

Laboratory tests also suggest that unburnt colliery shales, and burnt shales that fall outside the gradation specifications, can be stabilized with cement to render them suitable for subbase construction.

The only way in which a shale should be used as a roadbase material is when it is stabilized with cement. Most shales, both burnt and unburnt, are able to meet the grading requirements for soil-cement; however, the more stringent requirements for cement-bound granular material can be normally only met by burnt shales. No British shale, burnt or unburnt, can be made to meet the requirements for lean concrete without a considerable amount of (expensive) preliminary sieving and reconstitution of the fractions.

Normally, the addition of about 5 to 10 per cent cement by mass is required to enable burnt or unburnt shale to meet the compressive strength requirements for soil-cement and cement-bound granular material to be used in roadbase construction.

Detailed advice regarding the compaction of granular, cement-bound granular, and soil-cement (shale) materials is available in the literature[67].

## Spent oil shale

This material, which is the waste product of the now-extinct Scottish shale oil industry, is readily available in the West Lothian area of the central lowlands of Scotland. It is generally very similar in its physical and chemical properties to burnt colliery shale (see Chapter 3).

Unlike burnt colliery shale, however, spent oil shale cannot be used on its own in pavement subbases because of its high frost-susceptibility. However, stabilizing the shale with about 5 per cent cement on a premixed basis in order to reduce the frost heave to an acceptable amount has proved commercially viable and 0.5–1.0 million-tonnes of spent oil shale have been used in this way in subbase construction in the central lowlands of Scotland[68].

Present indications are that spent oil shale should not be used in the roadbases of main roads in Scotland.

### Pulverized fuel ash (pfa)

This material, which is a waste byproduct of the production of electricity at some coal-fired power stations, is generally considered[69] to be totally unsuitable on its own as a subbase material, because of its frost-susceptibility. However, British specifications do permit its usage in sub-bases if it is satisfactorily stabilized with cement or lime.

As is discussed elsewhere (see Chapter 5), the amount of cement required to ensure that pfa will meet the specification requirements varies from ash to ash, but typically it ranges between 5 and 15 per cent. As lime and cement cost about the same, and since lime requires a longer reaction time than cement to achieve a given strength, it is generally considered that cement is a better stabilizer of pfa for subbase construction in Britain.

In practice, British specifications make it extremely difficult to use pfa, even when stabilized with cement, in roadbases other than those of lightly-trafficked roads such as those in housing estates. Pfa does not appear to have been used to any significant extent in concrete pavements in roadworks.

### China-clay sands

The commercial extraction of china clay (kaolin) from kaolinized granite is concentrated in a relatively small area of South-west England. The china-clay industry produces considerable quantities of waste materials, including waste coarse sands. Over the years, these coarse sands have accumulated, and they are now estimated to total in excess of 125 million-tonnes.

China-clay waste sands generally meet pavement specifications in respect of grading, strength and frost heave, and can therefore be used in both subbase and roadbase construction.

When stabilized with about 6 per cent cement, these sand wastes will satisfy the requirements for a cement-bound granular material; as a comparison, it might be noted that 2–4 per cent cement is more usual with conventional materials. About 10 per cent cement is required to achieve strengths comparable with that of lean cement.

The major restraints upon the use of china-clay sand in highway pavements are geographic and economic[70]. The waste material is located in an area remote from the large potential market areas, and incurs a high transport cost for other than local usage.

**Slate waste**

Most slate quarries are located in remote areas, so that this waste material has had relatively little usage in road construction, even though there are very large accumulations of slate waste available.

Whilst it appears to have been used successfully as a subbase material in North Wales, relatively little is really known about the engineering potential of slate waste as a pavement material. It is reported[71] as having been used in the lowest 350 mm of a pavement composed of 90 mm of bituminous surfacing, 190 mm of roadbase, and 520 mm of subbase. The waste material was put down in two layers, each of which was rolled with twelve passes of a grid roller followed by six passes with a vibrating roller; good compaction was achieved and no trouble was experienced, even in very wet weather.

**Incinerated refuse**

Incinerated domestic refuse appears to have considerable potential as a road-making material (see Chapter 3).

Whilst ashes differ considerably from plant to plant, individual plants usually produce reasonably consistent material. Some ashes are suitable for use in pavements as a granular subbase material. For example, ash from the Edmonton (London) incinerator was used for this purpose after giving the results shown in Table 6.22. Frost-susceptibility tests also showed that this material was frost resistant, i.e. the mean heave at 250 h was only 2 mm (with a range of 1 to 4 mm), which is well within the maximum permitted value of 12 mm.

It might be noted that incinerator residue has been used successfully in a bituminous roadbase in the USA. Termed *littercrete*, this roadbase, composed of 9 per cent bitumen and 91 per cent incinerator residue, has been shown[73] to have performed as well as a conventional bitumen–rock-aggregate roadbase in an adjacent control section, after three years in service.

**Hardcore**

If hardcore is used in highway pavements, it is usually specified as any clean, rock-like material—such as broken, unreinforced concrete and sound brickwork free from mortar—which has few lumps greater than 100–150 mm.

Crushed brick (from brickworks) which was damaged or for some other

**Table 6.22** Summary of tests on Edmonton incinerator residue made for the consulting engineers before using the material in the subbase of a road[72]

| Test | Summary of result |
| --- | --- |
| Particle-size distribution | Conforms to (type 2) subbase specification |
| Breakdown on compaction | Meets 10% fines test requirements |
| *CBR* (%) | Top = 150, bottom = 65 at 9% moisture content |
| Soluble sulphate (%) | From 0.96–1.61 on three samples |
| pH value | From 10.0–11.1 on three samples |

reason was not suitable for sale has been used very successfully as granular subbase material in highway pavements in Britain. Crushed bricks from demolition, stabilized with cement, have also been used in a cement-bound granular material.

Crushed, unreinforced concrete is an accepted subbase material for use in highway pavements. Furthermore, limited work overseas would suggest that recycled crushed concrete could be a suitable aggregate for use in rigid pavement construction.

## Hand-pitched bases

Prior to World War II, hand-pitching (similar to the Telford-type of construction described in Volume 1, Chapter 1, of *Highways*) was the traditional method of roadbase construction in most countries. It consisted of hand-placing rough-cut, approximately rectangular, stones, each about 150–250 mm high by 100–150 mm wide, side by side on the prepared subgrade. Each stone was firmly settled in its seating and smaller stones were hand-wedged into the gaps between the larger stones. Projecting knobs of stone were then removed with a hammer, after which small stone was added to fill the surface voids. The layer was then compacted, extra material being added as necessary, until a roadbase having no surface depressions and true to the camber desired of the surfacing was obtained.

Hand-pitching is a very slow method of construction and requires a large labour force. For these reasons, it is no longer used in Britain. However, it still is, and will be for some time, an important method of pavement construction in developing countries where labour is cheap and the use of modern construction equipment may not be economical.

Apart from the problem of high labour costs, the hand-pitched roadbase has other disadvantages which render its use undesirable in modern highways. For instance, it can normally be laid only in about 230 mm layers, irrespective of what thickness of roadbase is specified by the design method. Furthermore, because of the slowness of construction and the openness of the completed roadbase, the subgrade is usually open to the ingress of water for a considerable period of time, with the result that the subgrade soil can become softened and begin to work its way up through the roadbase. In addition, experimental work has shown that layers composed of stone greater than about 100 mm in size are very difficult to compact sufficiently to meet modern traffic requirements. It has been found that excessive deformations have taken place *within* hand-pitched road-bases as a result of compaction under heavy traffic.

## Modern macadam bases

The modern macadam-type of construction is an outgrowth of the early macadam road (see Volume 1, Chapter 1, of *Highways*). Present-day requirements in highway construction have favoured the macadam-type of roadbase, principally because of its suitability for laying by mechanical means. This has led to higher speeds of road-building with a small labour force, and therefore to a lower initial cost of construction. Furthermore, with the type of equipment that is now available, the macadam-type of construction permits a bituminous surfacing to be laid once the roadbase is in place, instead of, as is customary with hand-pitching, laying the roadbase and then waiting for the traffic to complete compaction before regulating the surface and laying the final wearing course.

Several types of macadam pavements are used in highway construction today, the most common being dry-bound, crusher-run, premixed water-bound (wet-mix), and bituminous coated macadams. (The coated macadams are discussed under dense bituminous roadbases, see pp. 469–470.)

Aggregate materials used in macadam pavements are most usually crushed stone, crushed gravel, and crushed slag. All types of construction have a common stability mechanism: they primarily rely for their strength and resistance to deformation upon the interlocking of the individual crushed particles and upon the friction generated between the rough surfaces in contact. Some processes also utilize water or a bituminous binder to cement the particles together.

**Basic macadam preparation**

For economic reasons, unbound macadam bases are rarely greater than 600 mm deep, and are more usually 300 mm or less. The type of compaction to be used influences the method of construction. If heavy, smooth-wheeled rollers are to be used, then it is advisable to lay macadam in compacted layers not more than about 150 mm deep: a good rule-of-thumb states that the compacted layer thickness should be not more than 1.5 times the largest aggregate in the layer if good particle interlock is to be obtained. If, as is becoming more and more common, vibratory rollers are used, then single layers of up to about 225 mm compacted depth can be satisfactorily laid. In either case, the coarse macadam material is spread using a paving machine or spreader box operated with a mechanism which levels off the material to an even depth; this is usually about 125 per cent of the compacted layer thickness.

Before the first macadam layer can be laid, two essential preliminary construction procedures must be carried out to ensure the stability of the finished pavement. These are basic to all types of macadam construction.

Firstly the underlying material, on which the macadam construction will rest, must be thoroughly compacted so that it presents an unyielding formation. Good compaction is an essential ingredient to good pavement performance, and there is more than adequate evidence to support the view that whilst an increase in compactive effort may only cause a relatively small increase in density, it may result in a relatively large increase in strength. The degree of support provided by the subgrade influences the degree of compaction that can be achieved in any granular base.

If the subgrade is a silty or clayey soil, it is likely to soften under the influence of water and work its way up into the macadam layer. To obviate this, it is advisable to lay a capping or insulating layer of at least 150 mm of dry stone screenings or sand on top of the fine-grained soil. The gradation of this material will depend upon whether it is intended to act as a drainage layer as well. The macadam construction is then laid on top of this granular layer.

Secondly, because of the dependence for stability that is placed upon particle interlock and friction, it is desirable to prepare the edge of the roadway to resist the lateral thrust of the aggregate as it is being compacted. If the aggregate is not given stalwart support along the edges, it will give way laterally during compaction and much of the interlock strength will be lost.

Lateral support for the pavement can be provided by long steel or timber side forms laid alongside the edges. However, it may be more economical to construct and compact small earth embankments on either side and to use a blade-grader to cut back the soil to form the required vertical side supports. After the pavement is constructed, the earth embankments can be shaped to the desired contours.

Irrespective of the type of compacter used, macadam compaction is normally begun at the edges in a direction parallel to the centreline in order to lock the outer stones, and is extended progressively towards the centre of the road. In the case of a superelevated curve, however, compaction is initiated at the lower edge and continued progressively towards the higher edge. In either case, rolling is continued until there is no obvious creep of the aggregate ahead of the roller.

**Dry-bound macadam**
The term dry-bound, when used with reference to a macadam pavement, is concerned with the manner in which the crushed aggregate is laid. In Britain, the constituent aggregates are transported to the site in two separate sizes: a coarse material that is normally either 37.5 or 50 mm nominal size, and fine screenings graded from 5 mm to dust.

The first layer of coarse aggregate is spread on the prepared and compacted underlying material in an even layer 75–100 mm deep: the loose thickness should never be less than one-third greater than the desired compacted thickness, as otherwise it will be difficult to obtain the required compaction and the desired interlocking of the particles will not take place. Before compaction is initiated, the depth of the loose layer is checked very carefully in order to avoid any undulations of the compacted layer that may later be reflected in the surface. Preliminary rolling and shaping of the layer is then begun with a smooth-wheeled roller, after which the surface is carefully examined and any local projections or depressions corrected. After this, the dry fine aggregate is spread over the compacted layer. The reason for adding the fine aggregate is so that the voids between the larger particles can be filled (choked), thereby maintaining the interlock and increasing the internal friction. The fine aggregate is usually spread by some form of gritting attachment on the back of a lorry. Normally, a loose layer 25–50 mm deep or from 20 to 40 per cent by mass of the coarse aggregate, is required. The exact amount will vary with the size and grading of the coarse material, and can really only be determined by experience on the site.

This fine material is then compacted into the voids using a plate vibrator or a vibratory roller. Any open areas which develop during the vibration process are filled by brushing-in additional fines as compaction is continued. When vibrating is complete, i.e. when a dense compact surface with no 'hungry' patches has been obtained, the surface is broomed to remove excess fines and to leave the coarse aggregate standing 3–6 mm proud; the surface is then rolled again with a smooth-wheeled roller, until the rolls cease to mark the surface.

After the side supports have been repaired and built up as necessary, further macadam layers are laid as before until the macadam roadbase is fully constructed.

Dry-bound macadam has been shown to give excellent results in heavily-trafficked highway pavements. By using two separate materials of different sizes, segregation of the aggregate during stockpiling and transportation is kept to a minimum, and a uniform stable pavement can be obtained at a relatively moderate cost. Stability is ensured by proper compaction: the density of the compacted dry-bound layer is normally about 85–90 per cent of the calculated solid density of the ingredients.

The main drawback to dry-bound macadam construction arises during wet, or even damp, weather. While moisture has relatively little effect upon the compaction of the coarse aggregate, it is practically impossible to ensure that the voids are properly filled by vibration if the fine material is in a wet state before compaction. Often, when attempting to shift wet fines, the layer receives an excessive amount of vibration; as a result, the coarse material may ride upon a layer of fines with a resultant severe loss of stability. As a consequence of this moisture problem, and the fact that the method of construction tends to be relatively slow and labour-intensive, this type of base now tends to be used only in the smaller road projects, and a less-weather-susceptible material is normally specified for larger jobs.

**Crusher-run macadam**
Macadam pavements depend for their stability upon the interlocking and frictional characteristics of the ingredient particles. The extent to which these characteristics are utilized is dependent upon the density of the compacted layer. While high densities are achieved by the dry-bound process, it is obvious that higher, more economical and more predictable stabilities might be obtained if, instead of using two separate sizes of materials, just one material meeting high requirements regarding gradation and stability could be used in each layer. To achieve high stability, the grading of the aggregate should be such that the finer particles completely fill the voids between the coarser particles, thus providing a condition for achieving a high density after compaction.

This concept gave rise to the use of what is known in Britain as crusher-run macadam. It consists of natural or artificial aggregate which is generally passed through two stages of crushing to give a graded mixture of about 75 mm maximum size. This material is transported to the site, moistened and compacted in layers of up to 225 mm thickness.

This type of construction is normally relatively cheap since only one material has to be handled. It is spread easily and the required compaction can be obtained relatively quickly and with the minimum of hand-labour.

The main drawback to crusher-run macadam, and the one that has most limited its use, is concerned with its most important characteristic, its gradation. The gradation is selected so as to ensure the presence of particles of various size between the maximum and minimum sizes, so that a high density can be achieved—which in theory is an excellent concept. In practice, however, it means that while the material is being carried from the crushing plant to the construction site considerable segregation can occur, especially if transported over long distances. Thus when the material is spread it may consist principally of fines in some areas, whereas in others considerable amounts of choke material may be required. In addition, during laying and compacting the finer material will tend to fall to the bottom of the layer, resulting in a loose surface that can be most difficult to compact. As a consequence, crusher-run macadams are used relatively rarely in highway construction in Britain today.

**Premixed water-bound macadam (wet-mix)**
This consists of crushed, natural or artificial aggregate, usually of 50 mm maximum size, which is graded down to filler (see Table 6.23) so that a high density is obtained when the material is compacted. Gradings are generally derived from a combination of individual sizes, but crusher-run material of suitable grading is also used. The graded aggregate is mechanically mixed with a carefully controlled amount of water at the optimum moisture content for density, usually within the range of 2 to 5 per cent by mass. Great care is taken to ensure that a thorough mixing takes place and up-to-date machines have been specially designed for this purpose; where special plant is not available, the usual practice is to use bituminous macadam plant equipment.

Premixed water-bound macadam, or wet-mix as it is known in industry, has a basic cost that is slightly higher than those of the other macadams hitherto mentioned because of the processing of the material which is necessary before it is transported to the site. Its principal advantage is that because of the premixing with water, it can be transported over relatively long distances without significant segregation taking place. Similarly, relatively little segregation takes place during laying and compaction of the wet-mix because of the cohesion generated between the fines and the larger particles.

**Table 6.23**   Range of grading used with wet-mix bases[51]

| BS sieve size (mm) | Percentage passing |
|---|---|
| 50 | 100 |
| 37.5 | 95–100 |
| 20 | 60–80 |
| 10 | 40–60 |
| 5 | 25–40 |
| 2.36 | 15–30 |
| 0.600 | 8–22 |
| 0.075 | 0–8 |

The addition of moisture facilitates site work considerably and the amount of handwork required is negligible, since the premixed, graded aggregate can be laid speedily to the desired shape and thickness (usually in layers about 200 mm thick) by automatic pavers. Compaction is carried out with the minimum of delay since there is little necessity to add choke material to harsh areas. High dry densities are also more easily obtained because the moisture films allow the particles to slide more easily over each other into their interlocking positions as compaction is carried out. The amount of water which should be added is very critical; just enough must be added to provide the cohesive films about the particles. If too much is added, the cohesive bonds will not be formed and the particles will segregate out.

The mix moisture content is determined by the *vibrating hammer method of test*[74]. Care has to be taken to ensure that neither rain nor drying winds affect the moisture condition between the time of mixing and the time of compaction. On warm days or on wet days, it is necessary to sheet the wet-mix if it has to be transported any distance by lorry. For the same reason, laying in rain must be avoided.

Laying of the wet-mix must on no account be carried out on foundations that are inadequately drained, since the free mix water must be allowed to drain away during and after compaction. This is of particular importance if the macadam construction is being laid in a trench and there is a danger that the water will become ponded between the embankments. As soon as possible after compaction is complete, the uppermost layer should be sealed with a layer of bituminous coated grit or surface dressing. Assuming that the wet-mix is forming the roadbase construction, the desired bituminous surfacing is then placed on top of this sealing coat.

**Dense bituminous roadbases**
Since about the mid-1960s, premixed bituminous mixtures have come to be widely used in the roadbases of high-quality roadways in Britain. The three mixtures most well known in this capacity are *rolled asphalt* and the dense coated macadams, i.e. *tarmacadam* and *bitumen macadam*. (Since these types of mixtures are described in some detail in Chapter 7, this discussion will be concerned only with their basic functions in roadbases.)

As the term 'dense coated macadam' implies, dense tarmacadams and bitumen macadams utilize relatively well-graded aggregates which are premixed with either tar or bitumen before being placed in the pavement. Their main features are summarized in Table 6.24 for roadbases formed from crushed rock, gravel or steel slag and the most commonly used bituminous materials. The harder grade binders are always used with the more-heavily-trafficked (e.g. > 2 msa) pavements.

A major feature of the dense bituminous roadbases is their improved load-spreading properties as compared with other non-coated materials used in pavements (see Fig. 6.11).

Coated macadam[75] and rolled asphalt[76] roadbases should be well compacted, i.e. increasing compaction improves the stiffness of the material (and hence its load-spreading properties), as well as enhancing its resistance

**Table 6.24**  Compositions of bituminous-bound aggregate roadbases: (a) percentage by mass of total aggregate passing BS test sieves and (b) binder details

| BS sieve size (mm) | Bitumen/tar macadam | Rolled asphalt | | |
|---|---|---|---|---|
| | Nominal aggregate size (mm); nominal layer thickness (mm) | Nominal aggregate size (mm); nominal layer thickness (mm) | | |
| | 40; 60–105 | 20; 45–80 | 28; 60–120 | 40; 75–150 |
| 50 | 100 | – | – | 100 |
| 37.5 | 95–100 | – | 100 | 90–100 |
| 28 | 70–94 | 100 | 90–100 | 70–100 |
| 20 | – | 90–100 | 50–80 | 45–75 |
| 14 | 56–76 | 30–65 | 30–60 | 30–65 |
| 6.3 | 44–60 | – | – | – |
| 3.35 | 32–46 | – | – | – |
| 2.36 | – | 30–44 | 34–44 | 30–44 |
| 0.600 | – | 10–44 | 10–44 | 10–44 |
| 0.300 | 7–21 | – | – | – |
| 0.212 | – | 3–25 | 3–25 | 3–25 |
| 0.075 | 2–8 | 2–8 | 2–8 | 2–8 |

(a)

| Material property | Bitumen/tar macadam | | Rolled asphalt |
|---|---|---|---|
| | Bitumen binder | Tar binder | Bitumen binder |
| Grade | 200/100 pen | C50/C54 | 50/70 pen |
| Content* | | | |
| rock/slag | 3.5 | 3.9 | 5.7 |
| gravel | 4.5 | 4.6 | 5.5 |

*A tolerance of ±0.6 per cent is applied to all binder contents
(b)

to deformation and to fatigue cracking. Good compaction also decreases the permeability of the roadbase to water and hence the likelihood of stripping of the binder from the aggregate.

Another advantage of these roadbases is that the application of the first layer of the bituminous mixture early in construction affords immediate protection to the subbase and subgrade in bad weather. If desired, the next layer need not be superimposed immediately; indeed, the first layer may be used by traffic for short periods—a factor of particular importance in reducing traffic delays in urban streets. The material is normally laid by machine in layers of up to 100 mm thick to very accurate levels; this also means that the unsurfaced complete roadbase can be very often used to carry construction traffic, without undue damage, prior to the thin surface course being added upon completion of the construction.

## Stabilized bases

Cement-, lime- and bitumen-stabilized materials used in subbases and roadbases employ mix-in-place and central plant mixing operations in pavement construction. Both also utilize borrow-pit materials in their preparation. The central plant approach is that which is most widely used in Britain.

## Mix-in-place construction
The major difference between the mix-in-place processes for subgrade stabilization and the construction of stabilized pavement bases is the use of borrow-pit materials in the latter, with the consequent opportunity to get better stabilizer distribution as a result of mixing with the aid of a *windrow*, i.e. a low accumulation of soil material, perhaps 200–300 m long, with a trapezoidal cross-section. The following steps are typically utilized in subbase and roadbase construction employing windrows:

(1) soil preparation,
(2) stabilizer application,
(3) pulverization and mixing,
(4) compaction,
(5) curing.

Most of these steps are very similar to those previously discussed in relation to subgrade stabilization, so the following discussion will concentrate on those aspects which are different.

*Step 1* The first major preparation consideration is that of ensuring that the underlying construction layer—whether it be subgrade or subbase—is checked to remove all soft spots, compacted, and shaped to the desired grade and cross-slope. Another important element is the formation of a uniform soil-windrow on top of the subgrade/subbase; however, as most borrow-pit materials are granular, it is usually unnecessary to carry out any pulverization of the windrow prior to addition of the stabilizer.

*Step 2* Lime and cement are most conveniently applied directly to the windrow in bulk form. Pulverized fuel ash is normally conditioned with moisture (to avoid wind blowing) prior to bulk spreading on the windrow.

In the case of bituminous stabilization, water—very often about 3 to 5 per cent—is premixed with the raw soil prior to the addition of the bitumen, as this aids the subsequent mixing of the stabilizer and the soil. In the case of lime and cement, the stabilizers are premixed 'dry' with the windrow soil prior to the addition of moisture.

*Step 3* The mixing of the windrow materials is best carried out with parallel-shaft travelling pugmill mixers. Typically, the travelling plant passes over the windrow, picks up the soil and stabilizer, mixes them (with water being added as required) in the pugmill, and then drops the mixture to form a windrow of moist-mixed material behind it as it moves along. Normally, single-pass mixing is adequate, although additional mixes may be performed with a motor-grader prior to spreading.

*Steps 4 and 5* Whilst these steps are generally identical to those utilized in subgrade stabilization, there are two points which should be emphasized.

Firstly, if the stabilized layer is of sufficient thickness to justify multiple lifts, partial surface scarification of the lower lift is usually required for lime, lime–fly-ash, and cement stabilization, in order to ensure good layer interlock. In the case of a lime–soil mixture, it is also desirable to remove the top 12–25 mm of the compacted lower layer, as this surface depth is likely to be weakly cemented with calcium carbonate.

Secondly, it should be recognized that additional aeration time will usually be required prior to the compaction of bitumen-emulsion–soil mixtures and cutback-bitumen-treated-soil mixtures when windrows are employed, as there is only limited scope for the volatiles present in the bituminous material to escape during the mixing operation.

### Central plant construction

Whatever the type of stabilizer, stationary central plant mixing operations provide the best opportunity to produce maximum mixing efficiency and the most uniformly stabilized materials. These are the plant types most used in Britain, particularly for the manufacture of the cement-stabilized materials known as soil-cement, cement-bound granular material, and lean concrete.

Both hot and cold mixing operations are carried out in central plants. Penetration-grade bitumens normally require hot central plants for mixing; although emulsified and cutback bitumens have been used in warm mixing processes, they are most often used without the borrow-pit material having to be heated. Cold central plant operations are used with lime, lime–fly-ash, and cement stabilization.

Typical steps in central plant construction operations are as follows:

(1)   receiving and storage of materials,
(2)   mixing,
(3)   hauling,
(4)   spreading,
(5)   compaction and curing.

*Step 1*   In typical batch plant operations, the cement and lime are stored in vertical silos and delivered to the mixing plant by gravity and compressed air. For continuous plant operation where the cement and lime are metered by volume, the stabilizer is usually transferred from the large storage silos to small 'feed' vehicles capable of supplying a continuous, calibrated feed.

Pulverized fuel ash is normally stored in open stockpiles which have been pre-conditioned with sufficient water to prevent dusting. The conditioned pfa is normally charged into a feed hopper prior to mixing.

Bituminous materials are kept in storage tanks, the temperatures of which are adjusted to provide the correct binder viscosity for mixing.

Borrow-pit materials are normally stored in stockpiles of the desired gradation (see Table 5.5).

*Step 2*   Mixing must be accomplished in such a way that the amount of stabilizer is uniformly distributed. In practice, cement is for all intents and purposes the only stabilizer used in central plant stabilization operations in Britain.

Contrary to the conventional practice with concrete, with soil-cement and cement-bound granular material the admixed moisture content is normally about that for maximum dry density as determined by the *vibrating hammer method of test*[74]. Experience has shown[77] that the amount of water needed in lean concrete to achieve the specified strength is usually in the range of 5 to 7 per cent, i.e. a water to cement ratio of about 1:1. As a guide, the compaction moisture content for lean concrete is the maximum amount the mix can carry without free water in excess of a slight sheen appearing on the compacted surface after rolling, and without the roller tending to pick up material.

*Step 3* Lime-, lime–pfa- and cement-stabilized mixtures are normally hauled to the road site in conventional steel-lined dump trucks. If haul distances are long, agitators may need to be used. In the case of long hauls also, the transporting vehicles normally need to be covered with tarpaulins to protect the mixed material from wetting by rain, or evaporation and dust blowing in windy, dry weather. To minimize the possibility of segregation, a high level of discharge from the mixer to the truck at the loading point should be avoided and the mixtures should not be deposited in conical heaps. If segregation does occur, either at the mixer discharge or during transporting, it should be corrected by remixing during spreading.

Dusting is rarely a problem with bituminous-stabilization haul operations. However, covers may need to be used to prevent heat loss on cold days.

In all types of operation, sufficient haul vehicles will need to be made available to ensure that the mixing plant, spreaders, and rollers are able to operate at a steady, continuous pace rather than on a stop-and-go basis.

*Step 4* Spreading should be carried out with the minimum of segregation and as uniformly as possible. Spreader boxes, laydown machines and other equipment with automated grade-control provide the best results; blade-graders are also used, but with less satisfactory results. It is not essential to use forms to contain the mixed material when it is being laid, but it is advisable to do so; normally, the forms can be removed immediately after compaction, precautions being taken to avoid subsequent damage to the edges.

Layers of stabilized mixtures are normally spread to depths of about 15–20 per cent greater than the desired final compacted thickness. The amount of excess thickness is a function of the borrow-pit material type and sources, as well as the stabilizer and method of spreading, and so some experimentation may be necessary to determine the proper spread thickness in any given situation.

As a rule-of-thumb, a single stabilized layer after compaction should not exceed about 200 mm. If a greater thickness is required, the material should be spread and compacted in lifts, with the top layer being made as thick as possible consistent with obtaining good compaction, e.g. in the case of a 300 mm thickness of lean concrete, it is best to make the top layer 200 mm and the lower layer 100 mm thick. In the case of lift construction with lime, lime–pfa and cement mixtures, the time between compaction of the lower layer and the spreading of the upper one should be as short as possible, so that the lower layer does not 'set up' before the next layer is placed. However, in the case of lift construction involving emulsion- or cutback-stabilized layers, a time delay between layers is necessary to allow for the escape of volatiles from the lower layer and thus a gain in strength.

*Step 5*   In general, the compaction process is identical to that utilized for mix-in-place operations, with the exception of the urgency of compaction inherent in the use of hot bitumen stabilization, i.e. breakdown rolling should be completed before the mixture temperature drops to about 80 °C.

The compaction of a cement-bound mixture should be completed within, at most, 2 h of the water being added to the dry-cement–soil–aggregate. If it is not, then the desired high dry density will not be obtained, and the achievable strength will be considerably reduced. This may mean that the length of haul has to be limited in order to comply with the time requirement (in the case of cement-bound granular material and lean concrete).

Most cement-, lime- and lime–pfa-bound bases are laid without joints, except for day-work joints. Particular attention should be paid to compaction at these joints, which should all be cutback vertical butt-joints; poor compaction will result in weaknesses which may cause failure when expansion takes place. Transverse day-work joints can be formed by 'feathering off' at the end of the work; when work resumes the material should be cut back to a sound and vertical face. A preferable way of forming day-work joints is to lay heavy baulks of timber, or well-supported forms, against which the roller can work. If necessary, further compaction by ramming should be carried out to ensure the formation of a dense material at the joint.

Cement-, lime- and lime–pfa-bound bases require curing to prevent evaporation of moisture. Experience has shown that the omission of curing can lead to scaling of the surface of the layers, as well as to an acceleration of the cracking process to which all such layers are normally subject. In fact, these stabilized materials are considered to fall into the category of 'flexible' pavements because of their susceptibility to cracking; it is only in the stronger cement-bound materials in pavements of substantial thickness that general cracking can be avoided. Curing of the top layer is almost invariably by the application of a bituminous membrane, usually a quick-breaking bitumen emulsion applied at the rate of 0.9 litre/m². In the case of a roadbase, this membrane, which should be applied within 2 h of completion of compaction, can form part of a tack course on top of which the surfacing is laid. Normally, traffic is not allowed to travel on cement-bound bases until a seven-day curing period has expired, or twenty-eight days in the case of lime- and lime–pfa-stabilized materials.

# Selected bibliography

(1) *The WASHO Road Test—Part 2: Test Data, Analysis, Findings*, Highway Research Board Special Report No. 22, Washington DC, 1955.
(2) *The AASHO Road Test*, Highway Research Board Special Reports Nos 61A to 61E, Washington DC, 1962.
(3) Croney D and Loe JA, Full-scale pavement design experiment on the A-1 at Alconbury Hill, Huntingdonshire, *Proc. Inst. Civ. Engrs*, 1965, **30**, pp. 225–270.
(4) Lee AR and Croney D, Research on the design of flexible road pavements, *Proc. Australian Road Research Board*, 1962, **1**, Part 2, pp. 622–642.

(5) Thompson PD, Croney D and Currer EWH, The Alconbury Hill experiment and its relation to flexible pavement design, *Proceedings of the Third International Conference on the Structural Design of Asphalt Pavements*, 1972, **1**, pp. 920–937.

(6) Monismith C L and Finn FN, Recent developments in pavement design and structural rehabilitation, *Proc. Australian Road Research Board*, 1978, **9**, Part 1, pp. 113–142.

(7) Yoder EJ, Fundamental properties relative to behaviour under load, *Proceedings of a Conference on the Utilization of Graded Aggregate Base Materials in Flexible Pavements*, March 1974, pp. III-1 to III-11, Oak Brook, Illinois, National Crushed Stone Association.

(8) Monismith CL and Witczak MW, Moderator's report, *Proceedings of the Fifth International Conference on the Structural Design of Asphalt Pavements*, 1983, **2**, pp. 2–37.

(9) Whiffin AC and Lister NW, The application of elastic theory to flexible pavements, *Proceedings of the First International Conference on the Structural Design of Asphalt Pavements*, 1962, pp. 499–521.

(10) Burmister DM, The theory of stresses and displacements in layered systems and applications to the design of airport runways, *Proc. Highway Research Board*, 1943, **23**, pp. 126–144.

(11) Davis EH, *Pavement Design for Roads and Airfields*, Road Research Technical Paper No. 20, London, HMSO, 1951.

(12) van Vuuren DJ, Tyre pressure and its effect on pavement design and performance, *The Civil Engineer in South Africa*, 1974, **16**, No. 8, pp. 267–272.

(13) van Vuuren DJ, Relationship between tire inflation pressure and mean tire contact pressure, *Transportation Research Record 523*, pp. 76–87, Washington DC, The Transportation Research Board, 1974.

(14) Brown SF and Peattie KR, The structural design of bituminous pavements for heavy traffic, *Proc. Inst. Civ. Engrs*, 1974, **57**, Part 2, pp. 83–97.

(15) Newton WH, *Trends in Road Goods Transport 1973–1983*, TRRL Research Report 43, Crowthorne, Berks., The Transport and Road Research Laboratory, 1985.

(16) Shane BA, The relationship between goods movement and road damage, in: *The Estimation of Traffic for Road Pavement Design*, TRRL Report SR720, pp. 101–123, Crowthorne, Berks., The Transport and Road Research Laboratory, 1982.

(17) Addis RR and Whitmash RA, *Relative Damaging Power of Wheel Loads in Mixed Traffic*, TRRL Report LR979, Crowthorne, Berks., The Transport and Road Research Laboratory, 1981.

(18) Kennedy CK, *Pavement Deflection: Operating Procedures for Use in the United Kingdom*, TRRL Report LR835, Crowthorne, Berks., The Transport and Road Research Laboratory, 1978.

(19) Cooper KE and Pell PS, *The Effect of Mix Variables on the Fatigue Strength of Bituminous Materials*, TRRL Report LR633, Crowthorne, Berks., The Transport and Road Research Laboratory, 1974.

(20) Brown SF, Implementation of analytical pavement design: a case study, *The Highway Engineer*, 1980, **27**, No. 7, pp. 2–10.

(21) Lister NW, The transient and long-term performance of pavements in relation to temperature, *Proceedings of the Third International Conference on the Structural Design of Asphalt Pavements*, 1972, **1**, pp. 94–100.

(22) Lister NW and Addis RR, Field observations of rutting and their practical implications, *Transportation Research Record 640*, pp. 28–34, Washington DC, The Transportation Research Board, 1977.

(23) Peattie KP, Flexible pavement design procedures in Europe, *Transportation Engineering Journal*, 1977, **103**, No. TE1, pp. 115–123.

(24) Steel DJ, Discussion to classification of highway subgrade materials, *Proc. Highway Research Board*, 1945, **25**, pp. 388–392.

(25) Porter OJ, The preparation of subgrades, *Proc. Highway Research Board*, 1938, **18**, Part 2, pp. 324–331.

(26) Symposium on Development of the CBR Flexible Pavement Design Method for Airfields, *Trans Amer. Soc. Civ. Engrs*, 1950, **115**, pp. 453–589.

(27) BS 1377: *Methods of Test for Soils for Civil Engineering Purposes*, London, The British Standards Institution, 1975.

(28) Jansen DJ and Dempsey BJ, Soil-moisture properties of subgrade soils, *Transportation Research Record 790*, pp. 61–66, Washington DC, The Transportation Research Board, 1981.

(29) Croney D, Coleman JD and Black WPM, *Movement and Distribution of Water in Soil in Relation to Highway Design and Performance*, Highway Research Board Special Report No. 40, pp. 226–252, Washington DC, 1958.

(30) Road Research Laboratory, *A Guide to the Structural Design and Pavements for New Roads*, London, HMSO, 1970 (3rd edition).

(31) Department of Transport, *Notes for Guidance on the Specification for Road and Bridge Works*, London, HMSO, 1976.

(32) *Road Pavement Design*, Technical Memorandum H6/78, London, The Department of Transport, 1978.

(33) Thrower EN and Castledine LWE, *The Design of New Road Pavements and of Overlays: Estimation of Commercial Traffic Flows*, TRRL Report LR844, Crowthorne, Berks., The Transport and Road Research Laboratory, 1978.

(34) Currer EWH and O'Connor MGD, *Commercial Traffic: Its Damaging Effect, 1945–2005*, TRRL Report LR910, Crowthorne, Berks., The Transport and Road Research Laboratory, 1979.

(35) Powell WD, Potter JF, Mayhew HC and Nunn ME, *The Structural Design of Bituminous Roads*, TRRL Report LR1132, Crowthorne, Berks., The Transport and Road Research Laboratory, 1984.

(36) Technical Committee Report on Flexible Roads, *Proceedings of the XVII World Road Congress*, Paris, Permanent International Association of Road Congresses, 1983.

(37) *Shell Pavement Design Manual*, London, Shell International Petroleum Co. Ltd, 1978.

(38) Brown SF and Brunton JM, *An Introduction to the Analytical Design of Bituminous Pavements*, Nottingham, The Department of Civil Engineering, University of Nottingham, 1985 (2nd edition).

(39) *Proceedings of the First, Second, Third, Fourth and Fifth International Conferences on the Structural Design of Asphalt Pavements*, 1962, 1967, 1972, 1977 and 1982.

(40) *Deflection Measurement of Flexible Pavements: Operational Practice for the Deflection Beam and the Deflectograph*, Advice Note HA 24/83, London, The Department of Transport, August 1983.

(41) Brown SF, Mechanical properties of bituminous materials, *Journal of the Institute of Asphalt Technology*, 1978, No. 25, pp. 10–17.

(42) Ullidtz P, A fundamental method for the prediction of roughness, rutting and cracking in asphalt pavements, *Proc. Ass. Asphalt Paving Technologists*, 1979, **48**, pp. 557–586.

(43) Brown SF, A simplified fundamental design procedure for bituminous pavements, *The Highway Engineer*, 1974, **21**, No. 8/9, pp. 14–23.

(44) Lister NW and Porter J, Methodology for the design of bituminous roads, *Highways and Transportation*, 1984, **31**, No. 11, pp. 3–9.

(45) Powell WD, *Design, Performance and Specification of Bituminous Roadbases and Basecourses*, Paper presented at the Institution of Highways and Transportation National Conference on Bituminous Materials for Highways, held at Keele University, 19–20 September 1985.

(46) Goddard RTN, *Fatigue Resistance of a Bituminous Road Pavement Design for Very Heavy Traffic*, TRRL Report LR1050, Crowthorne, Berks., The Transport and Road Research Laboratory, 1982.

(47) Powell WD, Bituminous roadbases and basecourses, *Highways and Transportation*, 1987, **34**, No. 3, pp. 4–11.

(48) Taber S, Frost heaving, *Journal of Geology*, 1929, **37**, pp. 428–461.

(49) Jones RH, Frost heave of roads, *Quarterly Journal of Engineering Geology*, 1980, **13**, No. 2, pp. 77–86.

(50) *Roadway Design in Seasonal Frost Areas*, NCHRP Synthesis of Highway Practice No. 26, Washington DC, The Transportation Research Board, 1974.

(51) Department of Transport, *Specification for Highway Works*, London, HMSO, 1986.

(52) Sherwood PT and Roe PG, *Winter Air Temperatures in Relation to Frost Damage in Roads*, TRRL Research Report 45, Crowthorne, Berks., The Transport and Road Research Laboratory, 1986.

(53) Chamberlain EJ, Comparative evaluation of frost-susceptibility tests, *Transportation Research Record 809*, pp. 42–52, Washington DC, The Transportation Research Board, 1981.

(54) Roe PG and Webster DC, *Specification for the TRRL Frost-heave Test*, TRRL Report SR829, Crowthorne, Berks., The Transport and Road Research Laboratory, 1984.

(55) Ring GW, Seasonal strength of pavements, *Public Roads*, 1974, **38**, No. 2, pp. 62–68.

(56) *Construction of Embankments*, NCHRP Synthesis of Highway Practice No. 8, Washington DC, The Highway Research Board, 1971.

(57) Hamrahan ET et al, A series of three papers dealing with the problems of roads on peat and organic subsoils, in: *Journal of the Institution of Highway Engineers*, 1967, **14**, No. 4, pp. 8–38.

(58) Tressidor JO, *A Review of Existing Methods of Road Construction Over Peat*, Road Research Technical Paper No. 40, London, HMSO, 1958.

(59) Lewis WA, Murray RT, and Symons IF, Settlement stability of embankments constructed on soft alluvial soils, *Proc. Inst. Civ. Engrs*, 1975, **59**, Part 2, pp. 571–593.

(60) Robnett QL and Lai JS, Fabric-reinforced aggregate roads—Overview, *Transportation Research Record 875*, pp. 42–50, Washington DC, The Transportation Research Board, 1982.

(61) Potter JF and Currer EWH, *The Effect of a Fabric Membrane on the Structural Behaviour of a Granular Road Pavement*, TRRL Report LR996, Crowthorne, Berks., The Transport and Road Research Laboratory, 1981.

(62) Cross JE, *An Economic Assessment of Methods of Accelerating the Consolidation of Natural Soils*, TRRL Report SR203, Crowthorne, Berks., The Transport and Road Research Laboratory, 1977.

(63) Clarke AC and Johnson BW, Comparative designs, performance, and costs for a road on peat, *Journal of the Institution of Highway Engineers*, 1971, **18**, No. 3, pp. 25–30.

(64) Terrell, Epps, and Associates, *Soil Stabilization in Pavement Structures: A*

*User's Manual*, Volumes 1 and 2, Washington DC, The Federal Highway Administration, October 1979.

(65) McLellan JC, *Pavement Thickness, Surface Unevenness, and Construction Practice*, TRRL Report SR706, Crowthorne, Berks., The Transport and Road Research Laboratory, 1982.

(66) Department of Transport, *Notes for Guidance on the Specification for Highway Works*, London, HMSO, 1986.

(67) Sherwood PT, *The Use of Waste and Low-grade Materials in Road Construction: (2) Colliery Shale*, TRRL Report LR649, Crowthorne, Berks., The Transport and Road Research Laboratory, 1975.

(68) Burns J, *The Use of Waste and Low-grade Materials in Road Construction: (6) Spent Oil Shale*, TRRL Report LR818, Crowthorne, Berks., The Transport and Road Research Laboratory, 1978.

(69) Sherwood PT, *The Use of Waste and Low-grade Materials in Road Construction: (3) Pulverized Fuel Ash*, TRRL Report LR686, Crowthorne, Berks., The Transport and Road Research Laboratory, 1975.

(70) Tubey LW, *The Use of Waste and Low-grade Materials in Road Construction: (5) China Clay Sand*, TRRL Report LR817, Crowthorne, Berks., The Transport and Road Research Laboratory, 1978.

(71) Sherwood PT, Tubey LW, and Roe PG, *The Use of Waste and Low-grade Materials in Road Construction; (7) Miscellaneous Wastes*, TRRL Report LR819, Crowthorne, Berks., The Transport and Road Research Laboratory, 1977.

(72) Roe PG, *The Use of Waste and Low-grade Materials in Road Construction: (4) Incinerated Refuse*, TRRL Report LR728, Crowthorne, Berks., The Transport and Road Research Laboratory, 1976.

(73) Teague DJ and Ledbetter WB, Performance of incinerator refuse in a bituminous base, *Transportation Research Record 734*, pp. 32–37, Washington DC, The Transportation Research Board, 1980.

(74) BS 5385: Part 1: *Testing of Aggregates: Compactibility Test for Graded Aggregates*, London, The British Standards Institution, 1980.

(75) BS 4987: *Coated Macadam for Roads and Other Paved Areas*, London, The British Standards Institution, 1973.

(76) BS 594: Part 1: *Hot Rolled Asphalt for Roads and Other Paved Areas*, London, The British Standards Institution, 1985.

(77) Williams RIT, Lean concrete roadbases, *Highways and Road Construction International*, 1976, **44**, No. 1795, pp. 5–11, 26, and No. 1796, pp. 4–11.

# 7
# Bituminous surfacings

## General considerations

Bituminous binders (see Chapter 3) include tars derived from the destructive distillation of coal, naturally occurring asphalts, and refinery bitumens. These binders function in one or more of the following ways, viz. as a lubricant, sealant, and/or adhesive. These functions are the basis of all types of bituminous construction, including surfacings.

About 95 per cent of the roads in Britain have flexible pavements within which are included bituminous surfacings of various types and thicknesses. Where properly used and constructed, these surfacings have long and economic lives while performing satisfactorily the following functions[1], as seen by the road user and the highway engineer.

The *road user* requires the bituminous surfacing to provide a surface: (a) which is skid-free under all weather conditions, (b) which drains freely during rain, thus causing a minimum amount of spray and splash from moving vehicles, (c) which provides adequate visibility, even under wet conditions, (d) on which tyre–road noise is kept to an acceptable level, even at the maximum speed limit on the highway, and (e) which provides an acceptable riding quality.

In addition to the above functions, the *highway engineer* requires the bituminous surfacing: (f) to protect the underlying structural layers of the pavement from both water ingress and the abrasive and disruptive forces of traffic, (g) to give the type of performance which will provide a maximum maintenance-free life, and (h) to fulfil defined economic criteria.

The requirements are often very difficult to fulfil simultaneously and so a compromise must generally be reached between them in the final selection of the bituminous surfacing. In practice, the highway engineer must decide which functions are the most important at each site, taking into account the needs of the road user, the environment, the structural design of the pavement, and the economic implications.

## Types of surfacing

For the purpose of discussion, bituminous surfaces can generally be divided according to whether they are surface treatments (i.e. prime and tack coats, surface dressing and slurry seals), coated macadams, or mortar-type mixes (see Table 7.1). Highway engineers tend to have differing views as to whether surface treatments are or are not surfacings in their own right.

**Table 7.1** Some features of different bituminous processes and materials[2]

| Process/material | Use | Binder function | Binder viscosity (as constructed) | Aggregate system |
|---|---|---|---|---|
| Priming | Binds surface of new base in preparation for surfacing | Sealant | Low | Nil |
| Tack coating | Provides bond between existing surface and bituminous premix overlay | Adhesive | High | Nil |
| Surface dressing | Resealing and/or retexturing | Sealant and adhesive | Low/medium | Single-size chipping |
| Slurry sealing | Sealing open/'hungry'/cracked bituminous surfacings | Sealant/adhesive | Low | Dense, very fine |
| Macadams (including asphaltic concrete) | Bases, surfacings | Lubricant, adhesive | Medium/high | Angular, interlocking (very open to very dense) |
| Mortar-type mixes (including rolled asphalt) | Bases, surfacings | Adhesive/sealant | Very high | Very dense, may include stone |

Despite this, there is no doubt but that they at least help surfacings to meet all of the functions noted above, except that of distributing the applied traffic loads.

All bituminous surfacings, except prime and tack coats, are composed of a mixture of bitumen and/or tar and mineral aggregates.

As is reflected by Table 7.1, the success of a bituminous surfacing is very much dependent upon usage of the correct binder type and grade. Thus, in close-textured, dense mixtures, the binder is always a very viscous material, e.g. a penetration-grade refinery bitumen or a high-viscosity tar. In medium- and open-graded mixtures, the binders range from very viscous materials down to fluid ones such as cutback bitumens, low-viscosity tars, or emulsions.

The aggregate content of a mixture may be composed of coarse, fine and filler material. By *coarse aggregate* is generally meant the material retained on the 3.25 mm BS sieve, although some specifications refer to stone as that material retained on the 2.36 mm sieve; in either case, it may be crushed rock, slag or gravel. The *fine aggregate* is that which passes the 3.35 or 2.36 mm sieve (as specified) and is retained on the 75 $\mu$m sieve; it is usually composed of angular, natural sand particles, but can also consist of crushed rock or slag. The *filler* is the dust ingredient, all of which passes the 75 $\mu$m sieve; it is most usually composed of crushed-limestone dust, but may also be quartz, lime, cement, or pulverized fuel ash.

Fillers can play a number of roles in surfacing mixtures, of which the following are the most important.

(1)  They are a part of the mineral aggregate; as such, they fill the interstices and provide the contact points between larger aggregate particles and thereby strengthen the mixture.

(2)  When a filler is mixed with a binder, it forms a high-consistency binder or matrix which binds larger aggregate particles together; in effect, it transforms the original binder into one which closely resembles a higher penetration-grade bitumen or a more viscous tar.

(3)  The water-sensitivity of a bituminous mixture can be considerably influenced by the type and concentration of filler used, e.g. when a hydrated lime–bitumen mastic is used to coat hydrophilic aggregates, it assists in the creation of durable adhesion in the presence of water[3].

As will be discussed later in greater detail, a wide range of mix types fall into the category of macadam and mortar-type asphalts. Table 7.2 summarizes some 'typical' compositions of these mixes. Coated macadam, rolled asphalt and mastic asphalt are widely used in Britain, asphaltic concrete is heavily used in the USA, whilst Gussasphalt is a well-known German process.

Note that the macadam-type mixture shown in Table 7.2 has a high stone content, a low binder content, and a high voids content; as a result, this mixture tends to be quite porous. In practice, some other coated macadams are densely graded, somewhat like asphaltic concretes; these will be discussed later in this chapter. In contrast, the mortar-type mastic asphalt is very densely graded, has a relatively low stone content and a high

**Table 7.2** Typical compositions of some bituminous surfacing mixtures[4]: (a) aggregate percentages by mass, (b) aggregate percentages by volume, and (c) penetration-grade bitumens used

| Surfacing | Stone | Sand | Filler | Bitumen |
|---|---|---|---|---|
| Coated macadam | 86 | 7 | 3 | 4 |
| Asphaltic concrete | 52 | 33 | 9 | 6 |
| Rolled asphalt | 30 | 53 | 9 | 8 |
| Gussasphalt | 40 | 31 | 20 | 9 |
| Mastic asphalt | 30 | 26 | 32 | 12 |

(a)

| Surfacing | Stone | Sand | Filler | Bitumen | Voids |
|---|---|---|---|---|---|
| Coated macadam | 64.5 | 5.1 | 2.1 | 8.3 | 20.0 |
| Asphaltic concrete | 45.7 | 29.0 | 8.3 | 13.0 | 4.0 |
| Rolled asphalt | 25.7 | 46.0 | 7.8 | 17.5 | 3.0 |
| Gussasphalt | 34.5 | 26.7 | 17.2 | 20.6 | 1.0 |
| Mastic asphalt | 27.5 | 18.9 | 27.0 | 26.6 | 0.0 |

(b)

| Surfacing | Grade of bitumen (pen) |
|---|---|
| Coated macadam | 100–300 |
| Asphaltic concrete | 60–100 |
| Rolled asphalt | 40–70 |
| Gussasphalt | 40–70 |
| Mastic asphalt | 20–30 |

(c)

bitumen content, and is essentially voidless; as a result, it is essentially non-porous. The coated macadam uses a relatively soft bitumen and a low filler content, whilst the mastic asphalt utilizes a hard binder and a high filler content.

Note also that as the mix changes from the coated stone to the mastic type, its cost generally increases.

Asphaltic concrete is a material within which two stress-distribution mechanisms operate, viz. stone-to-stone contact and friction/interlock between the aggregates. Whilst both mechanisms also apply to rolled asphalt, the emphasis with this mixture is upon the role of the mortar. Gussasphalt can be poured or cast in-place, eliminating the need for rolling or compaction; its stress-distribution properties are mainly derived from the characteristics and relative proportions of the binder and mineral filler, and the influence of the coarse aggregate is of secondary importance.

All dense bituminous surfacings are composed of hot-mix, hot-laid mixtures of aggregate and a high-viscosity binder. These are manufactured at central plants where both aggregates and binders are heated to very high temperatures, properly proportioned and mixed while hot, then transported rapidly in covered lorries to the sites and, while still hot, laid by mechanical spreaders and compacted by rollers. The commonly used coated macadam mixtures are also mixed at central mixing plants, but mixing can take place at lower temperatures since lower-viscosity binders are used. When transported to the site, these mixtures may be laid hot, warm or cold, depending upon the viscosities of the materials involved and the circumstances of mixing and laying. In surface treatments the aggregates are usually laid cold in the field, while the binders may or may not be heated before application.

## How bituminous surfacings deteriorate

Before discussing the various types of bituminous surfacing and the methods of design which are used for dense bituminous mixtures, it is useful to review some of the principal factors which influence the performance of these surfacings. While this may seem at first sight to be a negative approach to the task of surface course design, it is a most useful one, as even today the state of the art worldwide is essentially one of design based on experience. This is particularly so in Britain where reliance is heavily placed upon the use of recipe-type specifications for bituminous surfacings which are (mainly) based on accumulated years of engineering experience with particular binder–aggregate mixtures.

Table 7.3 summarizes the structural ways in which bitumen surfacings in highway (and airport) pavements fail, and lists some features by which these failures are distinguished. Whilst this table refers to surfacings prepared with a bitumen binder, it should be noted that the failure categories of disintegration, instability, and fracture also apply to surfacings prepared with tar binders. The glossary of terms used, which follows the table, is also very useful in that it defines many of the 'short-hand' descriptions that are in common usage in the bituminous vernacular—and which can be very confusing to the young engineer entering the industry.

Although not included in Table 7.3, another form of surfacing failure results from a reduction in skid-resistance. This too is discussed here.

### Disintegration

Disintegration is the gradual break-up of the bituminous pavement under the abrasive action of traffic and under the mechanical or chemical actions of weathering. It is evidenced by the wearing or breaking away of loosened material, ranging from tiny particles to large chunks, generally from the surface pavement[5]. A bituminous surfacing which does not disintegrate as a result of weathering or under the abrasive forces of traffic is generally described as being durable.

If disintegration is to be prevented, the binder must have a high degree of adhesion for the aggregate surfaces and adequate cohesive bonds between the aggregate particles to hold them together. This requires a combination of the proper selection of binder viscosity to fit the aggregate gradation, the addition of sufficient binder to coat all the particles

**Table 7.3**   How bituminous surfacings fail[5] — types and causes of failure

| Types of failure | Causes of failure | | Distinguishing features | |
| --- | --- | --- | --- | --- |
| | Primary | Contributing | Specific | General |
| Disintegration | Low cohesion | Soft bitumen | Tenderness | Scuffing |
| | | Poor aggregate grading | Oversanded | Marking |
| | | Low density | Under compacted | Indenting |
| | | | | Gouging |
| | Low abrasion resistance | Insufficient bitumen | Dryness | Pitting |
| | | | Brittleness | Ravelling |
| | | Brittle bitumen | Crushed aggregate | Washboarding |
| | | Soft aggregate | Grooving | Potholing |
| | | Chains and studs | | |
| | Debonding of bitumen/ aggregate | Hydrophilic aggregate | Stripping | |
| | | Displacement of bitumen by water | | |
| | | Clay in aggregate | | |
| | | Displacement of bitumen by solvent | Fuel spillage | |
| | | Displacement of bituminous mix by jet blast | Blast erosion | |
| Instability | Low interparticle friction | Excess bitumen | Bleeding | Flowing |
| | | Smooth, polished aggregate | Lubricated | Pushing |
| | | Clay-water present | | Shoving |
| | | Rounded aggregate | Ball bearings | Rippling |
| | | | | Rutting |
| | | | | Corrugating |
| | Low mass stiffness | Soft binder | Tenderness | |
| | | Poor aggregate grading (insufficient rock) | | |
| | | Insufficient fines | | |
| | Low density | Insufficient compaction | Porous | |
| | | Cold compaction | | |
| | | Improper compaction | | |
| | Changing foundation support | Differential settlement | Bird bath | Longitudinal waves |
| | | Differential expansion | Dishing | Transverse waves |
| | | Frost heave | Mounding | |
| | | Trenching | Frost boil | |
| | | | Trench settlement | Porpoising |

**Table 7.3**  *(cont.)*

| Types of failure | Causes of failure | | Distinguishing features | |
|---|---|---|---|---|
| | Primary | Contributing | Specific | General |
| Fracture (or cracking) | Shrinkage | Absorptive aggregate Ageing bitumen Temperature fluctuations Volume change of coatings (paint, jet seals, mud, etc.) | Right-angle cracking Random cracking Curl cracking | Transverse cracking Longitudinal cracking Diagonal cracking Load-associated Non-load associated |
| | Brittleness | Bitumen embrittlement Burned bitumen Brittle base (e.g. cement-treated) Low-temperature exposure | Pattern cracking Block cracking Ladder cracking Low-temperature cracking | |
| | Fatigue | Resilient or 'springy' base Inadequate pavement stiffness Channelized traffic Poor drainage of pavement section | Alligatoring Chicken-wire cracking Wheel track cracking | |
| | Slippage | Insufficient bond between layers Low tensile strength of overlayer Thin overlayer No lateral support (e.g. shoulders) | Vee-cracking Crescent cracking | |
| | Reflection | Shrinkage forces Shear forces Bending stresses/ strains | Reflection cracking | |
| | Settlement and heave | Fill settlement (deep) Expansive soils | Settlement cracking Spread cracks Heave cracks | |

*Glossary of terms used*

**alligatoring**   load-associated cracking pattern in wheel track where asphaltic concrete pavement has segmented under repeated channelized loading into articulating sections able to accommodate high pavement deflections, giving appearance of an alligator's hide.

**ball bearings**   rounded smooth textured aggregates in mix, generally of sand size.

**bird bath**   dish-like depressions in pavement which hold water after rainstorm.

**blast erosion**   abrasion of surface by combination of heat and jet blast where jet blast impinges on (an airport runway) surface for sustained time interval.

**bleeding**   free bitumen at surface of pavement due to excess amount in mix or migration to surface from interior of mix due to compaction under traffic or to vapour pressures.

**block cracking**   a cracking pattern which segments the pavement into approximately equidimensional blocks of various sizes.

**brittleness**   bitumen binder in mix has become brittle, flakes off when probed with knife blade or screwdriver.

**chicken-wire cracking**   *see* alligatoring, except that cracking pattern smaller, giving appearance of chicken-wire.

**corrugating**   plastic deformation of unstable asphaltic concrete in form of parallel ridges transverse to direction of traffic movement, advance stage of rippling, generally found in deceleration and braking areas.

**crescent cracking**   crescent-shaped cracks which form in areas of load acceleration and deceleration where horizontal thrust exerted on pavement by wheels has resulted in slippage of asphaltic concrete layer, crescent points *forward* in acceleration and *rearward* in deceleration, generally found in take-off areas, braking areas and high-speed turnoffs at airports.

**crushed aggregate**   aggregate in mix has been broken during construction under compaction rolling or during service under traffic.

**curl cracking**   formation of a small cracking pattern where the edges of the crack curl upward, generally associated with shrinkage of a surface coating (e.g. paint stripes, jet seals, slurry seals).

**diagonal cracking**   cracks in the pavement diagonal to the direction of traffic.

**dishing**   a dish-like depression at the pavement surface up to a metre or more in diameter.

**dryness**   surface appears dry, low in bitumen content with evidence of uncoated aggregate particles.

**flowing**   plastic deformation of unstable asphaltic concrete in direction of traffic movement, except in acceleration lanes where deformations are to the rear.

**frost boil**   a mounding caused by ice lenses forming in subgrade soils in frost areas.

**fuel spillage**   spilling of jet fuels, gasoline or oils which soften or dissolve asphalt and displace it from mix.

**gouging**   pavement surface readily gouged when subjected to pressure from hard objects.

**grooving**   wearing away of mix in wheel tracks due to abrasive forces *or* lateral displacement of mix in wheel tracks under loading due to plastic deformation of mix, itself, or underlying basecourse.

**heave cracks**   cracks forming in pavements placed over expansive subgrade soils, generally in transverse direction but may be diagonal or transverse adjacent to non-expansive soil areas.

**indenting**   pavement surface easily indented by spike heels, aggregate particles pressed into surface, hand-held screwdriver, etc.

**ladder cracking**   load-associated cracking pattern in wheel track formed by long, parallel longitudinal cracks with short transverse cracks between them, giving appearance of a ladder, found mainly in asphaltic concrete pavements over cement-treated base.

**load-associated**   adjective used with descriptions of cracking patterns to indicate loading a factor.

**longitudinal cracking**   cracks in the pavement parallel to the direction of traffic.

**longitudinal waves**   widely spaced undulating waves in pavements parallel to direction of traffic, generally due to deep-seated differential heave or settlement.

**low-temperature cracking**   widely spaced non-load-associated cracking pattern (2.5–4.5 m), primarily in transverse direction with longitudinal offshoots, found in environmental areas where ambient temperatures remain at sub-zero levels for sustained time periods.

**lubricated**   mix appears rich in bitumen which is lubricating aggregate particles.

**marking**   pavement surface readily marked by tyre tread patterns, turning wheels, etc.

**mounding**   a hump at the pavement surface up to a metre or more in diameter.

**non-load-associated**   adjective used with descriptions of cracking patterns to indicate loading not a factor.

**oversanded**   mix contains more sand-size aggregate than necessary, makes asphaltic concrete difficult to compact and tender.

**pattern cracking**   cracking in pavement which appears to be repeated in a regular fashion.

**pitting**   loss of matrix from pavement surface around larger particles in mix, giving pitted appearance.

**porous**   mix appears to be full of voids and permeable to water.

**porpoising**   the vertical harmonic motion generated in a moving aircraft during a takeoff or landing run, caused by a series of inappropriately spaced transverse waves in the pavement, generally annoying to pilot.

**potholing**   formation of localized and deep depressions, generally where pavement is subjected to repeated impact from wheels, aggravated by presence of water.

**pushing**   plastic deformation of unstable asphaltic concrete generally sideways from wheel load, generally more pronounced under stationary wheel loads such as in parking areas.

**random cracking**   progressive cracking which meanders at the pavement surface in a random manner.

**ravelling**   removal of mix from pavement surface under abrasive action of rubber-tyred wheels, situation aggravated by use of chains and studs.

**reflection cracking**   cracks which develop in asphaltic concrete overlays in similar pattern existing in original asphaltic concrete or Portland cement concrete pavement, cracks 'reflect' through new overlay and may be either load-associated or non-load-associated.

**right-angle cracking**   progressive cracking which intercepts other cracks and pavement edges at right-angles, generally associated with shrinkage forces.

**rippling**   plastic deformation of unstable asphaltic concrete in wheel tracks forming ripples transverse to direction of traffic, generally in areas of deceleration and braking.

**rutting**   depression in wheel track under channelized traffic due to lateral plastic deformations in unstable asphaltic concrete *or* unstable basecourse (roadbase) *or* subgrade soils; generally, the narrower the rut, the closer to the surface the unstable pavement element.

**scuffing**   pavement surface scuffs when abrasive force applied such as stationary power steering wheel turn.

**settlement cracks**   cracks forming in pavement as a result of settlement and spreading of underlying earth fills, generally in longitudinal direction but may be diagonal or transverse where fill adjoins unfilled areas.

**shoving**   plastic deformation of unstable asphaltic concrete, generally where wheel loads exert thrust on pavement such as in braking and turning movements.

**spread cracks**   *see* settlement cracks.

**stripping**   displacement of asphalt films from aggregate surface by water, evident from uncoated aggregate particles.

**tenderness**   low resistance of mix to scuffing and marking under traffic *or* to penetration by blunt objects under pressure.

**transverse cracking**   cracks in the pavement transverse to the direction of traffic.

**transverse waves**   widely spaced undulating waves in pavements transverse to the direction of traffic, generally due to deep-seated differential heave or settlement.

**trench settlement**   settlement in trench backfill resulting in depression in trench with respect to original pavement grade, sometimes accompanied by cracking along edge of trench line adjacent to original pavement.

**under compacted**   mix not compacted to the degree normally required for paving.

**Vee-cracking**   V-shaped cracks which form in areas of load acceleration and deceleration where horizontal thrust exerted on pavement by wheels has resulted in slippage of asphaltic concrete layer, tip of V points *forward* in acceleration and *rearward* in deceleration, generally found in take-off areas, braking areas and high-speed turnoffs at airports.

**washboarding**   formation of a series of closely spaced ridges in advance stages of ravelling, generally in braking areas near intersections.

**wheel track cracking**   load-associated random cracking appearing in wheel tracks, generally representing early stages of more severe cracking, such as alligatoring, chicken-wire cracking and ladder cracking.

thoroughly, the use of hydrophobic aggregates, and adequate compaction to produce an impervious surfacing. Disintegration is generally minimized by high binder contents (i.e. thick films) since not only do they better waterproof the surfacings and bind the particles, but in addition the films formed are more resistant to hardening and thus less liable to become brittle at an early age.

As a binder ages in the field, a deficiency that emerges is a loss of matrix of binder and fines from around and between the larger aggregate particles, leaving behind protruding large aggregate particles. Initially, this appears as a pitting of the surface followed by ravelling of the larger particles as more matrix is lost. This process is normally first evident in the wheel track areas of accelerating, decelerating and turning traffic where the horizontal thrust imparted at the pavement surface is an abrading force. Longitudinal construction joints are particularly susceptible to the abrasive action of the vehicle wheels.

The higher the binder content, the greater the resistance to the above abrasion mechanism; although care must be taken to ensure that the binder content is not so great as to cause a lowering of stability. In theory, a 'soft' grade of binder should be used as its initial condition is further away from the hard and brittle state.

The period for which a mix is held at elevated temperatures during the manufacture and construction of a bituminous surfacing should be kept to a minimum, as the exposure to air at high temperatures can accelerate the ageing of the binder, thereby increasing its brittleness and susceptibility to disintegration.

Durability is also improved by keeping air and water out of the bituminous mixture, as the entry of water can encourage a loss of adhesion between the binder and the mineral aggregates. High binder contents and dense aggregate gradings contribute to reducing mix permeability, thereby rendering the mix more durable—which is why loss of adhesion is more likely to be associated with coated macadam mixes with high voids contents. For a mix in which the aggregate grading and binder content are held fixed, the lower the voids content achieved, the lower the mix permeability and, generally, the greater the durability.

## Why open-graded surfacings

As noted above, the disintegration of a bituminous surfacing is promoted by the presence of moisture, and is prevented by having dense impervious mixtures. Nonetheless, some high-quality bituminous surfacings are deliberately designed so as to be open-graded and to have high permeabilities [6, 7]. The basic objective underlying this type of surfacing mix design is to enable moisture to be removed as quickly as possible from the carriageway and/or to give a rougher surface texture than is achievable with conventional mixes, e.g. an open-graded surfacing laid 40 mm thick and having a voids content of 20 per cent will accept 8 mm of rainfall. Major advantages of these high voids content surfacings are as follows.

(1)   There is a reduction in the wet-road–tyre-rolling noise, e.g. the difference in noise levels between vehicles travelling on a wet rolled asphalt and a wet pervious macadam is about 6–8 dB(A)[8].

(2)   Hydroplaning during rainstorms is minimized.

(3)   Skid-resistance at high speeds during wet weather is improved.

(4)   Splash and spray during wet weather are minimized.

(5)   Wet-night visibility of road markings is improved.

Particular care must be taken with such mixes to ensure: (a) that the aggregate–binder adhesive bond is maintained in the presence of the water that the surfacing is designed to pass, (b) that the surfacing permeable layer is underlaid with a strong impervious substrate so that pavement stability is not threatened, and (c) that the removed water is allowed to drain transversely within the material to the edge of the carriageway where an unrestricted drainage channel is maintained, particularly if the roadway is kerbed.

To achieve its design objective, a pervious wearing course must maintain its open structure. However, traffic compaction and oil spilled from the engines of road vehicles tend to combine to close up the pores and render the mixture less effective.

## Instability

The stability of a bituminous surfacing is difficult to define, and it can mean different things to different authorities. There is general agreement, however, that stability refers to the resistance to deformation under traffic loading.

In this context, instability can be described as the vertical and lateral distortion manifested at the bituminous pavement surface under conditions of heavy or repeated traffic loadings, loss of foundation support, or deep-seated differential expansions and settlements. It is evidenced by plastic deformations within the pavement structure, loss of foundation support, or by localized depressions in wheel tracks or by undulating changes in elevations conforming to compressible or expansive foundation soils[5].

Unstable surfacings are very easily recognized in the field. For example, rutting is generally associated with traffic channelization. Shoving—which is one of the terms used to describe the transversely-ridged deformation which occurs at areas subject to severe accelerating stresses—is most noticeable at intersections (where traffic starts and stops), on hills where vehicles brake on the downgrade, and on sharp curves. In other words, shoving occurs at locations where the inertial resistance to slow-moving or stationary traffic cannot be developed to the extent possible under dynamic (fast-moving traffic) loading.

The bituminous surfacing designer is particularly interested in the resistance to deformation exhibited under the static or near-static loading conditions regularly encountered in urban areas. This non-dynamic resistance is a function of both the interparticle and the binder frictions. Interparticle friction is dependent upon the roughness of the surfaces of the particles and the intergranular contact pressure; it is lowered if too much binder and/or fine aggregate is present and the particles are kept apart. By binder friction is meant the contribution to the resistance to sliding which is provided by the binder (and filler) because of its viscosity characteristics. This means that sufficient binder must be present to coat all the particles, and that its viscosity must be high enough to give as great a stability as is necessary.

As can be seen from Table 7.3, the durability of the binder is not considered to be a cause of a stability-type failure. In fact, the ageing and consequent embrittlement of the binder component increase both the cohesiveness and the stiffness of the surfacing, resulting in a greater resistance to deformation under loading and, hence, higher stability.

## Fracture

Fracture is the cracking of the bituminous surfacing which is a manifestation of volume changes and of excessive strains under given traffic loadings or differential foundation support conditions. These cracks can occur abruptly or progressively with time or traffic.

With respect to fracture-type failures, there are two main causes to which the durability of the binder is a direct contributing cause: shrinkage cracking and brittleness cracking.

*Shrinkage cracking* results from a volume change in the binder during ageing, due to loss of volatiles, change in temperature, absorption of the binder by porous aggregates, or perhaps some internal structural readjustment in the binder such as that described by the term thixotropy. Shrinkage cracks are often found in old bituminous surfacings which have very high binder contents and are not heavily trafficked, e.g. large parking areas. They develop gradually in a meandering right-angled pattern as the binder ages but often appear initially in the longitudinal construction joints, where the pavement is generally weakest in tension.

In the case of *brittleness cracking*, as the binder becomes embrittled with age the surfacing initially develops load-associated block cracking in the wheel tracks, edge cracking along the perimeter of the pavement, and general edge spalling of all cracking patterns, whatever the initial cause of the cracking[5]. In the advanced stages of ageing, the surfacing will break up into the overall pattern of block cracking; the size of the blocks will be a function of the traffic loading applied with smaller blocks in areas of higher traffic loading and density.

A particular form of fracture that has manifested itself in recent years on new major roads soon after construction, is that of *slippage failure*[9, 10], associated with the presence of a plane of weakness at or near the bottom of the wearing course. Similar failures on older roads have previously been reported at locations where sudden braking of heavily-loaded vehicles is carried out.

Slippage failure occurs when the shear stress developed by traffic between two contiguous layers is greater than the shear or bond strength holding them together. It is usually manifested in the form of a lateral displacement of the surfacing with respect to the roadbase or by the movement of the bituminous wearing course with respect to the basecourse. It results in a very characteristic cracking or tearing of the surface in the shape of a crescent or V with the apex of the V opposite to the direction of travel.

There is no quantitative information available regarding the shear strength developed between contiguous layers in practice, although it is known that whilst the initial adhesion between dense bituminous layers on an untrafficked road is generally very weak, it increases rapidly under traffic. Similarly, it has not been possible to determine the absolute values of interfacial shear stress developed, as all results from theoretical analyses depend upon the stiffness moduli assumed for the different pavement layers. What is clear, however, is that the likelihood of slippage is related to the overall structural stiffness of the pavement and subgrade at the time of construction and to the in situ hardness of the binder in the wearing course. Thus bases of unduly low stiffness contribute significantly to failure by slippage. The viscosity of the binder in the wearing course during compaction has so critical an influence upon slippage that high rolling temperatures should be avoided. Table 7.4 gives advice regarding temperatures which are intended to ensure that the roller does not begin to compact the bituminous mixture until the viscosity of the binder exceeds 10 poise. The wearing course mixture should never be laid on a very cold basecourse material ( $< 5\,^{\circ}$C), except on very rigid structures.

Failure by fracture is also associated with the *fatigue cracking* which results from repeated bending under heavy traffic. In general, the number of load applications prior to failure by fatigue is dependent upon binder type and hardness, aggregate shape and grading, the air voids content in the mix, and the ambient temperature whilst the surfacing is in service. Fatigue failure is characterized by an alligator cracking pattern in the wheel tracks.

The effects of variations in the mix upon the fatigue properties of a bituminous surfacing are influenced according to whether a 'thick' layer ( $> 50$ mm) or a thin layer (say about 20 mm) is being considered. In the thick layer case, the fatigue mode is generally one of constant stress (i.e. where changes in the stiffness of the mixture have a significant effect upon

**Table 7.4** Characteristics of rolled asphalt wearing course mixtures which help to reduce slippage[9]

| Penetration of bitumen | Maximum softening point (R and B) ($^{\circ}$C) | Maximum temperature in paving machine ($^{\circ}$C) | Range of rolling temperatures ($^{\circ}$C) |
|---|---|---|---|
| 70 | 52 | 140 | 90–125 |
| 50 | 56 | 145 | 100–130 |
| 35 | 62 | 150 | 110–135 |

**Table 7.5** Factors affecting the fatigue life of asphalt concrete[11]

| | | Effect of change in factor upon fatigue life | |
| --- | --- | --- | --- |
| Factor | Change in factor | Structural layers (controlled stress test) | Non-structural layers (controlled strain test) |
| Bitumen penetration | Decrease | Increase | Decrease |
| Binder content | Increase | Increase | Increase |
| Aggregate type | Increase roughness and angularity | Increase | Decrease |
| Aggregate grading | Open to dense grading | Increase | Decrease |
| Air voids content | Decrease | Increase | Increase |
| Temperature (in-service) | Decrease | Increase | Decrease |

the deflection response of the pavement), and therefore the horizontal tensile strain in the surfacing and the vertical compressive strain in the subgrade vary according to the stiffness exhibited by the surfacing. In the thin layer case, the fatigue mode of loading is essentially one of constant strain (i.e. changes in the stiffness of the mixture have a negligible effect upon the deflection response of the underlying pavement structure), and therefore the horizontal tensile strain and the vertical compressive strain are essentially independent of the mix stiffness. In other words, in terms of the structural competence of a pavement the thick layers contribute to the total pavement performance whilst the thin layers serve as surfacings which conform with the underlying pavement.

Table 7.5 shows how the fatigue life of a bituminous mixture varies according to whether the fatigue test is one of controlled stress or controlled strain, as different composition factors are changed.

## Skid-resistance

High skid-resistance is generally promoted by the same factors which promote high stability, viz. low binder contents and aggregates with rough surface textures.

Many factors influence the frictional properties of a road surface, but in most instances the basic mechanism by which the road becomes slippery is the loss of microtexture brought about by tyres polishing the exposed surface. In the case of bituminous surfacings, the contact area of the exposed surface is composed largely of the mosaic of chippings—which is why in determining the skid-resistance of a road surface the type of aggregate, as characterized by its resistance to polishing (see Chapter 3), is the single most important property of the surfacing material. For example, a change of one unit of polished-stone value corresponds to a change of 0.01 unit of sideways-force coefficient at 50 km/h, as measured with the *sideways-force coefficient routine investigation machine*[12] (see Fig. 9.2). The sideways-force method is based on the contention that the critical maneouvre with regard to skidding is cornering. The test wheel is set at a predetermined angle to the direction of travel, and the sideways force acting normally to the plane of the wheel is measured. The sideways-force coefficient is then defined as the ratio of the sideways force to the vertical load.

As is discussed in Chapter 3 (see, for example, Fig. 3.10), the macrotexture of the surfacing also contributes to skid-resistance, particularly at high speeds. It facilitates the drainage of water from the area of contact with the tyre, and it enables energy losses which occur in the tread rubber when it is deformed by projections in the road surface to be used in absorbing vehicle kinetic energy. Loss of macrotexture can result from the progressive embedment of the exposed aggregate/chippings in the bituminous surfacing, or from the failure of the binder to weather at an appropriate rate.

Many other factors affect the skid-resistance, as measured in terms of sideways-force coefficient; they include type of binder, road temperature, road layout (e.g. excessive polishing is associated with braking or cornering forces), and size of stone (i.e. different sizes of the same stone may give different results under otherwise similar conditions). Overall, however, the most important external factor influencing the rate of skid-resistance deterioration is undoubtedly the volume–speed–mass of traffic. This deterioration is particularly noticeable on traffic lanes carrying heavy flows of heavy commercial vehicles. Nevertheless, it should also be pointed out that at the same time as traffic is tending to polish the surfacing, complex physio-chemical phenomena generally described as 'weathering' are tending to act in the opposite way to restore the microtexture of the exposed aggregate. Thus the resultant resistance to skidding measured at any given time is in effect a trade-off between the effects of these naturally occurring phenomena and the density of traffic.

Recommendations regarding aggregates suitable for use in bituminous surfacing mixtures at particular locations are given in Table 3.16. The skid-resistance of a surfacing can be predicted (correlation coefficient = 0.91) from the following equation:

$$sfc = 0.24 - \frac{0.663q_{cv}}{10^4} + \frac{1}{10^2 psv}$$

where $sfc$ = sideways-force coefficient, $q_{cv}$ = number of commercial vehicles per lane per day, and $psv$ = polished-stone value of the chippings.

The importance of this correlation is that it makes it possible to predict the level of skid-resistance at any reasonable site from a knowledge of the polished-stone value of the surface aggregate and an estimate of the traffic carried. The results should also serve as a guide in the selection of aggregates which are able to provide desired standards of skid-resistance. (References 13 and 14 summarize the sources of aggregates which can be used to give good skid-resistant surfacings, whilst references 15 and 16 provide excellent overviews of the results of research into skid-resistance carried out in Britain.)

## Design of dense 'hot-mix' surfacings

From the above it will be gathered that the design of bituminous surfacing mixtures can be quite complex. As a general guide, however, the following 'rules' regarding design can be given.

(1)   Select a good quality, relatively hard and hydrophobic, rough-textured aggregate of a grading which will meet the requirements of workability, permeability and economy, and (for a wearing course) with a high polish-resistant stone.

(2)   For the aggregate selected, choose a binder whose consistency is sufficiently soft to ensure good workability and long life, but is still hard enough to provide adequate tensile strength and resistance to moisture.

(3)   Use as much binder as possible in the surfacing without causing a loss of stability.

### Empirical design procedures

For mix design purposes, bituminous surfacing mixtures can be described as densely-graded, open-graded, or gap-graded.

Densely-graded mixes are made from graded aggregates of varying size, with or without an added filler material. They depend largely upon continuous grading and density for stability, and present a surface of close texture after compaction. Due to the high-density grading of the mix and the large surface area of the aggregate particles, the binder, aggregate and filler are normally heated as part of the mixing process (*hot-mix*), and a mixer of high efficiency is required in order to obtain a uniform product with quick and complete coating of all the particles with binder. The workability of a densely-graded mix is heavily influenced by its temperature, so it must be spread and compacted to its final shape whilst it still retains adequate heat (*hot laid*).

By workability is meant the ease with which the bituminous mix can be spread and compacted to the desired density, surface texture and finished level. If a mix is too harsh, it may tear under the screed of the spreading machine, and be difficult to compact; if the spread material is not well compacted, it will not develop the desirable properties of high stiffness, good fatigue-resistance, good durability, etc. However, a high degree of workability is usually consistent with low stability and higher binder contents, softer binders, uncrushed smooth-textured mineral aggregates, and open gradings. As a result, some compromise is normally required in order to achieve both workability and stability in a bituminous mixture.

Open-graded mixes are made from graded aggregates containing only small amounts of fine material and little or no filler. They depend largely upon mechanical interlock for stability, and present an open-textured surface after compaction. Depending upon the type of binder used, the mix may be a *hot-mix* (e.g. using penetration-grade bitumen), *warm-mix* (e.g. using cutback bitumen), or mixed at ambient or near-ambient temperatures, i.e. *cold-mix* (e.g. using bitumen emulsion). The hot-mixes are normally *hot laid*, whilst the warm- and cold-mixes are *cold laid*.

Gap-graded mixes, as the name implies, have a certain range of particle sizes missing from the total aggregate grading. They may consist of aggregates of a fairly uniform size which are blended with fine aggregate and filler, or a graded coarse aggregate blended with fine aggregate and filler (semi-gap-graded). As a consequence of the lack of good particle interlock—particularly when uniformly-sized coarse and fine aggregates are used—these mixes derive their stability from the mortar produced by the binder–sand–filler mixture. Since this, in turn, depends to a large extent upon the use of a high-viscosity binder, these gap-graded (dense) mixtures are always hot mixed and hot laid.

Laboratory methods have been most successfully employed in the mix design of continuously-graded dense mixtures using penetration-grade bitumens, and so the following discussion will concentrate on those types of mixtures. (References 17 and 18 provide overviews of the state of the art in relation to the mix design of liquid bituminous mixtures, whilst references 19 and 20 describe a proposed new method of designing gap-graded mixes.)

Before discussing any particular procedure, however, it is worthwhile seeing how the rules given above relate to the design of high-quality (dense) aggregate–bituminous-binder mixtures.

(1) *Selecting the aggregate*  Since dense surfacings are normally used at locations which are subject to high and heavy traffic stresses, the aggregates chosen for use should have angular, bulky shapes and rough surfaces so that high stabilities can be achieved. Although hydrophobic aggregates are to be preferred, relatively hydrophilic ones may sometimes be included in well-graded, densely compacted surfacings, since they are heated before being used with binder, and protected when compacted. For safety against skidding, the aggregates must have a considerable resistance to polishing.

The selection of an appropriate gradation is very often based on practicalities. For instance, from both the stability and economic aspects it may be desirable to use a particular maximum size of aggregate in the surfacing—this maximum size is also known as the *nominal size*—but practicalities of compaction will restrict the maximum size to not more than two-thirds of the thickness of a compacted basecourse or one-half in the case of a wearing course. Again, ideally, the gradation should be chosen so as to give as close-textured a mixture as possible, but this may not always be economically possible with the locally available aggregates. Extra care must be taken if gap-gradations are used as these are especially sensitive to minor changes in binder contents.

All mix design procedures in use at this time rely upon mechanical tests to predetermine the qualities of the aggregates which it is proposed to use (see Chapter 3) and rigid specifications control their acceptance. Specifications[21] also provide guidance on the range of gradations which may be used under particular circumstances.

(2) *Choosing the binder*  Binders composed of penetration-grade bitumens or high-viscosity road tars are automatically required at locations at which dense bituminous surfacings are normally justified, with the harder binders being utilized where the most severe conditions are encountered.

Again there is no rational procedure for determining which grade of material should be used in any specific situation, and so at the present time selection is based on experience and governed by specifications.

(3)  *Amount of binder*   It is towards determining the amount of binder which should be incorporated in the surfacing that most efforts have been directed in terms of designing dense bituminous mixtures. Many empirical and semi-empirical design procedures have been devised which first attempt to evaluate various properties of bituminous mixtures and then base the binder-content determination on these evaluations. Some of the more widely known of these tests are as follows: the Hubbard–Field extrusion test[22], the OTL bearing index test[23], the unconfined compressive test[24], the Smith triaxial test[25], the wheel-tracking simulative test[26], the Marshall test[27,28], the Hveem test[27], the splitting test[29], and the Lee–Rigden test[30].

It is not possible to present here the procedures involved and the relative merits of all these tests, and the reader is referred to the literature for further information regarding them. However, just one of these tests, the Marshall test, and its associated design method, will be discussed in detail here, as this test has the greatest international acceptance. However, before discussing the test and design method, it is necessary to review the fundamentals underlying the theory of bituminous mix design.

**Theory of bituminous mix design**
The design of bituminous surfacing mixtures, as with other highway engineering designs, is largely a matter of selecting and proportioning materials to obtain the desired properties in the finished construction. The overall objective is to determine an economical blend and gradation of aggregates and bituminous binder which will yield a mix having:

(1)  sufficient binder to ensure a durable surfacing,
(2)  sufficient mix stability to withstand traffic without distortion or displacement,
(3)  sufficient voids in the total compacted mix to allow for a small amount of additional compaction under traffic loading without flushing, bleeding, and loss of stability, but low enough to keep out harmful air and moisture,
(4)  sufficient workability to permit the efficient placement of the mix without segregation.

These principles indicate that for each mixture there is an 'optimum' binder content. There are two main approaches to determining this optimum content. These may be described as the *surface-area concept* and the *voids concept*.

*Surface-area concept*   As the name implies, this visualizes the optimum binder content as being a function of the surface area of the aggregate which is to be covered. This, in turn, is dependent upon the size, shape and surface texture of the ingredient mineral particles, their absorptive capabilities, gradation and relative density, and the type of binder. Typical of the many formulae which have been devised to relate surface area and binder content is the *Nebraskan formula*:

$$P = AR(0.02a) + 0.06b + 0.10c + Sd$$

where the symbols are as follows. $P$ is the percentage by mass of bitumen residue in the bituminous mixture prior to laying. $A$ is an absorption modifying factor for aggregate retained on the ASTM No. 50 (300 $\mu$m) sieve. $R$ is a relative density correction factor for aggregate retained on the ASTM No. 50 sieve; its value is given by

$$R = \frac{2.62}{\text{apparent relative density of aggregate}}$$

$a$ is the percentage by mass of aggregate retained on the ASTM No. 50 sieve. $b$ is the percentage by mass of aggregate passing the ASTM No. 50 sieve and retained on the ASTM No. 100 (150 $\mu$m) sieve. $c$ is the percentage by mass of aggregate passing the ASTM No. 100 sieve and retained on the ASTM No. 200 (75 $\mu$m) sieve. $d$ is the percentage by mass of aggregate passing the ASTM No. 200 sieve. $S$ is an experimental factor depending upon the fineness and absorptive characteristics of the material passing the ASTM No. 200 sieve.

At the present time, usage of surface-area formulae is confined: (a) to determining the amount of binder to be used in low-cost roads and (b) to a first estimation of the quantities of binder to be later used in laboratory design procedures based on the voids concept.

*Voids concept* According to this, the amount of binder which may be added is controlled by the voids space in the aggregate framework, and by the desired volume of voids in the final compacted mixture. Obviously, the amount of binder to be added will be influenced by the availability of the air voids in the aggregate framework—this, in turn, is predetermined by the aggregate gradation and method of compaction—and, desirably, as much binder as possible should be used to fill them. However, the compacted mixture must have a residue of air voids to allow for expansion of the binder and entrained air under hot weather conditions, to provide the mixture with a certain amount of elasticity, and to provide 'safety' space for further compaction of the surfacing under heavy traffic; against that, the residue of air voids should not be so great as to allow air and moisture to enter the surfacing and encourage disintegration. While it is generally agreed that maximum and minimum limits should be set on the amount of residual voids, there is considerable dissension as to what these limits should be. Recommended values have ranged from 2 to 3 per cent [31] to as high as 7 per cent maximum [32]. Experience would suggest, however, that good results are most likely to be obtained if the voids content of a bituminous surfacing is in the range 3–5 per cent, with use of the higher value being associated with hot climates, friable stones and well-channelized traffic, whilst the lower figure is more appropriate in colder climates and with scattered or low-intensity traffic [33].

Two points should be emphasized about the voids concept and its relation to bituminous mixture design. Firstly, it can only be applied to dense bituminous mixtures and not to open-graded ones. Where to draw the line between the two types of mixes, it is not possible to say; as a guide, however, it can be accepted that the concept is generally applied to mixtures whose gradations lie about those obtained by applying Fuller's gradation requirements for maximum density (see Chapter 5). If more-open-graded mixtures are used in conjunction with the voids concept, the binder content determined may be so great as to cause a significant reduction in stability. Secondly, it should be clearly understood that the voids concept is not used on its own to any great extent as a means of determining the optimum binder content. As will be shown in the discussion on the Marshall design procedure, it is used primarily as a means of ensuring that durability considerations are taken into account in a test in which the determination of binder content for maximum stability is the prime object.

## Marshall method of mix design

The concepts underlying the Marshall method of mix design were originally formulated by Bruce Marshall of the Mississippi State Highway Department, and improved and ultimately developed as a standard approach by the US Corps of Engineers. The Marshall test procedures have been standardized by the American Society for Testing and Materials, in ASTM Designation D15 559, *Resistance to the Plastic Flow of Bituminous Mixtures Using Marshall Apparatus*, and it is these which are most widely used throughout the world and are extensively quoted in the technical literature.

Generally, the Marshall method is applicable to hot-mix bituminous mixtures using penetration- or viscosity-grade bitumens and containing aggregates with maximum sizes of 25 mm or less. It requires the preparation and evaluation of a series of test specimens at different binder contents. Preliminary to this operation, however, it requires: (a) that the materials proposed for use meet the requirements of the project's specifications, (b) that aggregate blend combinations meet the grading requirements of the specifications, and (c) that the relative density on an oven-dried basis of all aggregates used in the blend, and the relative density of the penetration-grade bitumen, be determined (see Chapter 3) for later use in density and voids analyses.

The Marshall test uses standard cylindrical test specimens that are 101.6 mm diameter by about 63.5 mm high. The specimens are prepared using a prescribed procedure for heating, mixing and compacting the bitumen–aggregate mixtures. The two principal features of the Marshall method of mix design (USA method) are a density–voids analysis and a stability–flow test of the compacted test specimens. The stability test is a type of unconfined compressive strength test in which the test specimen (see Fig. 7.1) is compressed radially at a constant rate of strain of 50 mm per minute at 60 °C. The Marshall stability of each test specimen is the maximum load resistance in newtons that the specimen develops, whilst the Marshall flow value is the total movement or strain occurring in the specimen between no load and maximum load during the stability test. The 'optimum' binder content then selected for design is essentially a com-

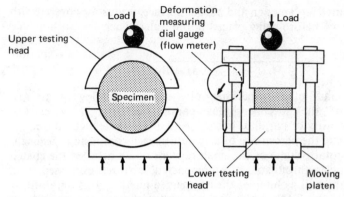

**Fig. 7.1**  Illustration of the Marshall stability test

promise value which meets specified requirements for stability, deformation and voids content. The manner in which this value is obtained can be outlined in a series of steps.

*Step 1*  Prepare a series of test specimens for a range of different binder contents so that the stability test data can show a well-defined optimum value at some binder content.

To establish the binder contents to be used in these tests, the optimum content must first be estimated, either on the basis of experience or by means of a surface-area equation to ensure that stability values for at least two binder contents on either side of the optimum binder content for maximum stability are obtained.

When preparing the individual Marshall specimens, each preheated mixture of aggregate and binder is placed in a preheated mould and compacted with a 4.535 kg standard hammer falling through 457 mm. A specified number of blows is given to each side of the specimen, so as to achieve a density close to that which the mixture might ultimately attain under traffic after rolling during construction. It is important that the same compaction pedestal be used for all the tests, as otherwise different results can be obtained.

*Step 2*  Determine the bulk density of each specimen.

This determination is usually made by one of two methods, depending upon the surface texture of the specimen being measured.

If the specimen has a compact, smooth surface, the determination can be made by measuring the mass of the specimen in air and in water and then calculating as follows:

$$d = \frac{M_A}{V} = \frac{M_A}{M_A - M_W}$$

where $d$ = bulk density of the compacted mix (g/cm$^3$), $M_A$ = mass of the specimen in air (g), $V$ = volume of the specimen (cm$^3$), and $M_W$ = mass of the specimen in water (g).

If the specimen has an open and porous surface, it must be covered with a paraffin coating before being placed in the water. Then

$$d = \frac{M_A}{V} = \frac{M_A}{M_{PA} - M_{PW} - (M_{PA} - M_A)/R_P}$$

where $M_{PA}$ = mass of the specimen plus paraffin coating in air (g), $M_{PW}$ = mass of the specimen plus paraffin coating in water (g), $R_P$ = relative density of paraffin, and $M_A$ and $V$ are as defined above.

*Step 3*   Calculate the percentage of air voids in each compacted specimen.

This is the total volume of the small pockets of air between the coated aggregate particles throughout the compacted mixture, expressed as a percentage of the bulk volume of the compacted mixture. It is obtained by first determining the theoretical or actual voidless density of the specimen and then expressing the difference between this and the bulk density as a percentage of the voidless density.

The theoretical density can normally be calculated from the formula:

$$\psi_t = \frac{M_A}{v_b + v_c + v_f + v_{mf}} = \frac{M_A}{\dfrac{m_b}{R_b} + \dfrac{m_c}{R_c} + \dfrac{m_f}{R_f} + \dfrac{m_{mf}}{R_{mf}}}$$

where $\psi_t$ = maximum theoretical density (g/cm$^3$), $M_A$ = mass of the specimen (g), $v_b$ = volume of the binder in the specimen (cm$^3$), $v_c$, $v_f$ and $v_{mf}$ = volumes of the coarse, fine and mineral filler fractions, respectively, of the aggregates in the specimen (cm$^3$), $m_b$ = mass of the binder used in the specimen (g), $m_c$, $m_f$ and $m_{mf}$ = masses of the coarse, fine and mineral filler fractions, respectively, of the aggregates in the specimen (g), $R_b$ = relative density of the binder, and $R_c$, $R_f$ and $R_{mf}$ = *apparent* relative densities of the coarse, fine and mineral filler fractions, respectively, of the aggregates in the specimen.

Two points should be noted with respect to this calculation. Firstly, the mass of each component fraction of the specimen (i.e. $m_b$, $m_c$, $m_f$ and $m_{mf}$) is determined by assuming each to be a proportional amount of the total mass of the specimen. Secondly, the relative density values of the aggregates used in this calculation are the apparent relative densities and not the relative densities on an oven-dried basis. In this way (*US Corps of Engineers method*), the volumes of the water-permeable voids in the aggregates are excluded from the calculation.

In practice, of course, the aggregate pores are *partially filled* with binder, i.e. with the non-effective binder content (see Fig. 7.2). To obviate errors therefore which might arise from the use of the Corps of Engineers approach, particularly in respect of porous aggregates, the voidless density should be determined directly by measurement (*J M Rice Correction Method—ASTM Test D2041-64T*) In this instance, the bituminous mixture needs to be warmed and broken up into loose particles so that all the entrapped air can escape. The mass of the coated, loose particles is then measured in air and in water and the actual effective voidless density determined directly from the formula:

$$\psi_t = \frac{M_A}{M_A - M_W}$$

where $M_A$ = mass of the coated mix in air (g), $M_W$ = mass of the coated mix in water (g), and $\psi_t$ = actual 'effective' voidless density (g/cm$^3$).

If the test is carried out correctly, then the 'effective' voidless density should lie somewhere between the bulk density and the theoretical voidless density.

The percentage of air voids in the compacted specimen is then obtained by subtracting the bulk density from the theoretical (apparent) or actual (effective) voidless density, as appropriate, and expressing the difference as a percentage of the voidless density. Thus

$$\% VTM = \frac{\psi_t - d}{\psi_t} \times 100$$

where $\% VTM$ = voids in the total mixture, i.e. in the specimen (%), $\psi_t$ = voidless density (g/cm$^3$), and $d$ = bulk density (g/cm$^3$).

*Step 4*  For each specimen, calculate the percentage of voids in the compacted mineral aggregate framework.

The 'percentage of voids in the mineral aggregate' is defined as the intergranular voids space between the aggregate particles in a compacted mixture (including the air voids and the effective binder content—see Fig. 7.2), expressed as a percentage of the total volume. It is calculated on the basis of the relative density on an oven-dried basis of the aggregate (see Chapter 3) and expressed as a percentage of the bulk volume, as follows:

$$\% VMA = 100 - \frac{RP_a}{R_{ave}}$$

where $\% VMA$ = voids in the mineral aggregate framework (percentage of bulk volume of the compacted mix), $R$ = relative density on an oven-dried basis of the compacted mixture, $P_a$ = aggregate content (percentage by mass of the total mix), and $R_{ave}$ = average relative density on an oven-dried basis of the coarse, fine and filler aggregate.

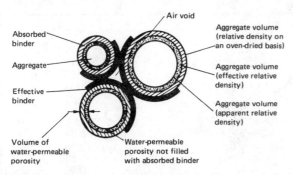

**Fig. 7.2**  Diagram illustrating the concepts of voids in the mineral aggregate, air voids and effective binder content in a compacted bituminous mixture

*Step 5* Determine the Marshall stability and flow of each specimen.

The Marshall stability of a test specimen is the maximum load, in newtons, required to produce failure when the specimen is preheated to a prescribed temperature, placed in the special testing head shown in Fig. 7.1 and the load applied at a constant rate of strain of 50 mm per minute. While the stability test is in progress, a dial gauge is used to measure the vertical deformation of the specimen; the deformation read at the load failure point is the flow value of the specimen.

*Step 6* Correct the measured stability values to those which would have been obtained if the specimens had been exactly 63.5 mm high.

This is done by multiplying each measured stability value by an appropriate correlation ratio. The correlation values shown in Table 7.6 are extracted from data derived by the US Corps of Engineers in the course of their investigations into the use of the Marshall test in the design of bituminous surfacings for airport pavements.

*Step 7* Prepare separate graphical plots for binder content versus each of the following: (a) corrected Marshall stability, (b) Marshall flow, (c) percentage of voids in the total mix, (d) percentage of voids in the mineral aggregate framework, and (e) density.

It should be noted that only the first three of the above are taken into account in the initial stage of the analysis. The manner in which this is done is best illustrated by assuming that the data in Fig. 7.3 represent the results of laboratory tests on a densely-graded asphaltic concrete mix (19 mm nominal maximum aggregate size) to be used in a highway surfacing under medium traffic conditions.

*Step 8* Determine the optimum binder content.

Whilst analysing the data in Fig. 7.3, the design criteria appropriate to the traffic and climatic conditions under which the pavement will operate should be borne in mind. Table 7.7 summarizes the design criteria

**Table 7.6** Marshall stability correlation values

| Volume of specimen (cm³) | Approximate thickness of specimen (mm) | Correlation ratio |
|---|---|---|
| 432–443 | 54.0 | 1.32 |
| 444–456 | 55.6 | 1.25 |
| 457–470 | 57.2 | 1.19 |
| 471–482 | 58.8 | 1.14 |
| 483–495 | 60.3 | 1.09 |
| 496–508 | 61.9 | 1.04 |
| 509–522 | 63.5 | 1.00 |
| 523–535 | 65.1 | 0.96 |
| 536–546 | 66.7 | 0.93 |
| 547–559 | 68.3 | 0.89 |
| 560–573 | 69.9 | 0.86 |
| 574–585 | 71.5 | 0.83 |
| 586–596 | 73.0 | 0.81 |
| 599–610 | 74.6 | 0.78 |

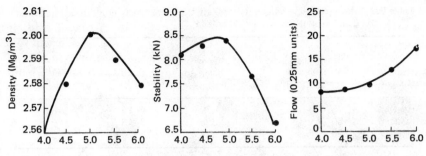

Binder content (% by mass of total mix)

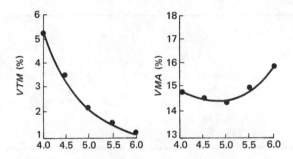

Binder content (% by mass of total mix)

**Fig. 7.3**  Typical Marshall test data

recommended[27] by the US Asphalt Institute for use with continuously-graded asphaltic concrete materials.

From Fig. 7.3, the following can be determined:

binder content at maximum density = 5.1%

binder content at maximum stability = 4.8%

and   binder content providing 4% *VTM* (median of 3–5% range for surfacing, medium traffic) = 4.3%

optimum = 4.7% (average)

*Step 9*  Check that the optimum binder content gives a mixture which will meet the criteria in Table 7.7.

Re-entering the curves in Fig. 7.3 with the average binder content, the following values are determined:

stability = 8.36 kN

flow = 9 (0.25 mm units)

% *VTM* = 2.8

and   % *VMA* = 14.4

In this instance, the stability value is well above the requirement

**Table 7.7**   Marshall design criteria used by the US Asphalt Institute: (a) stability, flow and % *VTM* criteria and (b) minimum % *VMA* criteria

| Traffic category | Number of compaction blows on each end of the specimen | Stability (minimum) (kN) | Flow range (0.25 mm units) | % *VTM* range |
|---|---|---|---|---|
| Heavy | 75 | 6.672 | 8–16 | 3–5 |
| Medium | 50 | 3.336 | 8–18 | 3–5 |
| Light | 35 | 2.224 | 8–20 | 3–5 |

(a)

| Nominal maximum aggregate size (mm) | % *VMA* |
|---|---|
| 1.18 | 23.5 |
| 2.36 | 21.0 |
| 4.75 | 18.0 |
| 9.50 | 16.0 |
| 12.50 | 15.0 |
| 19.00 | 14.0 |
| 25.00 | 13.0 |
| 37.50 | 12.0 |
| 50.00 | 11.5 |
| 63.00 | 11.0 |

(b)

(3.336 kN), the flow value is within the limiting range (8–18), and the percentage of voids in the mineral aggregate exceeds the recommended figure (14 per cent). In the case of the percentage of voids in the total mix, however, the optimum binder content for this aggregate grading gives a result which falls below the recommended minimum value (3 per cent). Therefore, in order to meet the Asphalt Institute criteria, it is necessary to reject the mix design as it does not have all test properties within the allowable limits.

*Step 10*   Adjust the grading of the original aggregate blend and carry out Steps 1–9 again.

*Discussion*   The Marshall test results shown in Fig. 7.3 are of particular interest in that they reflect some trends which are common to most laboratory tests for optimum binder content and, indeed, to most studies of actual road surfacing behaviour. Before discussing these, however, it is useful to comment briefly on the terms *optimum* and *effective* binder contents.

The optimum binder content selected by the Marshall method has two components. Firstly, there is the quantity of binder 'lost' by absorption into the aggregate particles, i.e. aggregates with high porosity tend to absorb relatively large amounts of binder, thereby increasing the construction cost of the bituminous pavement. Secondly, there is the effective binder content (see Fig. 7.2) which is the optimum content minus the absorbed quantity; it is this portion that remains as a coating on the outside of the aggregate particles, and upon which the in-service performance of a bituminous mixture depends.

From Fig. 7.3, the following may be deduced.

(1)  The density of the mixture increases with increasing binder content until a maximum value is reached, after which the density decreases. This characteristic is similar to that observed when moisture is added to a natural soil. At first the binder acts as a lubricant and helps the aggregate particles to slide over each other. Once an optimum amount of binder has been added, however, it acts only to displace the particles and so the 'wet' density decreases. If, therefore, a dense mixture is to be obtained, it is important that the amount of binder should not exceed the optimum for the compactive effort applied.

(2)  The stability value of the mixture also increases with increasing binder content until a maximum value is reached, after which stability decreases. Generally, the optimum binder content for stability is close to the optimum value for density but on the dry side of it. The optimum binder content for stability can be explained by noting that the Marshall test is actually a type of unconfined compressive strength test in which some degree of lateral support is given to the specimen; thus the maximum stability value occurs at the binder content at which the combination of the internal friction component of stability (provided by the interlocking aggregates) and the cohesive component (provided by the thin, viscous, 'effective' bituminous films coating the particles) is a maximum under the conditions of test. Of the two, the test is by far a more true measure of the cohesive component of stability than of the internal friction one. Whether it is an exact measure of the change in stability which would occur in the roadway itself is, of course, doubtful; there is no doubt, however, that each aggregate–bituminous-binder mixture placed in a pavement has an optimum binder content for stability under the prevailing environmental conditions.

(3)  The flow value increases as the binder content increases. In addition, the rate of deformation change is slow at low binder contents but increases rapidly as high binder contents are reached. Again this is what might be expected in a roadway. For instance, surfacings with abnormally low flow values and very high stability values tend to be rigid or brittle and may crack under heavy volumes of traffic; this is especially true where subgrade deflections are such as to permit moderate to relatively high deflections of the pavement. Surfacings with low stabilities and high flows deform easily under traffic.

(4)  The percentage of voids in the total mix decreases with increasing binder content until a value is reached at which it begins to level off. The %*VTM* is critical as regards durability, since the greater the air voids content, the more easily air and moisture can attack the binder and the binder–aggregate bond. When the air voids content is too low, perhaps approaching one per cent or less, the surfacing is likely to 'flush' or 'bleed' under traffic. Since the error in the air voids determination may be as much

as one per cent, due to the limits of precision of the standard test methods, the minimum air voids value which is normally recommended when using the Marshall test is 3 per cent.

(5)   The percentage of voids in the mineral aggregate generally decreases to a minimum value, and then increases with increasing binder content. It is important to note that, unless the % *VMA* is large, the paving mixture will be deficient in binder content or air voids, or both. When surfacings are deficient in binder, they become brittle and crack in early life and may ravel seriously under traffic; the effects of a low air voids content is, as has been stated, to promote flushing. Thus the voids in the mineral aggregate should be large enough to ensure that there is sufficient room between the particles in the thoroughly compacted mixture to contain at least 2 to 3 per cent air voids plus the minimum amount of binder required for a durable surfacing. Consequently, the voids in the mineral aggregate framework must be as nearly filled with binder as is possible.

### British (Marshall) mix design procedure

A variation of the above mix design method is now included in a British Standard[28] as an alternative to the recipe method of design as a means of determining the binder content to be used in a rolled asphalt wearing course.

In summary, the procedure involves preparing Marshall test specimens and, using data derived from these specimens, preparing graphs of binder content versus: (a) corrected Marshall stability, (b) Marshall flow, (c) bulk density, and (d) compacted aggregate density. In the British Standard, the bulk density of the specimen is described as the mix relative density, whilst the compacted aggregate density is determined from the formula

$$S_A = \frac{d(100 - m_b)}{100}$$

where $S_A$ = compacted aggregate density, and $d$ and $m_b$ are as described before.

The design binder content is then calculated as the mean value of the binder contents determined for maximum stability, maximum mix density, and maximum aggregate density, *plus* an additional binder content of 0, 0.7, 0.7 and 0 per cent for mix coarse aggregate contents of 0, 30, 40 and 55 per cent, respectively. In areas of the country where the prevailing weather conditions are characteristically colder and wetter than the national average, a further 0.5 per cent of binder may be added to improve the durability of the wearing course.

The Department of Transport will accept this design binder content for use in road construction, provided that Marshall specimens prepared at this design content meet the criteria in Table 7.8.

In this table, traffic is defined in terms of the estimated average number of commercial vehicles per lane per day in one direction during the year of laying. A commercial vehicle is described as a goods or public service vehicle of unladen mass exceeding 1.5 t. Where intense canalization of

**Table 7.8** Marshall design criteria used by the Department of Transport[34]

| Traffic | Marshall value of complete mix | |
| --- | --- | --- |
| | Stability (kN) | Maximum flow (mm) |
| < 1500 | 2–8 | 5 |
| 1500–6000 | 4–8 | 5 |
| > 6000 | 6–10 | 7 |

heavy goods traffic occurs, e.g. at approaches to traffic lights where heavy vehicles are continually braking and restarting, and where the rate of growth is expected to be abnormally high, the design criterion is based on the next highest traffic band.

*Comment*   In 1973 the Marshall test was accepted in Britain as an optional means of determining the optimum binder content of the blended sand and filler component of a rolled asphalt wearing course. The concept of using an empirical design procedure to derive the optimum binder content was subsequently well accepted by engineers and, following wide consultation, the 1973 procedure was amended and simplified. Some concern has been expressed at the modified procedure however, in relation to its usage for gap-graded mixes, as well as to the apparently arbitrary way in which the coarse aggregate correction factor is applied[35].

The Marshall method as originally developed in the USA was intended for use with continuously-graded asphaltic concrete mixes; the current British procedure requires the use of gradation specifications that are characterized by the gap-grading associated with the use of sands. A 50 pen bitumen is probably the binder that is most used in the design of rolled asphalt wearing courses, although harder binders (e.g. 35 or 40 pen HD) are used in designs for sites with intense traffic, and softer binders (e.g. 70 or 100 pen) on more-lightly-stressed pavements.

The Marshall design method is considered to be most suitable for use in the design of wearing courses for rolled asphalt where very intense vehicular traffic is expected, and/or there is little or no experience of the use of the proposed constituent materials, especially the fine aggregate component. This especially applies to projects involving large tonnages of wearing course material.

## Recipe-type bituminous surfacings

As noted above, it is not yet common practice in Britain to utilize laboratory tests such as the Marshall test in the design of bituminous surfacings. Instead, over the years, a considerable amount of information has been collected with respect to the performance of different types of surfacings under various traffic conditions, both on specially constructed test roads and on the normal roads of the country. The results of research on these data have been combined with commercial experience in formulating particular aggregate and binder compositions that ensure good durability while at the same time providing reasonable working tolerances for manufacture and laying. As a result, the quality of the bituminous surfacings in Britain is amongst the highest in the world—as well as being amongst the most expensive[33].

Recipe specifications have many *advantages*, not least of which are the following.

(1)   They have been proven successful in practice.
(2)   They are simple to use and applicable to all types of mix.
(3)   The highway engineer can easily specify the materials required in the surfacing.
(4)   The supplier at the mixing plant can more easily meet the fixed recipe requirements, rather than have to change the composition because of variations in the quality of the components.
(5)   The construction engineer can easily test for compliance with the specification.

Recipe specifications also have a number of important *disadvantages*, as follows.

(1)   The performance of a mix under traffic can depend upon workmanship as much as upon composition, and it is very difficult to specify workmanship via the recipe method.
(2)   If the recipe specification is used in a road environment that is very different from that for which the recipe was derived, modifications to the recipe may be required but no guidance is available as to what these should be.
(3)   If checks show that the material supplied does not comply with the specification, even though the differences may be only minor, there is no way of evaluating the seriousness of these variations.
(4)   Recipe specifications inhibit new developments and are restrictive with respect to the use of cheap, locally available pavement materials.
(5)   With the relatively large number of specifications available, it is possible for the inexperienced engineer to select an inappropriate recipe.

## British practice

Except as noted above in relation to the use of the Marshall test, all of the British Standard specifications for bituminous surfacings are of the recipe type, and are used nationwide. The number and apparent complexity of these surfacing mixtures can seem daunting to the person introduced to them for the first time. The emphasis in this discussion therefore will be upon those aspects which explain the system and illustrate how and why one surfacing is used as compared with another.

Table 7.9 gives the main types and usages of recipe-type bituminous surfacings specified for use in Britain[21]. Governmental advice regarding the practical usage of these surfacings is also given in Chapter 6.

**Table 7.9** The main categories and uses of recipe-type premixed bituminous-bound materials used in Britain

| Type | Description | Usage |
|------|-------------|-------|
| Asphalt | Rolled asphalt | |
| | low stone content | Wearing course |
| | high stone content | Wearing course, basecourse, roadbase |
| Coated macadam | Dense tar surfacing | Wearing course, |
| | Dense bitumen macadam | Wearing course, basecourse, roadbase |
| | Dense tarmacadam | Basecourse, roadbase |
| | Open-textured tarmacadam | Wearing course |
| | Open-textured bitumen macadam | Wearing course |
| | Bitumen macadam | Basecourse |
| | Tarmacadam | Basecourse, roadbase |
| | Cold asphalt | |
| | coarse | Wearing course |
| | fine | Wearing course |

## Asphalt

*Rolled asphalt*   Next to mastic asphalt, this hot-mix, hot laid surfacing is probably the most stable and durable bituminous road mixture used in Britain today. In essence, it is a mortar of fine aggregate and penetration-grade binder to which is added a quantity of coarse aggregate or stone. Low coarse aggregate content mixtures (e.g. 40 per cent or less retained on the 2.36 mm sieve) are used solely for wearing courses, while high stone content mixtures may also be used for wearing courses but are more usually limited to basecourses (and roadbases). Wearing courses containing no coarse aggregate are also termed *sand carpets* and *sand asphalts*.

Rolled asphalt surfacings possess considerable mechanical strength and this makes them more effective than most other types of surfacing in reducing the traffic stresses within the underlying parts of the pavement. Assessments of the relative economic value of various types of bituminous surfacings have indicated that a properly constructed rolled asphalt surfacing can be expected to have a maintenance-free life of about twenty years, provided that the pavement otherwise remains sound. Comparisons between rolled asphalt and some other common types of surfacing which will be discussed are given in Table 7.10.

The recipes for rolled asphalt surfacings are controlled by a British Standard[34] which at this time lists eleven acceptable wearing course and six basecourse and roadbase mixtures which may be used in highway pavements; these options are considerably reduced in number on those available a decade previously. The choice of which mixture to use in a given situation depends upon economic considerations, the thickness to be laid, site and traffic conditions, and the availability of particular types of aggregate and grades of binder.

**Table 7.10**   Relative merits of surfacing materials[36]

| Characteristic | Effective ratio | | |
| --- | --- | --- | --- |
| | Surface dressing | Pervious macadam | Rolled asphalt |
| Area surfaced per unit cost | 6 | 2 | 1 |
| Average life | 1 | 2 | 3 |
| Skid-resistance | 1 | 1 | 1 |
| Texture depth | 1 | 1 | 1 |
| Low spray | 2 | 6 | 1 |
| Low noise | 1 | 4 | 2 |
| Structural strength | 1 | 2 | 6 |
| Improved drive | 1 | 4 | 4 |
| Ease and speed of resurfacing | 4 | 1 | 1 |

Crushed rock, gravel, or slag are permitted as coarse aggregate in both wearing course and basecourse mixtures. The most commonly used wearing course material has a 30 per cent coarse aggregate content. For general basecourse use, a rolled asphalt with 60 per cent coarse aggregate is most commonly recommended. The maximum size of aggregate used in either layer is controlled by the thickness of the layer; the usual practice requires the maximum stone size to be between one-third and one-half of the thickness of the compacted layer. If too large a size is used, the graded aggregate will not compact satisfactorily under the rollers; if too small a size is used, there is a significant reduction in mechanical stability.

As noted previously, rolled asphalt is a dense, low air voids (generally 3–6 per cent) mixture composed of a mortar of sand, filler and binder to which is added a quantity of coarse material. Whilst the use of crushed fines is permitted by the specification, the fine aggregates most often used are natural sands, i.e. the grading envelopes given in the specification were historically developed so as to maximize the use of commonly available natural sands. The filler material is usually limestone dust or cement.

Binders listed as acceptable for use with rolled asphalt are penetration-grade refinery bitumens, lake-asphalt–bitumen (50 : 50 blend), and pitch–bitumen (25 : 75 blend). Whilst refinery bitumen is used in both wearing courses and basecourses, the other two binders are only used in wearing course work, because of their advantageous skid-resistance qualities. In general, 50 pen binders are commonly employed in wearing course, basecourse and roadbase construction in areas of intense canalized traffic in southern England, whilst 70 pen materials are frequently used in Scotland and northern England. The use of lower-penetration binders is associated with locations where the foundation material is strong and a high resistance of deformation is required, e.g. on heavily-travelled rural and city roads, particularly at severely stressed locations, such as bus stops. In contrast, high-penetration binders are associated with thin surfacings or those with high coarse aggregate contents or on less-heavily-trafficked routes. Rolled asphalt surfacings with high binder contents are necessary at locations which, when wetted, do not dry out easily; they are also used in roads carrying light traffic, since durability, and not stability, is the primary design factor here. Low bitumen contents tend to be employed in basecourses and in wearing courses carrying large volumes of traffic.

Rolled asphalt wearing courses containing about 40 per cent or less coarse aggregate present a relatively smooth surface texture upon completion of compaction, and so a surface dressing of pre-coated chippings is usually rolled in during the laying operation; this is to increase the resistance to skidding. If a rolled asphalt wearing course has a high coarse aggregate content, the addition of a surface dressing may not be possible; indeed, if the coarse aggregate is such that it does not polish easily under traffic, the surface dressing will not be necessary. Since adequate resistance to skidding is dependent upon the extent to which the chippings and/or aggregate are able to remain proud of the surface throughout its long life, the choice of binder is particularly important on very-heavily-travelled roads where binder contents tend to become more critical with, in particular, close-textured low voids content mixtures. The ability of chippings to stand proud is determined to a large extent by the nature of the binder and the way it permits the surface of the mortar to be slowly worn away by the combined action of traffic and weather (see Chapter 3).

*Mastic asphalt* Manufactured mastic asphalt [37, 38] consists of a hot-mix mortar of fine aggregate and binder—this may be refinery bitumen, lake asphalt, or lake-asphalt–bitumen (50:50) mix—with added coarse aggregate, which yields a plastic and voidless mass which is applied hot, and trowelled or 'floated' on a pavement to form a very dense, impermeable surfacing. The fine aggregate may be a crushed limestone or a finely-ground natural asphalt, which is a naturally occurring calcareous rock impregnated with bitumen (see Chapter 3).

Mastic asphalt is an 'old' surfacing; the records indicate that a number of the major streets in central London were surfaced with manufactured mastic asphalt as long ago as 1874. Although accepted as being perhaps the most stable and durable of the dense bituminous wearing courses, its usage is no longer recommended for British roads since, unlike rolled asphalt, it does not lend itself to mechanization and so must be laid by hand in the pavement.

As a result of its complete imperviousness, high resistance to deformation, and extreme durability, mastic asphalt is particularly suitable for use on bridge decks, on roads and areas that have to carry iron-wheeled and tracked vehicles, as well as at street locations subject to very high stresses. It has a very fine texture which provides little resistance to skidding and so pre-coated chippings are normally applied to the running surface to improve its skid-resistance characteristics. These chippings are rolled into the surface while the mastic material is still sufficiently plastic to allow them to become partially, but firmly, embedded. Here again refined lake asphalt has special wearing properties which render it most effective in maintaining the chippings proud of the surface.

**Dense tar surfacing (DTS)**
Although this surfacing is included in Table 7.9 under the general heading of coated macadam, it should be appreciated that its strength depends to a large extent upon its mortar—which is why DTS[39] is considered to be the tarmacadam-type surfacing which corresponds most closely to rolled asphalt. It is a hot-mix, hot laid wearing course material consisting of a mixture of coarse and fine aggregates, filler and high-viscosity tar, the proportions of which are selected so that, when rolling is complete, a dense and impervious surfacing is obtained which is capable of carrying heavy and varied traffic flows over long periods of time.

A close-textured DTS wearing course that is used as part of a two-course surfacing is laid on top of a densely-coated macadam with a high-viscosity binder or rolled asphalt; however, the lower material must be cold before the wearing course is placed upon it, as the temperature of laying can cause softening of the basecourse binder and consequent movement under rolling. On a sound substrate of good profile, one course of DTS is normally adequate for resurfacing work.

The dense tar wearing course mixtures are of two types, one of which contains 35 per cent coarse aggregate ( > 3.35 mm) and the other 50 per cent. If the lower stone content mixture is used on roads where skid-resistance is important, coated chippings must be rolled into the running surface to provide adequate surface texture. Fifty per cent coarse aggregate DTS with crushed rock or slag fine aggregate and 54 °C evt tar is the preferred mixture for the heaviest duty use, e.g. motorway service areas. Chippings cannot easily be applied to the surface of the 50 per cent coarse aggregate mixture, but then again this surface has a rough texture which renders the addition of chippings unnecessary if the right quality of stone is used. The maximum size of aggregate is determined by the desired thickness of layer; for good compaction, the maximum size is normally about one-third of the layer thickness.

The tars used in dense tar surfacings have viscosities that are as high as can be practically used without fuming occurring during mixing and the tar hardening too rapidly; this limits the tars to those with viscosities below 54 °C evt.

**Coated macadams**
These surfacings differ from the dense mastic-type asphalts in that they generally contain relatively little fine aggregate and filler material, and the intimate interlocking of the aggregate particles is a major factor in the strength of these surfacings. Furthermore, they are not initially impervious to water; in many instances also, the aggregates have to be more resistant to abrasion and crushing, since a matrix of fine particles is not available to protect the coarse particles from the traffic. These surfacings are normally laid at locations where all-weather roads are required but the traffic conditions do not justify the construction of the more expensive dense surfacings.

The coated macadams contain coarsely-graded mineral aggregates which are pre-coated with either tar or bitumen; the compacted mixtures have a substantial proportion of voids, i.e. 15–25 per cent in the case of the open- and medium-textured mixtures and 6–12 per cent in the more dense macadams. They are prepared in large plants situated in quarries or pits which, as a result of the geological formations of Britain, are sufficiently uniformly spaced throughout the country to provide surfacing materials at most road sites at economical prices. They are easy to manufacture and lay and, when properly designed, they provide adequate stability for all roads, except those carrying the heaviest traffic. At the present time, the compositions of most coated macadam road surfacings are controlled by a single British Standard specification[40].

Table 7.9 summarizes the coated macadam surfacings that are available. A two-course construction consisting of a wearing course on top of a supporting or regulating basecourse is most often used in the reconstruction of existing roads and as a surfacing in new roads carrying medium to light traffic. The nominal size of aggregate used in either of the layers of a two-course surfacing depends upon the compacted thickness, traffic conditions and, for wearing courses, the running surface texture desired.

A single-course construction, because it has to serve the dual function of being both a wearing course and a basecourse, is more densely graded than a normal coated macadam basecourse which would be used in a two-course surfacing. Single-course surfacings are considerably cheaper to construct than two-course ones, and so they are in wide use as reconstruction surfacings on existing roads. In new pavements they are confined to lightly-trafficked roads where the uniformity of the final running surface is not a major design criterion.

A coated macadam 'carpet' wearing course is used only when it is desired to give a new riding surface to an existing pavement, and its function is usually to remove minor irregularities in the running surface.

Coated macadam wearing courses are most usually described as being open-, medium- or close-textured. Open-textured mixtures have a low ( ⩾ 15 per cent passing the 3.35 mm sieve) fines content; this results in good workability during laying. Medium-textured surfacings have about 25 per cent fines, whilst close-textured or dense macadams have about 35 per cent fines. Dense macadam basecourses have been used extensively in new major road construction since the mid-1960s. Dense macadam wearing courses are suitable for use in pavements which carry all but the heaviest traffic. Open- and medium-textured macadams are generally used under light and medium traffic conditions. Current experience indicates that open surfaces, using 100 pen bitumen, at a thickness of 40 mm have a life of 5–8 years or more at traffic levels up to 50 000 vehicles per day[41].

Open-graded coated macadam mixtures have the disadvantage that they are more open to the disintegration effects of air and water. To resist these effects, they have available less tar or bitumen binder per unit volume of surfacing than any other premixed material. Since the coarse aggregates are no longer protected by the filler–binder matrix, the aggregates used in open-textured surfacings must have high resistance to abrasion and crushing.

Although the open mixtures have a wide tolerance in gradation with respect to stability, the tendency nowadays is to use the more-closely-textured mixtures in road surfacings. These have the dual advantages of providing more durable as well as more skid-resistant surfacings. Close-textured surfacings must be used if the underlying roadbase and/or subgrade are liable to be detrimentally affected by moisture percolating down through an open-textured layer. Close-textured basecourses must also be used under wearing courses formed from rolled asphalt and dense tar surfacings, since the open-textured ones utilize low-viscosity binders which would soften when the hot wearing course is applied. This, in turn, could result in surface deformations taking place beneath the roller during compaction, thereby producing a poor running surface.

Coated macadams may also be divided according to the manner in which they are laid. *Hot laid* macadams are those in which comparatively-high-viscosity binders are hot mixed with the aggregate and then transported to the site and laid at relatively high temperatures. They are used at locations where high stabilities are required. Since, however, these surfacings must be compacted while still hot, their use is limited to within short transportation distances of the mixing plant. The most widely used macadams are the *warm laid* ones. The bitumens used in these mixtures range from medium-curing cutbacks to high-penetration-grade bitumens, and the road tars have medium viscosities. The materials in these aggregate–binder mixtures must be heated if an intimate mix is to be obtained; if properly sheeted, they can be transported fairly long distances and still be laid warm the same day. The longer the journey or the colder the weather or the more lightly trafficked the road, the lower must be the viscosity of the binder which is used. *Cold laid* macadams can be made with low-viscosity tars or very fluid cutback bitumens and hence they are suitable for transporting over long distances or for storing for a period of time before laying. Full stability is not attained with these mixtures until the volatile oils present have evaporated, and so the surfacings cannot be sealed until this stage is reached. These surfacings are used only on lightly-trafficked roads or for patching more-heavily-travelled ones.

In general, the choice of binder content of a macadam mixture is related to the prevailing traffic conditions. If the traffic is heavy, binder contents towards the lower ends of the ranges are selected in order to avoid the bleeding which would be likely to occur as the traffic further compacted the surfacing. If the traffic is light, then as much binder as possible is included, since in this case durability, and not stability, is the prime design consideration.

*Cold asphalt*　This material is a special type of coated macadam which is usually manufactured with slag as the aggregate, although limestone aggregate is also used.

Cold asphalt mixtures may contain bitumens of various grades, ranging from medium-curing cutbacks to refinery bitumens of high penetration. Cutbacks of low viscosity are used when it is necessary to stockpile the material or when it is desired to lay it cold in the roadway. Cold asphalts can be divided into fine cold asphalt mixtures—these have 75–100 per cent passing the 2.36 mm sieve—and coarse cold asphalt mixtures—which have only 40–60 per cent passing the 2.36 mm sieve. With both types, the amount of material passing the 75 $\mu$m sieve is small.

Cold asphalts are used primarily as thin wearing coats or for patching purposes. In the latter case, the fine cold asphalt has the particular advantage that it can be premixed and stockpiled for several weeks prior to being laid.

When first laid, cold asphalt wearing courses are not impervious to water, and hence they are not used over pavements which are likely to suffer damage as a result of the entry of water. In time, however, these surfacings become less permeable under the kneading compaction of traffic.

When fine cold asphalt is laid and compacted it has a sandpaper texture which is slippery to fast traffic—which is why it is customary to apply a surface dressing of pre-coated chippings to the running surfaces of these mixtures. With the coarse cold asphalt surfacings, the surface dressing is not necessary.

Although originally devised for cold laying, the majority of the above carpet mixtures are now used with penetration-grade bitumens which require that they be mixed, laid and compacted whilst warm. However, cutback grades are still produced for cold laying and depot storage.

## Manufacture and placement of premixed bituminous materials

### Manufacture

Bituminous materials for road surfacings are manufactured at a bituminous plant by drying and heating aggregates and mixing them with binder in carefully controlled proportions under carefully controlled temperature conditions. Developments in this area have been towards larger and more efficient units, and modern plants can be likened to factories with computer-controlled processes.

Two basic types of bituminous plant have emerged to meet the needs of the bituminous construction industry, viz. batch plants and continuous plants. Of these, the batch plant is the more commonly used in Britain.

**Batch plant**

These plants are intermittent in operation. As is illustrated in Fig. 7.4, the aggregates are fed from stockpiles into several storage bins or hoppers, each of which might contain up to 20 t of a particular single-size aggregate or mixture of sizes. When the plant is in operation, aggregate batches are taken from these storage bins in controlled amounts; proportioning of the separate sizes is achieved either by using volumetric proportions or by automatic weighing into small hoppers beneath each bin. These batches are then carried by conveyor belts into an oil/gas-fired rotating dryer where they are dried by cascading through the flame provided by the burner. The slope of the cylinder, its rotation speed, diameter, length, and the arrangement of the 'flights' (i.e. the longitudinal channels attached to the inside of the drum) control the length of the time required by the aggregate to pass

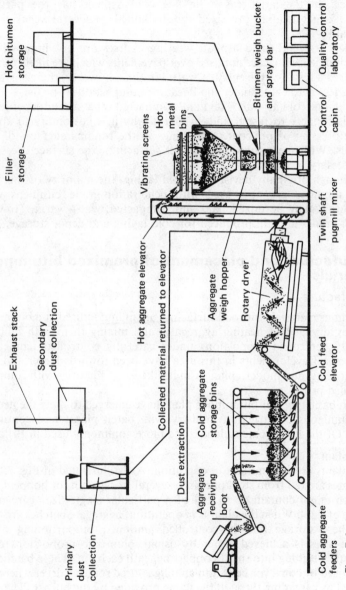

**Fig. 7.4** Layout of a typical batch plant used to manufacture bituminous materials

Hot bitumen storage

Filler storage

Bitumen weigh bucket and spray bar

Quality control laboratory

Hot metal bins

Vibrating screens

Control cabin

Twin shaft pugmill mixer

Hot aggregate elevator

Exhaust stack

Secondary dust collection

Collected material returned to elevator

Aggregate weigh hopper

Rotary dryer

Dust extraction

Cold feed elevator

Cold aggregate storage bins

Primary dust collection

Aggregate receiving boot

Cold aggregate feeders

through the dryer. The aggregates emerge from the dryer at a temperature somewhat higher than that which is required, i.e. to allow for cooling during further processing, and are carried to a set of screens (usually placed at the highest point in the plant) where they are again separated into different sized fractions and deposited into as many as six hot storage bins.

As material is required, a batch of perhaps 2 t or more is drawn off into a weigh hopper; this batch is made up of the exact proportions of the various sizes of aggregate and filler required by the mix design. The aggregate–filler mixture is discharged into a twin-shaft paddle or pugmill mixer, where the required amount of hot binder is added through a spray bar mounted in line with the paddle shafts and a thorough mixing is carried out. The mixed material is then discharged into a truck for direct transfer to the site, or transferred to heated, insulated storage bins for later usage.

The main advantage of a batch plant is its versatility. The plant structure can be erected and put into operation within a few days. It can use any type or combination of aggregates, and manufacture mixtures at high, medium or low temperatures. In addition, it can change relatively easily from manufacturing one bituminous material to another.

**Continuous plant**
These plants produce bituminous materials in a continuous process. One special type of continuous plant which has been introduced into Britain comparatively recently is the *drum mixing plant*.

The main feature of this process, which has been long established and proven in the USA [42, 43], is that the drying cylinder also serves as the mixer. With this type of manufacturing plant, the cold aggregate storage bins are fitted with highly-accurate proportioning devices which feed a continuous supply of correctly-graded aggregate and filler at a controlled rate into the dryer/mixer cylinder. Simultaneously, a binder metering device feeds hot binder into the drum at a controlled rate, so that the aggregate and filler are first dried and heated, and then mixed with the binder in one continuous operation. In contrast to batch mixing, the material is moved through the cylinder in the direction of the heating flame, so that it becomes hotter as it reaches the discharge point.

The main advantage of the continuous process is that high production runs of a mix material can be achieved at a lower cost than in a batch plant. The plant is also much simpler than the conventional batch plant in that the hot elevator, screens, hot bins, and pugmill mixer are dispensed with.

A disadvantage of this type of plant is that it requires hot 'surge' bins where the bituminous material can be stored for short periods of time after emerging from the dryer/mixer, to allow for intervals between truck movements. The use of large stockpiles of aggregate with consistent moisture contents is also necessary; furthermore, changing from one type of material to another entails considerable disruption.

## Laying

Bituminous materials can be laid by hand or by machine. Nowadays, however, hand-laying in developed countries is only used on construction projects where the use of machines is undesirable or impossible due to limited access or unsuitable foundations, e.g. footpaths, tennis courts, playgrounds. A large variety of machines are used to lay bituminous materials in highway pavements; these range from simple towed blade-scraper spreaders, through various types of mechanical mini-pavers, to large, automatic, floating-screed paving machines.

Figure 7.5 illustrates the basic operating principles of a modern, self-propelled paving machine, which combines the functions of spreading, levelling and partly compacting the bituminous mixtures. This paver consists of a tractor unit which drives the machine and spreads the material, and a screed unit which levels and partially compacts the bituminous mix.

The tractor unit travels either on large pneumatic tyres or on tracks. Pneumatic-tyred machines have the particular advantage that they can travel from site to site at relatively high speeds (up to 18 km/h), whilst tracked tractors are better for travelling on unbound or soft foundations which may be churned up by tyres.

A receiving hopper is mounted at the front of the tractor unit, into which feeder trucks from the manufacturing plant tip the mixed materials. A feeding arrangement then transfers the mix to the distributing augers. The floating screed unit is towed by the tractor unit. Mounted on this unit are a screed plate, tamper/vibrator, and heater.

Paving machines normally lay a 3 m width of bituminous material, but this can be reduced to 2 m with the aid of cutoff plates or increased to 5 m or more by fitting extensions. Recently developed pavers have hydraulically-extending screeds which can lay any width up to 4.25 m.

Levels are normally achieved with the aid of an automatic sensor working from the kerbline or a wire guideline or some other such reference. Stopping and starting result in bad levels—and hence in a poor final riding-quality of the surfacing—so it is important that the bituminous

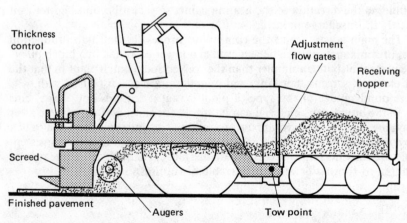

**Fig. 7.5**  Basic operating processes of a bituminous paving machine

laying operations are well planned and organized to ensure the continuity of laying necessary to achieve a high standard of finish. In this respect, the speed of the paving machine tends to be regulated by the rate of delivery of the materials from the manufacturing plant.

## Compaction

Compaction is the act of applying mechanical effort by means of rollers or other equipment to increase the density of a bituminous material[44]. The objective is to reduce the voids content and thereby enable the mechanical properties of the material to be fully realized[45]. The mechanical properties influenced by the state of compaction are as follows:

(1)  the stiffness modulus, which affects the load-spreading ability of the layer,
(2)  the fatigue properties, which give the number of repeated flexings that the layer can undergo before cracks are initiated and its service life affected,
(3)  the creep properties, which largely determine the resistance of the layer to shoving and rutting,
(4)  the durability properties of the mixture.

The British Standards and Department of Transport specifications which cover the laying and compaction of bituminous mixtures define the type and overall mass of roller to be used, limiting values of thickness of the compacted layers, and temperature limits for the delivery and compaction of the bituminous layers. Neither the number of rollers nor the number of passes is specified; rather the materials must be compacted to a specified density and thickness and, in the case of surfacing layers, to an acceptable surface regularity.

The time available for compaction is that which is taken by the binder to cool and stiffen to the point where its viscosity is such that it will absorb the applied compaction energy, without allowing the aggregate particles to move. In the case of bitumen, for example, this compaction cessation time normally occurs when viscosity increases to about 10–30 Pa-s[46]. Different binders achieve this cessation viscosity at different temperatures.

The important effect of compaction temperatures is reflected in Fig. 7.6. Note, for example, that the bitumen macadams rolled at 85 °C are far more difficult to compact than those at 130 °C. In all instances, the voids contents of the cooler materials are significantly higher than those for the corresponding hotter materials.

Whilst Fig. 7.6 indicates the trends to be expected when materials are compacted at different temperatures, it cannot be used to predict accurately the compaction obtained after a given number of roller passes. Factors such as the delivery temperature of the material on site, ambient air temperature, strength of the incident wind, layer thickness, and the intermittent nature of rolling complicate the relationship so that, in practice, much is left to the discretion of the engineer on site—and to the roller driver. As a consequence, the control mechanism quoted in the specifications is normally the minimum acceptable mix temperature at the completion of

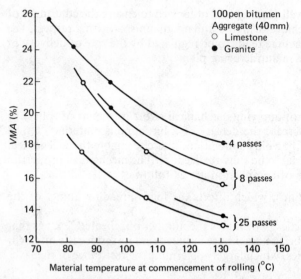

**Fig. 7.6** Variations of voids in the mineral aggregate with rolling temperatures, for dense bitumen macadam[47]

compaction, e.g. 85 °C for rolled asphalt mixes with 50 pen bitumen, based on a binder viscosity of approximately 30 Pa-s (300 poise)[48].

The adequacy of the density can be measured using the *Percentage Refusal Density* (*PRD*) test[21,49]. This test involves preparing samples in a standard mould, using a vibrating hammer to compact the bituminous mix material to 'refusal', i.e. no further compaction is deemed achievable after two minutes continuous compaction (with 2–10 s being taken for each compaction blow). The ratio of the average bulk density of core samples taken from the compacted surfacing to the average of the refusal densities as determined from the *PRD* test carried out on the material used in the surfacing, is termed the percentage refusal density value. A *PRD*-ratio of 0.93 is deemed acceptable for bituminous surfacing work in Britain.

**Equipment**
Bituminous materials are compacted by rollers which follow closely behind the paving machine. The types of compaction equipment used include steel-wheeled rollers (either static or vibratory), rubber-tyred rollers, or a combination.

*Static rollers*  Over the years, the traditionally accepted method of compacting bituminous materials in Britain has been to use deadweight rollers. The roller most commonly used is the 8–10 t three-point *steel-wheeled roller*. Tandem 8–10 t steel rollers are also quite common; as its name implies, this roller has only two rolls of similar size. Pneumatic-tyred rollers of the same mass are also widely used.

The importance of using large-diameter rolls and reducing drawbar pull is well established for steel-tyred rollers. A decrease in roll diameter causes an increase in lateral displacement, or pushing, ahead of the roller, which can result in decompaction of the mixture[44]; thus a large-diameter roll is preferable to a small-diameter one. The most desirable roller is one requiring the least drawbar pull—this is a measure of the horizontal force required to move a roller drum in a horizontal direction—and there is ample evidence to show that the only effective method of decreasing the drawbar pull is to increase the diameter of the roll. Rolling time using steel-wheeled rolls is also saved by using wide rolls in conjunction with large-diameter rolls.

The weight of the roller is transmitted to the mix through rolls and, consequently, the contact pressure should never exceed the supporting capability of the mix. As a general guide, heavier rollers can be used on harsher, more stable mixtures (especially for breakdown passes), whilst lighter rollers may have to be used on less stable mixes.

The strong point of a multi-wheeled *pneumatic-tyred roller* is the additional kneading action which results from its independently sprung wheels plus the action of the pneumatic tyres. In addition, it can travel at higher speeds than the steel-wheeled machines. As explained in respect of the steel-wheeled rollers, an increase in the diameter of the rolls reduces the decompaction effect ahead of the roller; in the case of a pneumatic roller, lowering the tyre pressure can achieve the same effect in minimizing decompaction.

Pneumatic-tyred rollers are able to achieve the same compaction as steel-wheeled rollers. In general, they are also able to provide a more tightly-knit, traffic-resistant surface; however, pneumatic rollers should not be used for the breakdown rolling of surface courses.

Whatever the type of equipment used, the bituminous material should normally be rolled in a longitudinal direction, starting at the sides and working gradually towards the middle. In the case of steel-wheeled rollers, the lateral overlap on successive passes should be at least one-half of the width of the rear roll; with pneumatic-tyred rollers, the overlap should be at least the nominal width of one tyre. As a general guide, the more passes the roller makes, the better the compaction achieved; in this respect, particular attention should be paid to achieving a high density in the critical nearside wheel path zone.

*Dynamic rollers*   Possibly the most controversial topic of technical conversation of recent years in the rolling world has been the use of vibrating rollers on bituminous materials. Vibratory rollers are widely used in the USA where the most important lesson learned has been that in order to use them effectively, the rollers have to fit the circumstances of the job[50,51]. All vibratory rollers do not fit all jobs, but many such rollers can be operated properly to fit many jobs.

Roller drum vibrations are produced by off-centre weights (eccentrics) on a spinning shaft. The speed of the shaft determines the frequency, i.e. the number of vibrations or downward impacts per minute. Frequency is defined as the number of cycles per minute, with one cycle being one full turn of the eccentric. As the shaft spins, the eccentric creates an outward force, and the faster it spins and/or the heavier it is and/or the further it is from the shaft, the greater the force. The higher the frequency used at any given roller speed, the smaller the impact spacing and the smoother the surface will be.

Amplitude is the greatest movement in one direction of a vibrating roller drum from an instantaneous 'at rest' position. For any given mass of drum, the heavier the eccentric and/or the further away it is from the shaft, the higher the amplitude will be.

Vibratory rollers can operate without vibration (static mode) or with vibration (dynamic mode). Those used for bituminous construction are self propelled; there are two basic models, however, viz. single-drum units and double-drum (tandem) units.

The general rule used in vibrating compaction is that the maximum total applied force should be applied which does not result in decompaction. If the mix material is very stable, compaction may be accomplished with both rolls (of a tandem roller) compacting; if the material is very unstable, or perhaps very hot, a number of static passes may be required before vibration can be applied. It should also be remembered that job conditions continually change whilst compaction is in progress, because the laid material becomes stronger and more stable as density increases and temperature decreases. Thus, when vibration is applied on subsequent passes, the frequency and amplitude may need to be changed for each pass in order to achieve the maximum increase in density without decompaction.

Exactly how to set frequency and amplitude cannot be stated, but general guidelines[50] are available, as follows.

(1)   When lifts are more than 50.8 mm thick, high amplitude and low frequency may be best. A heavy blow is needed to transmit force through a relatively large mass but should be applied at a low frequency to avoid decompaction caused by too much total force.
(2)   When the lift thickness is 50.8 mm or less, low amplitude and high frequency should normally be used. High amplitude should be avoided because a heavy blow will transmit through the carpet into the underlying material. If the underlying layers are weak, they will yield with resultant decompaction and surface roughness. If the underlying layers do not yield, the blow will reflect back to the surface with the same decompaction and roughness result, and perhaps roll chatter. High frequency is needed to provide enough total applied force and blows close enough to result in a smooth surface.

The travel speed of a vibratory roller is related to the frequency of vibration. If the travel speed is too high, the total applied force per unit area of carpet will be too low and satisfactory density, if at all achievable, will require too many passes. In addition, rough surfaces will be produced.

Two alternative empirical rules for controlling roller speed have been developed, as follows.

(1)   *The travel speed should be controlled so that the linear distance*

*between successive blows of the vibratory mechanism is equal to the depth of carpet.* For example, a frequency of 40 Hz working on a 38 mm carpet means that the roller speed should be $40 \times 38 = 1520$ mm/s (i.e. about 5.5 km/h). Experience suggests that this rule provides for practical travel speeds up to about 5 km/h; it should not be applied when the carpet thickness results in higher speeds.

(2) *The blows should be spaced 25.4 mm apart regardless of carpet thickness.* The roller speed in the above example would be $40 \times 25.4 = 1016$ mm/s (about 3.6 km/h) under this rule. Indications are that this rule, which was developed for thin overlay work, provides a practical roller speed for thin lifts, but it may not establish the maximum speed that could produce acceptable results.

The old rule, *roll as close behind laydown as possible while the carpet is hot,* is as applicable to vibratory rollers as to static rollers. Vibratory rollers can often operate at higher mix temperatures than static rollers because of their ability to adjust the total applied force to fit job conditions. As a result, it is possible to achieve the required density with fewer vibratory roller passes—and fewer passes require less rolling time and offer the potential of a more economical and less risky project.

Irrespective of whether a roller is of the dynamic or static variety, it should never be allowed to stand on a newly laid bituminous surfacing, as there is a risk that the surfacing will be deformed thereby.

# Surface treatments

'Surface treatment' is the general term used to describe work carried out to alter the qualities of a wearing surface, but which does not add appreciable thickness to it. While by far the most well-known type of surface treatment is that of *surface dressing*, other treatments which are also of importance are *sealing*, *priming* and *dust-laying*.

## Surface dressing

Laying a surface dressing normally consists of applying a thin film of bituminous binder to the surface of a roadway, footway or other trafficked area, distributing a thin layer of aggregate chippings upon the binder, and rolling the chippings to ensure their adhesion to the surface.

Surface dressings are used:

(1) to seal new or old surfacings against the ingress of water,
(2) to improve the skid-resistance properties of a surfacing,
(3) to arrest any disintegration which may already be taking place,
(4) to provide a clear demarcation between the carriageway and the shoulders,
(5) to improve the night visibility of bituminous surfacings.

Surface dressing is a long-established method used for the maintenance of over 40 000 km of the British road system every year. In relation to this usage, however, it must be emphasized that a surface dressing cannot restore the riding qualities of an already mis-shapen road, and to obtain good results the surfacing being treated must be sound, clean and have a uniform texture. A surface dressing is simply a thin layer of aggregate held by a film of binder and has no structural strength of its own.

Surface dressings are used successfully on all types of road, from very-lightly-travelled country lanes to motorways carrying many thousands of vehicles per day. They are applied to surfacings which range from those which are soft and rich in binder to those that are hard and stony. In addition, if it is necessary to protect the subgrade, subbase or roadbase from the effects of inclement weather during construction of a pavement, a surface dressing may be applied immediately after compaction of the appropriate layer.

When a surface dressing on a wearing course has a long and successful life, it is usually found that final failure occurs through the aggregate being worn away by the traffic; this may take as long as sixteen years, but it is more normally about five years. A surface dressing which fails prematurely does so either by 'scabbing'—i.e. early dislodgement of the stone from the dressing—or by 'bleeding' or 'fatting-up'—this occurs when the binder works its way up to the surface of the dressing. Thus the production of a good surface dressing consists primarily in designing to prevent scabbing or bleeding.

A considerable amount of research has been carried out worldwide into surface dressings, and the literature in this area is voluminous. In Britain, the art of surface dressing has been practised since the turn of the century, and accordingly historical experience combined with modern research has resulted in well-established principles and practices appropriate to the needs of the country (see, for example, references 52–56).

Surface dressing is a low-cost operation, and the process of specification development is simple and direct. The overall guiding principle in respect of design is that the size of chipping used at any particular site should be selected to offset the embedment produced by traffic forces in surfacings of different degrees of hardness.

The factors which determine whether scabbing or bleeding is likely to occur can be divided into the following three main groups.

(1) *External conditions*: hardness of pavement surface, traffic, and weather and time of year.

(2) *Properties of materials used*: (a) those pertaining to the aggregate chippings are type and strength, size and shape, and surface properties (i.e. texture, porosity, dryness and dustiness); (b) those pertaining to the binder are type and quality, and viscosity.

(3) *Method of application*: quantity or rate of spread of binder, quantity or rate of spread of chippings, mass and type of roller, and time interval before opening to traffic.

The following discussion relates to the influences which these factors have upon the quality of surface dressing work in Britain. The order in which they are taken into account in the development of design

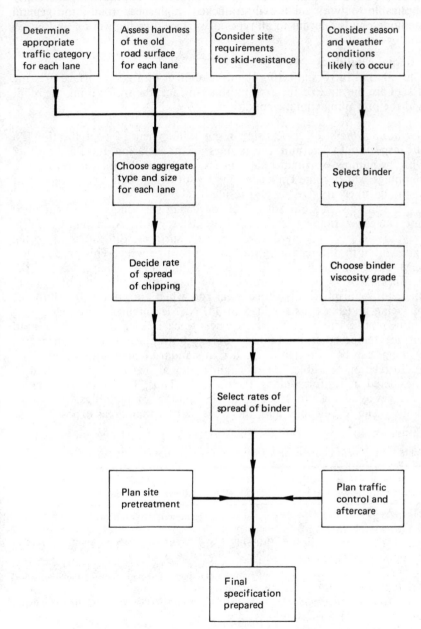

**Fig. 7.7** Flow diagram for the planning and specification of surface dressings[55]

specifications is summarized in Fig. 7.7. Whilst this approach is particularly applicable to work on heavily-trafficked, high-speed roads, the general methodology is relevant to all types of surface dressing work.

**External conditions**
The external factors affecting the development of a good surface dressing design are the state of the existing road surface, the traffic using the road, and the prevailing climatic conditions.

*Surface hardness*    A critical step in the development of a specification is a site inspection to determine the hardness of the surfacing. It is this, together with the number of commercial vehicles, which decides the extent to which chippings will become embedded in the surfacing, and hence the size of chippings likely to give the best results.

As can be seen from Table 7.11, pavement surfacings can be classified into categories ranging from very hard to very soft. Although it is fairly easy to identify very hard and very soft surfaces, difficulties are often experienced in differentiating the categories in between. This problem has been overcome with the aid of an instrument[57] which measures the hardness of a road by determining the depth of penetration of a 4 mm diameter hemispherically-ended steel rod when forced for 10 s into the surfacing under a constant load of 343 N. Measurements are made on a representative length of the inner-wheel track in each lane, and the road surface temperature is recorded during testing, so that the measured probings can be corrected to the design standard temperature of 30 °C.

In relation to Table 7.11, it might be noted that roads can seldom be considered as uniform along their length. Thus, for example, areas of carriageway shaded by trees or in the shadow of buildings, bridges or tunnels tend to be cooler and, therefore, harder than areas exposed to the

**Table 7.11**    Road surface hardness categories used in surface dressing design[55]

| Hardness category | Penetration at 30 °C (mm) | Classification of surface |
| --- | --- | --- |
| Very hard | 0–2 | Surfaces such as concrete or exceptionally lean bituminous mixtures with dry, stoney surfaces into which there will be negligible penetration of chippings under very heavy traffic |
| Hard | 2–5 | Surfaces containing some very hard bituminous mortar into which chippings will penetrate only slightly under heavy traffic |
| Normal | 5–8 | Surfaces into which chippings will penetrate moderately under heavy and medium traffic |
| Soft | 8–12 | Surfaces into which chippings will penetrate considerably under heavy and medium traffic |
| Very soft | > 12 | Surfaces into which even the largest chippings will be submerged under heavy traffic; such surfaces are usually rich in binder |

sun. Patched areas also are usually softer than the rest of the carriageway surface.

*Traffic*  A critical factor in the design of a specification is the volume of traffic the pavement is required to carry. Most important is the current number of commercial vehicles ( > 1.5 t) travelling in one direction in the lane under consideration, as it is these vehicles which contribute most to the embedment of chippings into the pavement surface. For surface dressing purposes, five categories of traffic are recognized in Britain, viz. 2000–4000, 1000–2000, 200–1000, 20–200, and < 20 commercial vehicles per day, with the heaviest volume classified as Category 1 and the lowest as Category 5.

It should be noted that the nearside, i.e. left-hand (in Britain), lane of both dual carriageways and three-lane roads usually carries the majority of commercial vehicles, whilst in urban streets parked vehicles tend to shift commercial traffic towards the centre of the road. Consequently, it is essential to prepare a separate specification for each lane of a multilane road.

*Season and weather*  A major function of the binder is to stick the chippings to the road surface. For proper adhesion to take place, therefore, it is best if surface dressing is carried out in fine warm weather—which in Britain generally means late spring and summer. Table 7.12 shows the binders recommended for use at particular times of the year and under particular traffic conditions; these are based on 'normal' temperatures for those times of the year. However, as British weather is notable for its vagaries, due consideration should be given to changing the binder in the event that the weather conditions at the site are significantly different from those expected.

As is discussed later, failure of a new surface dressing laid at the proper time of the year can occur as a result of rain falling during or soon after laying, so that the binder is displaced from the aggregate. This is particularly likely if the chippings are uncoated and damp, and the weather conditions do not encourage rapid drying. This problem can be minimized by the use of pre-coated chippings, or by the addition of one of a number of proprietary chemical compounds to the binder to improve its 'wetting'

**Table 7.12**  Binder viscosities recommended for use in surface dressing

| Traffic category | Period of year | Road tar[58] | Cutback bitumen[59] (s) | Tar–bitumen blends[60] (s) | Bitumen emulsions[61] |
|---|---|---|---|---|---|
| 1 | May to mid-July | S46 | 200 | 200 | — |
| 2 | May to mid-July | S46 | 200 | 200 | K1-70 |
| 3, 4, 5 | April, May and September | S34, S38 | 50, 100 | 100 ⎫ | A1-55, A1-60, K1-60, K1-70 |
| 3, 4, 5 | June to August | S38, S42 | 100, 200 | 200 ⎭ | |

properties. Correctly used in the proper proportions, these agents may promote adhesion between the chippings and the binder, even though the aggregate is damp and the weather conditions unsettled.

## Properties of materials

*Aggregate materials* Chippings used in surface dressing are controlled by British Standards[62, 63] and governmental specifications[21, 64].

The resistance to skidding of a surface dressing at low traffic speeds is primarily determined by the resistance to polishing of the chippings. Table 3.16 summarizes the polished-stone values that the chippings must meet in order to provide continued good resistance to skidding at particular locations and traffic intensities. At high traffic speeds, the macrostructure of the road surface becomes increasingly more important, and the value of a surface dressing in providing skid-resistance depends very much upon the way in which the chippings resist embedment in the road surface and abrasion by traffic.

If embedment is likely because of the soft nature of the surface and the intensity of traffic, then a large chipping must be used. Conversely, if the road surface is hard or the traffic is light, a small chipping is satisfactory. Figure 7.8 summarizes the manner in which these factors are taken into account in design. The use of a larger chipping than is necessary is both wrong in principle and uneconomical in practice; what should not be forgotten is that 100 per cent more stone is necessary when using a 14 mm chipping than when using a 6 mm one.

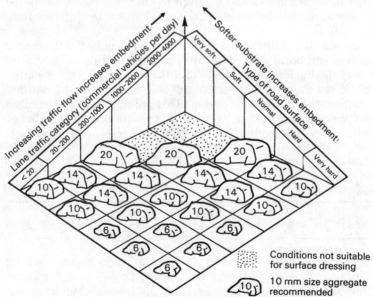

Conditions not suitable for surface dressing

10 mm size aggregate recommended

**Fig. 7.8** Nominal sizes of chippings used for surface dressings in Britain[55]

A further point to be noted about Fig. 7.8 is that only single-size chippings are recommended. Experience suggests that if the chippings contain a range of sizes, the smaller particles tend to prevent the larger ones from making contact with the binder film. Furthermore, if the chippings have an appreciable size range and segregation takes place, the smaller particles are likely to be almost entirely submerged in the binder layer, whilst the larger particles may only have a small depth of embedment when placed in the carriageway.

Whilst both slag and gravel aggregates are used for surface dressing work, hard igneous rock chippings are generally preferred because of their high resistance to both crushing and polishing. High crushing strengths are desirable because of the considerable stress imposed by the roller during the laying of the dressing and subsequently by traffic.

A chipping quality that is very important under heavy traffic is resistance to abrasion (see Chapter 3). The resistance to skidding of surface dressings placed on hard, unyielding concrete roads is particularly affected by the rate at which chippings wear under the action of traffic. For normal concrete roads, the recommendations in Fig. 7.8 for hard surfaces apply and chippings larger than 10 mm should not be used.

A major requirement for aggregate particles used as chippings is that they should not be flaky but should have angular shapes; this requirement means that gravel aggregates must normally be crushed beforehand. The roller and the traffic knead and orient the chippings so that they form a closely-knit interlocking mosaic which gives strength to the dressing; this effect is hard to achieve with flaky chippings. Furthermore, as flaky chippings tend to lie on their flat sides, they are not as deep as their nominal size would suggest; consequently, surface dressings with flaky chippings are likely to become smooth more quickly.

In order that the binder will adhere to the roadway and the chippings to the binder, both surfaces must be clean as well as dry. By their nature, chippings tend to be dusty and this prevents binder adhesion, the extent of which is dependent upon the amount of dust; for this reason also, soft aggregates should be avoided as they promote dusting.

The dust problem becomes most acute when the smaller sizes of chippings are used at low temperatures. This is best overcome by using chippings that are pre-coated with as thin a film of binder (usually 0.5–1.2 per cent by mass) as possible. In this way, surface dust is eliminated and rapid adhesion to the binder film is achieved even in wet weather or in conditions of high humidity. Correctly-coated chippings will separate from each other easily and flow readily through mechanical chipping spreaders; too-heavily-coated chippings will tend to bind together in warm weather and cannot then be applied mechanically.

*Binder materials* The binders used for surface dressing are road tar, cutback bitumen, bitumen emulsion, and tar–bitumen blends (see Table 7.12). A number of other modified binders are also available commercially, mainly under proprietary names for use in surface dressing; Table 7.13 gives

**Table 7.13**    Modified proprietary binders used in surface dressing[55]

| Basic binder | Modification | Where likely to be used |
|---|---|---|
| Cutback bitumen | Natural and synthetic rubbers | Single surface dressings on concrete |
| | Mineral fillers | All areas—often using heated chippings |
| | Various polymers (including ethene vinyl acetate and styrene–butadiene–styrene copolymer) | More-heavily-stressed sites (including urban) |
| Road tar | Various polymers (including polyvinylchloride and nitrile rubber) | More-heavily-stressed sites (including urban) |
| Bitumen emulsions | Natural rubber as latex | Important Category 3 roads (200–1000 commercial vehicles per lane per day) |
| Epoxy resins | Bitumen or road tar as extender | Most difficult sites (roundabouts, approaches to traffic lights, etc.) |

brief details of some of these materials, which generally are used at difficult sites.

Particularly notable in the past decade has been the growth in emulsion usage and, correspondingly, the decline in the use of other binders for surface dressing purposes. In 1985, the market shares in Britain were reported[56] as follows:

| | |
|---|---|
| bitumen emulsion (K1-70) | 57% |
| cutback bitumen | 19% |
| tar–bitumen blends | 15% |
| proprietary binders | 9% |

Note that the more expensive proprietary binders only account for about 9 per cent of the surface dressing activities. These binders, which are mainly applied to difficult sites, were divided between polymer emulsions (60 per cent), polymer cutbacks/tars (22 per cent), filled bitumen and high-penetration-index binders (15 per cent), and thermosetting epoxy binders (3 per cent).

Historically, the main advantage claimed for bitumen emulsions over conventional hot binders is that they can be applied to damp road surfaces; this has tended to extend the period during which surface dressing can take place and emulsions are often used in April and late September. Furthermore, emulsions do not require the use of scarce and expensive fluxing oils which are eventually lost to the atmosphere. The risk of fire during spraying operations is also much reduced with emulsions.

The principal considerations governing the choice of binder are, firstly, that when applied the adhesive must be sufficiently fluid to 'wet' the surface of the road and adhere to the chippings and, secondly, when cooled to road temperature—it takes only about two minutes for a hot binder to cool down—it must continue to adhere to the aggregates and hold them against dislodgement under traffic. The critical wetting viscosity and holding viscosity are clearly conflicting, so that the binder selected for any particular traffic conditions and temperature must represent a compromise between these two requirements. In Britain, this has resulted in the recommendations given in Table 7.12.

Note that, in general, heavy traffic volumes require binders of higher viscosity. The preferred binder for such traffic volumes is road tar—in the event of the binder rising to cover the applied chippings because of embedment, tar will tend to weather and wear rapidly at the surface, thereby re-exposing the aggregate and maintaining a skid-resistant surface. However, high-viscosity binders should not be used with uncoated chippings if the road surface temperature during application is likely to be below 18 °C for tar or 15 °C for cutback bitumen and tar–bitumen blends; in these circumstances, the use of lightly-coated chippings enables adhesion to take place more rapidly and there is less likelihood of dislodgement under traffic.

Tar has better 'wetting' properties than bitumen in the presence of moisture so that, in general, surface dressings which use tar are less vulnerable to wet weather failure than those which use cutback bitumen. Overall, however, cationic bitumen emulsions are superior to both and can be used in damp, unsettled conditions that would prohibit the use of other binders.

**Method of application**
The rate and uniformity of spread of binder are the most important controllable factors affecting the life of a surface dressing. A considerable amount of data has been collected regarding the rate of binder application, and this indicates that the correct rate of spread is primarily dependent upon the size and shape of the chippings and, to a lesser extent, upon the traffic intensity and the nature of the road surface.

The function of the binder is to bind the aggregate particles both to the road surface and to each other, while at the same time providing the chippings with the maximum possible support before the dislodging actions of traffic. This means that, since the chippings must first be embedded in the binder, their size is a major consideration; the depth of embedment must be sufficient to hold the particles in position but not so much that the aggregate will not remain proud and a slippery running surface is produced. There is a greater volume of voids present between rounded particles so gravel chippings require more binder to attain a given depth of embedment than do cubical particles of the same sieve size. Similarly, flat or flaky particles require less binder than do cubical ones. Once the aggregate particles are firmly embedded in the binder, the tendency is for them to be further pushed by the traffic into the surface of the road; the heavier the traffic and the softer the old road surface, the more this is likely to occur.

It is difficult to give exact criteria as to how to select the correct rate of spread for any particular surface, since such an assessment is still largely a matter of experience. For example, with old surfacings information regarding the rate of application of the binder may be best obtained by studying the old records for the road and assessing the performances of previous

**Table 7.14**    Target rates of spread of K1-70 cationic bitumen emulsion[55]

| | Number of commercial vehicles per lane per day | | | | | |
|---|---|---|---|---|---|---|
| | 200–1000 | | 20–200 | | < 20 | |
| Type of surface | Nominal size of chipping (mm) | Binder rate (l/m²) | Nominal size of chipping (mm) | Binder rate (l/m²) | Nominal size of chipping (mm) | Binder rate (l/m²) |
| Very hard | 6 | 1.3 | 6 | 1.5 | 6 | 1.6 |
| Hard | 10 | 1.3 | 6 | 1.3 | 6 | 1.4 |
| Normal | 10 | 1.3 | 10 | 1.3 | 6 | 1.3 |
| Soft | 14 | 1.2 | 14 | 1.3 | 10 | 1.3 |
| Very soft | 20 | 1.2 | 14 | 1.2 | 10 | 1.2 |

surface dressing applications. Some suggested rates of spread of hot applied cationic bitumen emulsion are given in Table 7.14; these target values, which apply to the midpoint of each lane traffic category range, should be increased by 0.1 litre/m² if the traffic volume is towards the lower end of the range.

A special problem arises in the case of an open-textured surface, e.g. a coarse-grade coated macadam may be hard and porous, whilst a newly-laid coarse asphalt may be soft and porous. Some of the binder will penetrate such porous surfaces and, unless allowance is made for this, insufficient will be left on the surface to hold the larger sizes of chippings. The usual practice in the case of any particular combination of lane traffic category and surface hardness is then to choose the rate of spread of binder as for an impervious surface, whilst the size of chipping is reduced to one size smaller than that given by Fig. 7.8.

To fulfil its function, the applied binder must fill all the voids in the lower half of the layer of chippings on the road surface, after rolling and compaction by traffic, when they have oriented themselves to lie with their least dimension vertical. The thickness of chippings applied must be therefore carefully selected and spread uniformly over the binder film. The rate at which chippings should be spread depends upon their size, shape and relative density, and the rates are normally selected from the ranges given in Table 7.15, bearing these points in mind.

British practice indicates that the most uniform application of the binder is obtained with the aid of mechanical tankers fitted with spray bars through

**Table 7.15**    Recommended rates of spread of chippings for surface dressing[55]

| Nominal size (mm) | Rate of application (kg/m²) |
|---|---|
| 6 | 7 ± 1 |
| 10 | 10 ± 1 |
| 14 | 13 ± 2 |
| 20 | 17 ± 2 |

which the binder is made to circulate at constant pressure and temperature. These spray bars have atomizing jets such that each jet makes a hollow cone of spray which overlaps others so that any one spot on the carriageway receives binder from four or five jets. There are British Standards[65, 66] which ensure the proper rates of application of binder from these machines.

Chippings should be applied uniformly in a single layer over the freshly sprayed binder film by a mechanical spreader fitted with a metering device which follows closely behind the sprayer. Self-propelled, forward-acting chipping spreaders operating at widths matched to the spray bar width are preferred to tail-board gritters for important work.

Immediately after the chippings have been laid on the binder film, they are rolled until a uniform, compact running surface is obtained. The roller has the dual function of pushing the chippings into the binder and then 'flattening' the layer so that it is less susceptible to dislocation by traffic. Best results are obtained by using a slow-moving rubber-tyred roller; unlike steel-wheeled rollers which tend to bridge low spots in the road surface, their multi-wheel action ensures that all chippings are pressed into the binder film after one or two passes so that maximum adhesion can occur. Repeated rolling with steel-wheeled rollers tends to crush chippings with loss of surface texture and increased risk of the surface dressing 'fatting-up'.

The success of a surface dressing, particularly if it is on a heavily-travelled road, is very much dependent upon the length of time before traffic is allowed on the new work, and then upon the control of traffic speeds during the initial phase of its life. In this respect, it should be kept in mind that a surface dressing is at its most vulnerable when newly laid. As roads are normally required to carry traffic immediately after being surface dressed, vehicle speeds should be restricted to 30 km/h or less until there is sufficient adhesion developed to ensure that the chippings are not dislodged; this normally takes 15–20 minutes in favourable weather, but, if it is humid or wet, the traffic control period may last for a number of days. For safety reasons[67] also, speeds should be controlled, and excess chippings removed by brushing or suction sweeping, early in the life of a surface dressing; this is particularly important when large-sized chippings are placed on heavily-trafficked, high-speed roads.

## Sealing

If a bituminous binder is applied in a thin film to a road surface in order to close the voids in the surface with the object of rendering it waterproof, the coating is called a sealing coat or a *mist spray*. Typically, seal coats are applied (in conjunction with a sparing quantity of fine grit) when road surfaces show early signs of fretting, or if macadam surfacings are unduly open-textured when laid. As such, a seal coat may be considered as a form of surface dressing.

Binders used for this purpose are road tar, cutback bitumen, tar–bitumen blends, or bitumen emulsions applied at the rate of 0.15–0.20 litre/m$^2$ for hot binders and 0.40–0.45 litre/m$^2$ for emulsions. A binding material normally consists of a fine aggregate of crushed rock, slag or sand containing not more than 15 per cent retained on the 6.3 mm sieve; it is applied at 5.0–7.0 kg/m$^2$, depending upon the texture of the surface. Rolling is not necessary, as the passage of vehicles is usually sufficient to work the coated grit into the voids in the road surface.

## Prime and tack coats

A *prime coat* is a film of binder—say a low-viscosity cutback bitumen spread at the rate of 0.4–1.0 litre/m$^2$—which is applied to a previously untreated porous layer so that it penetrates the top of the layer and is completely absorbed to a depth of at least 4–5 mm, leaving a matt, dry surface in about 24 h. Such coatings have a number of functions, of which by far the most important is to seal the porous layer and thereby aid in binding this layer to a superimposed one.

It is common practice to prepare a subgrade, subbase or roadbase and place over it a surface dressing which gives protection from the weather until completion of the pavement at a later time[68]; in this instance, the surface dressing binder would be applied directly to a dried prime coat, followed by the chippings as per the normal process. However, when a premixed surfacing is to be applied to a roadbase, it might be necessary to apply an additional tack coat to ensure interlayer adhesion, especially if the mix is of a dense type which has no large aggregate to give a mechanical 'key' with the roadbase.

A prime coat must be capable of wetting and penetrating the dust film of the layer being treated, coating the aggregate particles at the surface of the layer with a strongly adhering film of bituminous binder, and penetrating and sealing the top 5–10 mm of the layer. These requirements are best met if low-viscosity cutback bitumens or tars are used as the priming material[69]. Higher-viscosity materials are not suitable for coating a surface when dust is present, and they are only able to penetrate layers such as roadbases to a limited extent. Bitumen emulsions are not suitable as they will not penetrate densely-graded layers due to the speed with which the minute bitumen droplets coalesce to form a film on the surface of the layer.

A *tack coat* is a film of bituminous binder that is applied in order to assist in achieving adhesion between an existing surface and a new bituminous overlay or surfacing. A tack coat of bitumen emulsion is often used also as a curing membrane for cement-stabilized roadbases.

A tack coat is necessary in every case where doubt exists as to whether adequate adhesion can be obtained between a newly applied bituminous layer and an underlying one. It is commonly used when a new wearing course is to be placed on an old bituminous surfacing, or on a concrete pavement, or on a brick, stone or block pavement, as well as on a previously primed granular roadbase. It is normally unnecessary to apply a tack coat between two bituminous layers which are laid within a short time of each other; usually these are sufficiently plastic to interlock and there is sufficient binder at the interface to form a good bond. A tack coat can do more harm than good if applied where unnecessary or in too great a quantity, e.g. if extra tack coat binder is applied to a hot bituminous layer having a binder content already at the optimum for the mix.

It is essential that no traffic should be allowed to travel on a tack coat; thus, when carrying out work on an existing trafficked carriageway, only a limited length of the surface should be sprayed ahead of resurfacing operations. It is also undesirable for rain to fall on an uncovered tack coat.

## Dust-laying

As has been noted elsewhere in this text (see Chapter 5), a feature of many unimproved roads in newly-developing countries is the use of bituminous materials to abate the dust nuisance resulting from loose surface material. Bituminous materials used for this purpose might be low-viscosity cutback bitumens applied at the rate of $0.55-1.35$ litre/m$^2$ or, less preferably, crude oil or bunker-grade fuel oil, at heavier application rates.

The effectiveness of such treatments is governed mainly by the quantity of residual bitumen present in the binder used and, of course, by the application rate. On the whole, dust-laying cannot be considered as equivalent to priming, since loose material is being treated and the product is not durable. It is a palliative treatment with a limited life.

## Selected bibliography

(1) National Institute for Road Research, *Selection and Design of Hot-mix Asphalt Surfacings for Highways: TRH8*, Pretoria, SA, The Council for Scientific and Industrial Research, February 1978.

(2) Hitch LS and Russell RBC, Bituminous bases and surfacings for low-cost roads in the Middle East and other tropical areas, *Highways and Road Construction International*, 1977, **45**, No. 1806, pp. 5–10, and No. 1807, pp. 5–15.

(3) Ishai I and Craus J, Effect of the filler on aggregate–bitumen adhesion properties in bituminous mixtures, *Asphalt Paving Technology*, 1977, **46**, pp. 228–258.

(4) Edwards JM, Properties of bitumen–aggregate mixes, Lecture F in *Proceedings of the Residential Course in Flexible Pavements and Bituminous Surfacings*, Newcastle, The University of Newcastle-Upon-Tyne, September 1981.

(5) Vallerga BA, Pavement deficiencies related to asphalt durability, *Proc. Ass. Asphalt Paving Technologists*, 1981, **50**, pp. 483–491.

(6) *Open-graded Friction Courses for Highways*, NCHRP Synthesis of Highway Practice No. 49, Washington DC, The Transportation Research Board, 1978.

(7) Szatkowski WS and Brown JR, Design and performance of pervious wearing courses for roads in Britain, 1967–1976, *Highways and Road Construction International*, 1977, **44**, No. 1805, pp. 12–16.

(8) Garkabdm DG, *Rolling Noise and Vehicle Noise*, TRRL Report LR652, Crowthorne, Berks., The Transport and Road Research Laboratory, 1974.

(9) *Final Report of the Working Party on the Slippage of Rolled-asphalt Wearing Courses*, TRRL Report SR493, Crowthorne, Berks., The Transport and Road Research Laboratory, 1979.

(10) Kennedy CK and Lister NW, Experimental studies of slippage, in: *The Performance of Rolled Asphalt Road Surfacings*, pp. 31–56, London, The Institution of Civil Engineers, 1980.

(11) Balch IW and Touhey GJ, *Guide for the Design and Use of Asphaltic Concrete*, RRU Bulletin 31, Wellington, NZ, The National Roads Board, 1976.

(12) Hosking JR and Woodford GC, *Measurement of Skidding Resistance: Part 1, Guide to the Use of SCRIM*, TRRL Report LR737, Crowthorne, Berks., The Transport and Road Research Laboratory, 1976.

(13) Hawkes JR and Hosking JR, *British Arenaceous Rock for Skid-resistant Road Surfacings*, TRRL Report LR488, Crowthorne, Berks., The Transport and Road Research Laboratory, 1972.

(14) Hosking JR, *Aggregates for Skid-resistant Roads*, TRRL Report LR693, Crowthorne, Berks., The Transport and Road Research Laboratory, 1976.

(15) Salt GF, *Research on Skid-resistance at the Transport and Road Research Laboratory (1927–1977)*, TRRL Report SR340, Crowthorne, Berks., The Transport and Road Research Laboratory, 1977.

(16) Rhodes AH, Skidding and the road surface, Lecture S in the Proceedings as reference 4.

(17) Puzinauskas VP and Jester RN, *Design of Emulsified Asphalt Paving Mixtures*, NCHRP Report No. 29, Washington DC, The Transportation Research Board, 1983.

(18) Waller HF, Emulsion mix design methods: An overview, *Transportation Research Record 754*, pp. 1–9, Washington DC, The Transportation Research Board, 1980.

(19) Brien D, Research in the design of asphalt, *The Highway Engineer*, 1977, **24**, No. 10, pp. 14–21.

(20) Brien D, A design method for gap-graded asphalt mixes, *Shell Bitumen Review*, 1979, **56**, pp. 9–13.

(21) Department of Transport, *Specification for Highway Works*, London, HMSO, 1986 (6th edition).

(22) Hubbard P and Field J, A practical method for determining the relative stabilities of fine aggregate–asphalt paving mixes, *Proc. ASTM*, 1925, **25**, Part 2, pp. 335–348.

(23) Campden WH and Smith VR, A study of the Omaha Testing Laboratory's bearing index test for bituminous mixtures, *Proc. Ass. Asphalt Paving Technologists*, 1950, **19**, pp. 369–382.

(24) McLoughlin JF and Goetz WH, Comparison of the unconfined and Marshall test results, *Proc. Ass. Asphalt Paving Technologists*, 1952, **21**, pp. 203–236.

(25) Smith VR, Triaxial stability method for flexible pavement design, *Proc. Ass. Asphalt Paving Technologists*, 1949, **18**, pp. 63–94.

(26) Speer TL, Progress report on laboratory traffic tests of miniature bituminous highways, *Proc. Ass. Asphalt Paving Technologists*, 1960, **29**, pp. 316–361.

(27) *Mix Design Methods for Asphalt Concrete and Other Hot-mix Types*, Manual Series No. 2 (MS-2), College Park, Maryland, The Asphalt Institute, 1979.

(28) BS 598: Part 3: *Sampling and Examination of Bituminous Mixtures for Roads and Other Paved Areas: Methods for Design and Physical Testing*, London, The British Standards Institution, 1985.

(29) Livneh M and Shklarksy E, The splitting test for determination of bituminous concrete strength, *Proc. Ass. Asphalt Paving Technologists*, 1962, **31**, pp. 457–476.

(30) Lee AR and Rigden PJ, The use of mechanical tests in the design of bituminous road surfacing mixtures, Part 1: Dense tar surfacings, *J. Soc. Chem. Ind.*, 1945, **64**, No. 6, pp. 153–161.

(31) Campden WH, Smith VR, Erickson LG and Mertz LR, Factors that control asphalt content requirements of bituminous paving mixtures and a method for determining the proper asphalt content, *Proc. Ass. Asphalt Paving Technologists*, 1963, **32**, pp. 530–552.

(32) Weethan B and Hurlburt DW, The effect of asphalt viscosity on stability of asphalt paving mixtures, *Proc. Ass. Asphalt Paving Technologists*, 1947, **16**, pp. 249–263.

(33) Edwards JM, Design of bitumen–aggregate mixtures, Lecture H in the Proceedings as reference 4.

(34) BS 594: Part 1: *Hot Rolled Asphalt for Roads and Other Paved Areas: Specification for Constituent Materials and Asphalt Mixtures*, London, The British Standards Institution, 1985.

(35) Brown SF and Cooper KE, Hot rolled asphalt to BS 594: 1985—A commentary, *Highways and Transportation*, 1987, **34**, No. 1, pp. 29–30.

(36) *Spray Reducing Surfacings*, LF195: Issue 2, Crowthorne, Berks., The Transport and Road Research Laboratory, Undated (ca 1975).

(37) BS 1446: *Mastic Asphalt (Natural Rock Asphalt Fine Aggregate) For Roads and Footways*, London, The British Standards Institution, 1973.

(38) BS 1447: *Mastic Asphalt (Limestone Fine Aggregate) for Roads and Footways*, London, The British Standards Institution, 1973.

(39) BS 5273: *Dense Tar Surfacing for Roads and Other Paved Areas*, London, The British Standards Institution, 1985.

(40) BS 4987: *Coated Macadam for Roads and Other Paved Areas*, London, The British Standards Institution, 1973.

(41) *Technical Committee Report on Surface Characteristics to the XVII World Road Congress*, Paris, Permanent International Association of Road Congresses, 1983.

(42) Drum-mixed bituminous materials, *Highways and Road Construction International*, 1976, **44**, No. 1797, p. 10.

(43) *Asphalt Plant Manual*, Manual Series No. 3 (MS-3), College Park, Maryland, The Asphalt Institute, 1974 (4th edition).

(44) *State of the Art: Compaction of Asphalt Pavements*, Highway Research Board Special Report No. 131, Washington DC, 1972.

(45) Hills JF and Finey JT, The compaction of bituminous materials, *Civil Engineering*, 1976, Part 1 (April), pp. 46–51, and Part 2 (May), pp. 44–48.

(46) Rickards I, Asphalt compaction in cold weather, *Asphalt Review*, 1984, **3**, No. 2, pp. 4–7.

(47) Lister NW and Powell WD, *The Compaction of Bituminous Base and Base-course Material and Its Relation to Pavement Performance*, TRRL Report SR260, Crowthorne, Berks., The Transport and Road Research Laboratory, 1977.

(48) BS 594: Part 2: *Hot Rolled Asphalt for Roads and Other Paved Areas*: *Specification for the Transport, Laying and Compaction of Rolled Asphalt*, London, The British Standards Institution, 1985.

(49) Powell WD and Leech DE, Standard for Compaction of Dense Roadbase Macadams, TRRL Report SR717, Crowthorne, Berks., The Transport and Road Research Laboratory, 1982.

(50) *State of the Art: Vibratory Compaction of Asphalt Pavements*, Transportation Research Circular No. 242, Washington DC, The Transportation Research Board, April 1982.

(51) *Principles of Construction of Hot-mix Asphalt Pavements*, Manual Series No. 22 (MS-22), College Park, Maryland, The Asphalt Institute, 1983.

(52) Lee AR and Fudge GH, *The Technique of Surface Dressing with Tar*, London, British Road Tar Association, 1959.

(53) Wright N, *Recent Developments in Surface Dressing in the United Kingdom*, TRRL Report SR486, Crowthorne, Berks., The Transport and Road Research Laboratory, 1979.

(54) Nelson JR and Hardman R, *A Guide to Road Surface Dressing Practice*, TRRL Report SR627, Crowthorne, Berks., The Transport and Road Research Laboratory, 1980.

(55) Transport and Road Research Laboratory, *Recommendations for Surface Dressing*, Road Note 39, London, HMSO, 1981 (3rd edition).

(56) Heslop MFW and Elborn MJ, Surface treatment engineering, *The Highway Engineer*, 1986, **33**, No. 8/9, pp. 19–32.

(57) *Surface Dressing: Assessment of Road Surface Hardness*, TRRL Report SR573, Crowthorne, Berks., The Transport and Road Research Laboratory, 1980.

(58) BS 76: *Tars for Road Purposes*, London, The British Standards Institution, 1974.

(59) BS 3690: Part 1: *Bitumens for Building and Civil Engineering Purposes*, London, The British Standards Institution, 1982.

(60) BS 3690: Part 3: *Bitumens for Building and Civil Engineering Purposes*: *Specification for Bitumen Mixtures*, London, The British Standards Institution, 1983.

(61) BS 434: Part 1: *Bitumen Road Emulsions (Anionic and Cationic)*: *Specification for Bitumen Road Emulsions*, London, The British Standards Institution, 1984.

(62) BS 63: Part 2: *Single-sized Roadstone and Chippings*, London, The British Standards Institution, 1971.

(63) BS 1984: *Single-size Gravel Aggregate for Surface Treatment (Including Surface Dressing) on Roads*, London, The British Standards Institution, 1967.

(64) *Specification Requirements for Aggregate Properties and Texture Depth for Bituminous Surfacings to New Roads*, Technical Memorandum H16/76, London, The Department of Transport, 1976.

(65) BS 1707: *Hot Binder Distributors for Road Surface Dressing*, London, The British Standards Institution, 1980.

(66) BS 3136: Part 2: *Cold Emulsion Spraying Machines for Road: Metric Units*, London, The British Standards Institution, 1980.

(67) Wright N, *Surface Dressing: A Survey of Windscreen Damage*, TRRL Report

LR614, Crowthorne, Berks., The Transport and Road Research Laboratory, 1974.
(68) Road Research Laboratory, *Protection of Subgrades and Granular Sub-bases and Bases*, Road Note 17, London, HMSO, 1968.
(69) Guide on prime coats, tack coats and temporary surfacings for the protection of bases, in: *Surface Treatment*, Transportation Technology Support for Developing Countries Compendium 12, Text 2, Washington DC, The Transportation Research Board, 1980.

# 8
# Rigid pavements: design and construction

## General considerations

Rigid pavements are those which contain sufficient beam strength to be able to bridge over localized subgrade failures and areas of inadequate support. Thus, in contrast to flexible pavements, depressions which occur beneath properly designed and constructed rigid pavements are not reflected in their running surfaces.

While in theory it might be argued that pavements composed of many different types of material can be classified as 'rigid', in practice the only ones recognized as such are cement concrete pavements. There are three basic types of cement concrete construction, i.e. pavements which are: (a) jointed and unreinforced, (b) jointed and reinforced, and (c) continuously reinforced. In addition, prestressed concrete has been used in a limited number of highways.

Historically, concrete has been used in highway pavements in Britain for well over a century; it is reported[1] that the first documented example was of an access road to the Inverness freight yard in 1868. Nonetheless, and notwithstanding the establishment of a well-developed cement industry and the ready availability of suitable aggregates, concrete roads were slow to gain acceptance, e.g. in 1919, only a few kilometres existed in Britain, whilst 5000–6500 km were in use in the USA (where the first concrete road pavement was built at Bellefontaine, Ohio, in 1893).

In the 1950s and 1960s, the (then) Road Research Laboratory initiated a series of scientifically designed, full-scale concrete road experiments incorporating a wide range of design variables, and as a result greater interest was taken by engineers in this type of pavement.

In 1969, a major report[2] was released which concluded as follows (from pre-oil-crisis cost data).

(1)  Construction costs tended generally to be higher for concrete as compared with flexible pavements.
(2)  For rural motorway and arterial roads for which equal construction tenders were received, flexible pavements were still cheaper for the first twenty years when maintenance and associated traffic costs were taken into account, but concrete roads were cheaper after twenty years, e.g. by 2–10 per cent after fifty years.

The data in this report, combined with the Government's wish to conserve

**Table 8.1** Total trunk road construction in Britain[4]

| Type of road | Concrete (km) | Bituminous (km) |
| --- | --- | --- |
| Motorways | 270 | 1923 |
| Dual carriageways | 250 | 2200 |
| Single carriageways | 12 | 5400 |

resources and to ensure the viability of the concrete road industry, resulted in a policy decision being taken which required all major roadworks of length more than 1 km to be designed and put to tender in both rigid and flexible forms; the aim was to construct approximately 20 per cent of such major works in concrete every year.

In 1985, one study reported[3] that there appeared to be no outstanding differences in the costs of bituminous and concrete pavement construction, but that in the long term concrete roads appear to be cheaper even though initial costs tend to favour bituminous roads in most instances. In 1986, less than 6 per cent of the trunk road system had concrete pavements (see Table 8.1).

## Elements of a rigid pavement

As with flexible roads, the cross-section of a concrete road is composed of a pavement superimposed on the subgrade. With respect to the composition of the pavement, there are some differences in the literature in the nomenclature which is applied to the various layers. To avoid any misunderstanding, in this chapter the layer immediately below the concrete slab will be called the *subbase*, irrespective of whether it is part of a two- or three-layer rigid pavement system. Similarly, the layer immediately above this subbase will be called the concrete slab, again irrespective of whether it is part of a two- or three-layer system. When the concrete slab—the top of which is normally the running surface—is covered with a bituminous layer, this will be called a wearing course or surfacing.

## How concrete roads deteriorate

A rigid pavement may be distressed by a number of major mechanisms which can ultimately lead to its unserviceability, and it is the object of concrete pavement design to control these distress mechanisms. The following brief discussion regarding the main distress modes is based on an excellent review of concrete road design[5].

### Cracking

Cracking normally arises from over-stressing of the concrete due to traffic-induced or environmental stresses. Over-stressing due to traffic can arise from loads of excessive magnitude, fatigue, or loss of foundation support.

Cracks in concrete pavements have been classified by the Transport and Road Research Laboratory (in relation to its experimental road research) as hair, fine, medium, or wide. Hair cracks, which can be seen more clearly when the concrete is drying out after rain, do not detract from the performance of the pavement. Fine cracks can be defined as those up to 0.5 mm wide. Medium cracks are 0.5–1.3 mm wide; they are generally accompanied by the potential loss of aggregate across a fracture. Wide cracks are defined as those which exceed 1.3 mm in width; they are usually associated with a complete loss of aggregate interlock, and a failure of the steel in reinforced roads.

Cracking itself is not necessarily a direct cause of pavement failure, but it can lead to a number of problems. For example, water can enter the subbase and subgrade and lead to deformation and loss of support and, especially in colder climates, an accelerating rate of crack formation. Particles of debris can enter a crack and cause stress concentrations when the pavement flexes or the concrete expands; this encourages progressive spalling in the vicinity of the crack and affects riding quality. If the crack opens to the extent that the natural key transferring load is lost, *faulting* will occur, i.e. faulting occurs when the slab on one side of the crack is displaced relative to the other so that a step is caused in the riding surface.

It might be noted that internationally there has been a tendency to associate the failure of a concrete road with a fixed amount of cracking, e.g. 250–300 m of cracking per 100 m of road. The universal use of this definition of failure should be treated with caution, however, as it does not take into account the ability of reinforced thin slabs to accommodate a greater length of cracking before failure than reinforced thick slabs, e.g. research by the Transport and Road Research Laboratory showed that Alconbury Hill experimental slabs thicker than 152 mm failed before cracking reached the above level, whilst 127 mm thick slabs on the same highway had in excess of 380 m of cracking per 100 m and still remained in a serviceable condition.

## Joint failure

A pavement joint is sealed in order to prevent the entry of debris or water. If the seal fails, then pavement unserviceability can occur in the manner described for cracks.

If a formed or induced joint fails to transmit load by means of keys, dowels or particle interlock, faulting may occur and affect riding quality. If joint dowels do not effectively accommodate joint opening and closing movements, e.g. due to misaligned or jammed dowels, expansion movements can concentrate stress at the dowels and lead to spalling, whilst contraction movements can cause cracks.

If pavement expansion occurs which cannot be accommodated by the joint system, then two adjacent slabs may lock and lift at a joint. Known as *blow-up*, this is not normally a problem under British climatic conditions, provided that debris is not permitted to enter a joint.

## Pumping

By pumping is meant the forceful ejection of a mixture of water and subbase or subgrade materials from joints, cracks, and pavement edges during the passage of vehicles.

The process can be started by traffic-induced changes in pore-water pressure in a poorly-drained subgrade; this can lead to the creation of a space between the concrete and subbase, which then serves as a reservoir of water and accentuates the effect. Warping of the concrete due to differential shrinkage or temperature can also create the space within which the water may lie. If too much soil is removed, uniformity of support is lost and over-stressing of the concrete may occur. Pumping can also cause the deposition of fines beneath the approach slab, thereby leading to faulting.

## Loss of texture

Many accidents are caused by the low skid-resistance of carriageway surfaces. Concrete pavements have their surfaces textured in order to produce high skid-resistance. If unsatisfactory materials are used in the concrete, or poor construction materials are employed, the pavement surface will quickly suffer progressive loss of necessary texture under traffic, thereby creating a potential accident hazard.

# Subgrades and subbases

## Subgrades

The most important property of the subgrade in relation to concrete road design is whether or not it will provide *uniform* support for the slab. Water content and temperature are major climatic factors that influence the strength and deformation properties of a subgrade[6], and their detrimental effects are accentuated when the basement soils are not uniform. Accordingly, a first essential is to ensure that the water-table is lowered and/or prevented from rising to within 600 mm below the formation level, either by subgrade drainage or by raising the formation level at the design stage.

If the subgrade can be relied upon to provide uniform support throughout the life of the pavement, then the slab can often be laid directly on the prepared in situ soil and there is no need to construct a subbase. For example, surveys carried out in the late 1950s into the adequacies of 25–30-year old pavements showed[7] that they were generally in excellent condition where the highway profile stayed within a single soil horizon, i.e. where the subgrade was of good quality and naturally uniform; distress was largely limited to cut–fill transitions and other locations where there were abrupt changes in soil type, i.e. where subgrade support was not uniform and a well-designed transition zone was not provided.

Concrete used in highway construction normally has a high crushing strength, e.g. the target mean strength for pavement surface concrete of C40 grade is 48.2 N/mm$^2$ after twenty-eight days; this material has a significant beam strength. Its modulus of elasticity is correspondingly high,

**Table 8.2** Minimum thickness of subbase normally used in concrete pavements on subgrades of different strengths[8, 9]

| Subgrade *CBR* (%) | Minimum subbase (mm) |
| --- | --- |
| ⩽ 2 | 130* |
| > 2–4 | 180 |
| > 4–6 | 130 |
| > 6–15 | 80 |
| > 15 | 0 |

*On top of a capping layer of 280 mm; this layer should have a minimum *CBR*-value of 7 per cent, or 5 per cent above the normal subgrade *CBR*-value, whichever is the greater

which means that the concrete slab has a high degree of rigidity. By these properties of rigidity and beam strength, the wheel loads applied to a concrete pavement are distributed over a large area and so deflections are small and unit pressures on the subgrade are low. As a result, it has been concluded in Britain that subbases are not required on subgrades with *CBR*-values of 15 per cent or more (see Table 8.2).

If the subgrade is a gravel or sand that is well graded, can be compacted to a high density to give a good running surface for construction traffic, and is also frost resistant, a subbase will not normally be needed. Silt and clay subgrades generally require a subbase, as do chalk subgrades, except where construction traffic is minimal and some frost heave can be accepted. Surface irregularities in rock cuttings need to be regulated with lean concrete before placing the concrete slab; alternatively, if the surface is very irregular, it may be preferable to install a granular subbase as a regulating layer.

However, it cannot be too strongly emphasized that, notwithstanding the fact that the inherent strength of the subgrade plays a less important role in the design of a concrete road than it does in a flexible one, the old maxim 'a road is as good as its foundation' still holds for a rigid pavement. Thus adequate care must always be taken to ensure that the moisture and compaction conditions of the subgrade which are selected at the design stage are those which are likely to be experienced throughout the life of the pavement.

## Subbases

The *materials* used in a subbase may consist of granular materials, stabilized soils, or lean concrete. The range of granular materials includes naturally occurring sands and gravels, crushed stone or concrete, and industrial waste materials such as hard clinker, burnt colliery shale, spent oil shale, crushed slag, and pulverized fuel ashes. Such materials should have gradations which enable them to be compacted to a high density; when in this condition they should not be susceptible to shrinkage, swelling or loss of stability resulting from changes in moisture content. In addition, British practice is that all materials placed within 500 mm of the concrete slab should not normally have a soluble sulphate content greater than 2.5 g of sulphate (expressed as $SO_3$), whilst materials with more than 10 per cent passing the 75 $\mu$m sieve—these may be frost susceptible—must be stabilized if closer than 450 mm to the road surface.

The *surfaces* of subbases should be as regular as possible, for the following reasons[10]:

(1) to reduce the interlock and friction between the underside of the concrete slab and the top of the subbase, thereby promoting easier temperature movement and stress relief in the concrete slab,
(2) to assist in the construction of a slab of constant thickness and to lessen the need to make up to level with more expensive concrete materials, thereby contributing to the general economy of construction.

It is now normal practice to insert 125 $\mu$m of polythene sheeting as a *separation membrane* between the surface of the subbase and the bottom of the concrete slab. As well as reducing friction between the slab and the subbase when movements occur which are caused by temperature and/or moisture changes in the concrete slab, this waterproof membrane also prevents loose material on the surface of the subbase from becoming mixed into the bottom of the freshly-poured concrete and/or the loss of fine material from the concrete mix into a porous subbase. The only concrete pavement which does not use a membrane nowadays in its construction is a continuously reinforced concrete pavement; as is discussed elsewhere (see p. 273), this form of pavement design requires friction between the slab and the subbase.

As has been suggested above, the *function* of a subbase in a rigid pavement is not so much to increase the structural stability of the pavement as to counteract or correct unsatisfactory subgrade conditions which could lead to *non-uniform* support for the concrete slab, and eventual failure from fatigue. Whilst it can be shown that the tensile stress developed at the bottom of a slab by a moving wheel load can be 70 per cent greater when the pavement is on a weak subgrade as compared with a strong one, the fact is that substitution of the top of the weak subgrade by a stronger, unbound subbase has little influence on the stresses. For example, a gravel subbase 150 mm thick on a weak soil will reduce the tensile stress by only about 10 per cent in a thin slab and by less in a thicker slab[10].

Particular instances where subbases can be used to provide uniform, stable and permanent support for concrete slabs are when damage is anticipated from one or more of the following causes:

(1) frost action,
(2) poor drainage,
(3) mud-pumping,
(4) swell and shrinkage of high-volume-change soils,
(5) construction traffic.

## Preventing or minimizing frost action

Frost action in a soil can result in very severe differential heaving and softening of the subgrade, and this, in turn, can result in the break-up of the pavement (see also Chapters 4 and 6). Specific recommendations on how to deal with the frost-action problem with respect to concrete roads vary from country to country and from authority to authority. In general, it can be said that the only guaranteed solution to the frost-action problem is to remove the subgrade soil and replace it with a non-frost-susceptible subbase material to a depth equal to that of the frost-penetration below the road surface. Practically, however, it has been found that, because of the structural abilities of the concrete slab, it is very often sufficient to carry out subgrade removal and replacement to a depth equal to only about one-half of the frost-penetration into the subgrade.

As has been noted above, it is practice[10] in Britain to ensure that the water-table is at least 600 mm below the formation level beneath a concrete pavement. In addition, it is specified[11] that the total thickness of slab and subbase above a frost-susceptible subgrade should never be less than 450 mm.

Research work[12] has suggested that pavement damage caused by frost action in areas of severe winter climate can also be reduced by using a subbase material that provides both insulation and improved strength, viz. expanded polystyrene—concrete which is a form of lightweight concrete. The results of an analytical investigation have indicated that a 25 mm expanded polystyrene—concrete subbase is as effective as a 76 mm granular subbase in reducing subgrade frost-penetration.

**Improving drainage and minimizing the accumulation of water within the pavement**
Adequate subsurface drainage is another fundamental requirement for any road pavement (see also Chapters 2 and 6). Water which infiltrates through cracks and joints in a concrete slab, and which becomes trapped within the pavement, appears to be a major factor influencing the performance of many concrete pavements. It often results in the loss of uniform subgrade support and in pavement faulting due to the redistribution of subbase material[13].

A typical open crack or joint with an unfilled reservoir beneath can remove 70–97 per cent of the rainfall flowing across the pavement opening. One of the weakest parts of a pavement—shoulder system on a major road is the longitudinal joint formed between the concrete pavement and the adjoining bituminous-surfaced shoulder; indeed, leakage of water through this joint can lead not only to early cracking, settlement, and structural deterioration of the shoulder, but ultimately to cracking, transverse-joint faulting, spalling, and settlement of the pavement itself. Infiltrating water also contributes to frost heave in cold climates and to heave of expansive subgrade soils in both hot and cold regions.

A granular subbase designed to act as a drainage layer is essential whenever there is a danger of water accumulating within a pavement. Such drainage layers should extend through the shoulder to allow the water to escape. One proposal for a typical two-lane dual carriageway[14] is that a drainage blanket having a minimum permeability of 60–245 m per day will generally be able to provide for the drainage needs resulting from surface infiltration.

**Preventing mud-pumping at the joints, edges and cracks of pavements**
Pumping occurs with most severity on soils with high clay contents. It generally does not occur on natural subgrades or granular subbases with less than about 45 per cent smaller than 75 $\mu$m and a plasticity index of six or less[15].

Three factors must be present before pumping can occur. These are: (a) free water, (b) a soil that will go into suspension, and (c) frequent passage of heavy wheel loads. If any one of these three is missing, pumping will not occur.

The third factor emphasizes why soil-pumping can be expected on major concrete roads; it is a result of the frequent deflecting pumping action of the slab ends brought about by the heavy wheel loads which pass over the carriageway. The tendency of a slab to deflect and pumping to occur is minimized by limiting the number of expansion joints to as few as is absolutely necessary and substituting closely spaced and dowelled contraction joints.

Water which infiltrates through the pavement joints and cracks and along the edges of the pavement is invariably the source of the free water which causes pumping. If the subbase is poorly graded and the subgrade is not free draining, the soil will go into suspension where pockets of water are collected at void spaces in the subgrade, and it is this suspension which is ejected when the slab is deflected. Continued pavement deflection soon leads to the ejection of enough subgrade soil to leave the slab ends unsupported and extensive cracking will then occur. Thus pumping resulting from water entry is best minimized by ensuring that all pavement cracks and joints are adequately sealed against the infiltration of water, and that surface water is drained away over the shoulders as quickly as possible.

Finally, pumping can occur only if the subgrade soil is able to go into suspension in the water. This can be prevented either by chemically stabilizing the subgrade to an adequate depth or by providing a subbase composed of either densely-graded or open-graded materials. A densely-graded subbase is usually constructed in an undrained trench which is somewhat wider than the concrete pavement; to be successful, it must be graded and compacted so that it is practically impervious to water. If the gradation of the subbase is poorly designed, it will have a high moisture-holding capacity, while a lack of proper compaction will lead to pavement cracking at joints as a result of the traffic causing further compaction of the subbase. Open-graded subbases must also be properly compacted, but here the coarseness of the gradation must be such as to permit adequate drainage without itself becoming clogged by the intrusion of soil from the subgrade. As noted above (see also Chapters 2 and 6), this form of pumping-prevention entails constructing the subbase in such a way that it extends through the shoulders into shoulder drains or longitudinal pipe underdrains.

Table 6.20 shows the gradation requirements for unbound subbase material used in concrete roads in Britain. General American subbase requirements to prevent pumping are as follows: (a) the maximum aggregate size should not be more than one-third the thickness of the subbase, (b) the percentage passing the 75 $\mu$m sieve should not exceed 15 per cent, and (c) the liquid limit and plasticity index should not exceed 25 per cent and 6, respectively.

Internationally, there was a significant increase in the 1960s and 1970s in the number of countries using cement-bound subbases in concrete pavements to minimize the likelihood of pumping, particularly where the subgrade soils tend to be poor and high traffic intensities with heavy wheel loads are encountered [16, 17].

Cement-bound granular materials, especially lean concrete, are often used for subbase construction in Britain. The beneficial effects gained by so doing are illustrated in Fig. 8.4 (p. 571) and Table 8.3.

*Wet lean concrete* has also been used in recent years. Unlike dry lean concrete which must be roller compacted, wet lean concrete can be laid by a slip-form paver and, as a result, a better surface finish can be achieved. However, wet lean concrete requires a relatively high cement content to produce a strength similar to that of normal dry lean concrete, and it cracks more easily and more frequently [18]. Concern has been expressed at the use of wet lean concrete directly on top of fine-grained soils as the coincidence of subbase cracks with transverse joints might give rise to the possibility of subgrade pumping; however, it has been suggested [5] that subgrade stabilization might be an appropriate control against this possibility.

Current British practice, with respect to subbase thicknesses in concrete pavements, irrespective of whether the subbase material is cement bound or unbound, is summarized in Table 8.2.

It might be noted that the only major premature failure of a jointed concrete road identified in Britain took place by pumping as the result of saturation of a thin (80 mm), poorly-drained granular subbase con-

**Table 8.3**   Erodability of subbase materials under pumping action[18]

| Material | Cement content (%) | Mean erodability (g/minute) |
|---|---|---|
| Lean concrete | 2.2 | 57 |
| | 4.4 | 10 |
| | 6.6 | 6 |
| | 8.8 | 3 |
| Slag-bound | 20.0 | 168 |
| (Grave-laitier) | 20.0 | 193 |
| Treated silt | 7.0 | 350 |
| Cement-bound | 2.0 | 132 |
| (Grave-cement) | 3.0 | 30 |
| | 3.5 | 26 |
| | 4.0 | 12 |
| | 6.0 | 10 |
| | 9.0 | 98 |
| Graded-granular | 0.0 | 1231 |

taminated by subgrade material[18]. For the slab thickness, a life of about 40 million standard axles had been expected, whereas slab replacement was necessary after only a few msa.

Table 8.3 enables subbase materials to be classified in relation to their resistance to erodability by pumping action. It clearly demonstrates the superiority of strong cement-bound materials in respect of resistance to erosion.

### Minimizing volume changes

As has been described in Chapter 4, certain soils are highly susceptible to volume changes due to taking up moisture in wet weather and to giving up moisture in the dry season. Excessive differential shrink and swell of such soils can cause non-uniform subgrade support and, as a result, concrete pavements may become distorted enough to impair surface smoothness and riding quality. Conditions which may cause non-uniform and subsequent pavement warping are as follows[7].

(1) When expansive soils are compacted in too dry a condition, or when they are allowed to dry out prior to pavement construction, subsequent non-uniform expansion may cause high joints and loss or reversal of crown.
(2) When expansive soils are too wet prior to placing the pavement, subsequent non-uniform shrinkage may leave the slab edges unsupported, or may cause an objectionable increase in the pavement crown.
(3) When concrete pavements are placed on expansive soils that have widely varying moisture contents, subsequent shrink and swell may cause bumps, depressions or waves in the pavement surface.
(4) Similar waves may occur where there are abrupt changes in the volume-change capacities of the subgrade soils.

Partial design for combating a swelling subgrade may require chemical stabilization of the subgrade and/or the construction of a thick granular subbase, so that a sufficient thickness (and mass) of pavement is obtained which will both hold down the subgrade and act as a 'blanket' to absorb some of the expansion. Fortunately, the soil expansions and contractions which result in the development of rough riding surfaces are not common occurrences in Britain. They are most prevalent in arid, semi-arid and sub-humid regions of the world. However, objectionable distortion may also occur in more humid regions during periods of drought, during long, dry periods in summer months, or where subgrade soils are very expansive, i.e. where they have very high plasticity indices and very high liquid limits.

### Forming a working surface for construction traffic

A subbase is often utilized as a working surface by vehicles during the construction of a road. The construction used for this purpose should be a sufficient depth of either dense, well-compacted granular material or a chemically stabilized soil which is capable of withstanding the applied wheel stresses and protecting the subgrade from the detrimental actions of the weather. The usual practice is to increase the minimum subbase thickness to accommodate this usage, e.g. the thicknesses given in Table 8.2 include extra depths which provide for the use of heavy constructional equipment in the placement and compaction of the subbases. Should it be necessary to use a subbase to haul additional pavement materials about the site, then it may be necessary to make a further increase in the subbase thickness, especially in winter (see reference 19).

The capping layer of granular material (see Table 8.2) now recommended in Britain for use under subbases when the *CBR* of the subgrade at the time of construction is very low, minimizes the effect of variability in subgrade conditions and provides a working platform on which pavement construction can proceed with minimum interruptions from wet weather. It also provides a firm platform for compaction of the subbase and decreases the risk of damage during construction to any upper foundation layer of cement-bound materials. The extra capping layer surcharge also lessens the possibility of a reduction in the strength of the subgrade during construction in wet weather, and hence ensures a higher equilibrium strength.

## Concrete

Cement concrete is a mixture of cement, coarse aggregate, fine aggregate and water which is combined into a solid mass as a result of the chemical reaction which takes place between the water and the cement. In many ways, concrete is an excellent material for a highway pavement. As a consequence of its high-strength qualities, it can withstand heavy wheel loads and high tyre pressures. Well-designed and well-made concrete roads are known to last for at least forty years and need relatively little maintenance.

### Materials

The ingredients of a concrete mixture are cement, aggregate and water. These materials, and the chemical reaction which occurs when cement is hydrated, have been described elsewhere (see Chapter 3), and so this discussion is confined to emphasizing factors basic to the design and construction of a concrete pavement in Britain.

### Cement

Ordinary Portland cement is the binding material most often used in concrete road slabs. However, Portland blastfurnace cement may be necessary if a concrete slab is to be laid on a pulverized fuel ash or other subbase material containing soluble sulphates, as the separation membrane cannot be relied upon to afford protection against sulphate attack under these circumstances. In areas where the soil or groundwater contains soluble sulphates, the concentration of the sulphates in the upper layers of the soil is normally insufficient to cause damage to a concrete slab with ordinary Portland cement as they generally leach downwards[6]; however, where the road is provided in cutting, sulphate-resisting cement may need to be provided in the concrete slab if adequate intercepting drains are not installed.

In certain instances, as for example for aesthetic reasons or where it is desired to define a particular traffic lane, 'coloured' cements are utilized. These are made by mixing pigments with a white cement made from kaoline and chalk.

*Strength* The strength of the hardened concrete is the property which is of primary importance in the construction of a rigid pavement, and it is therefore tightly controlled. Grade C40 concrete[20] is normally specified in Britain[21] for use in unreinforced concrete, jointed reinforced concrete, and continuously reinforced concrete pavements. Each cubic metre of fully-compacted concrete must contain either 320 kg of ordinary Portland cement, or 340 kg of Portland blastfurnace cement, Portland pulverized fuel ash cement, or ordinary Portland cement blended with ground granulated blastfurnace slag or pulverized fuel ash. If a blend of ordinary Portland cement and pfa is used, the minimum permitted cement content is 220 kg/m$^3$ and the proportion of pfa by mass to the total cement must lie between 15 and 35 per cent. In the case of a cement-ground granulated blastfurnace slag blend, the maximum proportion of ground slag cannot exceed 50 per cent of the cement and slag combination.

During concrete production, inevitable and sometimes considerable variations can be obtained in the measured strength of a concrete mix. These result from variations in: (a) the quality of the materials used, e.g. different deliveries of cement may vary or the grading or particle shape of aggregate batches may differ, (b) the mix proportions associated with the batching process, and (c) sampling, making, curing and testing of the mix. Consequently, the mix must be designed to have a considerably higher mean strength than that which might normally be specified. This higher strength is called the *target mean strength*, whilst the specified strength is called the *characteristic strength*.

The characteristic strength is not a minimum strength. Rather, it is the strength below which a specified proportion of the test results—often called 'defectives'—may statistically be expected to fall.

The difference between the target mean strength and the characteristic strength of a conventional concrete mix is termed the 'margin'. Thus

$$f_m = f_c + ks$$

where $f_m$ = target mean strength, $f_c$ = specified characteristic strength, $k$ = a constant, and $s$ = standard deviation. The product $ks$ is the margin. The constant $k$ is derived from the mathematics of the normal distribution and increases as the proportion of defectives is decreased (see Table 8.4).

**Table 8.4** Relationship between the $k$-value used in margin calculations, and the proportion of defective strength tests

| Percentage of defectives | $k$ |
| --- | --- |
| 1.0 | 2.33 |
| 2.5 | 1.96 |
| 5.0 | 1.64 |
| 10.0 | 1.28 |

Thus, assuming a standard deviation of 5 N/mm$^2$, the normal target mean strength for pavement surface concrete of grade C40 is

$$f_m = 40 + 1.64 \times 5 = 48.2 \text{ N/mm}^2$$

Note that whilst there are several forms of strength test, the current British specifications[21] call for the use of the 150 mm cube compression test for the quality control strength testing of concrete.

**Aggregates**

Since mineral aggregates form roughly 80 per cent of the mass of a normal concrete slab, it follows that aggregate quality is of considerable importance in concrete road-making. Fortunately, however, good concrete can be made with most aggregates, even though they be of different mineralogical composition, and results are less dependent upon the type of aggregate than upon the grading, size and shape of the particles. Good-quality aggregates are free from coatings of clay or organic impurities which may prevent the full bond from being developed between the particles and the cement paste. In addition, good aggregates are essentially non-absorbent when in water and do not contain ingredients that are liable to decompose or change in volume from exposure to the atmosphere.

Experience has shown that limestone fine aggregate polishes quickly under traffic and consequently it is not recommended[10] for use in the running surfaces of concrete pavements. The coarse aggregate in a concrete mix does not have such a significant effect upon skid-resistance and therefore limestone coarse aggregate can be used, provided that the concrete produced meets minimum accelerated wearing criteria[21].

Whilst most aggregates used in concrete pavements are from natural sources[22], aircooled blastfurnace slag[23] is another material which is sometimes used. Irrespective of whether they are natural or artificial materials, aggregates used in concrete road-making are usually classified as coarse or fine. Coarse aggregate is composed of particles which are retained on the 5 mm sieve. Natural sand, crushed gravel or crushed stone which passes the 5 mm sieve is called fine aggregate or, simply, sand. The ratio of fine to coarse aggregate which is used in any mixture is dependent upon the individual gradations and upon the desired gradation of the combined materials.

As a general rule, the largest size of aggregate used in a mix should not exceed one-quarter of the thickness of the slab if the best combination of strength and workability is to be obtained. In practice, the maximum sizes which are most often used in concrete mixes in Britain are either 40 or 20 mm, with the smaller size being used with the thinner reinforced slabs. Whilst larger sizes can result in a reduced cement content in order to achieve a given strength, they give rise to construction problems at joints in the pavement.

For a given maximum size of aggregate, there is no such thing as an 'ideal' gradation which will satisfy all desirable criteria. For example, the most suitable proportion of fine aggregate to be used for a particular cement to aggregate ratio depends upon the actual grading of the fine aggregate, and the particle shape and the surface texture of both the fine and coarse aggregates. The aggregate gradations which are perhaps most widely used in Britain are shown in Tables 8.5 and 8.6.

**Table 8.5** Aggregate gradations used in concrete, percentage by mass passing BS sieves[22]: (a) coarse aggregate and (b) fine aggregate

| BS sieve size (mm) | Nominal size of graded aggregate (mm) | | | Nominal size of single-sized aggregate (mm) | | | |
|---|---|---|---|---|---|---|---|
| | 40–5 | 20–5 | 14–5 | 40 | 20 | 14 | 10 |
| 50 | 100 | – | – | 100 | – | – | – |
| 37.5 | 90–100 | 100 | – | 85–100 | 100 | – | – |
| 20 | 35–70 | 90–100 | 100 | 0–25 | 85–100 | 100 | – |
| 14 | – | – | 90–100 | – | – | 85–100 | 100 |
| 10 | 10–40 | 30–60 | 50–85 | 0–5 | 0–25 | 0–50 | 85–100 |
| 5 | 0–5 | 0–10 | 0–10 | – | 0–5 | 0–10 | 0–25 |
| 2.36 | – | – | – | – | – | – | 0–5 |

(a)

| BS sieve size (mm) | Overall limits |
|---|---|
| 10 | 100 |
| 5 | 89–100 |
| 2.36 | 60–100 |
| 1.18 | 30–100 |
| 0.600 | 15–100 |
| 0.300 | 5–70 |
| 0.150 | 0–15 |

(b)

**Table 8.6** All-in aggregate gradations used in concrete, percentage by mass passing BS sieves[22]

| BS sieve size (mm) | Nominal size (mm) | | |
|---|---|---|---|
| | 40 | 20 | 10 |
| 50 | 100 | – | – |
| 37.5 | 95–100 | 100 | – |
| 20 | 45–80 | 95–100 | – |
| 14 | – | – | 100 |
| 10 | – | – | 95–100 |
| 5 | 25–50 | 35–55 | 30–65 |
| 2.36 | – | – | 20–50 |
| 1.18 | – | – | 15–40 |
| 0.600 | 8–30 | 10–35 | 10–30 |
| 0.300 | – | – | 5–15 |
| 0.150 | 0–8 | 0–8 | 0–8 |

When the material used is crushed rock fines, the percentage of fine aggregate passing the 150 $\mu$m sieve can be increased to 20 per cent in Table 8.5 and to 10 per cent (all nominal sizes) in Table 8.6. The term 'all-in' aggregate used in Table 8.6 refers to aggregate consisting of a mixture of coarse and fine aggregate; it may be produced without separating into coarse and fine fractions, or it may be produced by combining coarse and fine fractions.

Coarse aggregate used in concrete pavement surface mixes normally has a *10 per cent fines* value of not less than 100 kN or, alternatively, an *aggregate impact* value of not more than 30 per cent. In the case of C20 to C35 concrete, the *flakiness index* should not exceed 50 for uncrushed gravel and 35 for crushed rock or crushed gravel; for concrete grades greater than C35, the flakiness index should not exceed 35 for either uncrushed gravel, crushed gravel, or crushed rock.

The proportion of fine aggregate used in a mix with a particular cement to aggregate ratio depends upon the actual fine aggregate grading used and the particle shape and surface texture of both the fine and coarse aggregates—and upon the paving plant to be utilized. For example, a typical sand content for a slip-form paving train is about 40 per cent, i.e. slip-form pavers apply less vibration to the surface of the concrete than fixed-form pavers and therefore require more fine material in the mix in order to get a good surface texture.

**Water**

The third ingredient of a concrete mixture is water. In most instances, specifications simply prescribe that the water should be potable. This requirement is normally sufficient to ensure that the water does not contain any impurities that will be detrimental to the quality of the cement paste.

**Additives**

In many instances, a fourth ingredient is added to a concrete mix for one of the following reasons:

(1)  to improve the workability of a relatively dry concrete mixture—this is a rare usage in concrete roadworks,
(2)  to increase the heat of hydration during setting so that the concrete can be mixed and placed at lower temperatures than are normally possible,
(3)  to decrease the susceptibility of the hardened concrete to frost action, de-icing salts, and/or bleeding, e.g. the current specifications covering the construction of roads[21] contain a mandatory requirement that at least the top 50 mm of a concrete slab in a pavement should be air entrained—this involves the addition of an air-entraining agent to the concrete.

*Accelerating agents*  The main advantage of these additives is that they reduce the setting time of cement and/or increase the rate of strength development so that higher early (and ultimate) strengths are achieved; as such, they are particularly useful in maintaining construction schedules during cold weather. Under normal conditions, they permit the early removal of concrete formwork and, generally, enable earlier project completion.

Until recently, most strength accelerators were based on formulations of calcium chloride. However, the use of these agents has now been banned in Britain in any concrete containing metal reinforcement, because of the corrosion effects associated with chloride. Whilst calcium chloride accelerators are still used with unreinforced concrete, they have now generally been replaced by chloride-free agents such as calcium formate in reinforced concrete[24].

Although the exact mechanisms by which both calcium chloride and calcium formate increase early strength is not yet fully understood, it is known that they increase the rate of hydration of the different chemical constituents in the cement. Whatever the type used, mixes containing accelerating agents must still be protected from frost during the early stages of setting, i.e. until strength has reached approximately 5 $N/mm^2$.

*Air-entraining agents*  If a wet concrete mixture is placed in the roadway, the coarse particles are liable to settle, with the result that there is a tendency for a layer of mortar to accumulate at the surface during compaction. This process, known as 'bleeding', can result in the surface-layer mixture having a high water to cement ratio which gives poor resistance to abrasion. If freezing temperatures occur, the surface layer is particularly liable to be attacked by frost action. This is made worse by the deleterious actions of the de-icing agents used in cold weather to keep the road surface safe for traffic.

The term 'air-entraining agent' is used to describe proprietary products which have the prime function of entraining air into a concrete mix to give it improved resistance to the otherwise deleterious effects of frost and de-icing salts. The addition of an air-entraining agent, e.g. rosin or vinsol resin, results in the concrete being intermixed with countless numbers of uniformly distributed, tiny air-bubbles which provide sufficient buoyancy to retard the settling of the coarse particles. After the concrete has hardened, it retains these tiny bubbles, with the result that they can act as 'expansion chambers' which help to relieve the hydraulic pressure developed in capillaries in the concrete in the initial stages of freezing. As freezing proceeds, the cavities limit the growth of microscopic bodies of ice, and thus protect the thin 'shells' of concrete surrounding them. The thickness of the shells between adjacent air voids (bubble spacing is critical) should be less than 0.25 mm and possibly as low as 0.05 mm. Bubbles should be as small as possible—they are usually 0.05–1.25 mm—so that the total volume of entrained air is low and any consequent strength losses are minimized.

In summary, it can be said that the purpose of air-entrainment in concrete is to reduce permeability and frost damage. Air-entraining agents also have a plasticizing effect.

Air-entrained concrete is more workable than ordinary concrete and is less subject to segregation and bleeding; these changes are the result of the ability of the air-bubbles to bear short-term loads, to interrupt the movement of bleeding water to the surface, to buoy up the solids, and to change the effective viscosity of the cement paste. Edge and joint deterioration are reduced where air-entrained concrete is used. Of particular importance is the contribution which air-entrainment makes to the resistance to freezing and thawing (especially when such exposure is aggravated by the use of ice-removal salts); it has tended to increase the useful service life of a rigid pavement by a significant factor.   .

Whilst the advantages associated with air-entraining by far outweigh the disadvantages, it must be pointed out that the entrainment of air does result in a reduction in strength and, consequently, in a reduction in such properties as abrasion resistance, elasticity, and bond strength to steel, as compared with ordinary concrete. A general rule-of-thumb is that a 5 per cent loss in compressive strength [24, 25] or a 4 per cent loss in indirect tensile strength [26] will result from each 1 per cent by volume of air entrained in the mix.

Due to the increased plasticity imparted by the entrained air, it is usually possible to reproportion concrete mixtures using lower water and sand contents at constant slump, so as to ensure that the strength reduction is minimal. In general, however, air-entrained concrete requires a slightly higher cement content than a non-air-entrained one for a given strength to be achieved; this particularly applies to mixes of high air content, high cement content, and large maximum size aggregate.

The amount of air required in order to give complete protection to concrete for the climatic conditions normally experienced in Britain is usually quite small, e.g. it is usually specified [21] that the total quality of air in air-entrained concrete shall be 5 and 4 + per cent by volume of the mix when the nominal aggregate sizes are 20 and 40 mm, respectively.

## Design of mixes

Before construction of a concrete road can begin, it is necessary to determine what proportions of cement, water, and aggregate (and air-entraining agent) should be present in the mixture. This is known as the mix design.

There are a number of different methods for 'designing' mixes, all of which have either directly or indirectly the ultimate aim of obtaining a concrete of the desired strength and workability at the lowest cost. Another characteristic which all the methods have in common is that, even though the selection of the initial combination may be based on well-tried data obtained from previous experience, the ultimate design is always a result of extensive trial mixes which are tested at the site.

Before commenting briefly upon concrete mix design as it is practised in Britain, it is appropriate to comment upon what is probably the most important concept in concrete engineering, viz. the relationship between the water to cement ratio and strength.

The water to cement ratio 'law' was formulated by Abrams nearly seventy years ago [27]. Essentially, Abrams stated that for a combination of cement and conventional aggregates in *workable* mixtures, under similar conditions of placement, curing and test, the strength of concrete is solely a function of the ratio of cement to the free water in the plastic mixture. When the water to cement ratio is too low, then the mixture is too dry to be compactable and, as shown in Fig. 8.1(a), this can result in low strengths. The peak point on the curve can be visualized as occurring where the concrete mix is just sufficiently workable to obtain near-complete compaction with the maximum energy which can be applied. As the water to cement ratio is increased beyond the peak value, the strength begins to fall, but the

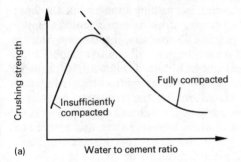

(a)

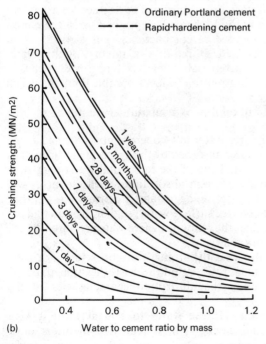

(b)

**Fig. 8.1**   Water to cement ratio versus strength: (a) basic concept and (b) actual relationships with 100 mm fully-compacted cubes

rate of decrease is less than that experienced for uncompacted conditions. It is here that the water to cement ratio law begins to operate, and it is seen that as the ratio is increased, the strengths obtained are decreased. Note, however, that because of the excess water, the mixtures are very workable and full compaction can always be obtained.

It is the right-hand side of the curve, i.e. the part which follows Abrams' law, in which the concrete engineer is most interested. Ideally, the engineer wants to utilize water to cement ratios which are neither too wet nor too dry but which result in strength values as close to the peak as is consistent with workability requirements. A very wet mix, while very easy to compact, results not only in a substantial reduction in crushing strength but also has a higher shrinkage factor, is subject to greater moisture movement in the slab, and is more susceptible to attack by frost. Conversely, if too low a water to cement ratio is used, then the mixture will be very difficult to compact and a smooth, sealed running surface may not be obtained. Figure 8.1(b) shows a family of curves of water to cement ratio versus strength which are based on normal concrete measurements carried out by the Transport and Road Research Laboratory. The water content of the water to cement ratio is the free-water content of the mixture, i.e. the moisture over and above that absorbed by the aggregate.

In the discussion so far, free use has been made of the term 'workability'. This is a term which is easily understood but is relatively hard to define. Perhaps the easiest way to do so is to say that the more workable a mix, the less work is required to compact it fully. The degree of workability required of the concrete on any road scheme is dependent upon the nature of the construction and the method of compaction. Thus a road slab in which mesh reinforcement is utilized requires a mixture with greater workability than a plain mass concrete slab, while a concrete mix which is to be compacted by mechanical vibration can be less workable than one which is to be tamped by hand.

Factors which affect the workability of a mixture are as follows.

(1)   *Free-water content*   The free water in a concrete mix is defined as the total water in the mix less the water absorbed by the aggregate to bring it to a saturated surface-dry condition. Thus, if the same total water content is used with dry aggregates having different absorptions, then the mixes will have different workabilities. In practice, aggregates are often wet, i.e. they contain both absorbed water and free surface water, so that the water added at the mixer is normally less than the amount of free water required by the mix to achieve a specified workability.

It might be noted here also that the strength of concrete is normally related to the free water to cement ratio, as on this basis the strength of the concrete does not depend upon the absorption characteristics of the aggregates.

(2)   *Cement to aggregate ratio*   If the water to cement ratio is kept constant, a rich mix, i.e. one having a high cement content, is more workable than a lean mix.

(3)   *Shape, size and grading of the aggregate*   The effects of these factors

can be observed by noting the results of adding aggregate to a neat cement paste of a particular water to cement ratio. It is found that the smaller the surface area of the added material in relation to the given quantity of cement, the greater is the workability, since more water is available to wet the surfaces of the particles; thus a concrete mix having smooth, rounded aggregate particles is more workable than one having crushed, rough, angular particles of a similar grading. Flaky aggregates result in the harshest and least workable concrete mixes. Workability also increases as the maximum size of the aggregate is increased. A corollary to this is that for a given degree of workability, the fines content of a mixture may be reduced as the maximum size of the aggregate is increased. In general, the better graded a mix, the more workable it is; this effect is more noticeable as the mix gets leaner.

Unfortunately, at this time there is no single test which is universally accepted as truly measuring workability. Three tests which have gained considerable acceptance are the compacting factor, V–B, and slump tests; of these, the compacting factor test, which is widely used in highway work, will be described for discussion purposes.

The *compacting factor test*[28] is a suitable workability test for most of the stiff mixes required for machine paving, particularly as it can be carried out alongside the paver to help ensure that workability is kept constant. It is an indirect measure of workability, since in essence it measures the degree of compaction which is achieved by a standard amount of work.

In the compacting factor test, the concrete is placed in the inverted frustrum of a cone which is fitted with a flap door at the bottom. When this is opened, the concrete falls a fixed distance into a lower frustrum which, being smaller, fills to overflowing; the concrete is then considered to be in a standard condition. The flap door on this frustrum is then opened and the concrete allowed to fall into a cylinder which is also filled to overflowing. The surplus concrete is carefully struck off and the mass in the cylinder is determined. The mass of the same volume of fully-compacted concrete is also determined, and the ratio of the observed mass of the concrete in the cylinder to the mass of the fully-compacted concrete in the same cylinder is called the compacting factor.

As might be anticipated, the more workable a concrete mix, the higher is its compacting factor. Low workabilities are required in the concrete to ensure that inserted dowel bars are retained in position. Higher workabilities are necessary to allow the texturing and finishing of the concrete surface to be completed satisfactorily within the time available. In practice, a compromise is required, depending upon the method of construction, the mixes and materials used, and the weather. Target compacting values are given in Table 8.7.

From Table 8.7 it can be seen that good mix design is concerned not only with obtaining a fresh concrete in which a free water to cement ratio is used that will give a required strength, but also with selecting a mix of sufficient workability so as to be properly, and economically, compacted with the construction plant available. As a general guide, the ratio of free water to cement should never exceed 0.55 by mass, as the wetter the mix, the greater

**Table 8.7** Target compacting factor values used in concrete road construction[22]

| Construction | Compacting factor |
|---|---|
| Single layer | 0.80–0.85 |
| Two layer | |
| top layer | 0.80–0.83 |
| bottom layer | 0.77–0.80 |

the tendency for the fresh concrete to flow under vibration down crossfalls and longitudinal gradients, thus affecting wet-formed transverse joints, the positions of dowel bars, and surface regularity.

**British mix design practice**
The initial information required to prepare any mix design can be divided into two categories:

(1)   specified variables, the values of which are usually nominated in specifications,
(2)   additional information, which is normally available to the producer of the concrete.

In British mix design practice these data are used in conjunction with reference information—these are readily available in the technical literature[26] in the form of figures or tables—to evaluate a number of 'derived' values which are also subdivided into two categories: (a) the mix parameters, several of which form intermediate steps in the derivation of the second category, and (b) the final mix proportions, which are defined in terms of masses of materials required to produce 1 m³ of compacted concrete.

The mix design process can be divided into five operational steps, as follows.

*Step 1* deals with strength and leads to the selection of the target free water to cement ratio.
*Step 2* deals with workability and leads to the selection of the free-water content.
*Step 3* combines the results of Steps 1 and 2 and leads to the determination of the cement content.
*Step 4* deals with the determination of the total aggregate content.
*Step 5* deals with the selection of the fine and coarse aggregate content.

Details of the use of these steps, with examples, are readily available in many standard textbooks on concrete mix design—and especially in governmental design manuals—and accordingly they will not be repeated here.

*Trial mix*   The aim of the computed mix design process is to produce a hypothetical concrete that has the desired properties of strength and workability. Once the computations are completed, it is necessary to check whether or not the mix will behave as anticipated, and so trial mixes are developed and tested for each source of material to be used, e.g. cements from different sources used with the same aggregates can have varying effects on the mix, even if the cube strength is similar.

The trial mixes should be assessed not only for strength but also for workability and the effects of vibration. The extent to which there is a need for any adjustments to the original mix design proportions will obviously vary according to how much the trial mix results differ from the design values which, in turn, will depend partly upon how typical the materials are of their classifications. Depending upon these, there are three courses of action open: (a) use the trial mix proportions in the field, (b) modify the trial mix proportions slightly in the field mixes, or (c) prepare further trial mixes incorporating major changes to the mix proportions.

## Stress considerations in concrete road slabs

Stresses in concrete pavements stem from a variety of sources, of which the applied wheel loads, changes in the temperature and moisture content of the concrete, and volumetric changes in the foundation soil are by far the most important. These factors tend to result in deformations of the concrete slab which cause tensile, compressive and flexural stresses of varying magnitude to be developed. Analysis of these stresses presents a most complex problem, and it is only in the past decade that finite-element analysis has been extended to enable the analysis of stresses and strains in concrete pavements to be carried out. However, these techniques are very expensive in computer time and complex models can make demands that exceed computer capacity. As a result, today's concrete pavement design, worldwide, is based on accumulated engineering experience gained by: (a) study and appraisal of existing pavements, (b) observation of trial roads and long-range experimental road tests under normal traffic, (c) accelerated controlled traffic tests on existing or specially constructed pavement sections, (d) laboratory experimentation, and (e) theoretical and rational analyses.

Most countries now have a standard approach to concrete road design, which is often mandatory for major highways (see, for example, references 29 and 30). British design practice relies considerably upon the experience accumulated over many years of concrete road construction, which takes into account fundamental stress-analysis concepts. Before discussing the empirical thickness design methods used in Britain, it is useful to consider the stresses in concrete pavements and how they are produced.

### Wheel load stresses

When a vehicle travels over a concrete carriageway, it obviously causes pavement stresses which vary with the position of the wheels at any given time. In theory, therefore, the stresses in each slab should be analysed when the wheel loads are at all points on the slab, and the most severe stresses then evaluated and used for design purposes. In this respect, it should be noted that, with the characteristics of concrete being what they are, a rigid pavement will fail under load when the load or bending moment is so great that the developed flexural stress exceeds the modulus of rupture of the concrete.

The most commonly used methods of theoretical/semi-theoretical analysis are based on that derived by Westergaard, which was first presented in 1925[31]. In his original analysis, Westergaard made the following assumptions.

(1)   The concrete slab acts as a homogeneous, isotropic elastic solid in equilibrium.
(2)   The reactions of the subgrade are vertical only and they are proportional to the deflections of the slab.
(3)   The reaction of the subgrade per unit of area at any given point is equal to a constant $k$ multiplied by the deflection at the point. The constant $k$ is termed 'the modulus of subgrade reaction', and is assumed to be constant at each point, independent of the deflection, and to be the same at all points within the area of consideration.
(4)   The thickness of the slab is uniform.
(5)   The load at the interior and at the corner of the slab is distributed uniformly over a circular area of contact; for the corner loading, the circumference of this circular area is tangential to the edge of the slab.
(6)   The load at the edge of the slab is distributed uniformly over a semi-circular area of contact, the diameter of the semi-circle being at the edge of the slab.

Westergaard then examined three critical conditions of loading; as is illustrated in Fig. 8.2, these are at the corners, edges and interior of the slab. For these cases, Westergaard developed the following *original* equations[32]

$$\sigma_c = \frac{3P}{h^2}\left[1 - \left(\frac{a\sqrt{2}}{l}\right)^{3/5}\right]$$

$$\sigma_i = 0.316\,25\frac{P}{h^2}\left[4\log_{10}\left(\frac{l}{b}\right) + 1.069\,3\right]$$

and   $$\sigma_e = 0.571\,85\frac{P}{h^2}\left[4\log_{10}\left(\frac{l}{b}\right) + 0.359\,3\right]$$

where the symbols are as follows. $P$ is the point load (lbf/in$^2$). $\sigma_c$ is the maximum tensile stress (lbf/in$^2$) at the top of the slab, in a direction parallel to the bisector of the corner angle, due to a load applied at the corner. $\sigma_i$ is the maximum tensile stress (lbf/in$^2$) at the bottom of the slab directly under the load, when the load is applied at a point in the interior of the slab at a considerable distance from the edges. $\sigma_e$ is the maximum tensile stress (lbf/in$^2$) at the bottom of the slab directly under the load at the edge, and in a direction parallel to the edge. $h$ is the slab thickness (in). $\mu$ is Poisson's ratio for concrete ($= 0.15$ in these equations). $E$ is the modulus of elasticity of the concrete (lbf/in$^2$). $k$ is the modulus of subgrade reaction (lbf per in$^2$ per in). $a$ is the radius of the area of load contact (in)—note that the area is

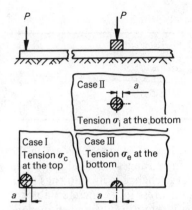

**Fig. 8.2**   Three cases of loading considered by Westergaard in his original analysis

circular for corner and interior loads, and semi-circular for edge loads. $b$ is the radius of equivalent distribution of pressure at the bottom of the slab (in) $= (1.2a^2 + h^2)^{1/2} - 0.675h$. Finally, $l$ is the radius of relative stiffness (in) $= [Eh^3/12 (1 - \mu^2)k]^{1/4}$.

The most critical situation illustrated by the above equations—which were later modified by Westergaard and by others—refers to the corner loading where, due to local depressions of the underlying material or warping of the slab, the corner portion may become unsupported and, in extreme circumstances, behave as a cantilever. Edge loading produces stresses that are slightly less than those caused by corner loading, whilst a load placed at the interior of the slab, away from edges and corners, generates the least stress.

In respect of corner loading, it might also be noted that the stress in a corner having an angle of 70 degrees may be up to 50 per cent greater than the stress in a 90-degree corner. Even greater stresses are developed with corner angles more acute than 70 degrees[10].

An important variable in these formulae is the modulus of subgrade reaction, $k$. This modulus is a measure of the stiffness of the supporting material; its units are load per unit volume of displaced subgrade (or subbase). It is most easily explained by considering a rigid slab which is constructed on a yielding medium. This slab will deflect when a load is applied and induce reactive pressures between the slab and the supporting material. It is normally assumed that the moment of reactive pressure bears a direct linear relationship to the magnitude of the deflection, viz.:

$$k = p/\delta$$

where $k =$ modulus of subgrade reaction, $p =$ reactive pressure, and $\delta =$ deflection of the plate.

Values of $k$ vary widely, depending upon the type of soil, its density and its moisture condition. Ideally, the modulus of subgrade reaction is determined by means of a plate-bearing test, but since the test is very time consuming, it is rarely carried out in a practical design but is estimated on

**Table 8.8**   $k$ values by type of soil

| Soil type | $k$ (MPa/m) |
|---|---|
| Plastic clays | 14–27 |
| Silts and silty clays | 27–54 |
| Sands and clayey gravels | 54–81 |
| Gravels | 81+ |

the basis of known relationships. Typical values of the modulus are in the ranges given in Table 8.8 [33]. In respect of these ranges, it should be noted that the influence of $k$ is such that a fairly large change in its value has but a relatively small influence upon the calculated stress in a concrete slab.

The least critical situation considered by Westergaard was when the load is applied at the interior of the slab. By assuming the pressure to be distributed uniformly over the contact area of a small circle, Westergaard determined that the critical stress is the tensile stress which is produced at the bottom of the slab under the centre of the circle. This stress is the critical stress, except when the radius of the circle is so small that some of the vertical stresses near the top become more important; this latter exception need not be considered, however, in the case of a wheel load which is applied through a rubber tyre.

The third situation considered by Westergaard was when the wheel load is at the edge of the slab, but at a considerable distance from any corner. When the load is applied, the edge deflects downwards immediately under the load and upwards at a distance away. The critical tensile stress is therefore immediately beneath the centre of the circle on the underside of the slab; the tensile stresses at the upper surface of the edge at a distance away are considerably smaller than the tensile stress at the bottom of the slab beneath the centre of the semi-circle.

**Other loading considerations**
The stress relationships developed for the three critical conditions which have just been described only refer, in general, to loading in the form of a single wheel load at rest. Obviously, therefore, the values given by any such equations have to be modified to take into account the effects brought about by multiple wheels and by moving traffic loads.

While the effects of multiple wheel loads are not yet fully understood, it is known that they result in increases in the stresses produced at the corners and interior of a slab and a reduction in the stresses caused at the edges of the slab. The multiple loading conditions which cause the greatest influence upon the maximum stresses are given in Fig. 8.3. Analyses which have been carried out suggest that the effect of multiple wheel load distributions is to increase the stresses caused by a single wheel load by about 25 per cent for corner loading and 50 per cent for interior loading; for edge loading, the effect can be considered as unimportant.

It is well known that the stresses caused by a statically applied load can be substantially increased by having it impact upon the surface. As has been

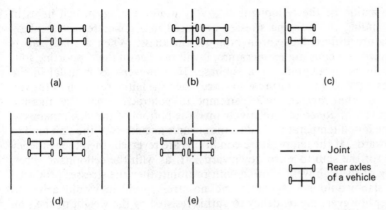

**Fig. 8.3** Loading positions for maximum stresses in concrete road slabs[34]: (a) at interior of slab, (b) at edge of longitudinal joint, (c) at free edge, (d) at edge of transverse joint, and (e) near corner

described in Chapter 6, the impact effect of a moving wheel upon a *smooth* road surface either is negligible or results in a reduction in maximum pavement stress; this is due to the mass and elasticity of the pavement preventing the full deflection from occurring before the wheel has moved on to another position. On a concrete road, however, impact effects may be quite considerable depending upon whether or not the adjacent slabs composing the pavement are 'flush' with each other, and whether or not particular joints (and cracks) are properly protected with effective load-transfer devices.

The effect of frequency of loading, i.e. intensity of traffic, is another factor which must be considered in any analysis of stresses within a concrete pavement. As is well known, considerable research has been carried out, particularly in the past twenty-five years, on the fatigue behaviour of concrete; however, most of this is based on regular repetitions of stress at quite high frequencies, and this is very much in contrast to what actually does occur on a roadway. On a highway, for instance, there is invariably a sufficiently long period of time between applications of the same successive heavy loads, and this allows time for recovery of the concrete. The fact that these recovery times are available is very important, since it is known that they reduce the magnitude of the detrimental effects brought about by repeated loading.

## Temperature-warping stresses

If a thin sheet of cellophane is placed on the (warm) palm of the hand, it will be found to curl upwards as a result of the thermal expansion of its lower surface. Placing it on a cool surface will cause curling in the opposite direction. A long, narrow sheet will curl either up or down about its major longitudinal axis, but, as the length to breadth ratio of the sheet approaches unity, the major curling or warping will shift to a diagonal direction.

The action of the cellophane is a very useful analogy which helps in understanding the warping stresses produced in a concrete pavement by temperature differentials throughout its thickness. When a road slab is maintained at a constant temperature, it will rest flat on the supporting soil, whether it be a subgrade or a subbase. If, however—as is usual in the evenings—the air temperature is lowered, then the initial reaction of the top surface of the concrete is to attempt to contract. Since the thermal conductivity of concrete is relatively low, the bottom of the slab remains at the same initial temperature and so the corners and edges of the slab tend to curl upwards. If the temperature conditions are reversed, then the tendency will be for the slab to warp downwards. If, as with the cellophane sheet, warping of the slab were allowed with restraint, then the stresses produced in the slab would be negligible and no stress problem would arise. In practice, however, the tendency to curl is resisted by the weight of the slab (and by load-transfer devices, or friction, at the pavement joints) so that warping stresses are induced which may result in the slab cracking, usually near its centre.

The problem of temperature-warping was also considered by Westergaard[35]. Using the assumption that the temperature gradient from the top to the bottom of a concrete road slab is in the form of a straight line, Westergaard developed equations for three different cases. In the simplest one of these, he assumed that the slab was infinitely large and derived the expression

$$\sigma_0 = E\varepsilon t/2(1 - \mu)$$

where $\sigma_0$ = tensile stress developed (lb/in$^2$), $E$ = modulus of elasticity of concrete (lb/in$^2$), $\varepsilon$ = coefficient of linear thermal expansion of concrete per degree fahrenheit, $\mu$ = Poisson's ratio for concrete, and $t$ = temperature difference between the top and the bottom of the slab (degrees fahrenheit).

In Britain, it has been shown that a temperature gradient of 5 °C can occur from the top to the bottom of a 150 mm concrete slab, so that on the basis of Westergaard's analysis the stresses caused by restrained temperature-warping can be quite large, even in a temperate climate. In general, the temperature–stress results given by Westergaard tend to be on the high side when compared with what actually does occur. To account for this, it has been shown that the temperature gradient is in fact closer to a curved line, and that the use of this latter form of gradient results in calculated stress values which are considerably lower than those given by Westergaard's analysis.

In practice, the stresses induced by temperature-warping are not as detrimental as might otherwise be expected. There are a number of reasons for this, as follows.

(1)    At slab corners, where the load stresses are actually the greatest, the warping stresses are negligible since the tendency of a slab to curl at these locations is resisted by only a very small amount of concrete.

(2)    At the interior of a slab and along its edges, significant curling stresses may be developed which, under certain circumstances, are additive to load

stresses. However, since concrete slabs are normally designed to have a uniform thickness based on the corner loading needs, the margin of strength present in the interior and edges of a slab is usually sufficient to offset the warping stresses which are produced at these locations.

(3) Long-term temperature record studies which were carried out overseas have indicated that the temperature at the bottom of the slab exceeds that at the top more often than the reverse, so that curling stresses in the interior and at the edges are more frequently subtractive than additive.

## Moisture-induced stresses

Differences in moisture content between the top and bottom of a slab also cause warping stresses. This is due to the ability of concrete to shrink when its moisture content is decreased and to swell when the moisture content is increased. Very little is known about the extent to which this type of warping occurs, and as yet it has not been possible to develop a method of analysis which enables the stress produced by this phenomenon to be calculated.

Generally, however, it can be assumed that the effects of moisture will oppose those of temperature, e.g. in summer the slab will normally shorten rather than lengthen and on drying out from its top surface will warp upward rather than downward. Overall, it is likely that the effects of moisture change on slab stresses are only important in climatic regions with pronounced wet and dry seasons, and are much less significant in Britain's more equable climate.

## Temperature-friction stresses

Stresses are also produced in concrete pavements as a result of the changes in the 'average' temperature of the slab, which cause it to expand and contract. In other words, as the pavement temperature increases or decreases, each end of the slab tries to move away from or towards the slab centre. If cooling takes place uniformly, a crack may occur about the centre of the slab. If expansion is excessive, and adequate joints are not provided, then blow-ups can result in adjacent slabs being quite dramatically jack-knifed into the air. (American experience [36] indicates that blow-ups more usually occur in the late afternoon when the air temperature in the shade is greater than $32\,^{\circ}\text{C}$.)

Assuming that adequate widths of joint were provided, the stresses due to 'average' temperature changes could be considered negligible, provided that there was no friction between the slab and the supporting soil. In fact, however, considerable friction may be developed between the slab and the soil, with the result that when the slab attempts to expand it is restrained from doing so and compressive stresses are produced at its underside. As the slab contracts, the same type of restraint is exerted but this time it results in tensile stresses in the bottom of the slab. It should be noted that stresses resulting from restraint of this type are only important when the slabs are quite long (say, over 30 m). They are critical only when conditions allow them to be applied when the combined loading and warping stresses from other sources are at their maximum. Since the maximum tensile stress due to frictional restraint only occurs when a slab is contracting and since the warping stresses resulting from temperature gradients are not at their maximum at this time, the net result is that, in practice, these restraint stresses can usually be neglected when calculating the maximum tensile stresses in a concrete road slab for thickness design purposes.

One further point which might be mentioned is that the magnitude of the restraint tensile stresses which are developed is heavily dependent upon the temperature conditions prevailing at the time the slab is laid. For instance, if a pavement is laid at an uncommonly high temperature of about $32\,^{\circ}\mathrm{C}$ in Britain, it can be expected that it will spend by far the greater part of its life in a state of permanent contraction, with consequent development of permanent tensile stresses. If, however, it is laid at a much lower temperature, then much of its life will be spent in an expanded state and the stresses developed will be compressive ones which the concrete is usually well capable of withstanding.

## Reinforcement in concrete road slabs

The previous discussion on stress considerations has dealt only with plain road slabs, and no mention has been made so far of the effects of the introduction of steel reinforcement.

Reinforcing steel is, and has been for many years, used in concrete road construction. It should be clear, however, that the term 'reinforcing' is used very loosely indeed in reference to concrete road slabs, as both the amount of steel used and its function are very different from those utilized in 'normal' reinforced concrete building construction.

When a bridge, a building or some other such structure is being constructed, the concrete is normally expected to carry only the compressive stresses which are produced, and reinforcing steel is incorporated in the structure to withstand the tensile stresses. The reason for this is that if the relatively low tensile strength of the concrete is exceeded, the result could well be the complete collapse of the structure, with perhaps the loss of many lives. With a concrete road, however, slab 'failure' does not result in any such dramatic happenings since the slab will still be supported. Indeed, if the pavement is on a good foundation the riding quality of the road may be so little affected that the only obvious damage is the aesthetic one of unsightly cracks in the surface. As a result, the generally accepted design approach has been primarily to include only sufficient reinforcing steel to minimize the development of cracks and only secondarily to regard the steel as taking any of the induced tensile stresses. A practical byproduct of this form of usage is that it allows a considerably greater spacing to be used between transverse joints in reinforced slabs, as compared with unreinforced ones.

Examination of the literature on concrete roads shows that in the past there have been considerable differences of opinion as to where and how much of the reinforcing steel should be placed in a concrete pavement.

If tensile stress resistance is the principal criterion, then it is, of course, logical that two layers of steel should be used, so that one layer is at the top and the other at the bottom of the slab. The function of the top layer of steel is to resist the load and warping tensile stress at the edges and corners of the top surface, while the bottom layer resists the tensile stresses set up in the interior of the underside of the slab. If only one layer of reinforcement is used and the governing criterion is again resistance to tensile stress, then the layer should be placed near the top of the slab, since it is there that the more critical stresses are induced. Even if it were possible to analyse these stresses exactly, it is doubtful whether in normal road construction the inclusion of sufficient steel in a road slab for complete resistance of the stresses would be justified; not only is it unnecessary from a safety aspect, but it is not an economical proposition either, since with modern construction methods additional load-carrying capacity could probably be secured at less cost by using additional thicknesses of concrete rather than by using the relatively large amounts of steel needed to increase the pavement's flexural strength to the same extent. Hence it is usual practice to add only the relatively small amounts of steel which are necessary to resist crack development at the top of the slab.

## Amount, type and position of reinforcement

Even when an unreinforced concrete slab is placed on an excellent foundation it can be expected to crack. If the slab is well designed and constructed, these cracks will only be of the 'hairline' variety, and of no dangerous consequence whatsoever. If, however, the joints between slabs are too far apart (say), then the cracks may be larger and more numerous so that foreign material can enter them and water can percolate easily to the subbase and subgrade. If traffic is heavy, the broken edges may become spalled, so that the cracks become wider, there is a loss in shearing resistance and, eventually, the pavement fails. Early maintenance in the form of cleaning out the cracks and then filling them with a plastic sealing compound can, of course, prevent too great a deterioration taking place. However, this is very expensive—not only because of the cost of the actual repairs but also due to the cost of the hold-ups to traffic—and in addition it results in an unsightly surface appearance about which the general public is likely to be very critical. In the past, this has resulted in otherwise structurally sound concrete pavements being 'damned' and in an unfair bias against this form of construction.

It can be seen, therefore, that the principal function of steel in concrete pavements is to *control* the opening of cracks in the slab, so that the interlocking faces of the concrete remain in tight contact; thus slabs act together as a vehicle approaches and load transfer is developed by aggregate interlock at the faces of the crack. The design aim is to furnish sufficient steel to resist the forces which tend to pull the crack faces apart. These forces develop when volume changes take place in the concrete slab as a result of a drop in temperature, concrete shrinkage, and/or a reduction in moisture content. As the slab contracts, the movements are resisted by the friction between the slab and the underlying subgrade or subbase. The resistance to movement produces a direct tensile stress which may cause the concrete to crack—which is when the tensile stress is transferred to the steel reinforcement. This tensile stress is greatest at the middle of the slab and so the steel is usually designed to withstand the stresses at this location. A simple expression which is used in the USA to calculate the minimum amount of longitudinal steel is as follows[33]:

$$A_s = 1000MLfg/2f_s$$

where $A_s$ = required area of steel per metre width (mm$^2$), $M$ = mass per unit area of slab (t/m$^2$), $L$ = length of slab (m), $f$ = average coefficient of friction between the concrete slab and the underlying layer (typically 1.5), $g$ = acceleration of free fall ($= 9.81$ m/s$^2$), and $f_s$ = allowable tensile stress in steel (MPa).

This equation is presented here to show that the area of steel required to control random cracking is a function of the length of the slab. It also enables the following principles of design to be enunciated.

(1)   For (short) slabs in the range 4.5–6.0 m, the required amount of reinforcing steel is nil, and plain concrete pavements constructed so that load transfer takes place by aggregate interlock will normally perform adequately (see, for example, reference 37).

(2)   For longer slabs, reinforcing steel must be used to control random cracking. As will be discussed later, dowel bars are also used at the joints to permit movement of the joints with load transfer.

(3)   As the length of the slab is increased to great lengths, e.g. 150 m or more, the amount of steel becomes quite substantial and the pavement becomes in essence a continuously reinforced concrete pavement.

As has been stated, the primary function of the steel in a concrete pavement is to limit the amount or scale of cracking that may develop. The beneficial effects of increasing amounts of steel upon crack propagation are graphically illustrated in Fig. 8.4. (This figure also shows the beneficial effects of using greater thicknesses of granular subbases and of changing a given thickness of subbase from granular to lean concrete.)

Since reinforcing steel is not designed to resist the induced flexural stresses, its exact location within the slab is not particularly important as long as it is well bonded to the concrete and adequately protected from corrosion. Common practice in Britain is to place the steel in a single layer about 60 mm below the slab surface in slabs less than 270 mm thick; 70 mm cover is provided in slabs more than 270 mm thick. Placing the reinforcement in a single layer at these levels has been shown to control the opening of cracks, and spalling, more effectively than reinforcement placed at the bottom of the slab, and to give results comparable with two-layer reinforcement; it is also more convenient for construction.

Reinforcement is normally either long mesh[38] or deformed hot rolled[39] or cold worked[40] steel bars. The steel used in the mesh reinforcement can be either hard-drawn wires or cold worked bars. Experience has shown that small bars or mesh are more effective reinforcing agents

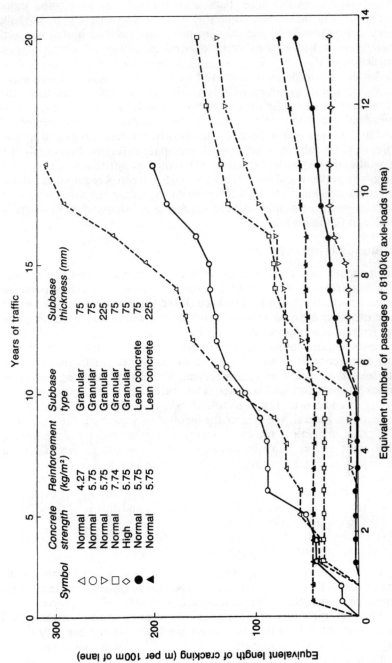

**Fig. 8.4** Development of cracking in 175 mm thick reinforced concrete slabs[37]

| Symbol | Concrete strength | Reinforcement (kg/m²) | Subbase type | Subbase thickness (mm) |
|--------|-------------------|----------------------|--------------|------------------------|
| ◁ | Normal | 4.27 | Granular | 75 |
| ○ | Normal | 5.75 | Granular | 75 |
| ▷ | Normal | 5.75 | Granular | 225 |
| □ | Normal | 7.74 | Granular | 75 |
| ◇ | High | 5.75 | Granular | 75 |
| ● | Normal | 5.75 | Lean concrete | 75 |
| ◀ | Normal | 5.75 | Lean concrete | 225 |

Years of traffic

Equivalent number of passages of 8180 kg axle-loads (msa)

Equivalent length of cracking (m per 100 m of lane)

than the same area of larger bars since they can be distributed more uniformly in the slab. This, combined with the fact that higher working stresses can be used with welded wire mesh, has resulted in this material being the most widely used form of steel in reinforced concrete road construction.

Typically, a reinforced concrete slab in a road pavement is seldom wider than 4.65 m and its length exceeds its width. With such a configuration, the reinforcement is normally only required to control transverse cracking as longitudinal cracking rarely occurs. Consequently, the reinforcement is placed in the longitudinal direction and transverse steel is provided to give rigidity to mesh fabrics or to support and space deformed bars. Only if a slab width of 4.65 m is exceeded, e.g. when constructing a three-lane carriageway in two equal widths, is extra transverse steel required to control longitudinal cracking. Detailed information regarding the arrangement of the reinforcement, e.g. joint and bar spacing, and lengths of mesh sheets, is available in the literature [41, 42].

## Continuous reinforcement

Concrete roads can also be built with no transverse joints if sufficient reinforcing steel is employed in their design. Roads which are so constructed and which contain enough steel to keep closed the many more cracks which can be expected are said to have continuously reinforced concrete pavements (commonly referred to as CRCPs).

Stresses within continuously reinforced concrete pavements are relieved by the occurrence of a random pattern of transverse cracks that are held tightly closed by the steel reinforcement, thereby maintaining aggregate interlock to give good load transfer. This cracking may first occur within a few days of construction, and almost all will be completed within three to four years. In general, the greater the amount of steel used, the closer will be the crack interval; if too little steel is used, the cracks will be formed further apart and be liable to widen. Concrete strength is also important with respect to crack spacing, i.e. the spacing increases with increasing concrete strength so that a greater amount of steel is required to hold the cracks closed. Experience suggests that the desirable spacing of the cracks for optimum life is between 1.5 and 2.5 m [43], and this is obtained with between 0.65 and 0.85 per cent of steel.

Performance studies on continuously reinforced concrete pavements that were performing satisfactorily indicate as follows [44].

(1)   The numerous fine transverse cracks are usually not visible to the driver or passenger in a vehicle, and crack widths remain insignificant under all conditions and sealing is not necessary.
(2)   Although the edges of the cracks will be under traffic, this is only a surface condition which does not affect the load-carrying capacity or the riding qualities of the pavement.
(3)   There is no spalling, faulting or pumping at tightly closed cracks.
(4)   When cracks are held tightly closed, the passage of water and the infiltration of solid material are prevented.

An important finding from the various studies of continuously reinforced concrete pavements is that longitudinal movements are limited to the end sections (60–150 m) and that the long central portion is, for all practical purposes, fully restrained. As a result, the polythene separation membrane normally imposed between the bottom of a concrete slab and the underlying layer is omitted in the case of continuously reinforced pavements so as to increase the level of subbase (or subgrade) restraint, and thereby restrict movement at the ends of the slab. Instead, the top of the subbase is simply sealed with a bituminous spray to prevent the loss of water from the overlying fresh concrete. In addition, terminal anchor blocks may be designed into the ends of the long slabs so as to restrain end movement and to distribute the stresses along the whole length of the pavement.

The major structural distress found in continuously reinforced concrete pavements is termed *edge punchout*; this occurs when a portion of the concrete slab near the outside edge of the carriageway breaks off and subsequently punches downwards[45]. This failure is first characterized by a loss of aggregate interlock at one or two cracks that are usually spaced less than 1.2 m apart. The cracks begin to fault and spall slightly, and this causes the portion of the slab between the closely spaced cracks to act essentially as a cantilever beam. As heavy commercial vehicles continue to pass over the cracks, a short longitudinal crack forms between the two transverse cracks, about 0.6 to 1.5 m from the pavement edge. Eventually, the transverse cracks break down further, the steel ruptures, and the pieces of concrete punch downwards into the subbase and subgrade. If this is not repaired, the distressed area will expand in size to adjacent transverse cracks and become quite large.

The main advantages of continuously reinforced concrete pavements are their considerably reduced maintenance costs and much improved riding quality. Unfortunately, they also cost more to construct, as well as requiring more steel, than normally reinforced slab-type pavements. Thus their usage at this time is generally limited to very-heavily-travelled roadways on which it is desired to keep traffic delays to a minimum, e.g. on busy city streets, especially on subgrades of doubtful quality or those extensively disturbed by excavations. This form of construction also minimizes the risk of uneven settlement where the pavement crosses areas formerly occupied by buildings. In Britain, continuously reinforced concrete pavements are normally not considered unless they are likely to carry in excess of 2.5 million standard axles during the design life.

It is usual practice to position the reinforcement so that, after the compaction of the concrete, it is at the mid-depth of the specified thickness of the slab. In Britain, it is also normal practice to cover the continuously reinforced slab with a bituminous surfacing.

## Prestressed concrete pavements

Although the principle of prestressing has been widely used in other structural fields, its application to pavement design has been relatively limited to date and its use in road construction is still considered somewhat of a novelty. Nonetheless, prestressed roads have been built in various countries and, on the basis of the available evidence, it appears[46] that the amount of steel used is not significantly more than that used for dowels and supports in joints alone in unreinforced pavements, and very much less than that used in reinforced or continuously reinforced concrete pavement designs; the saving in concrete pour is also appreciable. When the energy consumed in the production of steel, cement and aggregates is added to that required for transport and placement at the site, the figures indicate that the construction of prestressed pavements can result in a saving of one-third to one-half of the energy expended in conventional concrete pavements. American experience also suggests that the construction costs of prestressed pavements are within the range of conventional designs, and below the cost of continuously reinforced concrete pavements by actual bid comparisons.

The purpose of prestressing a concrete structure is to augment its tensile strength by inducing an initial compressive stress in the concrete before it is subjected to loading. Prestressing is carried out by two main methods. In the first of these, steel tendons are incorporated in the concrete, stretched and subsequently fixed to the concrete in such a way that the induced tension in the steel is balanced by compression in the concrete. Stretching may take place before the concrete has hardened (pretensioning by wires) or after the concrete has hardened (post-tensioning by cables or bars placed in protective ducts). The second method of prestressing is by casting the concrete between suitable rigid abutments which are of sufficient strength to receive the prestressing thrust. Jacks are then placed between the abutments and the concrete and operated to compress the concrete.

Prestressed concrete pavements can be classified according to whether they are of the individual slab type or of the continuous type.

With the exception of one experimental section of roadway designed by the Transport and Road Research Laboratory, it is probable that all of the prestressed concrete pavements built in Britain to date have been of the individual slab type. The method of construction employed is to cast the slabs so that they are separated only at expansion joints, and to prestress the slabs by internal tendons or cables. This constructional procedure allows each slab to expand or contract relatively freely and, since the coefficients of thermal expansion for steel and concrete are similar, the prestress in each slab remains essentially constant, except for the effects of subgrade friction. In addition to the customary construction equipment and processes, a prestressed slab pavement requires: (a) special jointing, since transverse joints may be 100–350 m apart, (b) sleeper slabs under the joints, (c) friction-reducing layers between the pavement and the subgrade or subbase, (d) steel tendons and conduits distributed throughout the area of the pavement, (e) filling the conduits with grout after the tensioning is completed, and (f) jacks for stressing the tendons.

The great majority of prestressed highway pavements built in the USA since 1970 have been 152 mm thick, with 122 mm or longer slabs, prestressed in the longitudinal direction only with post-tensioned steel. The slabs have been placed on friction-reducing membranes on treated bases. Plastic-encased strands have typically been used at 610 mm spacing to produce over $1.38 \text{ MN/m}^2$ prestress with 12.7 mm strand. The 610 mm spacing has been chosen to fit 3.65 m wide lanes and the common 0.3 m dowel spacing at transverse expansion joints.

In general, prestressed slabs are considered most suitable for use in roads with inferior subgrade conditions and curves. In contrast, the continuous type of pavement construction is more suited to fairly straight, level lengths of roadway over good subgrades. The continuous method utilizes jacks to apply the thrust and then, after the slab has been prestressed, the gaps in which the jacks are accommodated are filled, so that the strain remains in the slab. This means that, since the prestressed slab cannot expand between the abutments, the stress in it does not remain constant but varies with temperature and moisture changes.

The main advantages attributed to prestressing are reductions in the slab thickness, in the number of joints, and in the amount of cracking. Reductions in road slab thickness can result in a saving in concrete and, energy reasons apart, this is especially important in areas where good construction materials are not readily available. Fewer joints expedite and simplify construction of the road and result in the carriageway having a better riding quality. Fewer cracks result in a longer life and a considerable lowering of the maintenance cost for the roadway.

Major disadvantages associated with the use of prestressing are the difficulties encountered in applying prestress on vertical and horizontal curves and, in urban areas, the difficulty of repairing services located beneath the road since the prestress is destroyed by cutting trenches. A further disadvantage is that strict safety precautions must be enforced during the actual prestressing process.

## Joints in plain and reinforced concrete roads

As described previously, concrete is subject to changes in dimensions due to variations in temperature and moisture which cause it to warp and expand and contract. If these changes are entirely resisted, such high stresses may be induced in the pavement as to cause the concrete to develop tension cracks or buckling under compressive stresses to occur. It is to keep these stresses within safe limits, thereby conserving the strength of the concrete to resist the stresses induced by the traffic loads, that joints are primarily provided in concrete pavements.

Furthermore, joints provide for the differential movement of pavements at abutting structures, such as bridges or retaining walls, and at intersections with other pavements. They also, of course, enable the pavement to be divided into suitable lengths and widths for construction purposes.

Necessary though joints may be, their installation is the most prolific cause of defects in concrete roads. Joints are, in effect, deliberate planes of weakness inset into the pavement, and so the design engineer should take care that only those which are absolutely necessary are included in a design. The site engineer should ensure that the joints receive the highest standard of workmanship when they are being made. The cost of the extra attention to detail during construction is easily repaid by the increase in the life of the road, the reduction in maintenance costs, and the improvement in the riding qualities of the carriageway.

## Requirements of joints

The divisions between slabs can be longitudinal joints, which are parallel to the centreline of the road, or transverse joints, which are at right-angles to the centreline. Irrespective of the positions of the joints, the importance of the highest standards of care in their design and construction must be emphasized. There follows a summary of the chief functional requirements of joints if they are to be satisfactory constituents of a concrete pavement.

(1)   *A joint must be waterproof at all times.* This is perhaps the single most important criterion. If surface water is allowed to enter through a joint, softening of the subgrade will take place and the uniformity of its supporting power may be significantly reduced. If the underlying soil is clayey, then pumping may be promoted. This criterion emphasizes the importance of taking care in the selection and placement of long-life sealing materials in joints.

(2)   *Free movement of the slabs must be permitted at all times.* Both the filler and the sealing material must be capable of withstanding repeated expansion and contraction of the concrete. There is a particular danger with expansion joints that if grit and other such foreign matter gets between the slabs, then expansion of the concrete will be prevented, with resultant increased stresses in the concrete and subsequent spalling of the edges. This danger can only be overcome by taking care in the selection and pouring of the sealing compound.

(3)   *Joints should not detract from the riding quality of a roadway.* Improper design and/or construction can result in excessive relative deflections of adjacent concrete slabs. Not only is this structurally undesirable, but it also results in a most uncomfortable riding surface. Similarly, if adequate care is not taken when selecting and/or placing the joint sealing compound, the road user may experience an irritating and continuous series of impacts as the vehicle is driven over transverse ridges of sealing material which have been pushed above the level of the surface of the carriageway.

(4)   *A joint should not be the cause of an unexpected, undesigned structural weakness in a pavement.* For instance, transverse joints on either side of a longitudinal joint should not be staggered from each other, as transverse cracks will be induced in the slabs in line with the staggered joints. Furthermore, no joint should be constructed at an angle of less than 90 degrees to an adjacent joint or edge of the slab unless it is an intentional part of the design.

(5)   *Joints should interfere as little as possible with the placing of the concrete pavement.* The provision of joints should result in as little interference as possible with the construction of the pavement if paving is to proceed continuously. Not only do stoppages of the paving machine lead to additional costs, but they also tend to be associated with surface irregularities which result in an uneven surface profile which will be objectionable

to the road user. Easy and economical concrete road construction is facilitated by using the simplest types of joints, and as few of them as possible, consistent with the structural design of the pavement.

## Functions of joints

Joints may be classified according to the primary purpose for which they are installed in pavements. Thus there are expansion joints, contraction joints, warping joints, and construction joints.

**Expansion joints**
These joints are primarily designed to provide space into which expansion of concrete slabs can take place when the temperature rises above that at which the concrete was laid. Their provision prevents both the development of compressive stresses of damaging magnitude and the buckling or blow-up of slabs. As well as being used between slabs, expansion joints are necessary at locations where pavements join fixed structures, such as bridge abutments, or at intersections with other pavements.

Expansion joints are normally used transversely in a highway pavement. As is suggested in Fig. 8.5(a), each joint is formed by embedding in the concrete a vertical, non-extruding, preformed compressible filler material, shaped to ensure a complete division between abutting slabs. Any reinforcing in either slab is terminated about 60 mm from the centreline of the joint.

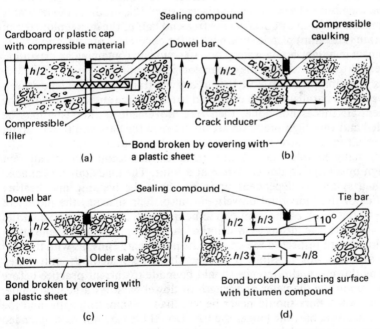

**Fig. 8.5**   Illustrations of typical joint details: (a) expansion joint, (b) dummy contraction joint, (c) butt contraction joint, and (d) tongue-and-groove construction joint (not to scale)

A wider space above the filler material is filled with a different sealing compound to prevent the entry of water and grit. The thickness of an expansion joint at the time of construction is usually 25 mm, and only rarely is it less than 12.5 mm. The narrower thicknesses are used only when the expansion joints are closely spaced and/or construction takes place during hot weather.

Mechanical load-transfer devices are desirable at all expansion joints, even though the edges and corners are designed to carry the wheel loads without over-stressing the concrete. Loads which pass over an unprotected joint may cause excessive deflections and consequent damage to the subbase and subgrade. This, in turn, can result in excessive vertical displacements of the slab ends and eventual faulting at the joints, even though the stresses induced in the concrete were not originally excessive. The load-transfer devices used at expansion joints are called *dowels*. They are placed across openings and lubricated so as to allow the joint to expand and contract freely while holding the slab ends on either side at essentially the same elevation. The deflection of either slab under load is then resisted, through the dowels, by the other slab, which, in turn, is also caused to deflect and carry its share of the load imposed upon the first slab.

The varieties of suitable load-transfer devices on the market are too numerous to describe here, and the reader is referred to a classical publication in which detailed and referenced information on the various types is given[47]. The most commonly used dowel is simply a round steel bar, one-half of which is anchored in either slab while the other half is free to move longitudinally within the adjacent slab. Longitudinal movement is economically ensured by covering the free-end half of the dowel plus 50 mm with a thin (1.25 mm) plastic sheath when the concrete is placed, and having it terminate in a tight-fitting waterproof 100 mm cup containing an expansion space equal to the width of the expansion joint gap.

It is most important to note that at a given transverse joint, the dowels must be placed parallel to each other and to the surface and centreline of the pavement. If this is not done, then free movement of the slabs may be restricted and very high pressures set up between the bars and the concrete, which result in over-stressing and cracking of the pavement.

Very many complex factors must be taken into account in any attempt to design by analysis a dowel system at a joint. The load-transfer capacity of such a system is dependent upon not only the bending and bearing capacities of the individual dowels, but also their spacing, the pavement thickness, the width of the joint gap to be spanned, the supporting qualities of the subgrade, the means by which the loads are applied, and the location of the loads with respect to the edge of the pavement. Thus, as with the slab thickness, it is not possible to utilize theoretical methods only when designing dowels, and reference should be made to current practice before deciding upon the diameter and length of dowel bars. As a general guide, however, dowel bars should never be less than 650 mm in length, and the thicker the dowel bar, the longer the bar. Dowel bars are not recommended for use in Britain in slabs of less than 190 mm thickness.

Expansion joints should be spaced so that they allow for slab move-

**Table 8.9** Spacings of contraction and expansion joints in reinforced concrete slabs[10]

| Slab thickness | Mass of reinforcement fabric (kg/m²) | Maximum spacing of joints (m) | |
|---|---|---|---|
| | | Contraction | Expansion |
| ⩾ 170–200 | ⩾ 2.6–3.2 | 16.5 | 49.5 |
| ⩾ 200–250 | ⩾ 3.2–4.4 | 20.0 | 60.0 |
| ⩾ 250 | ⩾ 4.4 | 28.0 | 84.0 |

ments caused by changes in temperature from that at which the slabs were constructed, to the maximum or minimum temperatures likely to occur when the slabs are in service. Table 8.9 shows examples of expansion joint spacings for use in reinforced concrete slabs; every third joint should be an expansion joint, the remainder being contraction joints.

The recommended maximum spacing of expansion joints in plain, unreinforced concrete pavements is 60 m for slabs of 200 mm or greater thickness, and 40 m for slabs of lesser thickness. For both reinforced and unreinforced concrete slabs, the expansion joints may be replaced by contraction joints if construction takes place in hot weather.

**Contraction joints**
The purpose of a contraction joint is to limit tensile stresses induced in the pavement due to contraction or shrinkage of the concrete and to prevent or control cracking. It also permits subsequent expansion, up to the original length of the slab, unless its effectiveness is reduced by dirt or grit entering into the joint.

As with expansion joints, construction joints are normally constructed at right-angles to the centreline of the roadway, as it is seldom considered necessary to allow for transverse expansion and contraction of highway pavements. Again, as with expansion joints, contraction joints permit some angular movement between adjacent slab sections, thereby providing some extra relief to the warping stresses developed within a concrete pavement.

There are two main types of contraction joint: butt joints and dummy joints. On large concrete road schemes, the most commonly used type by far is the dummy joint.

As illustrated in Fig. 8.5(b), a *dummy joint* consists essentially of a deliberate groove which is placed in a slab in order to form a vertical plane of weakness, and thus induce a controlled crack. Three main varieties of dummy joints are in use: these utilize a groove in the top of the slab, or a crack inducer inserted in the bottom of the slab, or (as illustrated) a combination of a groove in the top and a crack inducer in the bottom. Use of a bottom crack inducer alone results in the formation of an unsightly, irregular crack at the surface, which is not only liable to spall but is also difficult to seal as there is no deliberate surface groove; hence this type of contraction joint cannot be recommended.

By far the most widely used is the combination of surface groove and bottom crack inducer; however, when construction takes place in the summer period the bottom crack inducer may be omitted. The surface groove is formed by vibrating a groove former into the top of the plastic concrete to form a slot, so that the combined depth of the slot and the bottom inducer is normally (in Britain) between one-quarter and one-third of the thickness of the slab. As soon as the concrete has hardened, the groove is filled (i.e. assuming the former is not a permanent, preformed compression seal and has been withdrawn), and then sealed to prevent the ingress of water and grit.

Surface grooves can also be formed by using special, parallel high-speed saws to cut into the hardened concrete to a depth of between one-quarter and one-third of the depth of the slab. With this method, the bottom crack inducers are omitted as they are likely to cause cracking which is irregular, and possibly displaced from the correct line, before the sawing can be completed. Whilst this is a simple yet efficient method of construction, care must be taken to ensure that sawing takes place at exactly the right time. If sawing takes place too soon, aggregate may be pulled out of the concrete and the surface torn; if too late, uncontrolled cracking will take place in the pavement.

Experience worldwide has established that the maximum joint spacing necessary to control cracking in plain, unreinforced pavements is 4.5–6.0 m, depending upon concrete strength, the coefficient of thermal expansion of the aggregate, the climatic conditions during construction when the concrete is still fairly weak, and the in-service environmental regime[18]. In Britain, dummy joints normally are spaced at 5 m intervals; this spacing should ensure that uncontrolled cracks, which can open and spall rapidly, are avoided.

Practice in Britain in relation to the (longer) maximum joint spacings for reinforced slabs is shown in Table 8.9.

When contraction joints are less than 4.5 m apart, it is usually unnecessary to provide load-transfer devices at dummy joints. Normally, the crack opening will be small enough for the interlocking of the aggregate particles at the faces of the joint to be sufficient to provide an adequate amount of load transference without the need for dowels. If the grooves are more widely spaced, all contraction joints will need to be provided with dowel bars. These bars are similar to those in expansion joints, except that in this instance each bar, which is typically 20 or 25 mm in diameter at 300 mm spacing, is covered with the plastic sheath for two-thirds of its 400 mm length, and a receiving cap is not usually a necessity.

The *butt joint* is normally used only on small road schemes which utilize the alternate-bay method of concrete construction. As illustrated in Fig. 8.5(c), this is also a construction joint since it runs from the top to the bottom of the pavement. Irrespective of the distance between these joints, they should normally be provided with load-transfer devices.

When a concrete pavement is reinforced, the mesh is not carried through the joints; in other words, the reinforcing is used to control cracking *between* the contraction joints.

## Warping joints

Known also as hinge joints, warping joints are simply breaks in the continuity of the concrete in which any widening is restricted by tie bars, but which allow a small amount of angular movement to occur between adjacent slabs. These cracks do not allow for contraction or expansion of the concrete.

Transverse warping joints are used only in plain concrete pavements to control cracks which occur as a result of excessively high longitudinal warping stresses being developed, e.g. in long, narrow slabs. In reinforced concrete slabs, warping stresses, which are developed as a consequence of temperature gradients in the slab, are controlled by the reinforcing mesh, and load transfer is maintained by aggregate interlock. As the longitudinal movements in plain concrete slabs are likely to be relatively small, it is British practice to allow up to three consecutive contraction joints in these pavements to be replaced by warping joints with tie bars designed to relieve warping stresses.

Longitudinal joints are required in concrete roads in order to control the irregular longitudinal cracks that would otherwise occur as a result of thermal warping and loading stresses, and to enable the pavement to be constructed in convenient widths. The maximum bay width is normally 4.2 m, except in the case of reinforced slabs when widths up to 6 m are used. On multilane pavements, a joint spacing equal to the width of the traffic lanes serves the very useful dual purpose of crack control and reinforcing lane delineation. Joint locations along wheel tracks should always be avoided.

The tie bars used in both transverse warping and longitudinal joints are not normally intended to act as load-transfer devices; rather, they are designed to hold the joint tightly closed and to encourage load distribution by face-to-face aggregate interlock. The tie bars must therefore be firmly anchored at either end in the concrete. Whereas dowel bars are plain and relatively larger in diameter, tie bars are relatively thin (normally 12 mm diameter) and may be deformed to provide the necessary anchorage. As with dowels, tie bars are located at the mid-depth of the slab; however, because they do not have to allow movement between slabs, great accuracy in the placement of tie bars is not essential.

The tie bars in longitudinal joints are spaced further apart than in transverse joints because the distance between movement joints is smaller. Also, the number of axle loads crossing over these joints is less, demanding less rigid tying together of the slabs.

Longitudinal joints are frequently (but not necessarily) keyed.

## Construction joints

As the name implies, construction joints are those joints other than deliberately designed expansion, contraction or warping joints which are formed in the course of construction of the pavement. They are formed when construction work is unexpectedly interrupted, e.g. by mechanical breakdown or by the onset of bad weather, at points where joints are not normally required by the design.

The structural integrity of the pavement is best maintained by locating these at contraction joints or within the middle third of a slab bounded by contraction joints. Where transverse construction joints coincide with contraction joints in undowelled pavements, the joints should be keyed in; in dowelled pavements, the joints should be dowelled (Fig. 8.5(c)). Transverse construction joints located between contraction joints should be keyed in and tie bars provided (see Fig. 8.5(d)).

Good construction planning ensures that end-of-day joints are either contraction or expansion joints, coinciding with predetermined joint positions.

Details of the size and spacing of tie bars used in construction and warping joints are given in Table 8.10.

**Table 8.10**   Sizes and spacings of tie bars[21]

| Joints | Diameter (mm) | Length (mm) | Spacing (mm) |
|---|---|---|---|
| Transverse construction joints in continuously reinforced concrete pavements | As for reinforcement | 1500 | As for main reinforcement × 2 |
| Emergency construction joints in jointed reinforced concrete slabs (other than at contraction or expansion joints) | 12 | 1000 | 600 |
| Warping joints | 12 | 1000 (750) | 300 |
| All longitudinal joints (except where transverse reinforcement is permitted in lieu) | 12 | 1000 (750) | 600 |

*Note*: Lengths of deformed tie bars are given in brackets

## Grooves and crack inducers

Joint grooves at the top of the slab are normally preformed or sawn after placement of the slab. Transverse grooves are either sawn in the hardened concrete or wet formed in the plastic concrete; longitudinal joint grooves are normally wet formed.

Sawing is carried out as soon as the concrete has hardened sufficiently to enable a sharp-edged groove to be produced without disrupting the concrete and before random cracks develop in the slab. The grooves can be of any convenient width above 3 mm. Grooves are formed in the plastic concrete either by vibrating a metal blade into the concrete to the required depth and inserting a groove former into the groove, or by vibrating the groove former vertically into the plastic concrete.

Bottom crack inducers are triangular or inverted Y-shaped fillets, with a base width not less than the height, made of timber or of a rigid, synthetic material. They are firmly fixed to the subbase so as to remain in position during the whole process of constructing the slab. It is British practice to omit inducers from transverse contraction and warping joints in the summer period, 21 April to 21 October.

## Fillers and seals

Regardless of their function, all joints in a concrete pavement should be made waterproof at the time of construction and maintained in that way throughout the life of the pavement. Furthermore, any cracks which develop in the slabs throughout their life should also be made waterproof as soon as they are detected. Failure to prevent incompressible grit from entering joints can result in the development of stresses in hot weather which are great enough to cause spalling of joint edges and, in extreme cases, pavement buckling or blow-ups. Corrosion of embedded steel in concrete slabs is accelerated when the brine solution from de-icing salts placed on the carriageway in cold weather enters joints that are not effectively sealed. Water entering joints can be the cause of pavement pumping and the deterioration of uniform pavement support.

Notwithstanding the above, it should be appreciated that there is not complete agreement amongst highway engineers on the need for sealing all pavements joints. For example, it is reported[48] that the Technical Committee on Concrete Roads of the Permanent International Association of Road Congresses (PIARC) presented a report at the sixteenth World Congress in 1979 which concluded that, with joint spacings of 4–6 m, there is no disadvantage in leaving narrow transverse joints unsealed when: (a) traffic is light, (b) traffic is heavy but the climate is dry, or (c) traffic is heavy and the climate is wet but the pavement is dowelled.

### Fillers

These are used to provide the gaps for expansion joints at the time of construction and to provide support for the sealing compound. Materials which are to be used as fillers should satisfy a number of criteria. The most important of these are that a filler should be capable of being compressed without extrusion, sufficiently elastic to recover its original thickness when the compressive force is released, and unaffected by, and should not affect, the sealing compound used; furthermore, it should be able to retain these properties throughout the design life of the pavement.

Well-established, easily available filler materials used in joints which meet the above criteria are softwood, fibre-board impregnated with a light cutback bitumen or tar distillate, and cork.

Expansion joints formed with filler materials only neither are watertight nor do they prevent the ingress of grit. To be fully effective, therefore, they must be covered with a sealing material. Holes for dowel bars will need to be accurately bored or punched out in order to provide a sliding fit for the sheathed dowels.

### Seals

Joint seals (also commonly referred to as *sealants*) must meet a number of requirements[49] if they are to perform their functions satisfactorily. They should:

(1)  be impermeable,
(2)  deform to accommodate the total movement and rate of movement occurring at the joint,
(3)  sufficiently recover their original properties and shape after cyclical deformations,
(4)  remain in contact with the joint faces, i.e. for all seals, except those that exert a force against the joint face, the seal must bond to the joint face and neither fail in adhesion nor peel at corners or other local areas of stress concentration,
(5)  not rupture internally, i.e. fail in cohesion,
(6)  resist flow or unacceptable softening at high service temperatures,
(7)  not harden or become unacceptably brittle at low service temperatures,
(8)  not be adversely affected by ageing, weathering or other service factors for a reasonable service life under the range of temperatures and other environmental conditions that occur.

In addition, seals should, under all weather conditions, be able to resist the intrusion of incompressible foreign material, wear, indentation, pick-up, or attack by chemicals. Furthermore, they must not deteriorate when stored prior to use, be relatively easy to handle and install, and be free of substances harmful to the user and to concrete.

Some of these requirements contradict each other so it is therefore perhaps not surprising that no one material has yet been found which meets all of these criteria, and which does not require regular maintenance.

Joint seals can be divided into two main groups, viz. field-moulded seals and preformed seals.

*Field-moulded seals* are ones which are poured or gunned into the joint in a liquid or semi-liquid form, and take up the shape of the reservoir. They include hot and cold applied thermoplastics, and thermosetting (chemically curing and solvent-release) seals.

The hot applied thermoplastics include such materials as bitumen, rubber–bitumen, tar and rubber–tar. Whilst the tar-based fillers are fuel and oil resistant, and thus may be preferred for areas where spillage is expected, they have been largely replaced with a soft bitumen containing a high natural or synthetic rubber content[50]. Disadvantages of these thermoplastics are that they tend to lose elasticity and plasticity with age, to accept rather than reject intruding foreign materials, and to extrude from joints that are overfilled when they close appreciably. Probably the most common abuse of the compounds containing rubber is overheating during the preparation process.

Cold applied thermoplastic seals do not require heating to use; in practice, however, they may be warmed to facilitate application. These materials, which include acrylics and vinyls, set either by the release of solvents or the breaking of emulsions on exposure to the air. When the solvent or water is released, shrinkage and increased hardening can occur, and this reduces the permissible joint movement and serviceability; as a result, the use of these seal materials tends to be confined to joints with small movements.

Thermosetting seals, which typically are formed from polysulphides, silicone, urethane and epoxy-based materials, are either one- or (more usually) two-component systems that cure by chemical reaction to a solid state from the liquid form in which they are applied. Properties that render these seals of particular value are good resistance to weathering and ozone, flexibility and resilience at both high and low temperatures, and inertness to a wide range of chemicals, including some solvents and fuels. In addition, the resistance to abrasion and indentation of urethane seals is above average. Whilst initially more expensive, thermosetting chemically curing seals can accommodate greater movements than other field-moulded seals and generally have a much greater service life.

Hot and cold poured seals are best applied so that the installed depth to width ratio is between 1:2 and 1:1. The reason for this is that the smaller the depth to width ratio, the less the strains imposed on the seals as the joints open and close (see Fig. 8.6). Table 8.11 shows the sizes of the field-moulded joint seals used in practice in Britain.

*Preformed compression seals* are often cellular in cross-section, and the cells are designed to collapse as adjacent slabs expand. The preformed

| Depth to width ratio | Relative seal volume | Joint condition | | |
|---|---|---|---|---|
| | | As installed | Open | Closed |
| 1:2 | 1 | $s = 0$ | $s = 32\%$ | $s = 20\%$ |
| 1:1 | 2 | $s = 0$ | $s = 62\%$ | $s = 60\%$ |
| 2:1 | 4 | $s = 0$ | $s = 94\%$ | $s = 250\%$ |

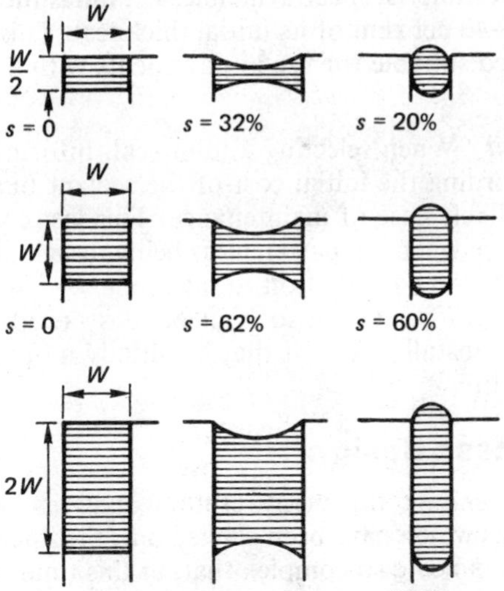

*Notes:* '$s$' is maximum strain occurring on the exposed parabolic surface of the sealant. Sealant is assumed installed at mean joint width.

**Fig. 8.6** Shape factors and strains in field-moulded joint seals[49]

**Table 8.11**   Dimensions of applied joint seals[21]

| Type of joint | Spacing of joints (m) | Minimum width of seal (mm) | Minimum depth of seal (mm) Hot | Cold | Depth of seal below surface (mm) |
|---|---|---|---|---|---|
| Contraction | ≤ 15 | 13 | 15 | 13 | 5 ± 2 |
|  | > 15–20 | 20 | 20 | 15 | 5 ± 2 |
|  | > 20–25 | 25 | 25 | 20 | 5 ± 2 |
|  | > 25 | 30 | 25 | 20 | 7 ± 2 |
| Warping | All | 10 | 13 | 10 | 5 ± 2 |
| Expansion | All | 30 | 25 | 20 | 7 ± 2 |
| Gulley and manhole slabs | All | 20 | 20 | 15 | 0–3 |
| Longitudinal | All | 10 | 13 | 10 | 0–5 |

compressed seal—typically ethene vinyl acetate foam or a neoprene rubber which when uncompressed has a width greater than the joint at its maximum opening—is inserted into the groove so that it exerts pressure against both faces of the joint. Properly installed, it is able to accommodate the normal expansion and contraction changes which occur in the joint width without allowing the entry of water or incompressible materials such as sand and silt.

A simpler type of preformed strip seal consists of a granulated cork board which is bonded with a water-soluble resin. After being inserted into the joint, water is sprinkled onto the opening and the cork strip then expands within the space available, i.e. it has the capability of expanding by up to 30–40 per cent of its initial thickness. This cork joint seal is generally considered suitable for use in pavements with a maximum joint movement of 3 mm.

*Comment*   When selecting a joint seal, information should be sought not only regarding the initial cost of the sealant but also about its anticipated life and likely ease of maintenance. This last consideration is of particular importance when the pavement is being designed to carry heavy volumes of traffic, i.e. the contribution to maintenance costs that accrue as a result of delays to traffic can be so high on busy roads that it is usually cheaper overall to install a sealant that is initially more expensive but has a longer working life.

## Thickness design

Notwithstanding the many erudite analyses of stresses within concrete pavements which have been carried out, the thickness design problem is still regarded as being so complex that, at this time, there is no highway agency in the world which attempts a completely theoretical analysis when designing a concrete road pavement. The fact is that whilst design theory enables stresses due to loading and temperature effects to be calculated for a slab of a given thickness, combined, and then compared with the strength of the concrete to show whether or not the concrete is over-stressed, the correlation between the calculated stresses and the pavement's in-service perform-ance is still uncertain. As a result, all concrete pavement theoretical design procedures, of necessity, make use of a number of assumptions and approximations which can have a profound effect upon the conclusions reached in relation to thickness requirements.

In Britain, concrete pavement design has tended to be entirely empirical, and to rely upon the results of full-scale road experiments [37] in order to gain design information re slab thickness, degree of reinforcement, spacing of joints, strength of concrete, and subbase thickness. Before discussing the results of these studies, and the design procedure that has now been developed from them, it is worth noting that until the mid-1980s the British concrete road design guidelines resulted in the same concrete thickness being used for both plain (unreinforced) and reinforced slabs. The result is that there was little incentive for reinforced concrete roads to be laid in Britain [29]. Similarly, whilst continuously reinforced pavements have been laid for trial purposes, they have not been adopted for general use.

## Unreinforced concrete pavements

The performance analysis of data gathered from twenty-nine different types of section on the Alconbury Hill test road [51] has given the following multiple regression equation linking the variables which mostly affect plain concrete pavement life.

$$\ln L = 5.094 \ln H + 3.466 \ln S + 0.4836 \ln M + 0.08718 \ln F - 40.78$$

where $L$ = cumulative traffic that can be carried before failure (msa), $H$ = thickness of concrete slab (mm), $S$ = twenty-eight-day mean com-pressive strength of cubes made from the pavement concrete (MPa), $M$ = equivalent modulus of a uniform foundation giving the same slab support as the actual foundation (MPa), and $F$ = percentage of failed bays per test section.

The probability of pavement survival associated with the above equation is 50 per cent.

The plain concrete experimental pavements from which the above equation was derived consisted of individual slabs divided into bays by contraction joints. Failure of sections usually proceeded gradually over a few years on a bay-by-bay basis, so that the performance of each type of unreinforced section was judged, at the time of inspection, by the per-centage of that type of bay that had failed.

The bays were judged to have failed if any of the following defects were present:

(1)  a crack of width equal to or greater than 0.5 mm crossing the bay longitudinally or transversely,
(2)  a longitudinal and transverse crack intersecting, both starting from an edge and greater than 0.5 mm wide, and each longer than 200 mm,
(3)  corner cracking wider than 1.3 mm and more than 200 mm radius,
(4)  a bay with pumping at a joint or edge,
(5)  a replaced or structurally repaired bay.

**Table 8.12**  Equivalent foundation modulus for a range of typical foundations for concrete pavements[51]

| Subbase | | | | | | | | |
|---|---|---|---|---|---|---|---|---|
| Upper layer | | | Lower layer | | | Subgrade | | Equivalent foundation modulus (MPa) |
| Type | Depth (mm) | Modulus (MPa) | Type | Depth (mm) | Modulus (MPa) | CBR | Modulus (MPa) | |
| Granular | 150 | 150 | Capping | 600 | 70 | 1.5 | 23 | 68 |
| Type 1 | | | layer | 350 | 70 | 2.0 | 27 | 65 |
| | 225 | 150 | None | — | — | 5.0 | 50 | 89 |
| Lean | 150 | 28 000 | Capping | 600 | 70 | 1.5 | 23 | 261 |
| concrete | | | layer | 350 | 70 | 2.0 | 27 | 268 |
| (C10) | | | | 150 | 70 | 5.0 | 50 | 358 |
| | | | None | — | — | 15.0 | 100 | 683 |
| Lean | 150 | 35 000 | Capping | 600 | 70 | 1.5 | 23 | 277 |
| concrete | | | layer | 350 | 70 | 2.0 | 27 | 285 |
| (C15) | | | | 150 | 70 | 5.0 | 50 | 383 |
| | | | None | — | — | 15.0 | 100 | 732 |

The multiple regression analysis showed that 75 per cent of the variability in performance of these unreinforced pavements was accounted for by the chosen variables, and that thickness was the most significant variable examined, i.e. thickness accounted for 67 per cent of the variation in observed performance. If typical values of 50 MPa for twenty-eight-day mean compressive strength, an equivalent foundation modulus of 270 MPa, and 30 per cent failure of bays are input into the above equation, it becomes

$$\ln H = (\ln L + 24.22)/5.094$$

Table 8.12 summarizes equivalent foundation moduli for various subbase and subgrade combinations which are capable of providing an all-weather working platform for pavement construction. In this table, equivalence is expressed in terms of a uniform elastic foundation of infinite depth which provides the same surface deflection, under a standard wheel load, as that of the actual combination foundation.

The experimental roads on which the above equations are based, were built without shoulders. However, shoulders abutting the carriageway are known to reduce the pavement stress induced in the concrete slab and increase the service life of the pavement; for best results, the shoulders should be tied and at least 1 m wide. The beneficial effect of a tied shoulder in terms of equivalent slab thickness, as evaluated using the method devised by the American Association of State Highway and Transportation Officials[52], is shown in Fig. 8.7 for a pavement with the following characteristics: probability of survival = 50 per cent, twenty-eight-day mean compressive strength of concrete = 50 MPa, and equivalent foundation modulus = 270 MPa. It might also be noted that the equivalences given by

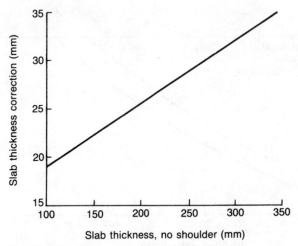

**Fig. 8.7** Contribution of a tied shoulder to concrete pavement life, in terms of equivalent slab thickness[51]. *Note*: Subtract the correction from the derived slab thickness if the pavement has tied shoulders at least 1 m wide

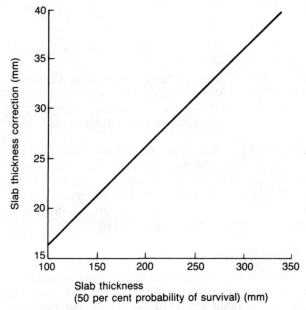

**Fig. 8.8** Increase in slab thickness required to increase the probability of pavement survival from 50 to 85 per cent[51]. *Note*: Add the correction to the recommended thickness

this figure are not significantly affected by changing the probability of survival from 50 to 85 per cent.

The additional slab thickness required to increase the chances of a pavement's survival from 50 to 85 per cent is given in Fig. 8.8. This correction applies to both unreinforced and reinforced concrete pavements.

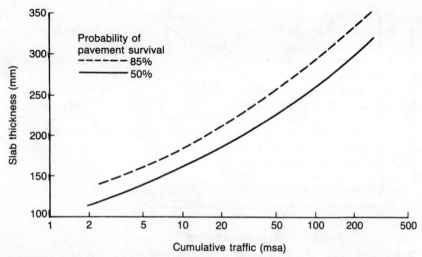

**Fig. 8.9**    Design curves for unreinforced concrete pavements with a tied shoulder[51].
*Note*: The curves assume an equivalent foundation modulus = 270 MPa and a twenty-eight-day mean compressive strength of concrete = 50 MPa

### Design curves

The multiple regression analysis, together with the relationships described above for the effects of tied shoulders and variations in a pavement's probability of survival, made it possible to predict the life of a range of different pavements, on the basis that the variables affecting their performance were not significantly different from those covered by the experimental highways. The resultant design curves for unreinforced concrete pavements are given in Fig. 8.9.

Note that the curves in Fig. 8.9 assume the use of a subbase and subgrade combination that is non-erodable and provides an all-weather working platform for pavement construction, whilst remaining stable throughout the predicted life of the pavement. The cemented subbase foundations described in Table 8.12 meet these criteria, and yield a minimum value of equivalent foundation modulus of 270 MPa.

### Reinforced concrete pavements

The performance analysis of thirty years of data from forty-two different types of section on the Alconbury Hill test road has given the following multiple regression equation linking the variables which mostly affect reinforced concrete pavement life.

$$\ln L = 4.786 \ln H + 1.418 \ln R + 3.171 \ln S + 0.3255 \ln M - 45.15$$

where $L$ = cumulative traffic that can be carried before failure (msa), $H$ = thickness of concrete slab (mm), $R$ = amount of reinforcement in the pavement-quality concrete (mm²/m, i.e. measured cross-sectional area of steel per metre width of slab), $S$ = twenty-eight-day mean compressive strength of cubes made from the pavement concrete (MPa), and $M$ = equivalent modulus of a uniform foundation giving the same support to the slab as the actual foundation (MPa).

The probability of pavement survival associated with this equation is also 50 per cent.

The regression analysis showed that 91 per cent of the variation in observed performance was accounted for by the following four variables (in order of significance): slab thickness, amount of reinforcement, concrete strength, and foundation stiffness. Of these, slab thickness, with 67 per cent of the variation in observed performance, was by far the most significant variable. These data were obtained from bays with lengths of 9.1, 24.4 and 36.6 mm.

If typical values of 50 MPa for strength, 500 mm$^2$/m for reinforcement, and an equivalent foundation modulus of 270 MPa are input into the above equation, it becomes

$$\ln H = (\ln L + 22.11)/4.786$$

**Design curves**

As has been described for plain slabs, a series of design curves has also been developed for reinforced concrete pavements (see Fig. 8.10), for different amounts of reinforcement and probabilities of survival. The benefits of additional reinforcement upon increased pavement life are clearly shown in this figure.

# Construction

Prior to 1935, all concrete road construction in Britain was carried out by hand. The only instances where mechanization was employed were in the batching and transporting of materials, the mixing of the concrete and, in some instances, its distribution from the mixer. About 1935, interest in the use of machines for spreading, compacting and finishing became aroused in Britain and this was accelerated during World War II. Now it is true to say that all major concrete road construction is to all intents and purposes completely mechanized, and hand-spreading is only used to lay small or irregular-shaped pavement slabs. Mechanized construction results in reduced labour costs, an increase in the speed of construction and, since it allows the use of leaner concrete mixes with low water to cement ratios, an effective saving in the cost of materials.

There are two basic types of mechanized concrete paving equipment, viz. the fixed-form plant and the slip-form plant.

## Fixed-form paving

With fixed-form paving, the spreading, compaction and finishing of the concrete and other associated operations are carried out between fixed side-forms. As well as supporting the edges of the plastic concrete, the side-forms also support and guide the individual machines making up the paving train.

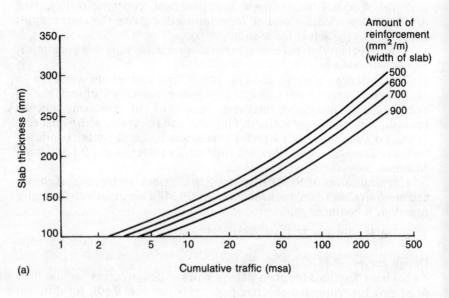

(a)

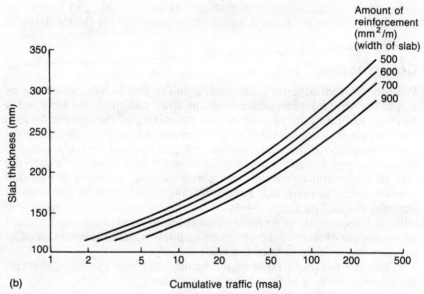

(b)

**Fig. 8.10** Design curves for reinforced concrete pavements with a tied shoulder and a probability of survival of[51]: (a) 50 per cent and (b) 85 per cent. *Note*: The curves assume an equivalent foundation modulus = 270 MPa and a twenty-eight-day mean compressive strength of concrete = 50 MPa

Figure 8.11 shows a typical arrangement of a fixed-form paving train. At the present time, this way of laying concrete pavements is more widely used in Britain than is slip-form paving.

The stages involved in conventional fixed-form concrete pavement construction can be summarized as follows:

(1)   subgrade and subbase preparation,
(2)   form laying,
(3)   mixing and placing the concrete,
(4)   compacting and finishing,
(5)   curing.

### Subgrade and subbase preparation

The preparation of the subgrade and subbase represents one of the most critical stages in the conventional construction process. Thus considerable care must be taken to ensure that each of these foundation layers is graded and compacted to a uniform hard surface.

A uniform subgrade is more important to concrete pavement performance than one compacted to a high density, since the pressures transmitted to the subgrade will be low. The subgrade should be dressed so that it conforms to the required line, profile and cross-section. If the pavement is to be constructed on top of an existing roadbed, it should be scarified to a depth of not less than 150 mm, and then recompacted and shaped to the correct line and grade in order to provide uniform support.

The subbase, whether it be compacted granular material, cement- or lime-treated soil, or lean concrete, will need to be laid to a regular and accurate surface level and maintained in a clean condition. Its use by construction traffic should be limited to the minimum necessary. In practice, however, the subbase—particularly on dual carriageway projects—is often used as a haul road, so its surface will need to be checked carefully before the concrete is poured to ensure that it contains no puddles, ruts, or soft spots.

Unlike flexible pavement construction, unevenness in the 'finished' subbase of a rigid pavement is not reflected in unevenness in the finished concrete surface; rather, it is reflected in variations in the thickness of the poured slab. Nonetheless, good control of the subbase surface level improves the uniformity of performance of a concrete road[54].

The subgrade or any bedding for forms should have sufficient strength to carry the concrete or paver without vertical movement. Cement-bound bedding should have sufficient time to reach the necessary strength before paving is initiated.

The type of equipment used to compact the subgrade and subbase is dependent upon the nature of the material being compacted. Thorough compaction is absolutely essential, and particular care should be taken during the back-filling of drainage excavations and other such openings.

### Form laying

After the subgrade and subbase have been compacted and graded, the next step is to lay the side-forms for the concrete. Formerly, timber forms were

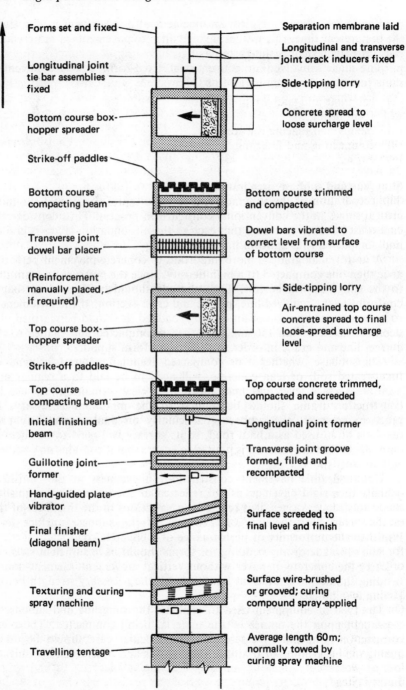

Direction of travel

Forms set and fixed

Longitudinal joint tie bar assemblies fixed

Bottom course box-hopper spreader

Strike-off paddles

Bottom course compacting beam

Transverse joint dowel bar placer

(Reinforcement manually placed, if required)

Top course box-hopper spreader

Strike-off paddles

Top course compacting beam

Initial finishing beam

Guillotine joint former

Hand-guided plate vibrator

Final finisher (diagonal beam)

Texturing and curing spray machine

Travelling tentage

Separation membrane laid

Longitudinal and transverse joint crack inducers fixed

Side-tipping lorry

Concrete spread to loose surcharge level

Bottom course trimmed and compacted

Dowel bars vibrated to correct level from surface of bottom course

Side-tipping lorry

Air-entrained top course concrete spread to final loose-spread surcharge level

Top course concrete trimmed, compacted and screeded

Longitudinal joint former

Transverse joint groove formed, filled and recompacted

Surface screeded to final level and finish

Surface wire-brushed or grooved; curing compound spray-applied

Average length 60 m; normally towed by curing spray machine

**Fig. 8.11** Typical arrangement of fixed-form paving plant for two-lane wide two-course pavement construction (based on reference[53])

used exclusively in concrete roadworks; it was found, however, that even the best quality timber formwork warped after contact with wet concrete on only very few occasions, and so today they have been supplanted entirely by purpose-made steel forms that are suitable for repeated use. Normally, these forms are 3 m long by up to 300 mm high, wide-based, steel sections that are temporarily fixed to the subbase; occasionally, however, they may be permanent concrete edge strips that are precast in advance of paving.

Forms serve dual purposes. Not only do they shape the sides of the concrete slab and define its top surface, but they also support flat-bottomed rails along which many of the paving machines operate during the laying of the pavement. As is suggested by Fig. 8.11, a paving train typically consists of at least a spreader and a vibratory compactor (both of which are often duplicated), an oscillating-beam finisher, and mechanical spraying equipment for the application of a curing compound. Additional equipment may be included in the train for such operations as the mechanical placement of joint tie bars and dowel bars, joint surface groove forming, and mechanized surface texturing. The major pieces of equipment are individually powered and self-propelled. Some smaller pieces, which are used more intermittently, may be moved manually along the form rails from one operating location to another, whilst others may be towed by a larger machine.

Since the equipment must be supported and guided by the rails on the side-forms, it follows that the forms need to be rigidly supported so that they will not be displaced in line or level by the lateral stresses and vibrations caused during the spreading and compacting of the fresh concrete.

The machines most commonly used in fixed-form paving trains in Britain are able to lay concrete widths of between 2.5 and 12.0 m. In practice, however, most concrete pavements are laid in either one or two-lane widths, as widths greater than about 7 m require considerably more substantial construction of the side-forms in order to maintain the desired rigidity.

Upon completion of form laying and aligning, the foundation layer (usually the subbase) is checked to ensure that its surface elevations and shape are exactly as desired. The plastic separation membrane is then placed on the surface prior to the fixing of any joint crack inducers or assemblies. Whilst the membrane needs to be positioned sufficiently far ahead to allow for subsequent preparation work, too much should not be laid in advance in order to minimize the risk of damage or of rainwater ponding upon it.

**Mixing and placing of concrete**
On large road contracts, well-organized fixed-form trains are capable of constructing up to 1 km of paving per day. For this to happen, concrete of a consistent quality must be available at the train not only in sufficient quantity but also steadily. Disruption to steady progress inevitably results in loss of workability, making finishing difficult and leading to bad riding quality. Steady progress requires a careful and realistic matching of mixing plant output and transport capability to the productive capacity of the paving train.

There are essentially three methods of organizing the mixing and delivery of concrete to large highway schemes, and all can produce effective and economic results if properly controlled. These methods are as follows.

(1)  *Batching at a central plant, and transporting the dry, batched materials to mixing and spreading machines at the construction site*  With this method, the aggregates and cement are batched by mass at a centrally located batching plant at the quarry or gravel pit away from the site. The dry materials are then transported by sheeted lorry to the site for wet-mixing and laying. At the site, the mixer may be a crawler-mounted machine travelling on the shoulder or mounted on a mobile framework spanning the foundation soil that is part of the fixed-form paving train. Whichever is used, the mixer travels forward in conjunction with the spreading and compacting machines so that the freshly-mixed concrete is always adjacent to the location where it has to be placed.

Whilst this method of organization can be criticized, for example on the grounds that a mixer must be available at the construction site which is constantly on the move, it has the particular advantage that there is continual and excellent control over the mixing time of the concrete, since setting cannot begin until water is added at the site just prior to spreading. It is very beneficial from the point of view of control of consistency and the proportioning of ingredients since, if any defect is found in the concrete during construction, it can be rectified immediately before another batch is started. Furthermore, if there is a breakdown in equipment at the site, the unmixed materials can be saved and used at another time.

(2)  *Batching and wet-mixing at a central plant, and transporting the fresh concrete to the spreading machines at the site*  This also requires the batching of the materials to take place at a central plant removed from the construction site. In this instance, however, the mixing machines are also located at the central plant and so wet-mixing takes place there. The wet concrete is then hauled to the spreader at the site by sheeted lorries or dumpers.

This method was almost universal in British concrete road construction in the 1970s[53]. It has the obvious advantage of obviating the necessity to move the mixer continuously in the course of construction. In addition, the permanency of the plant encourages the usage of more elaborate storage facilities and batching and mixing equipment, with a consequent beneficial influence upon the degree of quality control which can be attained. This method is particularly valuable when the central plant is capable of being used for several other concrete schemes in the same locality.

The disadvantages associated with this method are all concerned with the fact that the wet concrete has to be transported to the road site. Long hauls not only require more vehicles to keep the paving train in continuous operation, they also increase the risk of bunching of lorries in traffic and, consequently, the risk of an irregular supply to the train; this latter consideration can be of particular concern when concreting in urban areas and public highways have to be used for part of the haulage route. If travelling takes too long, say more than about 20 or 30 minutes, the concrete will begin to stiffen and its consistency and workability on arrival at the site may be detrimentally affected. Furthermore, if the haul road is bumpy, segregation may take place in the wet mixture; this will result in difficulty in discharging the material as well as defects in the compacted concrete. Finally, because the mixing and placing activities are separated, there is an inevitable loss in efficiency. Thus, for example, if a major piece of equipment at the site breaks down or if some defect is found in the concrete, all material in transit between the mixer and the site may have to be wasted if it cannot be diverted for other purposes.

(3) *Batching at a central plant, then mixing and transporting the batched materials simultaneously in an agitator vehicle* This can be considered a compromise between the previous two methods, since batching takes place at the central plant, and then wet-mixing is initiated either just before the mixture leaves for the site or en route during the trip. This method is most useful when the central plant is located a long distance from the road and working space at the site is limited. If the water is added and the mixing begun just prior to starting the journey, bulking is minimized and more material can be carried per unit volume of the mixer. If the journey is long and/or evaporation is likely to take place, water need not be added and mixing not initiated until the truck mixer is actually approaching the site. In either case, the fact that the concrete mixture can be agitated in the course of travel means that segregation is practically eliminated.

A major disadvantage of this method of operation is that of cost. Capital and operating costs of truck mixers are high and, as a result, the unit cost of the concrete may be higher than with the other two methods. Furthermore, truck mixers are slower to load and discharge than conventional end-tipping, side-tipping or ejector lorries. Also, the variability of concrete from truck mixers makes them unsuitable for large quantities of pavement-quality concrete, and they are best limited to supplying quality concrete for small, individual slabs[21].

Whichever of the latter two mixing methods is used, the size of each individual load hauled to the site should be equal to the capacity of the spreading hopper. The number of haul units required to ensure maximum spreader production is given by

$$\frac{\text{number of}}{\text{haul units}} = \frac{\text{loading time} + \text{journey time} + \text{unloading time}}{\text{spreading cycle time}}$$

It is usual also to provide at least one or two additional units so that, ideally, one vehicle is always waiting to discharge at the fixed-form train whilst another is waiting to load at the batching plant.

The placing of the fresh concrete should be carried out to obtain an even depth of uniform density with the minimum of segregation. The type of equipment most commonly used for this purpose in Britain is the traversing box-hopper spreader. This comprises a 4.5 m long hopper, of either 3.0 or 4.5 m$^3$ capacity, mounted on a self-propelled, rail-mounted frame. The usual procedure is for the power-operated hopper to receive concrete either directly from tipping lorries or by way of a side-feeding system working alongside; it then discharges the concrete through an adjustable bottom opening whilst moving across the width of the slab, with the machine frame either stationary or moving along the forms. The hopper is arranged so as to strike off the concrete to the desired surcharge level, i.e. the planned amount by which the initial depth of spread concrete exceeds the ultimate compacted slab thickness.

With fixed-form paving, good control of surface levels is mainly ensured by the spreader being able to spread the concrete evenly to the correct surcharge. It is bad practice to rely on subsequent regulating beams and the diagonal finisher to achieve the correct levels by a major planing operation[55]. If the first regulating beam in the compactor/finisher has too big a roll of concrete anywhere along the beam, the setting of the spreader should be changed. The roll in front of the regulating beam or diagonal finisher should be between 100 and 150 mm evenly distributed along the beam. If the roll is too great, then adjustment should be made at the spreader. If segregation occurs in the roll, adjustment to the workability of the mix may be necessary.

The *compacting factor test*[28] is a very useful measure of concrete workability at the site. For workability within the usual range of compaction factor values (say between 0.80 and 0.85), the concrete is usually spread to a depth between 25 and 18 per cent greater than that of the compacted slab. The amount of surcharge required decreases as the workability increases, as is illustrated by the following empirical formula which has been found to give heights close to those used in practice[56].

$$\text{surcharge} = \text{depth of slab required} \times \left( \frac{1}{\text{compacting factor}} - 1 \right)$$

In practice, the surcharge height is normally obtained by trial at the beginning of the work so that when fully compacted later it is level with the form elevations.

Other types of spreader include the *screw-auger spreader* and the *blade spreader*. With both types, the freshly-mixed concrete is dumped in small, well-distributed heaps on the subgrade or subbase, as the case may be, and is then distributed uniformly across the pavement width by the transversely-moving blade or screw-auger spreaders. A typical blade spreader has on its front a heavy reciprocating blade with a face inclined at 45 degrees in plan, which turns at the end of the stroke; thus it pushes the concrete forward and sideways at the same time. With the screw-auger spreader, the blade is replaced by a revolving screw which is similar to that used in a screw conveyor. This screw revolves alternately in each direction and distributes the concrete in front of strike-off paddles which, in a manner similar to that for the blade spreader, strike off the spread concrete at a predetermined height.

As with the box-hopper machines, the blade and screw-auger spreaders are part of wheel-mounted machines which can move longitudinally along the side-forms. Unlike box-hopper spreaders, however, the blade and screw-auger spreaders are rarely used in Britain, although they are in common usage in the USA.

With fixed-form equipment, unreinforced concrete may be placed to achieve the full slab depth in either one or two layers. With reinforced concrete construction, however, two-course construction is virtually unavoidable.

With reinforced work, the first course is spread and compacted to the reinforcement level. The steel fabric is then placed on the surface of the bottom layer and covered with a shallower, air-entrained concrete top course, using a spreader and compactor that immediately follow.

Unreinforced slabs can be spread to full depth in a single pass, provided that the equipment available is sufficiently powerful to ensure its proper compaction without unduly affecting the alignment of any dowel bars that may be used. In practice, however, many contractors prefer to use two-course construction when laying unreinforced slabs, for the following reasons.

(1)  Higher overall paving rates can be achieved.

(2)  The desired alignment of mechanically-placed, contraction joint dowel bars is easier to ensure if they are vibrated through a relatively shallow depth in the compacted bottom course rather than from the surface of a full-depth slab.

(3)  A high standard of surface regularity and riding quality is easier to achieve, particularly when laying concrete on steep gradients and crossfalls.

(4)  In some circumstances, lower-quality aggregates can be used in the bottom layer which are cheaper or more readily available, but which do not meet the more stringent requirements of top-course concrete.

**Compacting and finishing**

After the concrete has been spread to the surcharged depth, the next stages are its compaction, finishing and texturing. The sequence of operations is for the concrete to be compacted, then the finisher obtains the surface contour desired in the surface of the slab, after which the desired texturing is achieved.

The *compaction and initial finishing* of the concrete is carried out by a single piece of equipment composed of rotary strike-off paddles, a vibrating compaction beam, and an oscillating finishing beam.

The rotary strike-off paddles are mounted on independently-operated levelling screws at each side of the plant; these screws permit differential adjustments to be made which allow for carriageway crossfalls. The function of the paddles is to trim any minor irregularities which may still exist in the surface of the surcharged concrete.

The most common type of compaction beam normally applies vibration to the surface of the concrete at between 60 and 65 Hz, with the frequency used depending upon the characteristics of the mix; this permits satisfactory compaction of concrete to a depth of about 350 mm. In one model, the beam suspension incorporates a rocking or tamping action in addition to the vibration; this piece of equipment is able to provide satisfactory compaction to a depth of about 450 mm[10]. With all types, the height of the beam can be varied to allow for two-course construction, whilst each end can also be adjusted to compensate for the tendency of concrete to slump towards the low side of the pavement during compaction.

Overall, the aim of the compaction process is to obtain a dense, homogeneous slab of concrete which is free from voids, honeycombing and surface irregularities.

The oscillating finishing beam is usually a simple oscillating box-section float that is either mounted on the compactor machine carriage or carried on a trailing articulated framework. Only used for full-depth or top-course paving, this beam provides a regulated and partially finished surface which may be adequate as a 'final' finish on minor roads or industrial estates, but requires further treatment on higher-quality roads. When operating, the initial beam normally carries ahead of it a small amount of cement–sand grout—known as 'fat'—without coarse aggregate particles, which is uniform across the slab width.

It might be noted that the formation of longitudinal and contraction joints can be carried out immediately after the initial oscillating beam has completed its work. The longitudinal joint is formed with the aid of a hollow, vertical knife which travels submerged in the concrete; this knife is attached to the underside of a flat plate on which is mounted a small vibrator unit. Contraction grooves are most usually created with the aid of a vibrating guillotine blade which is caused to penetrate the concrete to the required depth; the vibration is then stopped and the blade withdrawn to leave the groove. Any disturbed concrete which results from these activities must be recompacted using manually-controlled vibrating plates.

The final finishing of the concrete, prior to texturing, is most often carried out by two diagonal finishing beams which oscillate in opposing directions and are mounted on an articulated, mobile framework. The leading beam vibrates and smooths the surface, whilst the rear beam acts as a float finisher. Diagonal rather than transverse beams are preferred as they reduce the area of finisher in contact with a joint former at any given time, with a consequent reduction in the likelihood of damage to the joint. The shearing action of the diagonal screed also results in a more uniform surface finish.

The last step in the finishing process is the *surface texturing* of the concrete. The purpose of this construction step is to provide a high-quality, skid-resistant surface.

As discussed previously (see Chapters 3 and 7), if a road pavement is to provide adequate resistance to skidding it must have both a macrotexture and a microtexture. The rough macrotexture is required to permit the displacement of the bulk of the water trapped between the tyre and the pavement, whilst the microtexture allows the remaining film of water to be penetrated so that the direct contact between the tyre and the pavement is maintained. In the case of concrete roads[57], the microtexture is ensured by incorporating a fine aggregate in the mix that is more resistant to abrasion than the matrix of the hardened cement paste, i.e. under traffic, the softer paste abrades so that the sand grains stand proud of the matrix. On British roads, the macrotexture is obtained by wire brushing or grooving the surface (at right-angles to the centreline), upon completion of the finishing process.

Wire-brush texturing is carried out manually from a travelling bridge or by means of mechanically-operated brushes. In either case, there are stringent requirements laid down regarding the brush system, and the average texture depth, as measured by the *sand patch test*[21], must be not less than 0.75 mm between 24 hours and seven days after construction of the slab, and not less than 0.65 mm not later than six weeks before the road is open to public traffic.

Grooving, which is undertaken mechanically using a vibrating head which traverses the width of the finished slab, is probably the better method of texturing. From a construction aspect, the method has the advantage that concrete of variable workability can be grooved, even when fairly stiff, as the speed and vibration of the head can be varied in intensity to suit the consistency of the compacted concrete. The desired texture is also easier and more consistently obtained. From a traffic safety aspect, water is removed more quickly and considerably less spray is thrown up by fast moving vehicles, due to the grooves forming continuous channels for the drainage of water across the pavement.

Measurements and subjective assessments of the riding quality of pavements constructed with grooves indicate that there is no significant difference between transversely-grooved and brushed concrete surfaces, when both texturing processes are properly carried out.

## Curing

This is the process which ensures that a satisfactory moisture content and favourable temperature are maintained in concrete during the period immediately following placement, so that hydration of the cement may continue until the desired properties are developed to a sufficient degree to meet the service requirements. Continued loss of moisture also results in drying shrinkage, and if curing is not properly carried out, plastic cracks may develop in the cement paste.

Conditions conducive to plastic shrinkage cracking include low humidity, wind, high concrete temperature, high air temperature, exposure to the direct rays of the sun, and concrete of low bleeding tendencies and/or a large surface area in relation to depth. The danger of plastic shrinkage cracking becomes very high when the evaporation rate reaches or exceeds 0.98 kg/m$^2$ per hour[58].

The best form of curing is to keep the concrete constantly damp. Means by which this is done are as follows.

(1) *Spraying waterproof membranes* The curing of road pavement slabs is most commonly carried out in Britain by mechanically spraying the surface of the concrete with an aluminized resin-base curing compound, immediately after the finishing process. Not only is the moisture prevented from evaporating by this impervious cover, but the aluminized membrane also reflects the radiant heat of the sun so that detrimental temperature

effects are lessened. The membrane has the further advantage that it needs no additional treatment after spraying and can be left to be worn off by vehicles when traffic is allowed on to the roadway.

Additional, immediate curing protection against not only the sun and wind, but also rain damage to the freshly-textured concrete, may be provided by the low-level travelling tentage which is normally towed behind the curing compound sprayer.

(2)   *Covering with damp fabric covers*   Used only for small areas now, this consists of placing damp fabric coverings, i.e. cotton matting, hessian, jute and cotton, directly on top of the concrete. This method is quite effective if coverings are sprinkled and kept constantly damp throughout the curing period. The principal disadvantages of this method are, firstly, that the coverings must not only be placed but also removed, and, secondly, that they must be constantly sprinkled with water; both of these factors increase the cost of the curing process.

(3)   *Covering with damp sand*   Once the initial hardening of the concrete is complete, i.e. the initial curing, it can be covered with about 5 cm of sand which is kept moist throughout the final curing period. While it is a quite effective curing procedure, it has the disadvantages of being both expensive and laborious, i.e. two separate coverings must be placed and removed, and again the sand must be kept constantly wet.

(4)   *Covering with plastic sheeting*   With this method, a layer of plastic sheeting is laid on top of the concrete, weighted down, and kept in close contact with the surface so that the wind does not penetrate beneath and free circulation of air is prevented. This allows droplets of condensed water to collect on the underside of the sheeting so that the concrete is cured under moist conditions.

(5)   *Water ponding*   This is a method of curing which was fairly widely used in the past but is rarely used now. Essentially, it consisted of building small clay dams about the slab and then flooding it with water. While this can be an effective way of curing a concrete slab, the disadvantages associated with it are obvious.

Even though the pavement may be structurally able to carry traffic from an early age, vehicles should not normally be allowed on hardened concrete until after about three weeks, as excessive wear of the surface texture might occur under heavy traffic. During prolonged hot weather it may be that this period can be reduced to two weeks, whilst in colder weather it is usual to increase the curing period by one day for each night that the temperature of the pavement surface falls below $0\,^{\circ}C$.

## Slip-form paving

An obvious problem associated with the use of conventional fixed-form paving is that the side-forms must be left in position for at least 4 h after completion of construction; in practice, they are usually left in position for about 24 h before being removed—most carefully, to avoid damage to the finished concrete—for cleaning and reuse. As a result, the road builder must always have available on site enough side-forms for about three days work at the normal rate, in order to ensure that enough time is available for the advance setting of the forms and their removal after paving.

In 1947, engineers at the Iowa State Highway Commission in the USA conceived the idea of a 'slip-form' paver which would lay concrete roads without the use of conventional side-forms. Originally considered by many highway engineers as a cute toy[59] which would never be used for major highway construction, slip-form paving has now become a conventional method of concrete road building throughout the world.

With slip-form paving, the preparation of the subgrade and subbase is similar to that for the fixed-form method, only now the rest of the conventional train is replaced by a single machine frame within which are combined the main operations of spreading, trimming, compaction, and finishing. The slip-form paver is self-propelled and mounted on caterpillar tracks—these minimize the pressure placed on the subgrade or subbase—which travel outside sliding side-forms attached within the length of the machine. The maintenance of the correct alignment and accurate levels during the paving process is ensured with the aid of automatic control systems on the machine which remain in continuous contact with tensioned guide-wires supported on stakes on each side of the pavement.

In a typical paving operation, the plastic concrete is deposited at the front of the moving paver and between the slip-forms; this is then struck off by a paddle or ram, leaving the desired surcharged height of concrete. The paver then forces a row of either poker vibrators or motorized angle plates through the concrete, which drive out the air and render the concrete fluid by intense vibration. As the machine moves forward—typically at a rate of 1–3 m per minute—it engulfs the concrete between the moving forms (up to 15 m long) on each side and a conforming plate bearing on the mix's surface; the concrete is still maintained in a fluid condition by a transverse vibrator placed in front of the conforming plate. By the time the concrete emerges behind the machine, it is beyond the effective range of vibration and is thus able to retain its shape. This is aided by the use of an air-entrained concrete with a low compacting factor, i.e. one which is sticky, cohesive and quite plastic.

The main features of a typical slip-form paver are illustrated in Fig. 8.12 which describes a paver developed in Britain[60] to lay plain concrete slabs in one operation.

Note that with this machine all the transverse contraction joint dowels and the longitudinal joint tie bars are automatically inserted by the paver as the slab is slip formed. Another important principle is the use of a plastic strip to create a vertical plane of weakness in the slab, thus cutting out the need for a longitudinal joint crack inducer. As is indicated in Fig. 8.12, the strips are towed on steel keels under the paver and under a joint seal-inserter through the green concrete whilst it is still being vibrated; the strip's length is such as to ensure that it leaves the concrete in a fully-compacted state outside the influence of further vibration. Another feature is the fitting of polythene membrane rolls in front of the concrete hopper so that the sheets are unrolled directly under the paver as it moves forward.

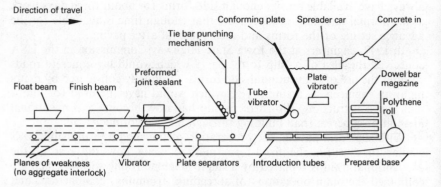

**Fig. 8.12**   Gunter and Zimmerman/McGregor modified slip-form paver

## Slip-form versus fixed-form paving

The following are generally regarded as being the two main *advantages* that slip-form paving has over fixed-form construction.

(1)   Higher daily outputs are possible as the plant is not restricted by the speed at which side-forms can be laid. Paving rates of 2–3 km per day are not uncommon: indeed, it is reported[59] that a slip-form paver laid 7.58 km of 7.3 m wide pavement in one long (23.5 h) working day.
(2)   Slip-form pavers are less labour-intensive as they involve fewer machines and there is no need to provide for the maintenance, setting and handling of large numbers of (expensive) side-forms.

The major *disadvantages* of slip-form paving are as follows.

(1)   The paving machine is far more complex than the traditional fixed-form train, and requires more expensive skills and experience for its proper maintenance and operation.
(2)   A relatively minor failure in the control system can result in the whole slip-form paving operation coming to a halt.
(3)   Greater stockpiles of cement and aggregates are required in advance to ensure that the higher output of the paving machine is maintained.
(4)   There is a tendency for edge slump in the concrete immediately after leaving the paver.

## Concrete block paving

The idea of using interlocking paving blocks for road construction is not new, e.g. many examples of hand-crafted stone roads built by the early Romans exist in Europe today. Stone sett paving was in wide use early this century, although its popularity soon waned in favour of cheaper materials such as tar macadam, due to its high cost and poor riding quality.

The modern use of concrete blocks for road construction came into prominence in the Netherlands in the 1950s, and since then its usage has grown considerably throughout the world. A major reason for the upsurge has been the development of block-making machinery which can rapidly produce concrete blocks of high compressive strength to close dimensional tolerances. There has also been a worldwide trend towards beautifying cities and more emphasis on controlling traffic with the aid of local area traffic management schemes, to which concrete block paving is well suited.

Characteristics of concrete block pavements which render them attractive to pavement designers are stated to be as follows[61]:

(1)   their ability to handle a wide range of wheel and point loads,
(2)   their ability to tolerate some subgrade movement without fatigue in the pavement surface,
(3)   the fact that the pavement gains stiffness with use, and is ultimately unaffected by increases in load or frequency of single wheel loads within the range 2–7 t,
(4)   the ease of their reinstatement in the event of areas of localized settlement occurring, with almost complete re-utilization of the pavement units,
(5)   the ease of access to underground services without the use of road-breaking equipment, and trench reinstatement without visible patching,
(6)   the simplicity of construction, i.e. the placement of block pavements does not require expensive plant and is generally suited to unskilled labour,
(7)   immediate access for traffic is provided upon completion of laying,
(8)   the delineation of areas of use and the location of underground services is facilitated by the use of contrasting coloured units,
(9)   the paving units may be used for temporary site access or as a traffic bypass prior to their final location in the pavement,
(10)   the blocks provide a wearing surface which has good durability and skid-resistance characteristics,
(11)   interlocking concrete pavements produce a noise differential with respect to adjacent pavements which can act as a safety measure to alert motorists, e.g. at intersections and pedestrian crossings.

## Design and construction

Concrete block paving is composed of small, individual, high-strength precast concrete units that are manufactured to very tight dimensional tolerances, placed on a bed of sand, and locked into place between edge restraints (see Fig. 8.13). Available in a variety of shapes, colours and textures, the blocks are based on a nominal 100 mm × 200 mm module and are normally laid without mortar joints.

The joints between the blocks—they are usually about 2–3 mm wide—are packed with dust and sand particles which prevent the blocks from being displaced. Horizontal interlock is provided either by a proprietary keying shape or, for plain rectangular blocks, by the use of a herringbone laying pattern. Edge restraint is provided by in situ or precast concrete kerbs, or flush edge strips.

A vertical load applied to a block laid in a paving causes it to behave in a flexible way; that is, the load is supported by that block, by those blocks surrounding it and, to a lesser extent, by blocks further away. Under traffic conditions, the interlocking blocks progressively stiffen and tend to lock together and share the load; this condition of 'lock-up' is also manifested by reductions in the rate of accumulation of deformation. Once this lock-up is achieved, the block pavement attains a stable equilibrium condition which is reported[61] to be unaffected by the volume of traffic or the magnitude of single wheel loads within the range 2–7 t.

At the time of writing, there are no governmental recommendations relating to the design of concrete block roads. However, design recommendations, based on those for flexible pavements in *Road Note 29*[11], have been developed by the Cement and Concrete Association (CCA) for lightly- and heavily-trafficked roads and paved areas (see references 62 and 63, respectively).

Figure 8.13 illustrates a typical pavement structure for a lightly-trafficked paved area. Note that it consists of a subbase, laying course (50 mm of clean sharp sand), surface course (normally 80 mm thick blocks for roads), and edge restraint. On the basis of research work which indicated that concrete blocks have a load-spreading capability similar to that of 160 mm of rolled asphalt, the CCA design for these roads allows the concrete block paving to be laid directly over a subbase designed in accordance with Fig. 6.20 for any subgrade and pavement life expectancy up to 1.5 msa.

In other words, the conventional flexible pavement's wearing course, basecourse, and roadbase are replaced by a layer of 80 mm thick concrete blocks and 50 mm of sharp sand. (The sand should contain not more than 3 per cent of silt and clay by mass and not more than 10 per cent retained on a 5 mm sieve.)

In the case of heavily-trafficked roads, the CCA design assumes the pavement structure to be composed of a layer of 80 mm thick concrete blocks, 50 mm of sharp sand, a cement- or bitumen-bound roadbase, and a subbase. The subbase thickness is determined from Table 6.5, whilst the roadbase thickness is derived from design curves relating cumulative numbers of standard axles to lean concrete, dense macadam, and rolled asphalt roadbase thicknesses.

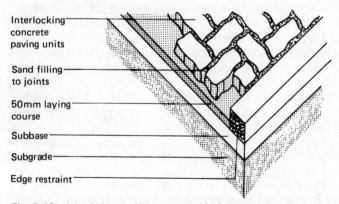

Interlocking concrete paving units

Sand filling to joints

50mm laying course

Subbase

Subgrade

Edge restraint

**Fig. 8.13**   A basic interlocking concrete block pavement

The construction of subbases and roadbases for concrete block roads is carried out as in the normal way for flexible pavements. In the case of the laying course, the sand is spread to a uniform height of about 65 mm, i.e. with a surcharge of about 15 mm. The blocks are laid by hand on top of this bed according to the pre-arranged pattern, and then vibrated down to the desired level using a plate vibrator. Additional sand is then brushed over the blocks to fill up the joints.

Joints in block pavement surfacings are not sealed, at least in the short to medium term. Consequently, there is opportunity for water to enter the pavement and damage the underlying layers. This is of particular concern when the subgrade is a weak material.

It might be noted also, however, that after a concrete block pavement has been in service for a short time, the joints between the blocks tend to become filled with fine material. As a result, the block road needs to be designed according to the normal longitudinal and crossfall requirements, to avoid ponding of rainwater on the surface.

*Comment*  Worldwide, the use of concrete blocks in road construction has mushroomed over the past decade. In Britain, for example, the number of manufacturing plants rose from four in 1975 to fifteen in 1980, whilst the annual production of concrete blocks reached 2.5 km$^2$ by 1983.

Experience suggests that concrete block paving is suitable for roads on which vehicle speeds are restricted to 50 km/h, and where the standards of riding quality that can be achieved are acceptable[10]. Typical applications are residential roads, pedestrian precincts, building forecourts, car parks, footways and landscaped areas. This form of paving is considered to be particularly suitable for use in residential areas where the pavement is to be shared between the pedestrian and the vehicle.

Particular care has to be taken when constructing block pavements at locations where vehicles brake and/or accelerate hard, e.g. a road junction on a longitudinal gradient. The blocks may creep at such locations and must be laid in a herringbone pattern to reduce this movement to the minimum.

The amount of research carried out on block pavements is still limited (see reference 64 for an excellent review of the literature), and there is a clear need to monitor a number of in-service concrete block pavements, especially construction details and performance data. Until this work is done, care should be taken in using concrete block pavements under heavy traffic conditions, especially over poor subgrade soils.

## Selected bibliography

(1) Lake JR, Lister NW and Thompson PD, Concrete road experience in Great Britain 1969–1975, *Proceedings of the International Conference on Concrete Pavement Design*, pp. 247–263, Purdue, Indiana, Purdue University, 1977.

(2) *The Cost of Constructing and Maintaining Flexible and Concrete Pavements Over 50 Years*, RRL Report LR256, Crowthorne, Berks., The Road Research Laboratory, 1969.

(3) Parry JD, Concrete roads in developing countries, *Highways and Transportation*, 1985, **32**, No. 8, pp. 13–17.

(4) Mildenhall HS and Northcott GDS, *Maintenance and Rehabilitation of Concrete Roads*, Paper presented at the Fifth International Symposium on Concrete Roads, Aachen/Aix-la-Chapelle, 2–4 June 1986.

(5) Tait JB, *Design and Construction of Concrete Road Pavements*, RRU Technical Recommendation TR6, Wellington NZ, The National Roads Board, 1983.

(6) Thompson MR and Dempsey BJ, Subgrade soils: An important factor in concrete pavement design, in the Proceedings as reference 1, pp. 399–432.

(7) Paving Bureau, *Subgrades, Subbases and Shoulders for Concrete Pavements*, Chicago, Illinois, The Portland Cement Association, 1960.

(8) Department of Transport, *Notes for Guidance on the Specification for Road and Bridge Works*, London, HMSO, 1976.

(9) *Road Pavement Design*, Technical Memorandum H6/78, London, The Department of Transport, 1978.

(10) Transport and Road Research Laboratory, *A Guide to Concrete Road Construction*, London, HMSO, 1978 (3rd edition).

(11) Road Research Laboratory, *A Guide to the Structural Design of Pavements for New Roads*, Road Note 29, London, HMSO, 1970 (3rd edition).

(12) Hanna AN, *Properties of Expanded Polystyrene Concrete and Applications for Pavement Subbases*, Research and Development Bulletin RD055, 01P, Skoki, Illinois, The Portland Cement Association, 1978.

(13) Ring GW, Drainage of concrete pavement structures, in the Proceedings as reference 1, pp. 365–378.

(14) Barksdale RD and Hicks RG, Drainage considerations to minimize distress at the pavement–shoulder joint, in the Proceedings as reference 1, pp. 383–398.

(15) Highway Research Board, Final report of committee on maintenance of concrete pavements as related to the pumping action of slabs, *Proc. Highway Research Board*, 1948, **28**, pp. 281–310.

(16) Walker BJ, *Dry and Wet Cement Stabilized Materials for Concrete Pavement Sub-bases*, Paper presented at the International Colloquium on Concrete Roads, Besancon, September 1978.

(17) Sharp R, *Standards and Practices for Concrete Roads: A European Survey*, Paper presented at the International Symposium on Concrete Roads, London, 13–15 September 1982.

(18) Lister NW and Maggs MF, *Research and Development in the Design of Concrete Pavements*, Paper presented at the International Symposium on Concrete Roads, London, 13–15 September 1982.

(19) Hardman R, Heaton BS, Jordan PG and Abell R, *The Economics of the Operation of Construction Traffic on the Sub-base of a Road Pavement*, TRRL Report LR606, Crowthorne, Berks., The Transport and Road Research Laboratory, 1973.

(20) BS 5328: *Methods for Specifying Concrete, Including Ready-mix Concrete*, London, The British Standards Institution, 1981.

(21) Department of Transport, *Specification for Highway Works*, London, HMSO, 1986.

(22) BS 882: *Aggregates from Natural Sources for Concrete*, London, The British Standards Institution, 1983.

(23) BS 1047: *Air-cooled Blast Furnace Slag Aggregate for Use in Construction*, London, The British Standards Institution, 1983.

(24) Rixom MR (ed.), *Concrete Admixtures: Use and Applications*, London, Construction Press, 1977.

(25) *Admixtures in Concrete*, Special Report 119, Washington DC, The Highway Research Board, 1971.

(26) Teychenne DC, Franklin RE and Erntroy HC, *Design of Normal Concrete Mixes*, London, HMSO, 1975.

(27) Abrams DA, *Design of Concrete Mixtures*, Structural Materials Research Laboratory Bull. No. 1, Chicago, Illinois, Lewis Institute, December 1918.

(28) BS 1881: Part 103: *Methods of Testing Concrete: Determination of Compacting Factor*, London, The British Standards Institution, 1983.

(29) Sharp R, European concrete road standards and practices, in the Proceedings as reference 1, pp. 73–96.

(30) Nissbaum PJ and Lokken EC, Design and construction of concrete pavements, in the Proceedings as reference 1, pp. 19–54.

(31) Westergaard HM, Stress in concrete pavements computed by theoretical analysis, *Public Roads*, 1926, 7, No. 2, pp. 25–35.

(32) Westergaard HM, Analytical tools for judging results of structural tests of concrete pavements, *Public Roads*, 1933, 14, No. 10, pp. 185–188.

(33) Yoder EJ, Design principles and practices—Concrete pavements, *Proceedings of the Australian Road Research Board*, 1978, 9, Part 1, pp. 149–171.

(34) Sparkes FN and Smith AF, *Concrete Roads*, London, Arnold, 1962.

(35) Westergaard HM, Analysis of stresses in concrete pavements caused by variations in temperature, *Public Roads*, 1928, 8, No. 3, pp. 54–60.

(36) Stott JP and Brook KM, *Report on a Visit to the USA to Study Blow-ups in Concrete Roads*, RRL Report LR128, Crowthorne, Berks., The Road Research Laboratory, 1968.

(37) Nowak JR, *The Concrete Pavement—Design Experiment on Trunk Road A1 at Alconbury Hill: Twenty Years' Performance*, TRRL Report LR887, Crowthorne, Berks., The Transport and Road Research Laboratory, 1979.

(38) BS 4483: *Steel Fabric for the Reinforcement of Concrete*, London, The British Standards Institution, 1969.

(39) BS 4449: *Hot Rolled Steel Bars for the Reinforcement of Concrete*, London, The British Standards Institution, 1978.

(40) BS 4461: *Cold Worked Steel Bars for the Reinforcement of Concrete*, London, The British Standards Institution, 1978.

(41) Gregory JM, *The Effect of the Revision of Road Note No. 29 on Reinforcement Requirements for Reinforced Concrete Pavements*, TRRL Report LR460, Crowthorne, Berks., The Transport and Road Research Laboratory, 1972.

(42) Parmenter BS, *The Design and Construction of Joints in Concrete Pavements*, TRRL Report LR512, Crowthorne, Berks., The Transport and Road Research Laboratory, 1973.

(43) Gregory JM, Burke AE and Pink A, *Continuously Reinforced Concrete Pavements: A Report of the Study Group*, TRRL Report LR612, Crowthorne Berks., The Transport and Road Research Laboratory, 1974.

(44) Committee on Rigid Pavement Design, *State of the Art of Rigid Pavement Design*, Special Report 95, pp. 1–33, Washington DC, The Highway Research Board, 1968.

(45) Darter MI, Lacoursiere SA and Smiley SA, Structural mechanisms in continuously reinforced concrete pavement, *Transportation Research Record 715*, 1979, pp. 1–7.

(46) Friberg BF, Prestressed pavements, theory into practice, in the Proceedings as reference 1, pp. 157–173.

(47) Road Research Laboratory, *Concrete Roads*, London, HMSO, 1955.

(48) Ray GK, Effect of defective joint seals on pavement performance, *Transportation Research Record 752*, 1980, pp. 1–2.

(49) Hodgkinson JR, *Joint Sealants for Concrete Road Pavements*, Technical Note 48, North Sydney, NSW, The Cement and Concrete Association of Australia, June 1982.

(50) Wright PJF, Full scale tests of materials for sealing expansion joints in concrete roads, *Roads and Road Construction*, 1963, **41**, No. 485, pp. 138–146.

(51) Mayhew HC and Harding HM, *Thickness Design of Concrete Roads*, TRRL Research Report 87, Crowthorne, Berks., The Transport and Road Research Laboratory, 1986.

(52) Joint Task Force on Pavements, *Proposed AASHTO Guide for the Design of Pavement Structures*, NCHRP Project 20-7/24, Washington DC, The American Association of State Highway and Transportation Officials, 1985.

(53) Walker BJ and Beadle D, *Mechanized Construction of Concrete Roads*, London, The Cement and Concrete Association, 1977.

(54) McLellan JC, *Pavement Thickness, Surface Evenness and Construction Practice*, TRRL Report SR706, Crowthorne, Berks., The Transport and Road Research Laboratory, 1982.

(55) Department of Transport, *Notes for Guidance on the Specification for Highway Works*, London, HMSO, 1986.

(56) Blake LS and Brook KM, *The Construction of Major Concrete Roads in Great Britain, 1955–1960*, Technical Report TRA/363, London, The Cement and Concrete Association, 1962.

(57) Murphy WE and Maynard DP, Surface texture of British concrete pavements, *Transportation Engineering Journal of ASCE*, 1975, **101**, No. TE1, pp. 115–136.

(58) Committee on Batching, Mixing, Placing and Curing of Concrete, *Curing of Concrete Pavements*, Transportation Research Circular No. 208, Washington DC, The Transportation Research Board, June 1979.

(59) Ray GK, Lokken EC and Packard RG, Slipform pavers prove their versatility, *Transportation Engineering Journal of ASCE*, 1975, **101**, No. TE4, pp. 721–736.

(60) Concrete road breakthrough: McGregor slips fully dowelled slabs in Essex, *New Civil Engineer*, 1972, October 12, p. 20.

(61) Hodgkinson JR and Morrish CF, *Design of Interlocking Concrete Pavements for Road Traffic*, Technical Note TN 40, North Sydney, NSW, The Cement and Concrete Association of Australia, March 1982.

(62) Lilley AA and Clark AJ, *Concrete Block Paving for Lightly Trafficked Roads and Paved Areas*, London, The Cement and Concrete Association, 1978.

(63) Lilley AA and Walker BJ, *Concrete Block Paving for Heavily Trafficked Roads and Paved Areas*, London, The Cement and Concrete Association, 1978.

(64) Sharp KG and Armstrong PJ, *Interlocking Concrete Block Pavements*, ARRB Special Report No. 31, Vermont South, Victoria, The Australian Road Research Board, 1985.

# 9
# Pavement maintenance and strengthening

Since the mid-1950s, the tremendous growth in the number and usage of motor vehicles has meant that the countries of the western world have spent immense sums on developing their road networks. In more recent years, the newly developing third world countries have also invested very considerable amounts in highway infrastructures in order to boost their burgeoning economies. As will have been gathered from previous chapters in Volumes 1 and 2 of *Highways*, the needs generated by the great increases in vehicle numbers and kilometres of road have given rise to major research programmes in traffic planning and engineering, and in pavement materials and design, which have led to notable improvements in highway construction and traffic operations.

Unfortunately, research into the preservation of the highway network has not paralleled that of planning, design, construction and traffic management. Partly as a result of this, and partly for financial reasons, this aspect of the road engineer's work has tended to be treated as the 'poor relation' of highway engineering.

In recent years, however, as major highway construction programmes have come close to completion, the need to preserve the road system as a national asset has become apparent to governments in many countries. Furthermore, many of the highways constructed in the 1950s and 1960s have neared the end of their design lives, and some have deteriorated very badly, e.g. in the UK, in 1984 the Department of Transport estimated that some 20 per cent of its motorway pavements had a life expectation of 0–5 years, 18 per cent had 6–10 years, 20 per cent had 11–15 years, and 42 per cent had 16 plus years. As a result, it is now clear that the 'after-care' of highways is going to become one of the most rapidly developing areas of highway engineering in the next decade and beyond.

## Terminology

Terminology concerned with highway preservation varies considerably from country to country; it also varies from urban area to rural area, and from highway authority to highway authority within rural and urban areas. In summary, there is no uniform terminology and, as will be discussed, the following definitions should not necessarily be assumed to apply to all locations and highway systems.

A well-established description of *highway maintenance* is that it is concerned with the task of preserving, repairing and restoring a system of roadways, with its elements, to its designed or accepted configuration[1]. Examples of system elements are as follows: carriageway surfaces, shoulders, roadsides, drainage facilities, bridges, tunnels, signs, markings and lighting fixtures. Included in the task are such traffic services as lighting and signal operation, snow and ice removal, and the operation of roadside rest areas.

*Highway maintenance programmes* are developed to carry out the above task, and to contain the detrimental effects of weather, organic growth, deterioration, traffic wear, damage and vandalism. Deterioration includes the effects of ageing, material failures, and design and construction faults. The preservation and repair of buildings, stockpiles and equipment essential to performing the highway maintenance task are also part of highway maintenance programmes.

A *routine maintenance programme* groups those activities that are carried out as frequently as required during each year on all elements of the highway (including its ancillary furniture and equipment), in order to ensure serviceability at all times and in all weathers. The main operations included are[2]:

(1)   the cleansing of carriageways, verges, ditches, drains, signs and signals, safety barriers, etc., as well as grass cutting and tree pruning,
(2)   the repair of minor damage to carriageways, verges, slopes, culverts, signals and signposts, barriers, lighting facilities, and buildings, as well as any urgent interventions required to restore disrupted traffic movement, e.g. removal of debris from the carriageway,
(3)   the replacement of ancillary furniture and equipment that has been damaged, e.g. signing, barriers, road markings, drainage tubes or small channels, planted areas, lighting facilities,
(4)   winter maintenance operations intended to retain serviceability in poor weather conditions, e.g. clearance of snow and ice, having regard to prevention and cure.

A *periodic maintenance programme* covers all longer-term programmable operations required within the service life of the road. These activities, which may be required only at intervals of several years, can be divided into two main groups, as follows:

(1)   the renewal or renovation of the wearing surfaces of carriageways that become worn or deformed by use, e.g. the regravelling of unpaved roads and the resealing/surface dressing of paved roads,
(2)   the restoration of road markings, culverts and ancillary items, and the repainting of metal bridges, etc.

*Extraordinary maintenance activities* aim to refurbish roads to their original condition, when they have severely deteriorated. Typically, they involve:

(1)   the strengthening and/or reconstruction of a pavement structure that has deteriorated,

(2)   major actions to protect roads against external agents, e.g. actions involving slope stabilization and falls of rocks, retaining walls, and protection against flooding and avalanches.

*Road strengthening*[3] is most usually accomplished by the application of one or more structural layers (*overlays*) to an existing pavement. It can also be accomplished in certain cases by the replacement of one or more existing pavement courses by new and generally higher-quality materials, by the reworking of existing in-place materials (i.e. *recycling*), by drainage works, by cement grouting in the case of cement concrete pavements or by the injection of other materials into underlying basecourses, and by stabilization in the case of unpaved roads.

If the effect of the pavement overlay(s) is to restore the initial pavement serviceability and/or to provide the extra structural capacity needed to withstand previously unexpected future traffic, the strengthening activity is sometimes described as *rehabilitation*. At the same time, however, it might be noted that at least one major workshop conference[4] has defined pavement rehabilitation as including the whole field of strengthening *and* maintenance.

If the highway strengthening also involves widening the pavement from, say, two lanes to three or four lanes and/or the use of lengthy portions of new alignment, so that the operational characteristics of the highway section are significantly improved, this process is normally termed *reconstruction*. The term reconstruction is also used to describe the situation where an existing pavement has failed and all or part of the surfacing, roadbase and subbase in the failed section is removed and the pavement is rebuilt to the same or greater thickness.

Highway maintenance activities can also be grouped and classified according to the purpose of the treatment. Thus the term *preventative maintenance* is used[5,6] to describe actions taken to prevent premature deterioration and/or to retard the progression of deficiencies, so as to reduce the rate of deterioration and effectively increase the useful life of a pavement. By contrast, the term *corrective maintenance*[5]—also known as *remedial* or *curative maintenance*[6]—is used to refer to maintenance actions taken to correct deficiencies which are potentially hazardous, e.g. to repair defects which seriously affect a pavement's operation, so as to keep the highway within a tolerable level of serviceability.

In general, preventative maintenance programmes automatically include routine maintenance activities, whilst corrective maintenance actions tend to encompass many of the activities carried out in the course of routine, periodic and extraordinary programmes. There are many instances, however, where preventative maintenance also includes actions carried out via routine and periodic programmes, e.g. the exclusion of water from a paved road through crack sealing can be classified as both preventative and routine maintenance, whilst surface dressing (resealing) can be described as both periodic and preventative maintenance.

## Maintenance management

### Maintenance organizations

The first comprehensive national report on the previously unfashionable subject of highway maintenance was published in Britain in 1970. This report—the *Marshall Report*[7]—paid particular attention to the organization and administration of maintenance work, and concluded that differences in local conditions and geography between highway authorities were such that no single maintenance organization could be recommended for all authorities. However, the report also emphasized the need for simple lines of authority responsibility and accountability, and for clear channels of communication in relation to maintenance management.

Subsequent investigation resulted in the recommendations[8] illustrated in Fig. 9.1 with respect to a desirable maintenance organization within a typical local authority in Britain. In practice, of course, maintenance organizations can (and do) differ considerably from this proposed structure. Nonetheless, it is useful to consider this proposal as it provides a convenient mechanism for summarizing the form of a maintenance organization. Furthermore, it emphasizes certain basic maintenance management concepts, e.g. the key theme underlying the proposed structure is the need for communication links, both vertical and horizontal, which will ensure the rapid flow of accurate information within the organization.

### Management structure

Different interpretations may be placed on designated posts in any management structure, and so the posts in the structure shown in Fig. 9.1 are described by numbered tiers. Typically, the County Surveyor and the Deputy County Surveyor would be regarded as operating in the first tier (not shown in the figure), whilst the line managers, e.g. the head of the maintenance organization, would be at the second tier. As the members of the first and second tiers form the corporate management of the Highways Department, this relationship ensures that the chief maintenance engineer not only has direct access to, but is also one of, the policy makers.

Where adequate support for the chief maintenance engineer is not available, the efficiency of the maintenance organization will be adversely affected. Consequently, the structure proposes that the maintenance group at the head office should contain, at the third tier, engineers with responsibility for works, surfacing and construction.

Typically, the *Engineer (Works)* would be responsible to the head of the maintenance organization for the day-to-day operation of a number of functions, such as:

(1)   liaison with district councils,
(2)   the collation of information from the Highways Management Services Section, its application and dissemination,
(3)   the operation of the *Public Utilities Street Works Act and Code*,
(4)   the maintenance and installation of street lighting,

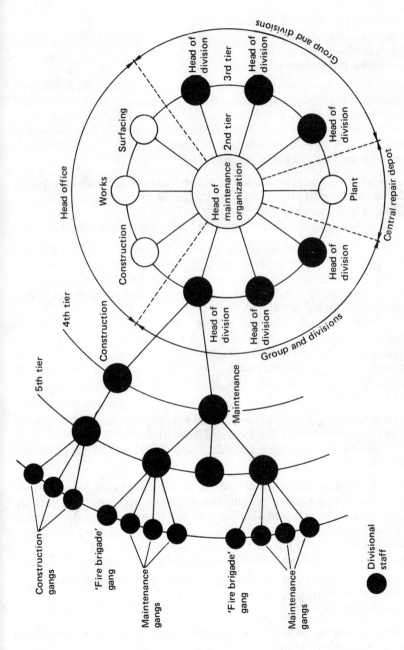

**Fig. 9.1** Suggested structure of a local authority's maintenance organization[8]

(5)   the road record system and its application (including maintenance assessment ratings),
(6)   plant utilization and allocation,
(7)   general correspondence,
(8)   safety officer,
(9)   training programmes.

A large proportion of the total maintenance expenditure on highways is directed towards structural maintenance, in particular to surfacing and surface dressing, e.g. the Marshall Committee reported that, on trunk roads, up to 75 per cent of the total maintenance expenditure was devoted to resurfacing and surface dressing. Accordingly, the *Engineer (Surfacing)* would be a specialist engineer responsible for:

(1)   the selection and specification of all surface treatments and the quality of the finished results (viz. riding quality and skid-resistance),
(2)   liaison with material suppliers,
(3)   the letting and administration of annual maintenance contracts.

In local authorities where major or complex construction works form a considerable part of the direct works programme, some central control is required to coordinate these activities. Thus the *Engineer (Construction)* would be responsible for the control and coordination of all major and/or complex construction works.

For economy and efficiency reasons, the Central Repair Depot is normally a service area that provides for the needs of the Highways Department as a whole, and not just for those of the maintenance organization. Typically, therefore, the *Engineer (Plant)* would be a qualified mechanical engineer with considerable management experience who would be responsible for:

(1)   the maintenance of all plant and vehicles of the Highways Department (and possibly of those for the local authority as a whole),
(2)   advice on the selection, suitability and utilization of all plant and vehicles.

The size of a maintenance division is ideally determined by analysis of operational considerations within the highway authority. In general, however, it can be expected that each of the maintenance organization's operational divisions would be responsible for lengths of road of between 1000 and 1600 km, subject to road and population density. A third tier *Head of Divisional Organization* would then be responsible for:

(1)   the organization and supervision of all of the division's maintenance activities, whether they be by direct works or by contract,
(2)   public relations.

The total number of supporting staff in each division would normally be based on the evaluation of the work load carried. However, to ensure that the overall functional responsibilities have a sound engineering basis, the report suggests that there should be at least *two appointments at the fourth tier in each division* as follows:

(1)   an engineer responsible to the divisional manager for the control of the divisional maintenance programme, and who can deputize for the manager in his or her absence,
(2)   an engineer responsible to the divisional manager for the control of the divisional construction programme.

At the *fifth tier*, the following posts are suggested:

(1)   personnel responsible to the fourth tier engineer (maintenance) for the planning and execution of routine maintenance, to be deployed on the basis of subdivisional maintenance areas of, typically, 150–500 km of road, depending upon area population and traffic intensities—each fifth tier appointee (who need not be a qualified engineer) would be responsible for the operation of three to four individually equipped and fully-mobile maintenance gangs deployed on a functional basis, and for one or two 'fire-brigade' gangs to deal with emergencies,
(2)   a person to supervise the operation of the *Public Utilities Street Works Act and Code*, estate development and highways works under planning consent,
(3)   depending upon the extent and geographic distribution of the direct labour construction programme, a person responsible for the execution of this programme.

## Assessment of maintenance needs

### Basic approach

Any assessment of maintenance needs starts with the following with regard to the highway section/system being studied:

(1)   a road inventory, including information regarding the soils, terrain and climate of the district serviced,
(2)   knowledge of the nature and amount of traffic using the road(s),
(3)   regular inspections of each road.

With this basic information, the maintenance engineer should be able to determine priorities and draw up purposeful programmes which will enable the required work to be carried out in a systematic and cost-effective way.

Simply gathering data represents a significant work load in its own right, and there is often a temptation to reduce the amount and scope of data-gathering when maintenance funds are tight. This should be resisted where possible, as adequate maintenance records are in many ways the key to credibility and, consequently, good road maintenance.

At the same time, it must be remembered that when establishing a maintenance databank, perhaps the most difficult management problem to overcome is that of defining precisely what information is required to meet management objectives and to refrain from asking for more data than is really necessary. It is easy to call for data, it is relatively easy to acquire and store data, it is possible to devise computer programs for the retrieval of these data at reasonable cost, but it is by no means easy to decide at the outset what data are immediately essential, what are likely to be required in future years, and what would be useful if acquired[2].

**Inventory**
As noted above, the inventory records basic data regarding the geometry and structure of the highway, as well as information regarding drainage, soils and climatic conditions. This is the basic reference material used in the planning and carrying out of maintenance operations and inspections. At its simplest, the inventory might be a road map of the maintenance district under consideration, marked up to show surface types, road widths, bridges, etc.; as the maintenance system is developed, the inventory is extended to cover other items such as those given in Table 9.1.

In respect of soils, topography and climate, it is not normally necessary for the maintenance engineer to have detailed knowledge of these features when establishing requirements for highway repair works. Rather it is important to know, for example, where expansive clay soils are located and

**Table 9.1**    Some basic inventory items required for maintenance purposes[9]

| Inventory item | Components |
| --- | --- |
| Alignment | Bends |
| Profile | Gradients |
|  | Vertical curves |
| Cross-section | Carriageway width |
|  | Shoulder width |
|  | Verge width |
|  | Camber |
|  | Superelevation |
| Construction | Carriageway |
|  | Shoulders |
| Earthworks | Cutting |
|  | Embankment |
| Side drainage | Side drains |
|  | Mitre drains |
|  | Turnouts |
|  | Cutoff drains |
| Bridges and culverts | Pipes |
|  | Box culverts |
|  | Bridges |
| Junctions | Location |
| Road furniture | Road signs |
|  | Road markings |
|  | Guardrails |
| Land use | Farming |
|  | Forest/bush |
|  | Town/village |
| Terrain | Soil types |
|  | Topography |
| Climate | Rainfall |
|  | Wind |

whether they are likely to cause maintenance problems, or where topographic and climatic features combine to give high and fast rainfall runoffs that are likely to cause side-slope erosion. It is also desirable to have available information regarding the engineering characteristics and distributions of soils, to help in decisions affected by the availability of suitable maintenance materials.

The Department of Transport has developed a system to hold information on computer files about the English primary road network of motorway and trunk roads. The data gathered fall into two main categories:

(1)  as-built records of new roads and major maintenance works, geometry of road layout, road lighting, etc.,
(2)  traffic and accident data.

Each group of files is free-standing, but is cross-referenced and correlated with each other group.

### Traffic

A most useful way of classifying roads for maintenance purposes is according to their real importance within the highway network, i.e. according to the traffic volumes carried. Such a classification can be very helpful in determining standards of maintenance and allocating funds for maintenance work. There is no ideal classification method, however, and systems vary considerably from country to country. The significant factor affecting the usefulness of any particular system is the extent to which it successfully meets the needs of the area within which it is applied.

A simple classification system recommended for roads in Britain (essentially all of which are surfaced) is given in reference 10.

### Inspections

Routine inspections should be programmed and carried out on all roads according to regular schedules. The basic objective of these inspections is to assess current maintenance needs, to update the road inventory, and to check the effectiveness of maintenance work. One suggested set of frequencies for the routine inspection of roads in Britain is given in Table 9.2.

More recent Department of Transport recommendations[11] for the motorway and all-purpose trunk road network specify that routine safety inspections should be carried out at seven-day intervals, whilst routine detailed inspections can be scheduled at much less frequent intervals, e.g. at six-month intervals in the case of hard shoulder inspections and at two-year intervals in the case of central reservation inspections. Safety inspections, which are normally carried out from a slow-moving vehicle by trained personnel, are designed to identify those defects which are likely to create a danger to the public and therefore require urgent attention. Detailed inspections are designed to establish programmes of routine maintenance tasks which do not require urgent execution, e.g. a central reservation detailed inspection may cover all items within the reservation, gullies and kerbing or edging adjacent to the central reservation, the centre and offside lanes of the carriageway (including all road markings and road studs).

**Table 9.2** Suggested frequencies for routine inspection of roads in Britain

| Type of area | Type of roads | Inspections per year |
|---|---|---|
| Rural | Trunk and important principal roads | 12 |
| | Other principal and important non-principal roads | 6 |
| | Other non-principal roads | 2 |
| | Roads in villages and shopping areas | 12–24 (according to importance) |
| | Roads in residential areas | 4–6 |
| Urban | Trunk and principal roads and main shopping areas | 24 |
| | Other roads in town centres and less important shopping areas | 12 |
| | Other roads | 4–6 |

A different approach to the question of inspection frequency is generally adopted in relation to roads in developing countries. For instance, one set of recommendations for rural roads suggests that the whole of the network should be inspected at least once every six months, e.g. one inspection during the wet season and one during the dry season. The wet season inspection is particularly important when assessing cracking in bituminous surfacings, as this is more easily identified when the carriageway is wet; also, the performance of the drainage system can only be assessed properly during the wet season.

Preprinted forms are normally used for inspections as they remind the inspector of items to be considered. Whatever form is used, it should be easy to understand and apply.

The following are some comments regarding factors affecting maintenance inspections.

(1) *Many of the defects encountered are likely to be repeated many times over.*

The Department of Transport has devised a *Code of Practice for Routine Maintenance*[11] which provides advice on groups of items to be reported upon in the course of safety and detailed inspections. For example, safety defects which are commonly noted, and which normally require immediate action, particularly if they constitute an imminent hazard, include: (a) potholes and other local defects in the carriageway, including defective ironware, (b) kerbing, edging and channel defects, (c) excessive standing water and water discharging onto and/or flowing across the highway, (d) damaged safety fences and other barriers, (e) debris and spillage in traffic lanes or on hard shoulders, (f) damaged lighting columns and other street furniture, (g) damaged, defective, displaced or missing traffic signs or signals, (h) dirty or otherwise obscured traffic signs and signals, (i) trees, shrubs and hedges which by virtue of their position or condition constitute a hazard to road users, (j) displaced road studs (particularly the cat's-eye type) which may be loose on the carriageway surface, (k) faults in highway structures, e.g. due to impact or flood damage, and (l) differences in level between abutting concrete slabs.

(2) *Defects are normally defined in relation to predetermined maintenance criteria or standards.*

The assessment of many defects and maintenance needs is necessarily dependent upon the maintenance engineer's view of what is satisfactory, what represents failure, etc., and upon the inspector's interpretation of the engineer's policies with respect to these. If standards are not defined (or are ill defined) for the inspectors, varying advice will be obtained regarding the same maintenance defect or need. Where possible, these standards should be set in terms which are capable of physical measurement.

(3) *Maintenance standards are normally established to meet local conditions.*

Maintenance standards acceptable for a road system in a newly developing country, with basically a rural economy, are not necessarily those which would be used in a highly-industrialized country. National standards recommended for use in Britain are readily available in the technical literature (see, for example, references 7, 10 and 11).

(4) *Maintenance standards normally indicate the remedial actions that need to be carried out.*

As well as indicating the nature/scale of the maintenance defect or problem, a well-defined standard will assist in describing the remedial action to be initiated. Often also, the standard will indicate the degree of urgency attached to the maintenance work.

(5) *Certain maintenance defects (and standards) can be determined with the aid of mechanical devices.*

Reference 12 provides a useful summary of the strengths and limitations of the devices currently used in Britain to help assess pavement condition.

For example, the adequacy of a road surfacing with respect to skid-resistance can only be determined with the aid of a mechanical testing device. The *sideways-force coefficient routine investigation machine* (*SCRIM*) is a machine developed in Britain[13] to provide a rapid, routine, method of measuring the resistance to skidding (sideways-force coefficient) under normal traffic conditions. The machine consists basically of a lorry-mounted water tank with a test wheel mounted between the front and rear wheels to measure skid-resistance in the nearside wheel track (see Fig. 9.2). The test wheel has a known constant vertical load applied to it, and the sideways force along the axis of rotation of the wheel is measured by means of a load transducer; the ratio of these two forces is known as the sideways-force coefficient. Associated equipment is used to provide a continuous measurement of skid-resistance as the machine travels along the highway, whilst items such as changes in surface material and road section codes are recorded simultaneously. SCRIM is widely used by highway authorities in Britain. It is capable of testing at speeds from 15 to 100 km/h. With one tank of water, 50 km of road can be tested in urban conditions

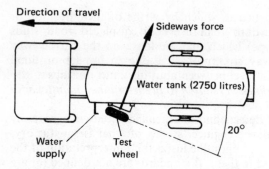

Direction of travel

Sideways force

Water tank (2750 litres)

20°

Water supply   Test wheel

**Fig. 9.2**   Diagrammatical representation of SCRIM, the sideways-force coefficient routine investigation machine

whilst operating in normal traffic, and up to 70 km can be tested on rural roads.

The most commonly used methods of measuring rut depth are based on conventional survey measurements of the transverse profile or on the use of a straightedge and calibrated wedge system. Both of these methods are slow, provide a relatively small sample of measurements and, unless the road is closed to traffic, can be hazardous for operators. To obviate these problems, a *high-speed road monitor* (*HRM*), based on the use of contactless displacement transducers, has been developed[14] which can measure up to 200 lane-kilometres of wheel-track rutting (and longitudinal profile, texture depth, and concrete groove dimensions) in a normal day, at speeds of between 5 and 80 km/h in the normal traffic stream. Data are stored in digital form on floppy disks and can be processed on board the vehicle using the system's computer facilities, or transferred to a mainframe computer for permanent storage and more detailed analysis.

Surface irregularity is an important factor in determining the comfort of ride afforded a road user; it is also of concern to people who live and work alongside roads as it causes traffic-induced vibrations in adjacent buildings. The *rolling straightedge* is currently used in Britain to check the regularity of the carriageway surface, most usually for new work. This 3 m long moving straightedge—it consists of a carriage running on forty wheels—is manually pushed along the carriageway parallel to the centreline, and irregularities at the centre of the straightedge are indicated on a dial. As well as being slow for routine maintenance work, this straightedge has the disadvantage that it only measures irregularities over short distances, and undulations of between 5 and 30 m which can cause acute discomfort to motorists are not recorded at all.

The *bump integrator*[15] provides a more rapid means of measuring riding quality. Basically, it consists of a single-wheeled pneumatic-tyred trailer of standardized design that is towed at a constant speed of 32 km/h. The sum of the vertical movements of the trailer wheel relative to the chassis divided by the distance travelled gives an index of irregularity, $r$, that is expressed in inches per mile.

**Determining priorities**

It is not enough to know where maintenance is required on a highway—the maintenance engineer must also be able to allocate the limited resources available to the maintenance organization in the way that most nearly satisfies the highway authorities' objectives and policies in relation to the maintenance of the highway system.

A basic, unsophisticated approach which might be used to assign priorities for roads in a newly developing country is as follows.

(1)   *Urgent work*—emergency repairs to roads that are cut, removal of debris, informing police of broken-down vehicles.

(2)   *Routine drainage work*—clean out and deepen ditches, clean out bridges and culverts, filling scoured areas, building check drains and scour control, repair of structures.

(3)   *Routine work on pavements*—dragging, brushing or grading of unpaved roads, patching, sanding and local sealing of paved roads.

(4)   *Other routine work*—filling on unpaved roads, shoulders and slopes, grass cutting, cleaning, repainting, repairing and replacing road furniture.

(5)   *Periodic work*—heavy grading and regravelling unpaved roads, surface dressing paved roads.

(6)   *Special work*—overlaying, reconstruction.

The logic underlying this priority system is straightforward. The need to give absolute priority to urgent work with safety overtones is self-evident, and sufficient funds and materials must be reserved for this. Routine drainage work is given priority over recurrent work on pavements because repairing surface defects which result from faulty drainage is a waste of effort unless the drainage is also corrected. Other routine work is considered to be of lower priority.

Not all funds should be expended on the first four categories, i.e. some should be retained for periodic work. This category of maintenance work can be considered as a series of discrete projects which can be carried out independently, can be deferred or brought forward as required, and can compete with each other for funds. Similarly, special projects of overlaying or reconstruction, whilst identified as a result of maintenance inspections, may be treated as 'capital' projects whose funding comes from a special source.

There are many more sophisticated approaches used in developed countries which aim, in one way or another, to indicate priorities between different maintenance needs within individual lengths of road and between different lengths of road, taking into account their traffic flow as well as their physical condition. One such approach applies a uniform points scale (say 1 to 100) to all defects, with the allocation of points being related to the quantity or extent of a defect, or to its severity. Weighting factors are then applied to the basic ratings in relation to the considered importance of the defect as affecting the need for maintenance, and traffic factors are applied in relation to traffic flows.

Two main lines of development have evolved in Britain to give the systems known as *MARCH* (*M*aintenance *A*ssessment, *R*ating and *C*osting for *H*ighways) and *CHART* (*C*omputerized *H*ighway *A*ssessment of

Ratings and *T*reatments). *MARCH*[16] was created and developed for use in urban areas, whereas *CHART*[9, 17] was initially considered to be applicable to non-urban highways. *CHART* was adopted by the Department of Transport in 1981–82 for use on the trunk road network; it is also used by the Scottish Development Department as well as by a significant number of other highway authorities in Britain, and it is inevitable that it will be further developed and more widely used.

Both of the above systems have the prime objective of producing annual maintenance programmes containing a priority list of structural maintenance requirements based on highway assessment, measurement and recording. Computer programs form an integral part of the systems, which both offer a considerable range of presentation of output information, e.g. *CHART* provides information regarding: (a) lengths of road which are substandard, (b) the apparent treatment needs of these lengths, and (c) the relative priorities of the need for treatment.

Notwithstanding the wide usage of the above and other assessment and priority making systems, it cannot be too strongly emphasized that they are only aids to engineering judgement. *The computer cannot make rational engineering decisions.* The degree of priority, timing, type and extent of maintenance treatment must always be the responsibility of the engineer. For example, the rating system might indicate that a carriageway pavement has reached the end of its design life and deserves a high priority in respect of overlay provision; however, proper engineering investigation might also indicate that bad drainage accelerated failure—in which case, it would be bad engineering practice to renew the structure without first correcting the drainage deficiency. As this would probably affect the cost of the repair very significantly, it could also affect its position in any priority listing.

**Allocation of resources**
The next step in the basic process is the estimation of the resource requirements for each item in terms of labour, equipment and materials. In theory, the total resources available to the maintenance engineer each year should match the total amount of maintenance work that needs to be done in that year. In practice, of course, this is rarely the case, so that the maintenance engineer, in concept, must work down through the needs file from the front (highest priority) and match the available resources to the work requirement, so as to determine the amount of work that can be carried out within the limited resources. Some flexibility and re-ordering of priorities may be appropriate at this stage to ensure that all available funds are used. Usually, the decision will also be taken that some works, most probably from the periodic programme, will have to be deferred until the following year.

A very sophisticated computer system, known as *RATE* (*R*esource *A*llocation and *T*echniques of *E*stimating), has been developed in Britain to aid management in the budgeting, estimating, planning and control of resources for highway construction and maintenance. The concept underlying *RATE* is founded in the belief that a realistic resources estimate can only be achieved when each item of work is analysed in its simplest elements (or operations) and the estimate of costs synthesized from factual information. The *RATE* system—details of which are readily available in the technical literature[18]—comprises a set of libraries and a suite of computer programs. It is capable of providing bills of quantities, priced or unpriced, together with schedules of the labour, plant and materials required for each maintenance job.

## Pavement condition surveys

The above discussion has concentrated on the basics of maintenance management as applied to highways, and the fundamentals upon which an annual maintenance action programme might be devised. What the approach described above does not do, however, is provide the maintenance engineer with an overall view of the condition of the highway system at any given time. For this, a *pavement condition survey* must be carried out.

A condition survey is not concerned with determining the structural adequacy of a pavement and, generally, it does not attempt to provide reasons as to why the pavement is as it is, or to indicate what type of maintenance is required. Rather, it attempts to provide a comparative assessment of the 'rideability' or acceptability of highway pavement sections as they might be judged by road users at a given time. As such, the results of a condition survey can be very valuable when determining priorities for maintenance funding within a major road system.

### Present serviceability index (*PSI*)

In concept, a pavement condition survey is carried out by a group of people who drive over the highway and rate each section according to its ability (in its present condition) to serve the traffic (travelling at a standard speed) that it is meant to serve. What is probably the most thoroughly researched rating system is that devised during the AASHO Road Test[19, 20].

In the AASHO study, the rating panel members were asked to drive over a large number of selected highway sections in three states, and to rate each section on a scale of 0 to 5, where 0–1 indicated a pavement in very poor condition, 1–2 was a poor pavement, 2–3 was fair, 3–4 was good, and 4–5 was very good. The panel members were also asked the extent to which their ratings were influenced by particular features of the pavement, viz. longitudinal and transverse distortions, cracking, faulting, and surface deterioration, and whether the road section was acceptable for its traffic. The average of the rating numbers for each section was termed the *present serviceability rating* (*PSR*) of the section.

The same road sections were also surveyed at the same time, and physical measurements obtained of the same features as were taken into account by the rating panel. These measurements were then correlated with the *PSR*-values using regression analysis techniques, and the following objective equations derived.

*For concrete pavements*:

$$PSI = 5.41 - 1.80 \log(1 + \overline{SV}) - 0.09(C + P)^{0.5}$$

*For flexible pavements*:

$$PSI = 5.03 - 1.91 \log(1 + \overline{SV}) - 0.01(C + P)^{0.5} - 1.38\overline{RD^2}$$

where $PSI$ = present serviceability index, $\overline{SV}$ = mean slope variance in both wheel paths (i.e. an assessment of surface irregularity), $C$ = lineal feet of major cracking per 1000 ft$^2$ area, $P$ = bituminous patching in ft$^2$ per 1000 ft$^2$ area, and $\overline{RD}$ = mean rut depth in inches (both wheel tracks) measured with a 4 ft straightedge (i.e. an assessment of permanent deformation).

This study constituted a break-through with respect to condition surveying, in that it resulted in the development of an objective method of pavement measurement which could be used to express, and substitute for, the subjective and qualitative ratings of road user panels regarding the 'rideability' of a highway section. In other words, the present serviceability index provides—with the aid of equipment used to obtain objective and quantitative measurements of the pavement condition—an estimate of the mean of serviceability ratings, which would otherwise be made by a panel of judges.

Following its development by the AASHO, usage of the $PSI$ approach to pavement condition surveying spread throughout the USA[21] and to many other countries of the world. Some highway organizations adopted the above equations as developed, whilst others modified them according to their own research findings and particular needs. The methodology is now widely used to help to define the order of priority of highway sections for structural maintenance. In the USA, $PSI$-values for new pavements can be expected to vary from 3.5 to 4.5, depending upon construction; lower $PSI$-values are obtained when the highway has been under traffic for a period of time. $PSI$-values below 2.0 typically indicate that the pavement section is in poor condition, unsatisfactory for most high-speed traffic, and deserves further detailed examination to determine whether and/or when structural maintenance is required. Bituminous surfacings with $PSI$-values below 1.5 are normally extremely poor, and tend to exhibit rutting and/or potholes, extensive cracking and, generally, a rough ride. Concrete pavements with similar $PSI$-values tend to exhibit a rough ride, severe cracking, spalling, pumping and faulting.

## Some common pavement defects and repairs

Highway maintenance techniques are not just applicable to road pavement defects. They also relate to shoulders and adjacent roadside areas; drainage systems; bridges and tunnels; highway appurtenances such as guardrails, crash barriers and cushions, fences, traffic islands, and kerbs; footpaths, underpasses and overpasses; traffic control devices; road lighting; snow and ice control—and to all aspects of accident prevention and safety.

Whilst a number of maintenance techniques relating to the above are dealt with in various ways in both Volumes 1 and 2 of *Highways*, space limitations do not make it possible to attempt to cover all aspects in any comprehensive detail. For this, the reader is referred to some excellent European[6, 7, 10, 22–25], Australian[26] and American[1] publications. The following discussion is concerned with some of the repairable deficiencies more commonly encountered in relation to the highway pavement. Before discussing these, however, it is useful to consider one aspect of highway maintenance that must always be given particular attention, viz. road safety whilst the work is being carried out.

## Safety during maintenance activities

Construction and maintenance work on existing highways present special problems in relation to road safety[27], and unless proper care is taken at work zones the accident rate will increase. Often, this increase will be reflected in changes: (a) from injury accidents 'before' construction to property damage accidents 'during' construction, (b) from rear-end 'before' accidents to fixed object 'during' accidents, and (c) from accidents in the peak period 'before' construction to accidents after dark 'during' construction.

When maintenance work is being carried out on or close to the carriageway, it is the maintenance engineer's responsibility to ensure that adequate care is taken to warn and protect road users and maintenance workers. The following can be considered as key elements in a safe construction zone.

(1) *Good visibility to ensure adequate warning is given to road users.* Methods of improving visibility stimuli for the motorist include the use of advance signs, barrier lighting, floodlighting, overhead and roadside sign lighting, and traffic signals.

(2) *Good alignment of any temporary lane or road diversion.*

(3) *A segregated work area within which the maintenance gang can freely work.* This will normally involve the use of signs and temporary barriers and/or cones to delineate not only the actual work area but also a transition zone at either end. The lengths of the transition zones will mainly depend upon the visibility conditions prior to and after the site, the traffic volume, and the speed reduction to be imposed.

(4) *Adequate capacity for traffic bypassing the site.*

(5) *Use of standard signs.* These should be in good condition and located according to a standard layout.

(6) *Regular checks as to the continued adequacy of the warning devices.*

(7) *Good maintenance of the bypass lane or carriageway.* The aim should be to ensure that it is kept clean and free from mud, dust and debris.

(8) *Wearing of distinctive, reflective safety vests by members of the workforce.*

## Soil—aggregate roads

Common defects on earth and gravel roads include corrugations, wheelruts, dust, and potholes.

### Corrugations

Also known under the terms *rippling* and *washboarding*, corrugations are transverse undulations located at closely and regularly spaced intervals. Encountered under dry weather conditions, they are formed as a result of the oscillatory pounding action that is produced when the tyres of moving vehicles encounter irregularities on the road surface. Corrugations can be formed on a gravel road independent of the volumes of traffic, speeds, and loads, although these parameters do enhance their formation[28].

By the use of such routine preventative maintenance measures as stabilized gravel, dust-retaining agents, watering, and more frequent grading, the problem of corrugations is now becoming of lesser importance in countries with soil–aggregate roads. When carried out, however, corrective maintenance involves scarifying the road surface to an appropriate depth, pulverizing the scarified material, admixing suitable stabilizing materials (if required), shaping to the desired crown, and compacting to a dense surfacing.

**Wheelruts**
These are longitudinal depressions that tend to follow the pattern of vehicle wheels. Usually associated with the settlement of the soil–aggregate pavement under traffic stresses and/or the dislodgement of material (especially in dry conditions), they can trap the front wheels of a vehicle and become a safety hazard. Filled with water, the ruts can create splash or icing problems.

Dragging and grading whilst the roadway is wet, followed by compaction, is the usual way of repairing ruts in soil–aggregate roads. In the course of the maintenance process, material should be bladed from the outside of the carriageway towards the centre so as to preserve the shape of the crown section.

**Dust**
The result of inadequate cohesion during dry weather, dust can become a severe safety hazard, an inconvenience to road users, a pollution problem, and a cause of excessive wear to vehicles.

Maintenance normally involves the application of liquid bitumen or chloride (see Chapter 5) to retain the dust. Calcium chloride is the chemical most often used for dust retention; it is usually added to the existing road surface in springtime or after rain, i.e. when the road is damp.

**Potholes**
Also known as *chuck-holes*, these are irregularly-shaped holes of various size and depth, which result from a variety of causes, e.g. poor initial compaction.

The patching of potholes on soil–aggregate roads is a continuing process. Materials used for temporary repair by filling are normally similar to those used in the existing road surface, improved possibly with the addition of calcium chloride. The success of the repair work can be directly related to good preparation of the hole and the amount of compaction applied to the fill material.

In well-developed countries, the repair of potholes by manual patching has largely been superseded in recent years by more permanent repairs consisting of blading, or scarifying the soil–aggregate surface, and admixing new material with the aid of motor graders. This type of maintenance is most usually performed in the spring of the year.

## Roads with bituminous surfacings

Common examples of surface distress in pavements with bituminous surfacings are potholes, cracking, shoving, bleeding, ravelling, wheelruts, and inadequate skid-resistance (see also Chapter 7).

### Potholes
When potholes are not accompanied by distortion of the adjacent surface, they generally result from a cracked bituminous surface which has allowed moisture to enter and soften the pavement or penetrate horizontally under the bituminous layer. Once water has entered, the cracked surfacing is prone to disintegrate and lift out under the action of traffic, particularly after rain, thereby initiating the formation of a pothole.

As a general rule, repairs to potholes should be carried out before the onset of inclement weather. Any pothole which is likely to be a potential hazard to traffic should be repaired immediately after detection, if necessary with temporary patches.

The patching process requires the squaring of a rectangular area encompassing the sides of the hole, and the removal of all loose or faulty material. The objective is to ensure that the edges of the infill patch are in contact with good-quality, supportive, pavement materials.

The most durable results are obtained when the backfill is a premixed, dense bitumen-bound material. If unbound gravel or crushed stone is used for backfill, the material will need to be moistened to facilitate its compaction, and compacted in layers not exceeding 100 mm thick with a mechanical tamping machine.

Before applying the final bituminous layer, the surface of the unbound backfill will need to be swept clean of dust and loose stones, and primed with a bituminous binder; the surface priming is unnecessary in the case of premixed bitumen-bound backfill, although the exposed surfaces of the hole may need to be lightly primed or tack coated before the addition of the backfill. The repair work is then completed with the placement of a bituminous material similar to that in the existing surface. In all instances, the amount of patching material used must be chosen to ensure that the surface of the compacted patch is flush with the surrounding carriageway.

### Cracking
A bituminous surfacing will crack for a variety of reasons and, if detected in the initial stages, the pattern of the cracking can indicate its cause. If cracks have developed and spread widely so that surface water enters and the surfacing material becomes vulnerable to dislodgement by vehicles, the cause can be difficult to detect and minor repairs are often not feasible. The definitions and causes of various forms of cracking in bituminous surfacings are discussed in Chapter 7.

Practice varies as to what corrective maintenance measures should be applied to cracks. These range from not filling any cracks, through filling only large cracks, to filling all cracks, to patching or providing overlays.

One commonly held view is that, where practicable, cracks should be sealed with a binder having a viscosity low enough to enable it to be poured or worked into the crack openings; a squeegee is useful in assisting the binder to penetrate narrow cracks. If the cracks are wide enough, they can be filled with a fine premix or bituminous slurry. When cracking is extensive, it is very often covered with a thin (non-structural) overlay. When it is caused by poor surfacing materials, e.g. excessive fines, local replacement of the surface course may be the only adequate remedy. Where cracking is associated with excessive pavement deflection, this latter problem will need to be corrected first; corrective maintenance in this instance may require the rehabilitation and possibly the reconstruction of the damaged pavement section.

### Shoving

The horizontal, transverse displacement of surfacing material, mainly in the direction of traffic, is known as shoving. Typically, shoving occurs at locations where vehicles generate high shearing stresses when accelerating or braking, e.g. at intersections and on hills.

As is discussed in Chapter 7, slippage/shoving failures occur when the shear stress developed by traffic between two contiguous layers is greater than the shear or bond strength holding them together. Repair work usually involves removing the faulty material down to a firm base, and replacing it with a hot-mix patch that is well bound to the underlying material.

### Bleeding

Also known as *flushing*, this is a condition caused by a concentration of excess binder, sometimes in the form of longitudinal spots at the surface of the pavement. Usually found in wheel tracks during hot weather, bleeding can result from a variety of factors, e.g. too high a binder content in the wearing course, increased compaction under traffic, too much binder in maintenance patches, the upward migration of binder from lower layers, and/or too soft a binder. In the case of surface dressings, bleeding can also result from the use of too small a size of chipping for the traffic conditions [29].

If left untreated, bleeding can create dangerous, slippery surfaces, particularly during wet weather. These surfaces are often described as being *fatty* or *slick*.

Slight to moderate bleeding can be repaired by blotting with sand or porous aggregates. Large areas will need to be returned to their originally constructed surface texture by the addition of a thin overlay or by the removal of the offending material and its replacement with a mixture having a suitably lower binder content.

### Ravelling

Sometimes termed *pitting*, this describes the condition which results from a bituminous surfacing progressively disintegrating from the top down, or from the edges inward, due to the dislodgement of aggregate particles under traffic. Ravelling is usually the outcome of poor construction practices, e.g. the use of too low a binder content or an overheated binder, wet weather conditions, or inadequate compaction, which are associated with the stripping of bituminous films from aggregates.

If detected in time, ravelling can be corrected by the application of a surface dressing (see Chapter 7) or a thin bituminous overlay. If it becomes extensive, ravelling will require resurfacing with a thicker (structural) overlay.

**Wheelruts**

Rutting usually takes the form of longitudinal depressions in the wheel tracks of vehicles. Usually the width of a wheel path, ruts can be dangerous to high-speed traffic in wet weather (from hydroplaning), cold weather (ice sheets), and dry weather (by directing the front wheels of vehicles).

Inadequate compaction during construction or an inappropriate mix design is often the cause of rutting. Studded tyres can also cause ruts through wear of the bituminous surfacing.

Provided that the rutting has not progressed to the stage where the pavement is deemed to have failed, maintenance treatment in the form of planing followed by the placement of a thin (non-structural) overlay can be used to remedy this defect.

**Inadequate skid-resistance**

This is a condition normally associated with heavy traffic wear of the carriageway surface, and is influenced largely by the type of bituminous mix and the quality of the aggregate used within it (see Chapters 3 and 7). The application of a surface dressing is the most common solution to this problem in Britain.

## Concrete roads

Notable examples of distress in concrete pavements are inadequate skid-resistance, surface spalling, cracking, blow-ups, pumping, and inadequate sealants (see also Chapter 6).

**Inadequate skid-resistance**

This results from inadequate microtexture and/or macrotexture, and can be caused by a number of factors, e.g. wear and tear of the concrete surface under heavy traffic, the use of an aggregate that is too soft, allowing rainwater access to a newly textured surface during construction before the concrete has gained sufficient strength, or inadequate texturing of a concrete in which the initial set had already taken place[30].

The most common method of restoring skid-resistance on low-speed concrete roads is by surface dressing (see Chapter 7). Sections of high-speed road have also been successfully treated with surface dressings.

In general, however, the currently recommended method of restoring skid-resistance to large sections of high-speed road surfaces is by using self-propelled, multisaw texturing machines to cut transverse grooves into the hardened concrete; for small areas, individual sawn grooves are acceptable. It is important that the grooves be randomly spaced and cut to the correct depth, i.e. if the grooves are uniformly spaced, an unacceptable single-toned noise is caused by traffic.

### Surface spalling

This is the term used to describe the progressive disintegration, with loss of aggregate, of the surface of an unsound concrete, e.g. a slab composed of a porous concrete or a concrete without air voids. The spalling results from the combined action of traffic and freeze–thaw cycles on the concrete.

If incipient spalling is detected at the fine crack stage, temporary protection can be obtained by impregnating the cracks with linseed oil. This will help to prevent water from entering the pavement.

The permanent repair of surface spalling involves the removal of all unsound concrete and its replacement with thin, bonded concrete or mortar patches. Cement mortar is normally used for repairs up to 20 mm deep; for greater depths, fine concrete, with 10 mm maximum size aggregate, is used. The repair concrete is placed with a small initial surcharge and surface vibration is applied to compact it and ensure a good bond. The surface of any repair patch should be brushed or grooved to obtain a skid-resistant surface texture compatible with that of the adjacent concrete.

### Cracking

Whilst all cracking is obviously undesirable, it can be particularly significant if the slab is steel reinforced, i.e. water or chlorides entering the cracks can corrode the steel and lead to the need for major repairs.

*Transverse* or *diagonal cracks*, extending from one edge of the slab to the other, can result from a variety of causes, of which the following are the most common: contraction joints that are sawn too late, inadequate subgrade support, insufficient slab thickness, the failure of one or more transverse joints to allow the longitudinal thermal expansion and contraction of the slabs, excessive length of slab, insufficient reinforcement and/or concrete strength, and as a sympathetic development of existing transverse joints, e.g. as in the case of unmatched joints in two parallel slabs.

*Long longitudinal cracks*, parallel to a longitudinal joint, can occur if the longitudinal joint is not deep enough or if the slab is excessively wide. *Short longitudinal cracks* which occur close to a longitudinal joint may be due to the omission of the bottom crack inducer or to its misalignment. Longitudinal cracking away from the joint may be due to subgrade failure or to the malfunction of the longitudinal joint.

*Corner cracks* normally link a transverse joint to a slab edge or to a longitudinal joint. They are most usually associated with acute-angled corners, subgrade failures resulting in cavities below the slab, overloading at the slab corner, weaknesses induced by gullies placed under the edge of the slab, or dowel bar restraint.

*D-cracking* can be described as a series of fine, hairline, crescent-shaped cracks in the concrete surface that usually parallel a joint or major crack and usually curve across a slab corner. Whilst the exact cause of this form of cracking is not yet known, it is generally attributed to freeze–thaw cycles in the case of concrete incorporating frost-susceptible aggregates.

The treatment of most cracks depends upon their severity and whether the slab is reinforced or unreinforced. *Fine cracks* (<0.5 mm) normally do not require treatment, except when they occur in unreinforced concrete immediately after construction. *Medium cracks* (0.5–1.5 mm) have only partial aggregate interlock and, hence, reduced load transference. In reinforced slabs, the steel requires protection, and this is provided by chasing out such cracks to a width and depth of about 25 mm and sealing the groove with a hot poured joint sealant. In unreinforced slabs, medium cracks should be tied by the insertion of tie bars into slots cut into the slab and transverse to the general line of the cracks; an epoxy-resin mortar is used to fill the slots. Any repair of *wide cracks* must include the provision of dowel bars to restore load transference, as there will be no aggregate interlock across the crack. In the case of wide cracks (and all corner cracks), a full-depth repair must be carried out, and, if necessary, the subbase and subgrade should be reinstated.

To minimize the stresses to which the new sealant and edges of the repaired crack will be subjected, crack treatments are best carried out when the weather is cooler and the concrete is in a state of contraction. Where possible, the reason for a crack forming should be determined and the causes which led to its formation should be eliminated before the repair work is carried out.

### Blow-ups

Also known as *buckling*, blow-ups are localized upward movements of slabs which occur at a transverse crack or joint. Blow-ups, which most usually occur in conjunction with transverse edge-shattering, result from hot weather expansion of two adjacent slabs. If insufficient space has been left at the joint between the slabs to allow for this expansion, tremendous longitudinal stresses will continue to be developed within the slabs until they are released by buckling.

Nowadays, blow-ups occur relatively rarely in concrete roads, especially in countries with fairly mild climates, such as Britain. At least partial reconstruction is required to repair a concrete pavement closed as a result of buckling.

### Pumping

By pumping is meant the ejection of mixtures of water, clay and/or silt from beneath a pavement, through transverse or longitudinal joints and cracks, and along the edges of the carriageway. Pumping occurs as a result of the repeated downward movement of a slab under heavy volumes of traffic with large axle loads, when free, non-draining water has accumulated in a fine-grained subgrade (see also Chapter 8).

Concrete slabs which have settled as a result of pumping can be lifted, and rocking slabs can be stabilized, by drilling holes through the slab(s) and subbase and injecting, under pressure or vacuum, a cement grout or a resin grout to fill the cavity. The technique is well established and is in common use in most countries where concrete roads are built.

The concrete slabs may also be lifted mechanically, after which the space beneath is filled with grout. This method of repair is used in the rare cases when pressure grouting is not effective, because the grout is able to escape through openings that cannot be sealed.

### Inadequate sealants

Joint sealing has two purposes, viz. to prevent the infiltration of surface water, and to prevent foreign material from lodging in the joints (see Chapter 8). Water will soften the subgrade, and also the subbase if it is not stabilized, whilst the brine from salt placed on the carriageway as a frost precaution may also corrode the dowel and tie bars if the joint sealing is defective. Stones in joints impair the free movement of slabs, and can cause edge-spalling.

An unsightly but less significant defect is the extrusion of the sealant above the carriageway in hot weather.

Loss or cracking of a joint seal can result from the use of a poor-quality product, a lack of adhesion between the seal and the sides of the sealing groove, cohesion failure resulting from cracks within the seal which are transverse or parallel to the joint groove, abnormal ageing (e.g. by overheating rubberized bitumen), or the use of an inadequately-shaped sealing groove. The protrusion of the sealant above the joint edges is usually associated with joints which have been overfilled with hot poured sealing material.

Sealant defects of the types described above are corrected by first using power-driven wire brushes and grit blasting to clean out the sealing groove, and then applying a good sealant in accordance with the manufacturer's instructions for its proper usage. In Britain, re-sealing is best carried out in the spring or autumn when the joints are neither fully open nor fully closed. In summer the joints are narrow and their subsequent opening may over-stress the sealing material, whilst in winter the joints are at their widest, adhesion to the concrete can be poor, and it may be difficult to avoid some extrusion in subsequent hot weather.

## Winter maintenance

Snow and ice are the cause of considerable costs to the community. In addition to the costs required for their treatment or removal—typically they amount to more than £100m per annum[31]—there are the costs of accidents, damage costs to road surfaces, bridge decks and vehicles, and the costs resulting from interruptions to normal, everyday commercial activities. In Britain, winter maintenance—which refers to the treatment or removal of ice and snow from highways and footpaths—is a duty imposed on highway authorities, and the associated responsibilities and the possible consequences of failing to execute those responsibilities are set out in law. Whilst governmental guidance is available regarding how to prepare for, and treat, snow and ice[32], it is not possible to lay down hard and fast rules which are applicable to all locations and all environmental conditions. As a consequence the interpretation of this law relies upon what is reasonable in the circumstances—and this can vary from one road to another, from one administrative area to another, and from one point in time to another.

Indeed, it might also be noted that the treatment of snow and ice can vary considerably according to:

(1)   the practices and materials in use in different countries, e.g. compare references 1, 2 and 32,

(2)   the type and amount of precipitation, e.g. whether a large or small amount of sleet, freezing rain, dry snow, wet snow, frost or ice is the target material,

(3)   the air and/or ground temperature experienced, e.g. whether the temperature is above or below freezing and the length of time for which it is sustained,

(4)   according to highway type and location.

## Preparation for winter maintenance

In Britain, the following three winter maintenance periods are defined for normal operational purposes:

(1)   high period, i.e. December, January and February, when severe conditions might reasonably be expected,

(2)   low period, i.e. November and March, when severe conditions may occur,

(3)   marginal period, i.e. October and April, when severe conditions are generally not to be expected.

A key step in the preparation of any operational maintenance programme is the provision of training for the persons involved, whether they be equipment operators or supervisory personnel, before the onset of winter conditions. Notwithstanding the problems which this may create, it is imperative that all engaged in these programmes should have full knowledge of their responsibilities and of the actions to be taken when emergencies occur. This training is reinforced by the production of procedure manuals which lay down chains of command, communication arrangements, snow ploughing and salting/gritting routes, and procedures to be adopted under particular emergency conditions.

The determination of priority routes for salting/gritting and snow ploughing is essential to the planning of any programme. For example, there follows one highway authority's[33] order of priority.

*Priority 1*—motorway and trunk roads, and important principal roads linking major centres of population, and town centres.

*Priority 2*—other principal roads, Class II and III roads giving access to major villages, farm milk/bulk feeding processing factories and associated vehicle depots, and accesses to emergency services premises.

*Priority 3*—Class III and unclassified roads linking to minor villages and hamlets, and 'normal' milk tanker/bulk feeding routes.

With this priority system, residential streets, and Class III and unclassified roads which provide secondary access routes, are only cleared as resources become available.

The organization of shift systems and other similar administrative necessities should be seen as part of the winter maintenance preparation process. Standards of maintenance for the different priority routes also need to be set; this inevitably involves specifying the quantities of salt and/or abrasives to be used under different circumstances. It might be noted that over the years—and partly due to the media attention given to snow and ice problems—public expectations have risen in respect of the speed with which these problems are supposed to be overcome, e.g. following heavy snow the public now expects at least the main routes to be clear by day two, and preferably all roads except those to isolated farms and communities[34].

If snow fences are to be employed, they should be placed in position well before the ground becomes hard or frozen and the expected snow problems develop. The experience of previous years is usually necessary to determine locations where snow fences can be effectively used. The adequacy of existing post delineators, and markings which locate drains and kerbs or traffic islands likely to catch snowplough blades, should also be checked well in advance of the time when they are expected to be needed, so that any remedial actions required can be put in hand before the onset of winter.

Arrangements should be made for the maintenance organization to be provided with early-warning weather forecasts from the meteorological service. There is a limit, however, to the amount of information which these forecasts can provide, e.g. whilst long-range meteorological forecasts can be used to alert the maintenance organization to the severity of the weather likely to be experienced over a period of time, they cannot usually give details of individual snow storms. Only short-range forecasts can predict the intensities of local storms—and even these are sometimes noted for their miscalculations.

Before winter begins, decisions will also have to be taken as to whether and where night patrols are to be used on major routes, so that instant warning can be provided when adverse conditions begin to set-in on the carriageway. In some areas, it may be appropriate for moisture- and temperature-sensitive devices to be placed in the carriageway surface to give warning of adverse conditions or to activate heating installations. Sites for these devices are normally selected on the basis of local knowledge; however, this approach has been criticized as being subject to bias, and recent research has encouraged the use of thermal mapping[31]: (a) to decide where to locate sensors, (b) to decide how many sensors are required to give adequate coverage of a road network, (c) to provide a systematic fingerprint of carriageway surface temperatures in given weather conditions, so that existing sensors can be calibrated, and (d) to redesign salting routes so that selective salting of cold routes can be carried out on marginal nights.

The planning arrangements should also enable immediate information on road conditions to be transmitted to the general public through the news media, motoring organizations, and the police. Two-way radios should be supplied to every snow and ice control vehicle; these are essential for safety, the reporting of critical conditions, and to enable equipment assignments to be changed.

## Snow and ice treatments

### Road heating

One method of combating ice and snow on the carriageway is to supply enough heat to the carriageway surface to prevent their accumulation. Locations where road heating is employed typically include crucial sites where snow ploughing, gritting and/or salting are normally unable to prevent the development of severe operational difficulties, e.g. at interchanges.

Various pavement heating systems have been used in different countries, the most common being embedded electric resistance elements or pipes carrying a heated fluid. However, because these systems have either poor reliability, high costs, or restrictive power sources, they have not had widespread application[35].

The reliability of *electrical heating systems* can be quite low. For example, shielded resistance wires embedded in the roadway are susceptible to wire breakage due to concrete cracking, to shorting due to moisture, and to corrosion as a result of salt penetration. Bare electric resistance wire is even less reliable. The high cost of power for electrical systems causes their operating costs to be very high; even if the electrical system is activated only when needed, standby power costs are incurred. The high thermal resistivity and large heat capacity of a highway pavement means that an electrically-protected road requires either several hours lead time or a high start-up wattage to warm the surface so that snow or ice will melt. Consequently, highway authorities with such systems have argued that it is often preferable to maintain the surface at a temperature above freezing, and that continuous operation at low wattage is sometimes desirable.

Use has also been made of *heated liquids*, e.g. mineral oils, circulating in piping set in the pavement to warm the carriageway. These liquid heating systems are most commonly employed at locations where suitable quantities of excess heat are easily and cheaply obtained, e.g. at sites adjacent to power stations. However, the temperature at which the fluids are moved causes expansion and contraction problems that can be sufficiently severe to cause expensive leaks to develop.

*Infrared systems* have also been used to heat roads. This type of heating has the advantage that it can be installed under bridge decks without disturbing the pavement, and the bottom insulated to reduce heat loss. However, whilst this method has been used successfully to protect bridge carriageways, it is generally considered not to be very practical because of the length of the lead time required to warm the pavement.

If installed overhead or along the roadside, infrared systems must be sufficiently far away to ensure that stopped vehicles are not damaged, but the further the infrared source is from the pavement, the less efficient it is. The operating cost of an overhead system can be quite high as it must be turned on before any accumulation of snow, as otherwise the snow's high reflectivity will make the system ineffective. Overhead systems must also be made safe against an impacting vehicle.

For geographical areas having moderate winters, the earth's temperature below the frost line is generally in the range of 10–15 °C, which is approximately the average annual air temperature at the ground–air interface. In recent years, research work has been initiated into the use of *earth heat-pipe systems* to transfer this natural energy to the pavement surface to protect it from freezing temperatures.

Whilst the initial cost of constructing an earth heat-pipe system is considered to be comparable to constructing a conventional electrical heating system, it has two major advantages[35, 36], as follows. Firstly, it automatically becomes active when the pavement temperature drops below the temperature of the earth, thereby warming the surface prior to the onset of snow or ice. Secondly, as the energy transferred is naturally stored solar energy, all subsequent power costs are eliminated. Furthermore, heat-pipes constructed of steel are not easily broken by minor pavement movement, and their maintenance costs are therefore minimal.

**Use of chemicals and abrasives**
The chemicals that have been most accepted internationally for snow and ice treatment and removal are sodium chloride and calcium chloride. Calcium chloride is usually supplied in pellet or flake form, whilst sodium chloride is usually obtained as a (considerably cheaper) rock-salt. Calcium pellets dissolve more rapidly and dissolve about 20 per cent more ice than calcium flakes.

The effectiveness of the chlorides for ice and snow treatment is based on their ability in solution to reduce the freezing point of water (see Chapter 5). In Britain, rock-salt is most normally used for winter maintenance purposes. To avoid storage, loading and spreading difficulties, the salt is normally pretreated with sodium ferrocyanide as an anti-caking agent.

Ideally, stored salt should be located on a well-drained, air-entrained cement concrete base, covered with black polythene or butyl rubber sheeting, and encircled by a cutoff drain. An exposed stockpile will form crusts on the surface, whilst wet salt which is subjected to prolonged low temperatures may also solidify as a result of the formation of sodium chloride dehydrate. Runoff from stored salt can detrimentally affect fishing waters or watercourses to which livestock have access, as well as resulting in the dehydration of plants.

When frost or light snow is expected, a common British practice[32] is to carry out precautionary salting at the rate of 10 g/m$^2$. When freezing conditions are expected after snow, the precautionary rates may be increased to 25–40 g/m$^2$, depending upon the amount of humidity present and the temperatures expected. When continuous snow is forecast, precautionary spreading rates of 25–40 g/m$^2$ are also applied; in this instance, of course, the precautionary salting causes the initial snowfall to melt, thereby ensuring a wet surface beneath subsequent snow and easing the task of snow clearance.

If ice has formed on the carriageway surface, salt is usually spread at the rate of 40 g/m$^2$, depending upon the amount of ice to be removed and the air temperature.

Sustained low temperatures are rare in Britain. However, for each degree drop in temperature below $-5\,^{\circ}$C, the general rule-of-thumb is that the amount of sodium chloride needed to maintain the equivalent melting effect increases by about 14 g/m$^2$. However, if the road is subjected to heavy traffic, little or no increase is required until sustained temperatures below $-10\,^{\circ}$C are reached.

Abrasives such as crushed or screened rock and sand are still used in many countries to help vehicular traction when there is more than 25–50 mm of ice or hard-packed snow on the carriageway. Cinders, where available, are also excellent for this purpose. Quarry rock that splinters when crushed is not a good abrasive. Chemicals and abrasives are also mixed for effective results.

The general trend internationally is for the use of abrasives to decrease whilst that of chlorides—especially the cheaper rock-salt—grows. The main reasons for this are probably that salt can now be readily stored for long periods of time and still remain friable, it may be spread very quickly, and it does not leave a residue that can block roadside drainage systems. This trend towards an increase in the use of salt instead of abrasives has been paralleled and encouraged by developments in the equipment available for spreading the salt material.

**Spreaders**

Tailgate-mounted spreaders are now in common usage which utilize an adjustable-speed auger to feed salt automatically to a spinner at the rear of the vehicle. The spinner then broadcasts the salt uniformly over the carriageway to a width that is in excess of the width of the spreading vehicle. The speed of the spinner regulates the length-of-throw or spreading width. The speeds of spinners and augers are regulated from the driver's cab in relation to the speed of travel and the quantity of material to be placed per unit area. Spreading patterns, i.e. to the right, left or directly behind the spreader, are regulated by adjustments to the spinner assembly. Salts are normally spread along the high side or crown of the highway so that the melt will flow across the rest of the carriageway.

## Snow clearance

In Britain, the maximum salt spreading rate recommended[32] for melting up to 4 cm of fresh snow at $0\,^{\circ}$C is 40 g/m$^2$. At snow depths greater than 4 cm, the normal practice is to initiate snow ploughing; however, each pass of the plough may be supplemented by salt spread at the rate of 10 g/m$^2$ so as to prevent the snow from compacting, and so ease the passage of the plough.

Snow clearance technology centres around the use of equipment (see reference 37 for an overview of equipment easily available in Britain). The two main pieces of equipment used for clearance purposes are the fixed-blade plough and the rotary plough.

The operational characteristics of the two basic forms of *fixed-blade plough*, i.e. the vee plough and the straight or side-clearing plough, are well known and need not be elaborated upon here. Basically, however, the vee plough—its blade is mounted at the front of the propulsion vehicle—is most effectively used for drift-breaking and when the snow depth on the carriageway is between 1 and 2 m. The blades of straight ploughs are sometimes mounted beneath and behind the propulsion vehicle, as well as in front of it; this type of plough is mostly used to cast the snow either to the left or to the right of the carriageway in the course of constant high-speed ploughing, the aim being to prevent accumulation of any significant depth of snow.

Whilst the ploughs are usually fitted with replacement blades of materials such as steel with tungsten-carbide inserts, rubber blades have proven effective for snow removal at temperatures not too far below freezing. Rubber blades also have the advantage of causing less damage to road studs and other markers set into the carriageway. Ploughs equipped with serrated blades are more effective in removing compacted snow and ice than straightedge blades.

*Rotary ploughs*, also known as *snowblowers*, are used to pump or blow snow from the carriageway. Whilst augers or ribbon-cutters are used to cut into the snow ahead of the plough and feed it into the blowers, ribbon-cutters have a much greater operational efficiency than augers[1]. Initially developed for use in dry snow conditions, snowblowers have been modified so that they can now deal with the wet snow and slush conditions prevalent in Britain. They are most effectively used when the depth of snow on the carriageway is in excess of 0.5 m.

As well as being effective when properly used, snowblowers have a dramatic appeal to the general public and provide the maintenance organization with a good public image. In practice, however, this type of equipment is very expensive and has limited seasonal use in Britain.

## Snow disposal

The most usual method of snow clearance involves pushing the snow to the outside of the roadway or onto a central reservation, and then waiting for warmer weather to cause the snow to melt naturally. In many instances, particularly in urban areas and at major intersections and overpasses, the roadside areas are not adequate for snow storage and additional removal and disposal methods must be arranged.

The most usual way of solving this problem is to use front-end loaders with large buckets (as the snow is normally light), or blowers, to transfer the snow into lorries which transport it to dump areas such as landfill sites or rivers. In the case of rivers in particular, disposal practices for ice and snow containing salt will need to be considered carefully to ensure that there are no subsequent detrimental ecological effects.

Obviously, the shorter the distance the lorry must travel with the load of snow, the fewer will be the number of vehicles required to remove the snow. In certain instances, e.g. in large urban areas, melting stations have been used to shorten the travel distance. At these stations, heat is used to convert the collected ice and snow into water which is then removed via the normal sewer system. The locations of melting stations should, if practical, be adjacent to stockpiles of chemicals and abrasives so that a lorry carrying snow to a melter is able to carry a payload on its return trip. Overall, however, the cost of melting snow by the application of heat is very high and so this method of snow disposal is only used when other methods are not possible.

## Structural design of overlays

### When overlays are used

Over 6500 km of motorways and major highways have been built in Britain since the mid-1950s. Since 1970 most of these roads have had their pavements designed on a twenty-year life cycle based on estimates of the number of millions of standard axles (msa) expected to pass over them during that design period. Some parts of this highway network have already reached their design life in years, whilst nearly the whole of the system has been subjected to a dramatic increase in damage due to the considerable increases both in the gross mass of vehicles and in the use of heavier vehicles since the early 1970s. As a result of this latter development, the design life in msa units of many highway sections has been exceeded on many occasions within a life span of fewer years than intended.

In many countries, it is the practice for strengthening to be carried out on a roadway *after* much damage has been caused to the pavement, and this damage is evident at the road surface. Often, however, the road condition by this time has deteriorated to the extent that rebuilding of the whole (full reconstruction) or upper layers (partial reconstruction) of the pavement is necessitated. In other instances, a concrete or (more usually) a bituminous overlay is provided; however, because of the significance of the structural damage to the pavement, the thickness of overlay required is large. Either of these solutions is very expensive, and usually costs more than would the earlier application of a thinner overlay, e.g. before major surface deterioration is apparent and before the structural integrity of the pavement is seriously compromised.

Consequently, the trend in recent years in Britain has been to plan to place an overlay on a pavement *before* it fails, e.g. when the pavement is deemed to be in a critical but not a failed condition. Table 9.3 describes the pavement surface conditions which are generally reflective of the pavement condition as a whole. Note that the term 'critical' as used in this categorization does not necessarily imply that the pavement is in immediate danger of failure—in fact, there may be many years of useful life left after the onset of critical conditions. Rather, the term is used to attempt to define the condition when an overlay thickness can be assumed to be the most effective strengthening treatment. After the onset of critical conditions, deflections will increase at a faster rate and be less predictable, and will

**Table 9.3** Road surface conditions which are broadly comparable with the condition of the whole pavement[38]

| Wheel-track cracking | Wheel-track rutting under a 2 m straightedge (mm) | | | |
| --- | --- | --- | --- | --- |
|  | < 5 | 5 to < 10 | 10 to < 20 | ⩾ 20 |
| None | Sound | Sound | Critical | Failed |
| Less than half-width* or single crack | Critical | Critical | Critical | Failed |
| More than half-width* | Failed | Failed | Failed | Failed |

*Half-width is likely to be in the range 0.5–1.0 m. If there is no rutting to define the wheel tracks, use 0.5 m as half the wheel-track width

require corresponding increases in the overlay thickness needed for a given future life.

When a pavement is deemed to have failed, it usually implies that all or part of the pavement structure has to be reconstructed.

Strengthening by overlay has the advantage that it enhances any residual life in the existing pavement. Compared with the reconstruction approach, it is also quicker, reduces traffic delays, and is less sensitive to weather conditions. Furthermore, the problems associated with damage to drains and the restrictions which existing drainage levels may impose on design when a reconstruction solution is adopted, are avoided.

Notwithstanding the advantages of overlays, the following factors need to be considered before detailed design is proceeded with: (a) the maximum thickness of overlay that can be accommodated by bridge structures, and (b) the ease with which changes in overlay thickness can be made, having regard to the effect on the longitudinal profile and surface water drainage paths.

The extent to which an existing surface is badly damaged is also a major factor influencing decision-making in relation to overlays. This applies particularly to pavements with lean concrete bases, when reflective cracking has propagated to the road surface, i.e. even a considerable (e.g. 200 mm) thickness of bituminous overlay material cannot be guaranteed to prevent further upward propagation of the existing cracks.

When an overlay is used, it is normally extended over all lanes of the carriageway and the hard shoulder, regardless of which lanes have deteriorated[39]. This also means that safety barriers, other roadside equipment, and verges may have to be lifted to suit the new carriageway level, and so the overall cost of an overlay can be quite high.

From the above, it is clear that the decision as to whether or not to have an overlay, and what thickness to utilize if it is justified, is one which deserves considerable attention. In this respect, it is useful first to consider a basic way in which the structural performance of a bituminous pavement can be evaluated.

## Measuring structural performance

The primary indicator of the strength of a flexible pavement is the deflection measured under a rolling wheel load[38,40]. In Britain, the devices used to measure this deflection are the *deflectograph*[41,42] and the *deflection beam*[41,42]. (Other devices are used in other countries to measure deflections, e.g. see reference 43.)

The roles of the above two devices in the carrying out of a comprehensive evaluation of the condition and performance of a pavement are outlined in Fig. 9.3. Note that the full process outlined in this flow diagram may not be necessary, depending upon the needs of the scheme at hand, e.g.

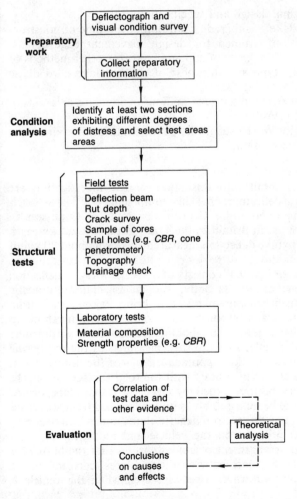

**Fig. 9.3** Sequential process of structural examination for a bituminous pavement[40]

newer highways for which full records are available normally require less investigation than older, undesigned roads that have been altered both laterally and vertically and for which few records are available.

## Preparatory work

The deterioration of a pavement is best investigated by identifying areas of pavement exhibiting different degrees of distress and then relating performance to significant structural differences between the areas. For this purpose, the following preparatory information is normally required:

(1)  general information, i.e. location, road layout, road type, dates of construction and opening, and relevant information on geology or topography,
(2)  details of the original design and specification,
(3)  construction details, e.g. subgrade condition at the time of construction versus the condition assumed for design, pavement edge details, drainage details, type and thickness of capping layers (or other methods of subgrade improvement), type and thickness of subbase layers, roadbase layers, basecourse, and wearing course,
(4)  cumulative traffic carried in terms of millions of standard axles (msa),
(5)  previous remedial measures,
(6)  the present condition of the subgrade, pavement layers and drainage,
(7)  visual condition survey data,
(8)  deflection data.

The deflection data input into this stage of the investigation are normally provided by a deflectograph. This equipment, which was originally developed by the Laboratoire Central des Ponts et Chaussees in France and modified for use in Britain by the Transport and Road Research Laboratory[44], is able to take deflection measurements over about 20 km of carriageway per working day.

The deflectograph (see Fig. 9.4) consists of a special lorry, a deflection beam assembly located beneath its body, and an associated automatic recording system. When measurements are being taken, the beam assembly—which is of tubular steel construction to the dimensions shown in Fig. 9.4—rests on the carriageway, suitably aligned between the front and rear axles of the vehicle; deflections are then measured as the rear wheel assemblies (each loaded to 3175 kg) approach the tips of the beams which, during this period, are at rest in contact with the road surface. When the maximum deflection has been recorded by electrical transducers located near the beam pivots, the beam assembly is pulled forward (at about twice the speed of the vehicle) by an electromagnetic clutch and winch assembly until it is at its initial position on the vehicle and ready for the next measurement cycle. An arrangement of guides ensures that the beams are 'aimed' at the centre of the space between the two tyres (each inflated to $690 \text{ kN/m}^2$) of the rear twin-wheel assembly, even when the vehicle is negotiating bends.

The deflectograph automatically measures deflections at 3.8 m intervals

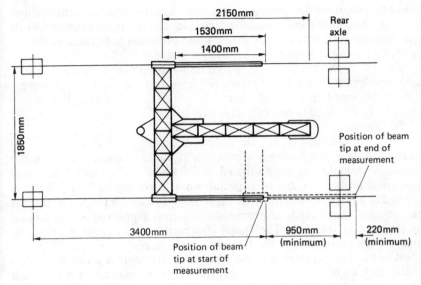

2150mm

1530mm

1400mm

Rear axle

1850mm

Position of beam tip at end of measurement

3400mm

950mm (minimum)

220mm (minimum)

Position of beam tip at start of measurement

**Fig. 9.4** Deflectograph equipment used to measure pavement deflections

at a velocity of 2 km/h, thereby permitting 10–12 km of pavement to be surveyed in a working day.

**Condition analysis**
In order to relate the performance of a pavement to important structural features that explain its deterioration, its present condition must be determined at locations that exhibit different degrees of distress. Thus at least two test areas (each about 100 m long) are selected for examination on the basis of the deflectograph and visual survey data. At least one of these areas should be selected to represent a section with little or no sign of distress, for comparison with another/others showing varying levels of distress.

**Structural tests**
For each test area, deflection beam measurements are gathered at about 10 m intervals in the nearside wheel path of the slow lane. These are supplemented with measurements of rut depth and 150 mm diameter cores taken at the same locations. The cores are taken: (a) to determine the thickness of each bound layer and the degree of bonding, (b) to see if there is any evidence of stripping of binder from the aggregate or the presence of detritus where there is a lack of bond between layers, (c) to assess compaction levels by measuring density, (d) to indicate the depth of cracking, and (e) to provide samples for composition analysis and the measurement of the properties (especially penetration and softening point) of the recovered binder. Trial pits are also dug, as appropriate, near the centres of the test areas, so as to obtain detailed information regarding

grading, classification, moisture content, and bearing capacity of the subbase, the capping layer, and the subgrade. The adequacy or otherwise of the drainage system is determined and any problems noted and examined carefully for the reasons why they are occurring.

Known in the USA as the Benkleman beam (after its inventor), the deflection beam measures the elastic response at the surface of a pavement that is subjected to a known load; it is then assumed that this elastic response can be used to determine the overall condition, and the existing life of the pavement.

As is indicated by Fig. 9.5, the deflection beam consists of an aluminium alloy beam that is sufficiently slender to fit within the space between the walls of the dual tyres (each inflated to 590 kN/m$^2$) of either of the wheel assemblies on the rear axle of a special two-axle loading lorry. The beam is pivoted at a point 2.44 m from the tip giving a 1 : 2 length ratio. The pivot is carried on a frame made of aluminium, which is supported on the ground by three adjustable feet. The frame also carries a dial-gauge arranged to measure the movement of the free arm of the beam.

When a measurement is to be taken, the test point is identified with a chalk mark on the carriageway; this is normally in the nearside wheel track of the road, 0.9–1.2 m from the nearside verge. A transverse line is then drawn on the carriageway 1.3 m behind this point of measurement, and the loaded lorry—each wheel assembly carries 3175 kg—is stationed parallel with the verge and its rear wheel directly over the line. The transverse positioning is such that, when the vehicle is driven forward, the gap between the nearside dual rear wheels passes directly over the test point. The deflection beam is then placed centrally between the dual tyres so that the beam tip is directly over the test point, and the loaded vehicle is driven forward at creep speed until the rear wheel is at least 3 m beyond the test point. The carriageway deflection is then taken as the sum of the maximum

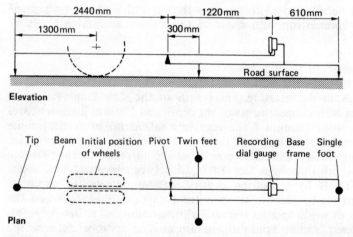

**Fig. 9.5**  Deflection beam equipment used to measure pavement deflections

reading and the difference between the maximum and final readings. (The sum of deflection is not meaned because of the 2 : 1 ratio of the beam arms.)

The deflection measured as a loaded wheel passes over a point on the carriageway is the summation of the individual deflections in each layer of the pavement and in the subgrade. However, the stiffness of a bituminous layer changes with the temperature of the binder (see Chapter 7) and, consequently, the magnitude of the measured deflection will vary according to the temperatures of the constituent bituminous layers. For routine measurement purposes, however, it is not feasible to measure temperature gradients through the pavement structure, and so the simple procedure has been adopted of representing the temperature of the pavement structure by a single temperature measurement at a fixed depth. The standard deflection value is then the equivalent deflection beam deflection value measured at a pavement temperature of 20 °C at 40 mm below the surface. The actual process (which now makes use of a computer program), whereby the measured deflection is converted to this standard deflection, is described in references 41 and 45.

Deflection measurements are best made when the pavement temperature is close to 20 °C, and measurements outside the range 10–30 °C should be avoided because of the extra-large temperature correction which this would require. In Britain, this means that the spring months, mid-March to June, are preferable for deflection surveys although, as an alternative, the months of September and November may be suitable.

Before or after the deflection measurement is carried out with the deflection beam, the structural condition of the pavement should be assessed according to Table 9.3. If a gross mismatch appears to occur between the measured deflection and the visual condition of the pavement, a check should be made to ensure that there are no mistakes in the measurement and analysis of the deflection results. In this respect, it should be emphasized that inaccurate estimates of standard deflection can occur when pavements which are sited on either very strong or very weak subgrades are tested at temperatures close to the extremes of the working range; in these cases, check measurements of deflection should be carried out at another temperature.

The deflection beam is a relatively slow (and expensive) way of collecting data. Depending upon the condition of the surface, deflections are measured at intervals of 12–25 m, permitting about 1 km of pavement to be surveyed in a working day. By comparison, the deflectograph is clearly able to collect considerably more data than the deflection beam in a given length of time. As a consequence, the deflectograph will probably eventually supersede the deflection beam.

Results obtained with the deflectograph, which are normally lower than those obtained with the deflection beam, have been correlated with those from the deflection beam (see Fig. 9.6) within the test temperature range 10–30 °C. This relationship is based on experimental evidence collected from pavements containing crushed stone, and cement-bound and bituminous-bound roadbases which are built on subgrades with *CBR*s ranging from 2.5 to 15.0 per cent. Pavements with rolled asphalt, bitumen

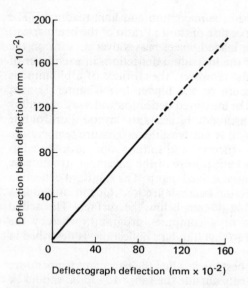

**Fig. 9.6**   Correlation between deflection beam and deflectograph deflection measurements[45]

macadam and tarmacadam surfacings were also included in the correlation study. It should be noted that the correlation methodology requires that the deflectograph deflections be translated to their equivalent deflection beam deflections *before* any temperature correction is applied to the deflection results.

### Evaluation

A comparison of the information gathered on the two or more test areas should reveal the main contributions to the deterioration in overall pavement strength. The recommended format for the presentation of results is a strip map which shows the pattern of cracking and rutting in each 100 m length, together with deflection results and the thickness of pavement layers.

Differences in deflection can reasonably be ascribed as due to foundation layers if analysis of the pavement layers for composition, compaction, penetration and softening point of recovered bitumens, thickness, and degree of cracking show no significant differences between sections. Whilst the load-carrying capability of foundation layers is best judged by direct measurement of their strength, e.g. by *CBR*-testing, a comparison of densities may give an indirect indication of differences where foundation materials of identical composition are compared.

Conversely, large differences in layer properties, e.g. in composition and/or compaction of bound layers above a uniform foundation, would point to these layers as being the main contributors to differences in measured deflection. In addition, the lack of bond between adjacent pavement layers may be important in explaining pavement deterioration.

For dual carriageways, differences in pavement condition and deflection levels between different traffic lanes can be interpreted to provide further information regarding overall pavement deterioration.

Where the above comparisons are inconclusive, e.g. where large variations are apparent in bound and foundation layers, detailed laboratory testing may need to be carried out on samples of the bound layers in order to provide the necessary data for subsequent theoretical analysis.

**Deflection–performance relationships**

The deflection of a pavement at a given point does not remain constant with time, but increases slowly as the pavement deteriorates. Studies made on experimental roads have enabled deflection histories to be built up from construction to the onset of critical conditions for a large number of highway sections, and these have been consolidated into the four performance charts shown in Fig. 9.7. The deflections in this figure are expressed in terms of measurements made with the deflection beam at 20 °C, and are valid for flexible pavements surfaced with the bituminous materials in common use in Britain.

Note that the individual charts in Fig. 9.7 are differentiated according to roadbase type. The type and thickness of granular subbase are not identified, however, as they have little effect on the deflection–performance relationships.

A pavement is classified as having a *granular roadbase with natural cementing action* when more than 150 mm of this type of material is present; any associated cement-bound layers should be less than 100 mm thick, whilst any bituminous layers should be less than 150 mm thick. Where there is doubt as to the cementing action, such action is normally assumed as more conservative results are then obtained. A pavement is considered to have a *granular roadbase without cementing action* when more than 150 mm of this type of material is present, given the above provisons regarding the presence of other materials.

A pavement is classified as having a *cement-bound roadbase* if more than 100 mm of such material is present, even if it is located beneath a considerable thickness of bituminous surfacing and roadbase material. A pavement is considered to have a *bituminous-bound roadbase* when more than 150 mm of bituminous material is present, providing that there is no more than 100 mm of cement-bound material also present. (The bituminous layers used in the calculation can be separated by intervening layers of granular materials.)

Note also that the trend lines of deflection in each of the charts in Fig. 9.7 lead to four envelope curves defining different levels of probability that the critical life of the pavement will be achieved. The life expectancy of any particular pavement is determined by following the deflection trend from a point defined by the present level of deflection and the past traffic (in standard axle units) to the envelope of the selected probability level.

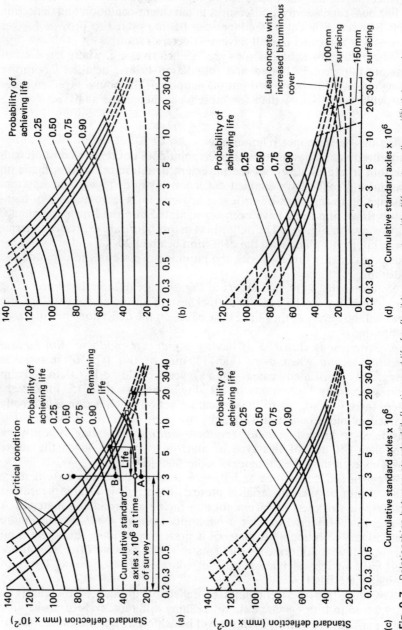

**Fig. 9.7** Relationships between standard deflection and life for flexible pavements with different roadbases[45]: (a) granular roadbases whose aggregates exhibit a natural cementing action, (b) non-cementing granular roadbases, (c) bituminous roadbases, and (d) cement-bound roadbases

## Overlays on flexible pavements

Overlay design methods for flexible pavements can be broadly divided according to whether they are based on engineering judgement, on non-destructive procedures, or on quasi-mechanistic procedures.

The Asphalt Institute's simplified method of overlay design for lightly-trafficked roads[46] is a useful example of a method based essentially on engineering experience and judgement. The Transport and Road Research Laboratory's method of overlay design for flexible pavements[45] is a good example of a non-destructive method based on deflection measurements related to the structural strength of the pavement. The Shell method of overlay design is an example of an analytical method which also utilizes performance parameters but uses elastic theory to calculate the overlay thickness; this is not discussed here, however, and the reader is referred to reference 47 for useful descriptions of this and other quasi-mechanistic methods.

### Asphalt Institute simplified method

With this method, which is widely used in the USA to design overlays for pavements carrying no more than 100 heavy commercial vehicles per day, each layer of the existing pavement is assigned an equivalency factor (see Table 9.4) which is used to convert the existing thickness of the layer to an equivalent thickness of asphaltic concrete. The sum of the equivalent thicknesses is then subtracted from the total design thickness (see Table 9.5) required to cater for the future traffic, to give the thickness of overlay.

The use of this method is most easily shown by an example.

### Example

Consider a secondary road carrying an average of 10 commercial vehicles per day. The existing pavement is composed of 40 mm of asphaltic concrete surface course on top of 150 mm of untreated, crushed stone roadbase containing some plastic fines. The subgrade is of the medium category, and the surface course has large cracks and some rutting in the wheel paths. Determine the required overlay thickness.

*Solution*
*Step 1* If the pavement was full-depth asphaltic concrete, the thickness required would be 125 mm (from Table 9.5).

*Step 2* The effective thickness of the existing pavement (from Table 9.4) is $(40 \times 0.6) + (150 \times 0.15) = 24.0 + 22.5 = 46.5$ mm.

*Step 3* By subtraction, the required overlay thickness of asphaltic concrete is $125 - 46.5 = 78.5$ mm; use 80 mm for design purposes.

### TRRL method

Reference has already been made (see, for example, Chapter 6) to the very extensive full-scale pavement experiments carried out by the Transport and Road Research Laboratory. A number of these test sections were overlaid

**Table 9.4** Asphalt Institute factors used to convert existing courses to equivalent thicknesses of asphaltic concrete[46]

| Pavement course | Minimum requirements | Equivalency factors |
|---|---|---|
| Asphaltic concrete | Stable, generally uncracked with little or no deformation in the wheel paths | 0.9–1.0 |
| | Stable, some fine cracking or slight deformation | 0.7–0.9 |
| | Much cracking and crack patterns, or appreciable deformation | 0.5–0.7 |
| Emulsified or cutback asphalt mixtures | Stable, generally uncracked and exhibiting little deformation in the wheel paths | 0.7–0.9 |
| | Stable, some fine cracking, some ravelling or aggregate degradation and slight deformation | 0.5–0.7 |
| | Extensive cracking, much ravelling or aggregate degradation, appreciable deformation and lack of stability | 0.3–0.5 |
| Portland cement | Stable, undersealed and generally uncracked | 0.9–1.0 |
| | Stable, undersealed, some cracks but no pieces < 1 m² | 0.7–0.9 |
| | Appreciably cracked and faulted, cannot be undersealed. Slab fragments (1–4 m²) have been well seated on the subgrade by heavy pneumatic rolling | 0.5–0.7 |
| | Pavement broken into small pieces (0.6 m maximum dimension). Use upper range when subbase is present; use lower range when slab is on subgrade | 0.3–0.5 |
| Aggregate | Granular subbase or roadbase of fairly well-graded, hard aggregates with some plastic fines and $CBR \geqslant 20$. Use upper range if $PI \leqslant 6$; use lower range if $PI > 6$ | 0.1–0.2 |
| Soil | Improved subgrade or native subgrade | 0 |

**Table 9.5** Typical thicknesses of full-depth asphaltic concrete pavement used on light- to medium-trafficked roads in the USA[46]

Typical subgrade properties

| Category | CBR (%) | Resilient modulus (MPa) | Thickness (mm) | | | | | | |
|---|---|---|---|---|---|---|---|---|---|
| | | | Average number of heavy commercial vehicles per day in the design lane | | | | | | |
| | | | ⩽5 | 10 | 20 | 30 | 50 | 70 | 100 |
| Poor* | 3 | 30 | 165 | 180 | 200 | 215 | 230 | 240 | 250 |
| Medium† | 8 | 80 | 115 | 125 | 150 | 165 | 180 | 190 | 200 |
| Good to excellent‡ | 17 | 170 | 100 | 100 | 100 | 115 | 125 | 140 | 150 |

* Poor soils have appreciable amounts of clay and fine silt, and become soft and plastic when wet
† Medium soils include loams, silty sands and sand–gravels with moderate amounts of clays and fine silts
‡ Good to excellent soils are relatively unaffected by moisture or frost, e.g. clean sands, sand–gravels, and gravels

with rolled asphalt, usually at a stage when they were approaching failure. Systematic measurements of deflection were made before and after the application of the overlays, and these enabled histories of the overlaid pavements to be developed. From these studies[48], the information essential to the development of an overlay design method was obtained, viz. the reduction in deflection brought about by an overlay of any given thickness, and the deflection levels measured on the overlaid pavement required to give any given extension of pavement life.

One set of the *design charts* derived from these studies is given in Fig. 9.8. The 0.5 probability level relationship is presented as it is that which is normally used in trunk road assessments and redesign schemes[38]; it is considered to represent the best estimate of the relationship between deflection and the cumulative traffic carried at the onset of critical conditions. Note that these charts specify the thickness of rolled asphalt overlay required to strengthen a pavement of given deflection in order to achieve a desired extension of life, expressed in millions of standard axles. In defining the thickness of overlay required, the charts take into account any remaining life in the original pavement.

The thickness derived from the design charts are for overlays using rolled asphalt materials only. However, these thicknesses can be converted to equivalent thicknesses of coated macadam using the factors given in Table 9.6. It might also be noted that the research report from which these data are extracted recommends that overlays in these materials should be limited to 100 mm thickness, i.e. wearing course and basecourse materials only. Furthermore, the open-textured macadams are normally recommended only for overlaying pavements carrying traffic of intensities lower than those for which the overlay design charts are intended.

The design charts recommend a minimum thickness of 40 mm for rolled asphalt structural overlays. This is because of the difficulty in predicting the performance of thinner overlays, and because of the uncertainty in the observed structural performance of thin overlays (often associated with construction problems). This limitation should certainly be adhered to on important highways.

In respect of the design thicknesses obtained from Fig. 9.8, it should be remembered that they do not include the depth of any rut in the pavement surface. When the ruts are wide, signifying structural damage in several or all of the pavement layers, the shoulders of the ruts are used to define the datum for the overlay. Narrow ruts generally indicate a deformed wearing course which may be removed before overlaying is carried out; when it remains in place the overlay datum should be that of the road surfacing away from the ruts.

The charts were derived from observation of pavements constructed on subgrades in the weak to medium category, with the majority having *CBR*-values in the range 2.5–15.0 per cent. If the classification of subgrade strength is outside this range, the overlay design method may not be fully applicable and should therefore be applied with due caution.

The use of any of the charts in Fig. 9.8 requires estimates to be made of the cumulative number of standard axles carried by the existing highway

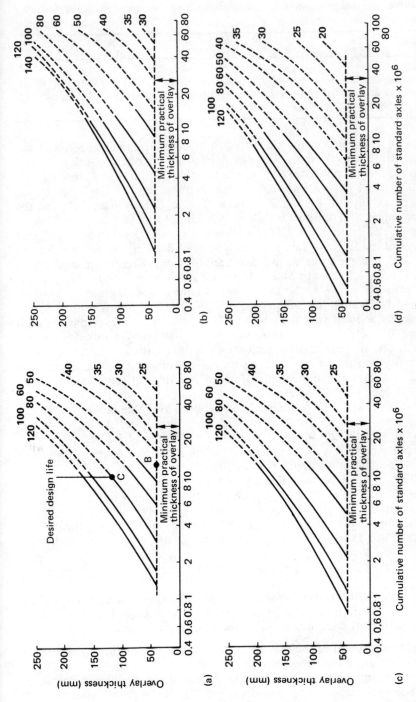

**Fig. 9.8** Overlay design charts (0.50 probability) for use with pavements with[45]: (a) granular roadbases whose aggregates have a natural cementing action, (b) non-cementing granular roadbases, (c) bituminous roadbases, and (d) cement-bound roadbases. *Note:* Deflections before overlay (mm × 10⁻²) are shown in bold

**Table 9.6**   Overlay thicknesses for coated macadams in relation to the requirements for rolled asphalt[45]

| Material | Thickness factor |
| --- | --- |
| Rolled asphalt | 1.0 |
| Dense coated macadam containing 100 pen or B54 binder | 1.0 |
| Dense coated macadam containing 200 pen or B50 binder | 1.3 |
| Open-textured macadam | 2.0 |

since its construction (or since its last structural maintenance), and the future traffic (msa) expected during the desired life of the overlay. This in turn requires a knowledge of past and future traffic flows and growth rates.

The above flows are normally based on traffic records. For example, for the period up to 1978, the General Traffic Census data held by the Department of Transport is able to provide information on 16 h flows of commercial vehicles for 6300 non-random sites on motorway, trunk and principal roads; these data are in the form of flows for an average August day and, in some cases, an average April/May day. Factors are available to convert the 16 h flows to 24 h *AADF*s (see also Volume 1 of *Highways*). For the period after 1978, the Department's core or rotating census provides 24 h *AADF* values for commercial vehicles. The core census consists of 170 randomly selected sites for which traffic is counted on three days in each month of the year; 110 of these sites are on motorway, trunk or principal roads. The six-year rotating census, which was started in 1980, covers all links between major intersections on the motorway, trunk and principal road system; a random sample of about one-sixth of the sites is counted once in each year of the cycle.

Growth rates can be interpolated between available census years, and these rates used for forward or backward projection. Alternatively, an average growth rate taken over the life of the road to date can be used without serious loss of accuracy. For trunk roads and motorways, it may often be sufficient to apply a future growth rate of 2 per cent[38].

The formulae for determining the total number of standard axles have been described in Chapter 6 (see the Nottingham method of flexible pavement design) and will not be repeated here. The value for the traffic carried up to the time of the deflection survey enables the estimation of residual life, in terms of millions of standard axles, based on the deflection level of the pavement. The future traffic, expressed as standard axles in each year, is used to predict the year in which the remaining life will expire.

*Summary of information required*   The following is a summary of the input information required by the Transport and Road Research Laboratory method of designing overlays for flexible pavements:

(1)   the deflection of the existing pavement measured either by the deflection beam or by the deflectograph,
(2)   the temperature of the pavement at a depth of 40 mm below the carriageway,

(3)   the cumulative number of standard axles carried by the existing highway since its construction (or since its last major structural maintenance),

(4)   an estimate of the future traffic (msa) expected during the desired life of the overlay,

(5)   information to identify the type and condition of the pavement for the purpose of: (a) correcting measured deflections to standard values at 20 °C, (b) estimating the remaining life of the pavement, and (c) designing any overlay required,

(6)   a broad classification of subgrade strength to determine whether or not it lies in the range of *CBR*-values between 2.5 and 15.0 per cent,

(7)   information regarding cut and fill and other factors relevant to the drainage conditions under and near the highway,

(8)   the type of material to be used in the structural overlay.

The manner in which the design charts are used to estimate the remaining life of a pavement of given deflections, and to determine the thickness of overlay required to achieve a desired extension of this life, are best illustrated by a basic example. Before this, however, the reader is reminded that deflections measured in a survey of structural strength along the length of a highway typically show considerable variations, which reflect differences in subgrade strength, in the type of pavement, and in its structural condition. In concept, this means that successive test points on the pavement could require different thicknesses of overlay. In practice, of course, the test points are grouped into pavement sections, each of which is then provided with a compromise 'optimum' thickness of overlay. As a general rule, this optimum thickness is based on the 85th percentile of the deflection measurements taken over each design length[38] (normally 100 m), i.e. on that value of deflection in the section at or below which 85 per cent of the deflections lie.

**Example**
A highway has the following characteristics.

| Pavement course | Thickness (mm) | Details |
|---|---|---|
| Surfacing | 100 | Rolled asphalt |
| Roadbase | 200 | Crushed rock with a natural cementing action |
| Subbase | 200 | Type 1 crushed rock |
| Subgrade | — | *CBR* = 6% |

It has carried 3 msa since it was initially constructed and now appears to require major maintenance. Determine the overlay needs of lengths of the highway having 85th percentile temperature-corrected deflection beam deflections of 25, 45 and $80 \times 10^{-2}$ mm, in order to obtain a future life of 10 msa with a 0.50 probability of achieving at least the design life.

*Solution*

*Step 1*   Determine the remaining life for each section.

This is done by plotting the 85th percentile points on the appropriate deflection–performance chart in Fig. 9.7; in this instance, use Fig. 9.7(a). Providing that the points lie below the 0.50 critical curve, the trend lines from the points to the critical curve can be sketched in and the remaining lives read off.

A deflection of $25 \times 10^{-2}$ mm (point A) gives a remaining life of $22 - 3 = 19$ msa. This is greater than the desired overlay design life of 10 msa, and so no overlay action is necessary on this first section. However, the result should be noted and used to time a future deflection survey when the road will be closer to critical conditions.

A deflection of $45 \times 10^{-2}$ mm (point B) gives a remaining life of $6 - 3 = 3$ msa. An overlay is therefore required to achieve the desired design life in the second section.

A deflection of $80 \times 10^{-2}$ mm (point C) lies above the critical condition curve for a pavement which has carried 3 msa. The pavement is obviously structurally weak and strengthening action is required immediately. (Also shown for information in Fig. 9.7(a) is the maximum deflection on the existing pavement that will give a 0.50 probability of achieving the desired additional design life without overlaying, viz. $29 \times 10^{-2}$ mm.)

*Step 2*   Determine the overlay thicknesses of rolled asphalt required for the deflections of $45 \times 10^{-2}$ and $80 \times 10^{-2}$ mm.

The thicknesses are obtained by plotting these deflection values, in association with the desired life of 10 msa, on the appropriate overlay design chart. In this instance, use Fig. 9.8(a).

A deflection of $45 \times 10^{-2}$ mm (point B) requires less than the minimum recommended thickness of overlay. Use 40 mm; this should give a future life of about 12.5 msa.

A deflection of $80 \times 10^{-2}$ mm (point C) requires an overlay of 120 mm. In this example, the position of the deflection–traffic coordinate in relation to the critical curve suggests that the pavement may be already badly damaged, and could be in need of full or partial reconstruction. Reconstruction measures, if adopted, will depend upon whether the weakness is in the pavement, in the subgrade, or in both. Alternatively, a thick overlay may be applied to the pavement section; in practice, however, level restrictions should be checked to ensure that they do not preclude this solution.

## Overlays on rigid pavements

### Construction options

The normal method of overlaying a concrete road is to apply a *bituminous carpet*, usually of hot rolled asphalt or dense bitumen macadam. Unlike the situation with flexible pavements, there are no preferred thicknesses specified in Britain, i.e. they are considered to depend upon such local circumstances as the mass of the slab, slab movements, life required, and the general structural condition of the pavement[25].

On major concrete roads, the minimum thickness of bituminous material generally applied is 100 mm. It is considered that, with this thickness, a life of about ten years may be expected before the reflected cracking will require further major maintenance; however, this will depend upon the degree of slab movement existing.

In some countries, *concrete overlays* are applied to rigid pavements. Generally, the economics of this type of treatment and the length of time for which vehicles have to be kept off the new surfacing have tended to mitigate against the use of cement concrete overlays in Britain.

One British recommendation[25] for the use of concrete overlays is that the unbounded overlay slab thickness on heavily-trafficked concrete pavements should be not less than 150 mm, whilst for lightly-trafficked roads the concrete overlay thickness should be not less than 100 mm. The use of concrete to overlay existing roads is known to have been employed in the USA from as long ago as 1913. The trend towards the selection of resurfacing type based on life-cycle costs rather than initial costs, combined with concerns regarding the uncertain future of bitumen supplies, has resulted in a significant growth in the use of this type of overlay in the USA since the mid-1970s.

These concrete overlays may be either unreinforced, jointed or continuously reinforced slabs; the latter two are more commonly employed in Britain. Whatever the type of overlay slab utilized, any vertical movement that might occur at joints or cracks in the existing slab should be stabilized either by pressure or (preferably) by vacuum grouting (see reference 23), surface levels should be regulated where necessary, whilst any spalling at joints should be rectified with bituminous materials.

Concrete overlays may be bonded, partially bonded, or unbonded[49]. The partially bonded or unbonded overlays are generally used over (American) asphaltic concretes. For bonded overlays or unreinforced, partially bonded overlays, joints must match those in the original pavement to prevent reflective cracking. For reinforced, partially bonded overlays, transverse joint matching is preferred but not required. Joints need not be matched in unbonded overlays.

*Bonded overlays*, predominantly unreinforced concrete, are placed on existing Portland cement concrete pavements after the surface has been completely cleaned by surface scarification, sandblasting, waterblasting or shotblasting. A commonly used bonding agent is a 50:50 mix of sand–cement grout brushed into the clean, dry pavement surface. Water–cement grouts are also practical for spray application. Early projects depended upon brooming dry cement into the wetted pavement surface to establish bond.

*Unbonded overlays* have a positive separation course between the existing pavement and the overlay. The unbonded overlays are generally thicker than bonded overlays, and may be installed with or without steel reinforcement. The bondbreaker (unbonding) materials may be lean concrete, bituminous materials (e.g. hot applied mats, seal coats or slurry seals), or polythene film in a double layer. The slurry seal option has the advantage of action as a levelling course as well as a bondbreaker; adequate levelling of an old bituminous surfacing also makes an important contribution to the quality and ease of installation of a cement concrete overlay.

*Partially bonded overlays* are placed directly on an existing pavement with the minimum of surface preparation, such as the cleaning of loose debris and excess joint seal. No special effort is made either to bond or to prevent bond of the overlay. Sometimes the existing concrete is broken and left in place with 7–9 cm size pieces at the surface. Before overlaying bituminous surfacings in rough condition, scarification or milling of the surface may be necessary.

### Thickness design

Empirically derived design formulae that are widely used to determine plain cement concrete overlay thicknesses over existing jointed plain concrete slabs are reported[50] as follows.

(1)   Where no bond is assumed to exist between the overlay and the existing slabs, then

$$h_r = (h_1^2 - Ch_0^2)^{1/2}$$

where $h_r$ = overlay thickness (mm), $h_1$ = monolithic thickness of pavement slab required for estimated traffic (determined from normal concrete pavement design analysis) (mm), $h_0$ = existing pavement thickness (mm), and $C$ = factor depending upon the existing pavement condition. The factor $C$ takes the following values:

$C = 1.00$ if the pavement is in good condition with little or no structural cracking

$C = 0.75$ if the slabs have broken corners or some structural cracking

$C = 0.35$ if the pavement is badly damaged or cracked

(2)   If the overlay is placed directly on the existing slabs and partial bonding is achieved, then

$$h_r = (h_1^{1.4} - Ch_0^{1.4})^{1/1.4}$$

A modification to this second formula that is used on the Continent is

$$h_r = (h_1^{1.87}/423.64 - Ch_0^2/645.16)^{1/25.4}$$

(3)   Where no bond is assumed between the overlay and the existing slabs, but the flexural strengths in the two concretes differ by more than $0.7 \text{ N/mm}^2$, then

$$h_r = [h_1^2 - C(h_1h_0/h_2)^2]^{1/2}$$

(4)   If the overlay is placed directly on the existing slabs and partial bonding is achieved, but the flexural strengths in the two concretes differ by more than $0.7 \text{ N/mm}^2$, then

$$h_r = [h_1^{1.4} - C(h_1h_0/h_2)^{1.4}]^{1/1.4}$$

A method of design used in the USA for continuously reinforced concrete overlays on top of jointed rigid pavements is also available in the literature[51]; this is reported to result in a near-maintenance-free pavement at a very competitive cost, as compared with equivalent resurfacing types. It is also reported that conventional Portland cement concrete and continuously reinforced concrete overlays have been successfully placed over existing bituminous pavements which required major maintenance.

Reference 52 provides a very useful summary of practices in the various states in the USA with regard to concrete overlays.

## Rehabilitation with recycled pavement materials

In recent years, there has been a growing interest in environmental protection and in the conservation of scarce highway materials. Thus, when

**Table 9.7**   Major advantages and disadvantages of recycling categories[54]

| Category | Advantages | Disadvantages |
| --- | --- | --- |
| Surface | Reduces reflection cracking<br>Promotes bond between old pavement and thin overlay<br>Provides a transition between new overlay and existing gutter, bridge, pavement, etc., that is resistant to ravelling (eliminates feathering)<br>Reduces localized roughness<br>Treats a variety of types of pavement distress (ravelling, flushing, corrugations, rutting, oxidized pavement, faulting) at a reasonable cost<br>Improves skid-resistance<br>Minimum disruption to traffic | Limited structural improvement<br>Heating–scarifying and heating–planing have limited effectiveness on rough pavement without multiple passes of equipment<br>Limited repair of severely flushed or unstable pavements<br>Some air quality problems<br>Vegetation close to roadway may be damaged<br>Mixtures with maximum size aggregates greater than 25 mm cannot be treated with some equipment |
| In-place | Significant structural improvements<br>Treats all types and degrees of pavement distress<br>Reflection cracking can be eliminated<br>Frost-susceptibility may be improved<br>Improves ride quality | Quality control not as good as central plant<br>Traffic disruption<br>Pulverized equipment repair requirement<br>Cost<br>Cannot be easily performed on Portland cement concrete pavements |
| Central plant | Significant structural improvements<br>Good quality control<br>Treats all types and degrees of pavement distress<br>Reflection cracking can be eliminated<br>Improves skid-resistance<br>Frost-susceptibility may be improved<br>Geometrics can be more easily altered<br>Better control if additional binder and/or aggregates must be used<br>Improves ride quality | Increases traffic disruption<br>May have air quality problems at plant site |

a maintenance investigation shows, for example, that a new surfacing is required on an existing highway, consideration is now often given to maximizing the use of the existing pavement material in whatever rehabilitation process is decided upon. Thus it is reported[53] that in a typical British wearing course recycling project, the demand for new material can be reduced by about 50 per cent when compared with a conventional resurfacing operation, so that there are appreciable savings in both aggregate and (imported) binder.

The recycling concept is not particularly new to the highway field. Various methods, some quite successful, have been practised in a limited manner since about 1915. However, the ready availability of cheap aggregates and binders did not make these methods very attractive to the highway engineer, and it required the 'energy crisis' which followed the 1973 Arab–Israeli conflict to re-awake interest in this rehabilitation method. The developing interest has been worldwide, with many countries now becoming increasingly involved in various forms of pavement recycling.

Pavement recycling is usually categorized by either the procedure used, the type of materials, or the structural benefit to be gained. Of these, the procedure approach has tended to become most widely accepted, and on this basis recycling can be divided according to whether it is: (a) surface recycling, (b) in-place surface and base recycling, or (c) central plant surface and base recycling. Table 9.7 lists advantages and disadvantages of each of these recycling categories.

## Surface recycling

This method normally consists of reworking the surface of a bituminous pavement to a depth of 25 mm or less[54,55]. As is indicated in Fig. 9.9, there are two basic processes in use for recycling surfaces: one utilizes the heating of the pavement, the other does not. Within either process, a host of

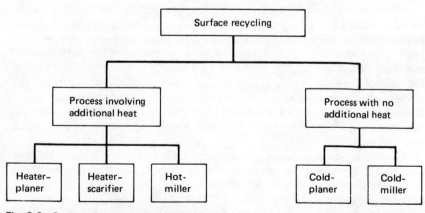

**Fig. 9.9** Basic surface recycling processes

recycling equipment types, and innovative techniques, have been developed, e.g. at least nineteen distinctive hot surface recycling processes, all based on the heating–scarifying approach, have been identified by one investigator[56]. The following discussion therefore concentrates on the overall concepts involved, and the uses to which they are put.

**Hot processes**

The *heater–planer* is a piece of equipment that heats the bituminous surfacing and shears up to 25 mm of the hot material with a steel blade or plate. Any material that is removed from the roadway can be reused, if desired and appropriate, in further work.

The heater–planer is mostly used to maintain longitudinal grades and transverse cross-slopes on pavements. Other uses include removing surfacings from bridges to reduce the dead weight, maintaining proper clearances in tunnels, at underpasses, and under bridges, removing improperly designed or constructed surface dressings, and removing surface irregularities from rough pavements. It is also common practice to heat and plane a road surface prior to placing an overlay for rehabilitation purposes.

The heater–planer may be used to improve a bituminous surfacing with poor skid-resistance, particularly when flushing and bleeding occur. With this process, known in Britain as *regripping*, a layer of polish-resistant aggregate is spread on the surface by a conventional chip-spreader; the heating unit is then used to heat the surfacing and this is followed by a steel-wheeled roller which compacts the chippings into the old material.

The *heater–scarifier* can be visualized as an extension of the heater–planer in that the equipment heats the pavement surface and then rips it to a depth of up to 25 mm by raking spring-loaded steel points over the hot layer. The heating systems—as those on the heater–planers—are usually either indirect radiant-heat emitters or direct open-flame burners; in either case, they are enclosed in a hood that directs the heat downwards into the surfacing. Carbide-tip steel blades on spring-mounted scarifiers or air-bag operated scarifiers are used to loosen and process the heated surfacing.

The basic operation consists of preparing, heating, and scarifying the surface, adding additional materials if required, compacting, making final adjustments to manholes and drainage structures, and then opening the highway to traffic. As with heater–planers, production rates with heater–scarifiers vary according to the equipment used, the thermal properties of the material being scarified and its temperature prior to heating, the scarification depth required, and restrictions imposed by auxiliary operations, e.g. the addition of a softener to dissolve and enliven the binder (the *reclaimex* process) or a bitumen emulsion (the *retread* process), reprofiling and recompacting.

Uses to which this process is put are similar to those for the heater–planer. Heater–scarifiers are also used to remove surface irregularities, whilst the bond between an old surfacing and a new bituminous overlay may be improved by the use of this equipment prior to placing the overlay. Reflection cracking, a major consideration in overlay design, may be reduced by the use of the heating–scarifying technique prior to overlaying bituminous surfacings.

In Britain, the main surface recycling activity has centred about a process commonly known as *repaving*[57]. In the repave process, the road surface is heated and then scarified to a depth of 20 mm. The scarified material is reprofiled as necessary and then overlaid with a relatively thin (usually 20 mm) bituminous mixture before compaction. If only a single lane of a carriageway requires repaving, some of the existing surfacing is removed in order to accommodate the new material and maintain the existing levels across the carriageway; in such instances, the existing surface is pre-planed as a separate operation and, after heating and scarifying the freshly exposed surface, the new material is inlaid.

If the heated and scarified material is reprofiled and compacted without any new material being added, the process is known in Britain as *re-forming*. Fairly recently, modifiers have been developed which are used to replasticize binders by replacing certain constituents lost through oxidation and polymerization. Sometimes these modifiers are added to re-formed surfacings immediately after compaction, and allowed to soak into the carriageway for a few days, after which a conventional bituminous overlay is added; this combined process is known as *rejuvenating* a surfacing.

The *hot-miller* is a piece of equipment which heats the surfacing, and then mills or grinds the in-place material to a depth of up to 50 mm with a rotating drum that has cutting tips mounted on its cylindrical surface. This process, which is less widely used than the other two hot processes, is limited to bituminous surfacings and is carried out for the same reasons as given for cold milling (see below).

When circumstances permit, material reclaimed by hot milling (and hot planing) can be immediately processed through a bituminous central plant. In practice, however, it is more likely that the hot milled material will be stockpiled and this can present major problems, e.g. the millings are either degraded by the mixing-in of sand to prevent congealment, or else it congeals thus necessitating further breaking-up and crushing before reprocessing at the central plant. In addition, if a poor technique is used, size segregation will occur during stockpiling; not only will this adversely affect the resultant mix but it is also likely to be the cause of additional air pollution during reprocessing[58].

A further point to be noted in respect of the potential for reusing surface material removed by milling (and other hot methods) is that haulage distances are quite crucial in recycling economics. Typically, haulage economic balances depend upon the following: (a) the haulage distance from the project to the central plant, (b) savings in the haulage costs of new material, (c) the haulage distance from the project to the tip or other conventional disposing site, and (d) savings in tipping fees or the loss of revenue by not utilizing the material's conventional reuse value.

**Cold processes**
The *cold-planer* process is usually carried out in the heat of summer, on bituminous surfacings. The equipment most commonly used is a motor

grader with hardened-steel blades. Typically, it is used to remove corrugations and other stability failures, to reduce the amount of rutting, and to remove badly designed or constructed surface dressings.

As with the heater–planer process, the removed material can be recycled for use in another pavement, but is generally not returned to rehabilitate the original pavement.

*Cold milling* is performed on both bituminous-surfaced and Portland-cement-concrete-surfaced pavements in order to remove surface deterioration. The types of pavement distress normally treated by cold milling include rutting, ravelling, flushing and corrugations of bituminous surfacings, and rutting, ravelling, scaling, faulting and spalling of Portland cement concrete pavements. Additional applications include repairing a rough-riding road and improving the surface texture to provide better skid-resistance. The improved surface texture will also result in an increase in the bond or shear strength between the old surface and a new bituminous overlay.

The cold millings can be reclaimed for usage in other pavements in stabilized or unstabilized bases or surface courses. They can be treated either in-place or at a central plant, e.g. as they are already reduced in size, the cold millings are normally suited for direct central plant recycling without further reduction, except for the possible scalping-off of oversized chunks. In fact, the main problem experienced with recycling cold millings has been the generation of excess fines.

## Comment

Surface recycling is the most widely used of the recycling processes. However, the publications on which the above discussion is based clearly show that the state-of-the-art of surface recycling is still in a state of transition. It is used principally to conserve materials and energy, and to reduce the costs of correcting or minimizing surface deficiencies in respect of skid-resistance, deformation and cracking. Present indications are that the most significant improvements to the present processes are likely to be in respect of the equipment used.

## In-place recycling

This method of pavement rehabilitation is usually carried out cold, and without heating the reused material. As with surface recycling, it is normally used in order to conserve materials and energy, and to improve pavement surface conditions; in addition, however, it can be used to improve the load-carrying capacity of the pavement[59]. There are several ways of improving a pavement's load-carrying capacity, viz. overlaying with a substantial thickness of new bituminous surfacing, reconstructing by removing all or part of the old pavement and building a new pavement, and strengthening the existing pavement by cold recycling, normally with the addition of a binder, without changing the horizontal or vertical geometry of the road.

In-place recycling of old flexible and rigid pavements is not new. Since

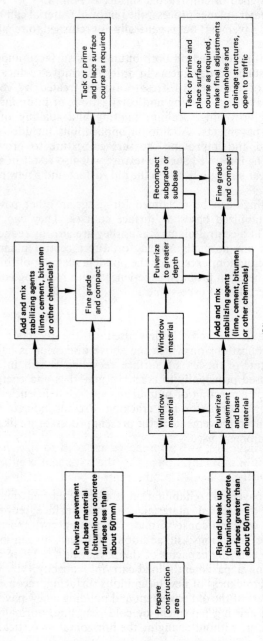

**Fig. 9.10** In-place surfacing and base recycling alternatives[54]

the early 1940s at least, conventional construction equipment, such as bulldozers, vibratory compactors, and rollers, has been used to crush old pavement material for reuse. However, the development of pulverizing equipment and processing techniques which use travelling hammer-mills for recycling bituminous surfacings is among the more important recent refinements of in-place recycling.

The various alternatives for in-place pavement recycling with no additional heat are shown in Fig. 9.10. This indicates that two basic approaches have developed which depend upon the thickness of the pavement to be treated. If the surfacing is about 50 mm or less thick, pulverization equipment can be used with preliminary ripping and breaking. If the surfacing is greater than 50 mm, motor graders with scarifiers or dozers with ripper teeth are usually used for the initial break-up; heavy equipment, e.g. dozers or rollers, can then be used if additional breakdown is required prior to pulverization.

**Comment**
In-place cold recycling is little used in Britain at this time, although it is widely used in the USA. However, its usage will probably grow, particularly in respect of the rehabilitation of unsurfaced roads and roadways with thin bituminous wearing courses [60].

## Central plant recycling

With this method of reusing pavement materials, the pavement layers are removed from the roadway, crushed or pulverized as necessary, and a mix-design analysis is then carried out on the resulting blend. Controlled amounts of new aggregate and binder (with or without a rejuvenating agent) are added to the recycled aggregate at a central plant. The resultant mix is then placed in a pavement using conventional equipment and construction techniques, and compacted using normal rollers.

Figure 9.11 summarizes the basic processes involved in central plant recycling. As this indicates, two approaches are used to size the material prior to recycling it in the central plant, i.e. the pavement is either reduced in size in-place and then hauled to the central plant or it is ripped and removed from the site and crushed at a later time at the central plant. In-place removal and sizing is performed with equipment usually associated with surface and in-place recycling, viz. hot and cold milling machines, heater–planing equipment, and on-site pulverizers.

In the case of hot bituminous mixes, the processing at the central plant can be categorized according to whether the material is handled by direct flame heating, indirect flame heating, or as a superheated aggregate.

*Direct flame heating* is typically performed with a drum mixer wherein all materials are mixed simultaneously in a revolving cylinder with a flame at one end.

*Indirect flame heating* is performed in special drum mixers with internal exchanger tubes. These tubes, which transfer hot gases, prevent the

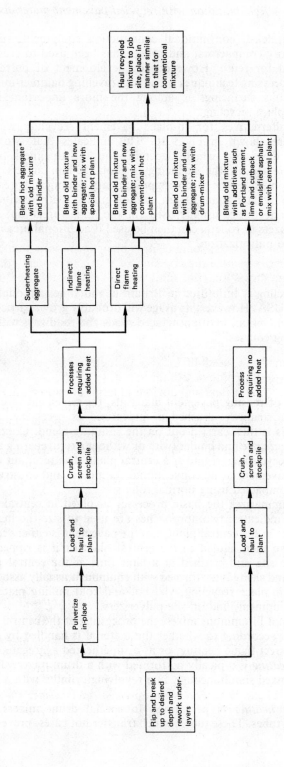

**Fig. 9.11** Central plant recycling techniques[(54)]

*Binder may include a modifier; new aggregate may be used as required to correct mix design and control air quality problems.

materials from coming into direct contact with the flame and extremely high gases.

With the third method, *superheated aggregate* is used to heat the recycled bituminous material. For example, with the tandem drum mixer method, new aggregate is dried and heated at a high temperature in a conventional dryer, whilst a second cylinder is used to heat the recycled material to a lower temperature, with the exhaust gases from the first dryer acting as the heat source for the second cylinder. The superheated aggregate and the heated recycled material are then fed into a pugmill where they are admixed with additional binder and modifier according to the mix design; the resulting mix is carried to a surge hopper where the mixture is temporarily stored, prior to being carried to the construction site. (Details of the many types of equipment used at central hot-mix plants which deal with recycled materials are readily available in the literature[54,58].)

As Fig. 9.11 also indicates, some central plant operations require no heat. These can simply involve the crushing of Portland cement concrete and bituminous pavement material until the mix is suitable for use in unstabilized basecourses, or until a cementitious binder can be admixed, e.g. cement has been often used as a binder to form a concrete pavement—in the USA, this product is sometimes described as *Enoncrete*.

**Comment**
Although it is commonly used in the USA, there is as yet very little experience of hot-mix recycling in Britain.

The case for recycling is clear and obvious in terms of conserving energy and mineral resources. It would also appear to be justified on structural grounds, e.g. research has shown[61] that a hot rolled asphalt containing reclaimed material has stiffness and deformation characteristics which are, for all practical purposes, indistinguishable from those for conventional hot rolled asphalt. Furthermore, the following parameters have been shown to have no practical effect upon the performance of a hot rolled asphalt mix containing recycled material, viz.: (a) reclaimed material content, (b) source of reclaimed material, (c) the removal process, and (d) the type of softening agent used.

## Selected bibliography

(1) *AASHTO Maintenance Manual*, Washington DC, The American Association of State Highway and Transportation Officials, 1976.
(2) Technical Committee Report on Maintenance, *Proceedings of the XVII World Road Congress*, Paris, The Permanent International Association of Road Congresses, 1983.
(3) Road Research Group, *Road Strengthening*, Paris, OECD, September 1976.
(4) *Proceedings of the HRB/FHWA Workshop on Pavement Rehabilitation*, TRB Report No. FHWA-RD-74-60, Washington DC, The Transportation Research Board, June 1974.
(5) Blum WE and Phang WA, *Preventive Pavement Maintenance Concepts*, Downsview, Ontario, Ministry of Transportation and Communications, January 1981.

(6) Road Research Group, *Maintenance Techniques for Road Surfacings*, Paris, OECD, October 1978.

(7) *Report of the Committee on Highway Maintenance*, London, HMSO, 1970.

(8) Parmenter BS, Lancaster IE and Cox BE, *Highway Authorities' Maintenance Organisation*, TRRL Report LR615, Crowthorne, Berks., The Transport and Road Research Laboratory, 1974.

(9) TRRL Overseas Unit, *Maintenance Management for District Engineers*, Overseas Road Note 1, Crowthorne, Berks., The Transport and Road Research Laboratory, 1981.

(10) Wingate PJF and Peters CH, *The CHART System of Assessing Structural Maintenance Needs of Highways*, TRRL Report SR153UC, Crowthorne, Berks., The Transport and Road Research Laboratory, 1975.

(11) *Code of Practice for Routine Maintenance*, London, The Department of Transport, 1985 (and as amended to June 1987).

(12) Snaith MS, Pavement condition assessment techniques, *Highways and Transportation*, 1985, **32**, No. 1, pp. 11–16.

(13) Hosking JR and Woodford GC, *Measurement of Skidding Resistance: Part 1—Guide to the Use of SCRIM*, TRRL Report LR737, Crowthorne, Berks., The Transport and Road Research Laboratory, 1976.

(14) Cooper DRC, *The TRRL High-speed Road Monitor: Assessing the Serviceability of Roads, Bridges and Airfields*, TRRL Research Report 11, Crowthorne, Berks., The Transport and Road Research Laboratory, 1985.

(15) Orr DM, Snaith MS and Thompson A, Pavement riding quality assessment with the Bump Integrator, *Highways and Public Works*, 1978, **46**, No. 1820, pp. 4–7.

(16) *MARCH Highway Maintenance System User Manual*, Manchester, Greater Manchester Council, 1975.

(17) *The CHART User Manual*, HECB R/16, London, The Department of the Environment, 1976.

(18) Parmenter BS, *Estimating Resources and Costs for Highway Works—Development of the 'RATE' System*, TRRL Report LR957, Crowthorne, Berks., The Transport and Road Research Laboratory, 1980.

(19) Carey WN and Irick PE, The pavement serviceability-performance concept, *Highway Research Board Bulletin 250*, 1960, pp. 40–58.

(20) *The AASHO Road Test: Report 5—Pavement Research*, Special Report No. 61E, Washington DC, The Highway Research Board, 1962.

(21) *Collection and Use of Pavement Condition Data*, NCHRP Synthesis of Highway Practice 76, Washington DC, The Transportation Research Board, 1981.

(22) TRRL Overseas Unit, *Maintenance Techniques for District Engineers*, Crowthorne, Berks., The Transport and Road Research Laboratory, 1981.

(23) Mildenhall HS and Northcott GDS, *Manual for the Maintenance and Repair of Concrete Roads*, London, HMSO, 1986.

(24) Road Research Group, *Catalogue of Road Surface Deficiencies*, Paris, OECD, October 1978.

(25) Transport and Road Research Laboratory, *A Guide to Concrete Road Construction*, London, HMSO, 1979 (3rd edition).

(26) NAASRA, *Road Maintenance Practice*, Sydney, National Association of Australian State Road Authorities, 1975.

(27) Committee on Visibility, *Visibility in Construction and Maintenance Work Zones*, Transportation Research Circular No. 232, Washington DC, The Transportation Research Board, October 1981.

(28) Ola SA, Corrugations on gravel and lateritic roads, *Transportation Engineering Journal of ASCE*, 1978, **104**, No. TE2, pp. 227–237.

(29) Wright N, *Methods Available for the Renovation of Fatted Surface Dressings*, TRRL Report SR304, Crowthorne, Berks., The Transport and Road Research Laboratory, 1977.

(30) Mackay HJ, Concrete carriageway repairs, *The Highway Engineer*, 1982, **29**, No. 10, pp. 2–7.

(31) Thornes JE, The prediction of ice formation on roads, *Highways and Transportation*, 1985, **32**, No. 8, pp. 3–12.

(32) *Winter Maintenance of Motorways and Trunk Roads: Statement of Service and Code of Practice*, London, The Department of Transport, August 1984.

(33) Elliott HE, Winter maintenance in Somerset, *Highways and Public Roads*, 1979, **47**, No. 1827, pp. 5–7.

(34) Chorlton E, The use of weather monitoring equipment in the management of highway maintenance, *Municipal Engineer*, 1986, **3**, No. 5, pp. 245–256.

(35) Space-age technology for deicing highway surfaces, *Public Roads*, 1975, **39**, No. 3, pp. 89–95.

(36) Long DC and Baldwin JS, *Snow and Ice Removal From Pavement Using Stored Earth Energy*, Report No. FHWA-TS-80-227, Springfield, Virginia, National Technical Information Service, February 1980.

(37) Winter maintenance of road pavements, *Highways and Public Works*, 1980, **48**, No. 1845, pp. 12–27.

(38) *Deflection Measurement of Flexible Pavements: Analysis, Interpretation and Application of Deflection Measurements*, Advice Note HA25/83, London, The Department of Transport, August 1983.

(39) Russell DJ, Strengthening and reconstruction of pavements, in: *Proceedings of Seminar Q on Highway Construction and Maintenance*, Volume P215, pp. 88–93, London, PTRC Education and Research Services, 1981.

(40) *Structural Examination of Bituminous Pavements*, Advice Note HA30/85, London, The Department of Transport, June 1985.

(41) *Deflection Measurement of Flexible Pavements: Operational Practice for the Deflection Beam and the Deflectograph*, Advice Note HA24/83, London, The Department of Transport, August 1983.

(42) *Strength Testing of Flexible Pavements by Deflection Measurement*, Departmental Standard HD10/83, London, The Department of Transport, August 1983.

(43) Monismith CL, Pavement evaluation and overlay design: Summary of methods, *Transportation Research Record 700*, 1979, pp. 78–81.

(44) Kennedy CK, Fevre P and Clarke C, *Pavement Deflection: Equipment for Measurement in the United Kingdom*, TRRL Report LR834, Crowthorne, Berks., The Transport and Road Research Laboratory, 1978.

(45) Kennedy CK and Lister NW, *Prediction of Pavement Performance and the Design of Overlays*, TRRL Report LR833, Crowthorne, Berks., The Transport and Road Research Laboratory, 1978.

(46) *A Simplified Method for the Design of Asphaltic Overlays for Light to Medium Traffic Pavements*, College Park, Maryland, The Asphalt Institute, 1987.

(47) Finn FN and Monismith CL, *Asphalt Overlay Design Procedures*, NCHRP Synthesis of Highway Practice 116, Washington DC, The Transportation Research Board, December 1984.

(48) Kennedy CK and Lister NW, *Deflection and Pavement Performance: The Experimental Evidence*, TRRL Report LR832, Crowthorne, Berks., The Transport and Road Research Laboratory, 1978.

(49) Pavement rehabilitation with portland cement concrete, *Concrete Construction*, May 1985, pp. 413–423.

(50) Gregory JM, *The Continuously Reinforced Concrete Overlay on Trunk Road A3 at Horndean*, TRRL Report SR742, Crowthorne, Berks., The Transport and Road Research Laboratory, 1982.

(51) Renner KH, Design criteria for continuously reinforced concrete overlay based on performance, *Proceedings of the International Conference on Concrete Pavement Design*, pp. 447–467, Purdue, Indiana, Purdue University, 1977.

(52) Hutchinson RL, *Resurfacing with Portland Cement Concrete*, NCHRP Synthesis of Highway Practice 99, Washington DC, The Transportation Research Board, 1982.

(53) Goodsall GD, *In-situ Recycling of Asphalt Wearing Courses in the UK*, TRRL Report SR675, Crowthorne, Berks., The Transport and Road Research Laboratory, 1981.

(54) *Recycling Materials for Highways*, NCHRP Synthesis of Highway Practice 54, Washington DC, The Transportation Research Board, 1978.

(55) Jimenez RA, State-of-the-art of surface recycling, *Transportation Research Record 780*, 1980, pp. 40–50.

(56) Servas VP, Hot surface recycling, *The Highway Engineer*, 1981, **28**, No. 12, pp. 8–13.

(57) Cooper DRC and Young JC, *Surface Characteristics of Roads Resurfaced Using the Repave Process*, TRRL Report SR744, Crowthorne, Berks., The Transport and Road Research Laboratory, 1982.

(58) Servas VP, Hot mix recycling of bituminous pavement materials, *The Highway Engineer*, 1980, **27**, No. 12, pp. 2–8.

(59) Alcoke WH, Cold recycling of failed flexible pavements with cement, *Transportation Research Record 734*, 1979, pp. 22–27.

(60) Epps JA, State-of-the-art cold recycling, *Transportation Research Record 780*, 1980, pp. 68–100.

(61) Stock AF, Structural properties of recycled mixes, *Highways and Transportation*, 1985, **32**, No. 3, pp. 8–12.

# Index

# Highways

**Volume 2**
Highway Engineering

*This textbook is dedicated to my sister*

Kathleen

*for whom I have much love and respect
for her courage in the face of adversity*